The
2011
Arrivc
Bus Hand.

CW00664927

British Bus Publishing

Body codes used in the Bus Handbook series:

Type:
A	Articulated vehicle
B	Bus, either single-deck or double-deck
BC	Interurban - high-back seated bus
C	Coach
M	Minibus with design capacity of 16 seats or less
N	Low-floor bus (*Niederflur*), either single-deck or double-deck
O	Open-top bus (CO = convertible - PO = partial open-top)

Seating capacity is then shown. For double-decks the upper deck quantity is followed by the lower deck. Please note that seating capacities shown are generally those provided by the operator. It is common practice, however, for some vehicles to operate at different capacities when on certain duties.

Door position:
C	Centre entrance/exit
D	Dual doorway.
F	Front entrance/exit
R	Rear entrance/exit (no distinction between doored and open)
T	Three or more access points

Equipment:-
T	Toilet	TV	Training vehicle.
M	Mail compartment	RV	Used as tow bus or engineers' vehicle.
L	Lift for wheelchair (post 2005 express coaches are fitted with lifts as standard)		

Allocation:
s	Ancillary vehicle
t	Training bus
u	out of service or strategic reserve; refurbishment or seasonal requirement
w	Vehicle is withdrawn and awaiting disposal.

e.g. - B32/28F is a double-deck bus with thirty-two seats upstairs, twenty-eight down and a front entrance/exit.
N43D is a low-floor bus with two or more doorways.

Re-registrations:
Where a vehicle has gained new index marks the details are listed at the end of each fleet showing the current mark, followed in sequence by those previously carried starting with the original mark.

Annual books are produced for the major groups:
The Stagecoach Bus Handbook
The First Bus Handbook
The Arriva Bus Handbook
The Go-Ahead Bus Handbook
The National Express Coach Handbook (bi-annual)
Some editions for earlier years are available. Please contact the publisher.

Regional books in the series:
The Scottish Bus Handbook
The Welsh Bus Handbook
The Ireland & Islands Bus Handbook
English Bus Handbook: Smaller Groups
English Bus Handbook: Notable Independents
English Bus Handbook: Coaches

Associated series:
The Hong Kong Bus Handbook
The Malta Bus Handbook
The Leyland Lynx Handbook
The Postbus Handbook
The Mailvan Handbook
The Toy & Model Bus Handbook - Volume 1 - Early Diecasts
The Fire Brigade Handbook (fleet list of each local authority fire brigade)
The Police Range Rover Handbook

Some earlier editions of these books are still available. Please contact the publisher on 01952 255669.

2011 Arriva Bus Handbook

The Arriva Bus Handbook is a Major Group edition of the *Bus Handbook* series which contains the various fleets of Arriva plc, one of the major operators across Europe. The *Bus Handbook* series is published by British Bus Publishing, an independent publisher of quality books for the industry and bus enthusiasts. Further information on these books may be obtained from the address below.

Although this book has been produced with the encouragement of, and in co-operation with, Arriva plc management, it is not an official group fleet list and the vehicles included are subject to variation, particularly as the vehicle investment programme continues. Some vehicles listed are no longer in regular use on services but are retained for special purposes. Also, not all out of use vehicles awaiting disposal are listed. The services operated and the allocation of vehicles to subsidiary companies are subject to variation at any time, although accurate at the time of going to print.

To keep the fleet information up to date we recommend the Ian Allan publication *Buses*, published monthly or, for more detailed information, the PSV Circle monthly news sheets.

Edited by Bill Potter and Stuart Martin

Acknowledgments:

We are most grateful to Tom Johnson, Harry Laming, Peter Marley, Colin Martin, Kevin O'Leary, the PSV Circle and the management and officials of Arriva Group plc, and their operating companies, for their kind assistance and co-operation in the compilation of this book. The front cover picture is by Mark Doggett, the rear cover views are by Richard Godfrey and the frontispiece by Mark Lyons.

ISBN 9781904875291

Published by British Bus Publishing Ltd
16 St Margaret's Drive, Telford, TF1 3PH

© British Bus Publishing Ltd, February 2011

Telephone 01952 255669 - www.britishbuspublishing.co.uk

CONTENTS

ARRIVA plc

The Arriva Group: A Company Profile

Arriva plc is one of the largest transport services organisations in Europe, employing more than 38,000 people and delivering more than one billion passenger journeys across eleven European countries every year. It operates an extensive range of services including buses, trains, commuter coaches and water buses. In the UK it is also engaged in bus and coach distribution.

The group was acquired by Deutsche Bahn, one of the world's leading passenger and logistics service providers, in August 2010 after being quoted for forty-five years on the London Stock Exchange and firmly established as one of the UK's top 250 companies.

Deutsche Bahn acquired Arriva to strengthen and expand its competitive position in a consolidating European transport market. Arriva is now Deutsche Bahn's growth division for regional passenger transport outside of Germany, maintaining the Arriva name and brand and providing continuity of management to its operations in 11 countries.

For the year ended 31 December 2009 Arriva's group revenue was more than £3 billion. With a proven track record, having tripled revenue from its mainland European operations in the six years from 2002, the group was awarded The Queen's Award for Enterprise: International Trade 2009.

Arriva in the UK

In the UK, Arriva is one of the largest regional bus operators, with 6,300 vehicles serving customers in the North East, North West and South East of England, the Midlands, Yorkshire, Scotland and Wales. The core activity is the operation of urban, inter-urban and rural bus services, and commuter and express coach services within England, Scotland and Wales. In the capital, the group also runs buses under contract to Transport for London and in addition operates The Original Tour sightseeing buses.

Many of the operating companies in Arriva's UK Bus division are long established but the grouping emerged out of the privatisation of public sector transport companies, following the Transport Act 1985, and the subsequent consolidation of the sector. The division is organised into autonomous operating subsidiaries in order that management teams and staff can focus upon the discrete local and regional markets that they serve.

The group makes significant capital investment in the replacement and improvement of its vehicles and facilities. Arriva's UK bus division has made significant investments in new vehicles adding a further 330 new buses to its UK bus fleet during 2010, improving the passenger experience and bringing the total investment in new buses over three years to £180 million. During 2010 Arriva UK Bus also completed the roll-out of EcoManager, a dashboard-mounted fuel-saving system, which helps cut exhaust emissions.

Recent years have witnessed a renewed interest in rapid transit systems and the development of intermediate technologies. Arriva has been actively positioning itself within this broadened public transport market. Fastrack, the award-winning bus rapid transit system in North Kent in the UK, is operated by Arriva on behalf of Kent County Council and Kent Thameside. It is being delivered through one of the best examples of a public/private sector partnership which has proved successful in attracting people out of their cars.

Arriva Bus and Coach is the group's bus and coach distribution business with exclusive import rights for all VDL chassis supported by a wide range of bus and coach bodywork options, from Van Hool of Belgium, Ikarus from Hungary, Temsa from Turkey and Plaxton from the UK, to meet new market demands.

Arriva's UK trains division operates two passenger rail franchises – Arriva Trains Wales and CrossCountry. Arriva Trains Wales stretches from Manchester, through north and south Wales and across to Birmingham and Gloucester. CrossCountry is the UK's most extensive rail franchise stretching from Aberdeen to Penzance and from Stansted to Cardiff.

Arriva in mainland Europe

Over the last ten years Arriva has developed a unique position in mainland Europe, setting itself apart from other UK public transport sector peers. Arriva's footprint has deepened and widened, with operations now in eleven countries. Management teams have been strengthened, further reinforcing the group's unrivalled knowledge and experience, and the continuous development of a strong network of relationships which has been key to Arriva's success.

Across Europe Arriva provides passenger transport services in the Czech Republic, Denmark, Italy, Hungary, the Netherlands, Poland, Portugal, Slovakia, Spain, Sweden, and in 2011 begins operations in Malta after winning a ten-year contract to provide scheduled bus services on Malta and Gozo.

The Cowie name - early years.

In 1931, the Cowie family started a motorcycle repair business in Sunderland. In 1934 the first sales outlet opened on what became the location of the Group Head Offices. Business came to a halt in 1942 because of the effects of the war, but reopened in 1948 and benefited from the boom in personal mobility offered by the motorcycle. A second motorcycle shop was opened in Newcastle in 1952. Further expansion occurred in 1955 with another branch in Newcastle, and new branches in Durham and Stockton-on-Tees. A move into the Scottish market was taken with the acquisition of the J R Alexander motorcycle dealerships in Edinburgh and Glasgow in 1960. However, there were signs that the market was moving against the motorcycle and in favour of the motor car which was becoming a more mass market item in availability and price.

In 1962, Cowie acquired its first car dealership in Sunderland, and such was the pace of change that, by 1963, motor car sales constituted 80 per cent of revenue. On the back of this change, a public company, T Cowie plc, was formed in 1965 and, in that year, a further two car dealerships were acquired, one in Redcar and a second in Sunderland. In 1967, there was investment in new car showrooms for the Ford franchise in Sunderland; there has been a long association with Ford over the years. In 1971, this was strengthened with the acquisition of Ford Blackburn and a further Ford dealership, this time in Middlesbrough. By 1971, the group turnover reached £8m per annum.

Growing on the motor business.

The first exposure to the bus and coach industry came in 1980. In that year, Cowie took over The George Ewer Group which had various motor interests including Eastern Tractors and these assets were bought with the business. It also included the long established Grey Green coach operation and this was to lead to a sea change in the make-up of the business.

In 1984 Cowie acquired the Hanger Group and this brought Ford dealerships in Nottingham and Birmingham and, significantly, Interleasing, the contract hire business. Expansion continued in 1987 when seven main dealerships were acquired from the Heron Group. On the leasing side, Marley Leasing was acquired. Further growth in this business area came in 1991 when RoyScot Drive and Ringway Leasing were also acquired, adding to the prominence of this activity for the group.

1992 was the year that Cowie very nearly took another step into the bus and coach market, narrowly failing to purchase Henlys which, by that time, had ownership of Plaxtons along with several car franchises. Consolation came with the addition of a Ford dealership in Swindon, a Peugeot dealership in Middlesbrough, and a Toyota dealership in Wakefield. In 1993, the Keep Trust Group was acquired, the dealership network being boosted by seventy per cent.

Another notable event in 1993 was the retirement of Sir Tom Cowie, the Chairmanship of the business being taken up by Sir James McKinnon in 1994 and continuing until he retired at the end of 1999, when Gareth Cooper took over the role.

Explosion into Buses

Grey Green, which had operating bases in Stamford Hill and Dagenham in London, and in Ipswich in East Anglia, participated in historic operations such as East Anglian Express, the Eastlander Pool, and joint services to Scotland in association with Scottish Bus Group. Private Hire coaching also played a large part in the business.

Great opportunities were perceived in the 1980s in commuter coaching after the deregulation of coach services under the 1980 Act. Commuter coach services thrived for a while, but the involvement in British Coachways was not successful. In the mid 1980s, Grey Green's involvement in the East Anglian Express Pool was taken into the National Express operation.

Early success in London Bus tendering brought the Grey Green operation into to the very heart of London, notably on route 24 which passes the Palace of Westminster. After that, Grey Green gradually ceased all coach activities and concentrated entirely on tendered bus services in London.

The privatisation of the newly created subsidiaries of London Buses offered the opportunity to build on the favourable experience of Grey Green in the London bus market. Leaside was acquired in 1994 and was renamed Cowie Leaside. Later in 1995, the South London company was purchased, becoming Cowie South London. These two acquisitions made Cowie the largest single operator in the London Buses area. As the London operations were tidied up, the former Kentish Bus/Londonlinks operations at Cambridge Heath, Battersea, Croydon (Beddington Farm) and Walworth, and the East Herts & Essex operations from Edmonton were gradually incorporated into the London operation.

In 1996, Cowie purchased County Bus from the National Express Group, adding to the group's presence in the south-east of England. Then, in August 1996, Cowie completed the acquisition of British Bus plc and, at a stroke, became the second largest bus operating group in the United Kingdom. The acquisition of British Bus plc added a whole raft of bus companies across the country and very nearly brought all the disparate elements of the former London Country company, including Green Line Travel, under one ownership. There was a Monopolies and Mergers Commission inquiry into the acquisition of British Bus, with particular focus on the situation in London and the South East, but the report did not require any divestment.

The final acquisition of 1996, also in August, brought another previously divided company back under common ownership. In 1986, United Automobile Services had been split into two separate companies for privatisation: North East Bus and Northumbria. Northumbria was sold to Proudmutual, a company which had been set up to facilitate the management buyout and was acquired by Cowie in 1994. United Auto was sold in December 1987 to Caldaire who sold it on, as North East Bus, to West Midlands Travel. West Midlands Travel itself then merged with the National Express Group which decided to concentrate on its core operations and, in 1996, sold first County Bus then North East Bus to Cowie.

The former British Bus headquarters at Salisbury, which dated back to Drawlane days, was wound down and closed at the end of 1996, with the group administration being moved to Sunderland.

The growth of British Bus plc

With the acquisition of British Bus plc, Cowie became the second largest bus operating group in the United Kingdom. This move led to the reclassification of the enlarged group from being motor trade to transport.

Drawlane Ltd

The privatisation of the National Bus Company followed the 1985 Transport Act with the National Bus Company becoming a vendor unit selling its subsidiaries to pre-qualified parties. Endless Holdings Ltd was one of those interested parties, being a group of companies based in the cleaning and building management sector with a head office on Endless Street in Salisbury. The prime mover in Endless was Ray McEnhill. Endless set up a subsidiary called Drawlane Ltd to bid for NBC companies as they were made ready for sale.

The first company bought by Drawlane was Shamrock & Rambler in July 1987. This was the major part of the coaching activities of Hants and Dorset and was based at a modern depot in Bournemouth. The business was heavily dependent on National Express contracts, although a minibus operation was set up to compete with Yellow Buses in the Bournemouth area. Shamrock & Rambler did not survive for long: its bus operations were quickly reduced in scale, and difficulties with the National Express contracts led to notice of termination being given to Shamrock & Rambler which sealed its fate. National Express set up a local joint venture company called Dorset Travel Services Ltd to take over the workings of Shamrock & Rambler using other vehicles and based as a tenant of Yellow Buses at Mallard Road. Yellow Buses eventually purchased Dorset Travel Services. The Shamrock & Rambler vehicles were dispersed around the then Drawlane Group fleets and Shamrock & Rambler was wound up.

Drawlane was preferred bidder for three more companies: Southern National, North Devon, and London Country (South West). Each purchaser was limited to three NBC companies in the first instance. However there was concern that Drawlane might be related to another bidder called Allied Bus which had been selected as preferred bidder for another three companies: Lincolnshire Road Car, East Midland Motor Services and Midland Red North. The concern was sufficient for the preferred bidder status to be withdrawn from both and offers were re-invited.

Drawlane was successful in acquiring Midland Red (North) in January 1988 which, at the time of purchase, had 248 vehicles and 491 employees. The following month, London Country (South West) Ltd was purchased with 415 vehicles and 1250 employees, although the garages were purchased separately by Speyhawk Properties, who then leased them to the bus company with varying securities of tenure, reflecting the premium value of property in London and the South East. Finally, in March 1988, Drawlane acquired the 'new' North Western Road Car Company Ltd based in Bootle, with 340 vehicles and 870 staff.

Drawlane had also bought East Lancashire Coachbuilders from the industrial conglomerate John Brown. East Lancs was based in Blackburn and had a strong customer base in the local authority sector.

Further expansion for Drawlane would now come from acquiring bus operations from other sources. ATL (Western) Ltd had purchased Crosville Motor Services from NBC in March 1988 and in early 1989 was ready to sell. Drawlane purchased the company adding a further 470 vehicles.

A quick overview of the future of Crosville is appropriate here. In an exercise to realise value from the company, the South Cheshire operations at Crewe and Etruria were transferred to Midland Red North, the Runcorn and Warrington depots were transferred to North Western, and the Macclesfield and Congleton depots were merged into Bee Line Buzz, of which more later. The remaining operations at Rock Ferry and Chester, together with the vehicles, were sold to PMT Ltd along with the 'Crosville' trading name. The original Crosville Motor Services Company was

Greenline was the name used by London Transport for its commuter services into and through the city. The name lives on with Arriva's commuter services from The Shires. VDL SB3000 with Prima bodywork numbered 4055, R455SKX, is seen in Hemel Hempstead. *Richard Godfrey*

renamed North British Bus Ltd, and, though it existed for some time thereafter, it did not trade as a bus company.

Midland Fox was bought from its management team in September 1989 along with a minority share holding in the company from Stevensons of Uttoxeter. Bee Line Buzz operations in Manchester had been started up by BET, which had sold its bus operations in 1968, venturing back into bus operation in the UK. A similar operation was started in Preston. Both were sold to Ribble's management buyout team who, in turn, sold Ribble Buses to the Stagecoach Group. As part of an exchange of assets with Stagecoach in the Manchester area, Drawlane bought Bee Line Buzz from Stagecoach along with Hulme Hall Road depot in Manchester and added into the company the former Crosville operations at Macclesfield and Congleton. Bee Line had an independent existence within the group until 1993, when its operations were merged into North Western, with Macclesfield depot going to Midland Red North.

Drawlane in Transition

In 1991, Drawlane became a partner in a consortium with several banks setting up a company called Speedtheme Ltd in a bid to buy National Express Holdings from its management team. As well as the main National Express business, National Express Holdings owned Crosville Wales Ltd and its Liverpool subsidiary Amberline Ltd, Express Travel in Perth, and Carlton PSV the Neoplan coach dealer in Rotherham. Speedtheme Ltd did not want Crosville Wales and Amberline/Express Travel, and these were immediately sold to a company, called Catchdeluxe Ltd, set up by two of the main shareholders of Drawlane, Ray McEnhill and Adam Mills. Although not part of Drawlane at this time, these two companies were under common management, and it was not long before they became part of the Drawlane Group.

Ray McEnhill became the Chairman and Chief Executive of National Express Group and, as this group prepared for its floatation on the Stock Exchange, Ray McEnhill and Adam Mills severed their involvement with Drawlane. The London & Country business called Speedlink Airport Services was sold by Drawlane to National Express at this time, though Drawlane retained the Green Line Travel Company, along with the Green Line trading name.

There was, in effect, a management buyout of Drawlane in the autumn of 1992 to coincide with the successful floatation of National Express and shortly thereafter Drawlane was renamed British Bus plc. (British Bus Ltd had been a dormant subsidiary of National Express Holdings, originally set up by NBC to market the Britexpress card overseas.)

British Bus grows

Throughout this period, there were various smaller acquisitions by the group companies but these are dealt with in the short histories of these companies that follow.

In 1993, British Bus purchased Southend Transport and Colchester Transport, both former municipal operations which had been offered for sale after being weakened by competition from Badgerline subsidiaries, Thamesway in Southend and Eastern National in Colchester. After acquisition, the two companies were put under common management and the supervision of London & Country. A programme of rationalisation put both back onto a firm footing, though downsized.

In 1993, North Western acquired Liverline of Liverpool which, by then, had grown to a fifty-one vehicle company. It was run as a separate subsidiary until 1997. North Western had by this time absorbed the bus operations of Amberline.

Also in 1993, Tellings Golden Miller was sold back to its original owners. Tellings had been taken over by Midland Fox and came into the group. At the time of its sale, it had bases in Surrey and Cardiff. In the latter location, Tellings had become the joint operator of the Trawscambria service with Crosville Cymru. That role then passed to Rhondda Bus in which British Bus had a share holding for a while.

At the end of 1993, British Bus became the preferred bidder for the purchase of GM Buses North, but the position was overturned by the vendors and new bids were invited. The outcome of this exercise was a winning bid from an employee-based team which was eventually completed in the spring of 1994. They subsequently sold out to First.

Further growth was funded by expanding the capital base of the group through investment by two merchant banks who took a share of the increased equity in a new parent company British Bus Group, though operational control remained with British Bus plc.

During 1994, ownership of both East Lancashire Coachbuilders Ltd and Express Travel was transferred out of the group, though they were still associated companies. East Lancs in particular was still a preferred supplier to the group for bus bodywork.

The National Greenway programme was coming to an end at this point. This programme involved the stripping down and re-engineering of Leyland National shells with a new Gardner or Volvo engine, new gearbox and new body panels mounted on the shell framework. The stripping down and mechanical overhaul work was carried out at London and Country's Reigate garage, though later some of this work was carried out by Blackburn Transport, as this was closer to East Lancs. East Lancs then produced the bodywork with customer options as to the front design. Significant numbers were carried out both for Group companies and other operators.

Luton, Derby, Clydeside and Stevensons

In July 1994, British Bus acquired Luton and District Transport from its employees. By this time, the business included the former London Country Bus North West and a large part of the Stevenage operations bought from Sovereign Bus. This meant that a sizeable part of the former London Country company was now back in common ownership.

Luton and District had also assisted other employee buyouts such as Derby City Transport in which it had a 25 per cent share holding, and Clydeside 2000 plc, where there was a 19 per cent share holding. In both companies, the shareholders voted to accept offers from British Bus for the balance of the shares and they became fully owned members of the British Bus group. A third company, Lincoln City Transport, had not met with success and the employees had already agreed its sale to Yorkshire Traction-owned Lincolnshire Road Car Company Ltd before the British Bus take-over.

At the same time, there were discussions about the acquisition of Stevensons of Uttoxeter. Stevensons had grown dramatically after deregulation and operated well away from its traditional area. A strong expansion in the West Midlands was initially successful but West Midlands Travel responded to the competition and used its Your Bus acquisition to start up operations in Burton-on-Trent which was by then the heartland of Stevensons. A long struggle looked in prospect and a sale to British Bus was agreed. Operations in the West Midlands were scaled down and surplus vehicles were distributed around the group. After this process was complete, the geographically separated Macclesfield depot of Midland Red North was transferred to Stevensons control in January 1995.

Proudmutual and Caldaire Holdings

In the summer of 1994, British Bus also acquired the Proudmutual group. Proudmutual had been the buyout vehicle for the management team of Northumbria Motor Services to buy their business from NBC. It had also acquired some smaller businesses in the North East, including Moor-Dale.

Proudmutual had previously purchased Kentish Bus, the former London Country South East from NBC in March 1988. They had considerable success in the London Transport tendering process and further LT work was added when the LT contracts of Boro'line were purchased in February 1992. The Proudmutual acquisition thus gave British Bus a very strong position in LT tendering when the activities of London and Country and the LDT group were taken into account. It also brought another part of the former London and Country into common ownership.

The privatisation of the London Transport Bus companies brought no success for British Bus but, as seen earlier, the Cowie Group was successful in acquiring two of the subsidiaries. In March of 1995, the Caldaire group was acquired. Caldaire was the buyout vehicle with which the management of West Riding Group had purchased their business from NBC in January 1987. In the December of that year they also bought United Auto from NBC. A demerger later on saw the United business being separated off again into North East Bus. The long-established independent South Yorkshire Road Transport was acquired and formed one of the trading identities of the Caldaire Group, the others being West Riding, Yorkshire Woollen, and Selby & District. After acquisition, the group of companies was renamed Yorkshire Bus Group by British Bus.

Maidstone & District

What turned out to be the last major acquisition by British Bus was made in April 1995. Maidstone and District had been one of the earliest of NBC sales in late 1986. It had purchased New Enterprise of Tonbridge in 1988, and the assets of Boro'line Maidstone in 1992. Under British Bus ownership, the company was put under common management with Kentish Bus and Londonlinks as the Invictaway Group with its head office at Maidstone.

Floatation or Trade Sale?

Throughout 1995, preparations for floatation had been underway with the appointment of advisors. However, in the summer of 1995, these plans were thrown off course by reports of alleged irregularities involving support from the Bank of Boston for British Bus at an earlier point in the group's history. The timing of these allegations led to the postponement of the floatation. The alternative route for shareholders and the investing banks to realise their investment was a trade sale of the group and discussions were held with various interested parties.

Concurrently, the group was also looking to expand its interests into other modes of transport as the opportunities in the bus industry were becoming scarce owing to the growth of the major players. The subsequent sales of the two former GM Buses companies by their employee owners and that of Strathclyde Buses were opportunities for growth, but British Bus was not successful. In June 1996 the Cowie Group made an offer to acquire British Bus. There was a Monopolies and Mergers Commission investigation into the take-over in view of the concentration of operation in London and the South East in the combined business. However, the resulting report made no recommendation about disinvestment, recognising the considerable presence of the other groups in the area. The acquisition by Cowie was completed in August 1996.

Trams and trains

As part of its drive to expand its business, British Bus pursued tramway operations and had become a partner in the Eurotrans consortium which bid for both the Leeds Supertram and Manchester Metrolink concessions. British Bus was also part of a consortium bid for the Croydon Tramlink project.

Eurotrans was selected as the preferred bidder for the South Leeds Supertram Project which was being promoted by West Yorkshire PTE. This was a PFI project where bidders were fighting for the concession to design, build, operate, and maintain the tramway for a period of thirty years. The Eurotrans consortium included big construction companies such as Taylor Woodrow, Morrison Construction, and Christiani & Neilsen. The tram supplier was Vevey Technologies of Switzerland, now part of the Bombardier Group. The intention was for Arriva Yorkshire to set up a tram-operating subsidiary to operate the tramway for the concession life on behalf of Eurotrans. The project stalled waiting for UK Government funding commitment, but was revived, in expanded form, in 2001 when funding was secured.

British Bus was also active in the process of franchising of the Train Operating Companies by OPRAF although none of their bids were successful. However, the exposure to the process paid off in arranging through ticketing deals with the successful bidders later on.

From Cowie to Arriva

Arriva was born in 1997, bringing together the many different company backgrounds under the Arriva flag. Also in that year Arriva acquired its first business on the European mainland – Unibus Holdings in Denmark.

In 1999 Arriva decided to focus its management and financial resources to enable the group to capitalise on opportunities in passenger transportation in the UK and mainland Europe. Subsequently the group successfully disposed of a number of major motor retailing and finance businesses. This process was completed by the summer of 2003 and the sale of its vehicle rental division followed in 2006.

The group continued its expansion in Europe firmly establishing itself as one of the leading transport services organisations.

Arriva in London

When the Arriva name was introduced, Grey Green was renamed Arriva London North East. Cowie Leaside became Arriva London North, and Cowie South London became Arriva London South. The three companies gradually moved closer to functioning as one unit, with the London North East operations absorbed into London North in 2003 with the head office for Arriva London at Wood Green. The Beddington Farm depot of Londonlinks transferred from Southern Counties to London South in October 1999. The Leaside Travel coach and bus contract hire fleet retained a separate livery until operations ceased at the end of 2005. Arriva London now concentrates private hire activities on its Routemaster operations, for which a number of these historic vehicles have been retained under the title "The Arriva Heritage Fleet".

Today the group operates approximately 20 per cent of the London bus market under contract to Transport for London (TfL), covering almost 66 million miles a year. Also in London, Arriva runs The Original Tour, which provides sightseeing tours of the capital.

Arriva provided the first low-floor double-deck buses in London and in 2007 joined forces with TfL to trial the world's first Hybrid double decker bus in the capital. Hybrid buses, which use a combination of diesel and electric power, are central to the Mayor of London's and TfL's plans for a cleaner, greener fleet, and will contribute to cutting the capital's carbon dioxide emissions. In 2010 Arriva added twenty more hybrid buses to its London fleet, with twenty more set to enter service during 2011.

County Bus and Coach into Arriva East Herts and Essex

County Bus & Coach was established at the beginning of 1989 to carry on the eastern operations of the former London Country North East, which in itself was one of the four parts into which London Country was divided. Operations were based at Harlow, Hertford and Grays. Ownership had progressed through the AJS group in 1988, the South of England Travel group in 1989 and the Lynton Travel group in 1990. The company was then purchased by the West Midlands Travel holding company, becoming part of the National Express Group when WMT merged into NEG. A retraction into core business led NEG to sell County to Cowie in 1996. A significant acquisition in 1989 was the bus interests and depot of Sampsons of Hoddesdon.

A restructuring of responsibilities saw County Bus take over the controlling supervision of Southend Transport and Colchester Borough Transport from London & Country and, during 1998, this responsibility passed to Arriva The Shires with overall control of what was now Arriva East Herts and Essex. The Edmonton operation passed to the Arriva London group in a rationalisation of responsibilities within London. During 1999 the fleets of these various component operations were renumbered into a single series. In a further restructuring in 2001, responsibility for Colchester, Grays and Southend passed to Arriva Southern Counties.

The Shires becomes Arriva the Shires and Essex Ltd

In 1986, United Counties Omnibus Company Ltd was divided into three parts, the southernmost of these being Luton and District Transport Ltd which took over operations in Aylesbury, Dunstable, Hitchin and Luton. The new head office of the company was in Luton.

In August 1987 Luton and District became the first employee-owned bus operator in the UK when its employees bought it from NBC. In the period from January 1988 to October 1990, LDT expanded the size and the area of its operations through a number of acquisitions. The assets and business of Red Rover Omnibus Ltd, operating bus services from a depot in Aylesbury, were acquired in January 1988. In June 1988, Milton Keynes Coaches was acquired, joined in May 1990 by two-thirds of the bus services operated in the Stevenage area latterly Sovereign Bus Ltd.

In October 1990, LDT acquired London Country North West Ltd. LCNW operated a vehicle fleet of a similar size to LDT from a head office and depot in Garston and other depots in Hemel Hempstead, High Wycombe, Amersham, and Slough. LDT assisted in the employee buyouts of two other companies and acquired a share holding in both, Derby City Transport in 1989, and Clydeside 2000 plc in 1991.

In July 1994 LDT became part of British Bus. In October 1994, the bus operations of Stuart Palmer Travel based in Dunstable were taken over, followed in May 1995 by Buffalo Travel of Flitwick, and Motts Travel of Aylesbury in July 1995. April 1995 saw the launch of a brand new blue and yellow company livery with local trading names replacing the previous red and cream of LDT and green and grey of LCNW. The legal name was changed to LDT Ltd in May and the corporate operating name became The Shires.

In late 1997, Lucketts Garages (Watford) Ltd was acquired. In addition to local bus services in Watford there were substantial dial-a-ride operations and a commercial workshop. Lutonian Buses was acquired in March. There had been a ruling that the business should be sold under competition regulations and the group's challenge was unsuccessful and Lutonian was later sold during 2000. The Arriva branding saw vehicles carrying the name 'Arriva serving the Shires', except at Garston garage which carries 'Arriva serving Watford'. Management responsibility for Arriva East Herts & Essex now falls to Arriva the Shires and Essex Ltd. Responsibility for Colchester, Grays and Southend passed to Arriva Southern Counties in 2001.

In February 2006, Arriva acquired Premier Buses Limited, the holding company of MK Metro Limited (MK Metro), of Milton Keynes for £5.6 million. MK Metro operated commercial and tendered services in Milton Keynes, Bedfordshire and Northamptonshire adding 260 employees and 120 buses to the fleet.

Kentish Bus part of Arriva Southern Counties

Kentish Bus started as London Country South East on the division of London Country Bus Services in 1986. It had its Head Office at Northfleet and in April 1987 was relaunched as Kentish Bus and Coach Ltd with a new livery of cream and maroon.

In March 1988 Kentish Bus was sold to Proudmutual on privatisation. There was considerable expansion into the LT tender market for which new buses were added, many with registration indices originating in the North East. In February 1992 there was further expansion in this area when Kentish acquired the LT tendered work of the troubled Boro'line Maidstone operation, along with some fifty-seven vehicles.

After the acquisition of the Proudmutual group by British Bus in 1994, Kentish Bus and Londonlinks were jointly managed from Northfleet. However, on the acquisition of Maidstone and District by British Bus, the management was relocated to Armstrong Road, Maidstone under the Invictaway grouping. The balance of the operation continued to be controlled from Maidstone after the re-allocation of the two London depots to South London and Leaside.

Its size was significantly reduced by the transfer of operations at Battersea to the control of South London and the operations at Cambridge Heath to Leaside.

However the local Kent Thameside network was expanded and upgraded with low-floor vehicles upon the opening of the Bluewater shopping centre in 1999. This was followed by a successful Kickstart scheme on routes 495, 498 and 499 which brought in new Dennis Dart MPDs. A major development has been the operation of the award-winning Fastrack services which commenced in 2006 with a new fleet of Volvo/Wrights vehicles running on significant lengths of busway. A second route started in June 2007 which features cashless operation on the bus and a dedicated bus bridge over the M25.

The Dartford operation has seen an increase in the number of London contracts operated and this now forms the vast majority of the operation there. The Arriva identity was applied as 'Arriva serving Kent Thameside' to the operations at Dartford and Northfleet.

London & Country into Arriva Surrey and West Sussex

London & Country was the trading name of London Country Bus (South West) Ltd, which was one of the four operations that London Country Bus Services Ltd was divided into prior to the privatisation of NBC. The former head office of LCBS at Reigate became that of L&C. The company was bought by Drawlane, as outlined previously, in February 1988. However, the properties were leased back having been sold separately. The company was relaunched with a new livery and trading name in April 1989.

London & Country was successful in winning LT tenders and this led to the addition of new vehicles and the high profile opening of an impressive new garage at Beddington Farm in Croydon. Responsibility for this operation passed to Arriva London in 1999.

In 1990 the Woking, Guildford, and Cranleigh operations of the former Alder Valley business were purchased, and though kept as a separate operating company - Guildford and West Surrey - they were put under the same management as London & Country. Also in 1990, a separate company called Horsham Buses was established for operations in the Horsham area.

Spare capacity at the Reigate garage allowed the development of the National Greenway concept in conjunction with East Lancs and many vehicles were prepared at Reigate.

Briefly, L&C had two subsidiaries in Dorset: Stanbridge and Crichel and Oakfield Travel. Both of these were later sold to Damory Coaches. Another subsidiary was Linkline Coaches of Harlesden in London, which specialised in coaching and corporate work. This was later sold to its management.

1993 saw the acquisition of Southend Transport and Colchester Transport and many L&C influences followed. These companies transferred to the supervision of County Bus but returned to Southern Counties in 2001.

The Croydon based operations and other LT tender operations at Walworth were transferred into a new company called Londonlinks. In 1995 Londonlinks was put under common management with Kentish Bus and Maidstone and District as part of the Invictaway Group. Reallocation of responsibilities in the enlarged group later saw the Croydon depot of Londonlinks return to L&C control before finally passing to London South.

A consequence of the property sales was the vacation of Reigate garage and its replacement by a facility at Merstham. The Head Office functions were consolidated in 1997 when the Reigate office closed as the functions moved to other premises including Crawley garage.

The three companies were renamed as Arriva Croydon and North Surrey, Arriva West Sussex, and Arriva Guildford and West Surrey. In August 1998 the Countryliner coaching operation was sold to its manager. In 2001, the Crawley operation and depot was sold to Metrobus and the Merstham depot was closed.

In Guildford, significant investment has taken place with the depot completely rebuilt in 2002 and the fleet updated. Major new contracts are now operated for Surrey County Council and in partnership with the University of Surrey.

Maidstone and District becomes Arriva Kent & Sussex

This is the original Maidstone and District Motor Services Ltd which was founded in 1911. Under NBC, it shared common management with East Kent from 1972 to 1983. In 1983 the Hastings and Rye area services were hived off as Hastings and District.

Maidstone and District was one of the first NBC companies to be privatised, being bought by its management team in November 1986. In 1988 New Enterprise of Tonbridge was purchased and kept as a separate entity. In June 1992 the assets of Maidstone Boro'line Maidstone including the premises at Armstrong Road were purchased.

In April 1995 the company was sold to British Bus, and in November the Head Office at Chatham was closed and staff moved along with Kentish Bus head office staff from Northfleet to the former Maidstone Boro'line premises at Maidstone under the Invictaway banner.

Under British Bus Cowie control, the group acquired a number of additional operators including Mercury Passenger Services of Hoo, Wealden Beeline of Five Oak Green, and the Grey Green (Medway) bus operation. In May of 1997 the Green Line operations in Gravesend and the Medway Towns were sold to the Pullman Group (London Coaches).

Developments have included a substantial "Operation Overdrive" investment at Gillingham, a Kickstart scheme in Sittingbourne and further investment under a Maidstone Quality Partnership.

The Arriva branding used three identities, 'Arriva serving the Medway Towns', 'Arriva serving Kent and Sussex', and 'Arriva serving Maidstone'.

Midland Fox turns into Arriva Fox County Ltd

Midland Red East Ltd was formed in 1981 to take over the Leicestershire operations of Midland Red. In 1984 the company name was changed to Midland Fox Ltd, and there was a major relaunch of the company with a new livery and fox logo. There was also the launch of a new minibus network in Leicester under the, now discontinued, Fox Cub brand.

In 1987 the company was bought from NBC by its management with the help of the directors of Stevensons of Uttoxeter who, separately, bought the Swadlincote depot. Several smaller operators were also taken over. These included Wreake Valley of Thurmaston, Fairtax of Melton Mowbray, Astill and Jordan of Ratby, Shelton Orsborn of Wollaston, Blands of Stamford, and Loughborough Coach and Bus.

In 1989 Midland Fox was acquired by Drawlane. The following year it acquired Tellings Golden Miller in Byfleet and this business, in turn, acquired the Coach Travel Centre in Cardiff, amongst others. Tellings bus operations eventually became part of London and Country, while Tellings was sold back to its management in 1994 before its expansion into bus operations in Cardiff.

In 1994 Pickering Transport was purchased by British Bus. Pickering build lorry bodies at their extensive site at Thurmaston, and now offer body repair and painting services which has resulted in many group vehicles appearing there. The site also housed one of Fox's three Leicester area depots. 1996 saw a launch of high quality services under the Urban Fox brand in a striking new blue livery.

Derby City Transport Ltd was a long established municipally owned bus company. In August 1989 it was sold to its employees who were assisted by Luton and District Transport. Luton and District took a 25 per cent share holding in the business. There was a competitive interlude in Derby where Midland Red North started operations, but this ended with Derby buying out the competition in February 1990.

In 1994, after the acquisition of Luton and District by British Bus, the shareholders in Derby decided to accept an offer from British Bus for the rest of the share capital of the company. After a period of autonomy, the business was relaunched under the City Rider brand name and a yellow, red and blue livery. In January 1996, Derby City Transport was incorporated into the Midland Fox group; full integration and renumbering of the fleet took place at the start of 2000.

In 1990, "75" Taxis started as a division of Derby City Transport, building up a fleet of London style taxis. In September 1994, Midland Fox launched a new taxi service in Leicester marketed as Fox Cabs, but this operation was sold in 2001.

In September 1996, the Head Office of Midland Fox moved to the Pickering of Thurmaston premises along with a depot facility. It was later joined by the British Bus head office, now Arriva Passenger Services Ltd, which later moved to new premises on the other side of Leicester.

The Arriva branding had vehicles carrying the 'Arriva serving the Fox County', or 'Arriva serving Derby' identities as appropriate. The taxi business remains under its previous brand. Special liveries included four vehicles in Quick Silver Shuttle for Leicester Park and Ride, Airport Car Park Shuttle and Airport Rail Link, three vehicles in a blue livery for East Midland Airport, two buses in a Corby to Kettering Rail Link for Midland Main Line, and two vehicles in a green livery for a Marks and Spencer shuttle service.

In 2003 Arriva Fox County and Arriva Midlands North merged to become Arriva Midlands.

Midland Red North & Stevensons become Arriva Midlands North

Midland Red North Ltd was founded in 1981 when the Midland Red company was divided into four operating parts by NBC. The company traded with local network names such as Chaserider for a considerable time. These were based upon the networks generated from the Viable Network Project later carried out across NBC as Market Analysis Project (MAP). The area included the new town of Telford where a network of new services was introduced displacing many of the long-traditional operators.

The company was sold to Drawlane in January 1988 after a false start as described earlier. In 1989, it took over the Crewe and Etruria depots of fellow Drawlane subsidiary Crosville Motor Services Ltd. In 1992, Midland Red North purchased the Oswestry and Abermule operations of Crosville Wales Ltd, then an associated company. In 1993, with the dispersion of the Bee Line Buzz Company, the Macclesfield depot of that company which had traded as C-Line was taken over, having been part of Crosville for some time.

Stevensons of Uttoxeter commenced services in that part of Staffordshire in 1926 and continued as a small but successful family owned business. During the 1980s, and particularly after deregulation, significant growth occurred. In 1985 a controlling interest was acquired in the East Staffordshire Borough Council's bus operations in Burton-on-Trent. In 1987, the Swadlincote depot of Midland Fox and the Lichfield out station were purchased from NBC.

Growth in the West Midlands and the acquisition of a number of small companies including Crystal Coaches in Burslem and Viking Tours and Travel saw the company become a major independent operator in the early 1990s.

In April 1994, however, West Midlands Travel used its Your Bus subsidiary to retaliate in the Burton area against the significant level of operation Stevensons then had in the West Midlands area. This led to the sale of the company to British Bus in August 1994 and a significant scaling down of Stevensons operations in the West Midlands.

Macclesfield depot was transferred from Midland Red North into Stevensons in January 1995. From April 1995, Midland Red North and Stevensons were jointly managed. The closure of the Stevensons Head Office at Spath with the provision of central administration services from the Cannock head office became effective in 1996. A common livery was established between the two fleets though the Stevensons fleet name was retained on vehicles allocated to former Stevensons depots. Viking coaches retained a separate livery of two shades of grey until the operation was sold. The application of Arriva livery and branding saw the trading identity 'Arriva serving the North Midlands' applied to all buses.

In May 1998, the Shifnal depot of Timeline was acquired along with nineteen vehicles. The bus operations of Matthews Handybus in the Newcastle under Lyme area were acquired in February 1998, but no buses were involved. In August of the same year, the local bus operations of Williamsons of Knockin Heath were taken over and four vehicles came with the work.

1999 saw many SLF Dennis Darts arrive and these were followed by thirty Volvo B6BLE buses fitted with Wright Crusader 2 bodywork. All private hire coaching operations along with the vehicles were disposed of during the year.

In February 2003, Macclesfield, Crewe and Winsford depots were transferred from Arriva Midlands North to Arriva North West. The remaining depots of Midlands North were combined with Arriva Fox County to become Arriva Midlands.

More recently in 2010 Arriva Midlands acquired Wardle Transport, a leading provider of transport solutions in the Potteries. With a fleet of twelve deckers, six coaches, nineteen buses and twenty-seven minibuses, core services include private hire, school buses and football bus services, as well as a range of local bus services.

North Western Road Car Co Ltd becomes Arriva North West

Ribble Motor Services was another NBC company divided in preparation for privatisation. The dormant Mexborough & Swinton Traction Company was renamed as above to take over the Merseyside, West Lancashire and Wigan operations of Ribble in September 1986. The head office of the new company was sited at Hawthorne Road, the Bootle area office north of Liverpool.

The company was acquired by Drawlane in March 1988. In 1989, the Runcorn and Warrington depots of Crosville were acquired. Expansion saw North Western open a depot in Altrincham, though eventual rationalisation saw the operations assumed by the Bee Line Buzz Company during its independent existence as a Drawlane subsidiary.

In 1993 Bee Line was put under the same management as North Western and a few weeks later, Liverline of Bootle was acquired along with fifty-one vehicles. Both were maintained as separate identities under the same management. Also acquired in 1993 was the bus operations of Express Travel, which at the time were still branded as Amberline, though this identity was not maintained.

The head office of the company later moved to Aintree depot, though a subsequent move saw the depot sold and redeveloped leaving the head office building free standing.

1995 was a busy year with two operations in the Wigan area acquired; Little White Bus and Wigan Bus Company. Also acquired in 1995 was Arrowline Travel based in Knutsford, which traded as Star Line. This brought luxury coaches on airport-related work as well as a modern fleet of mini and midi buses. The Star Line operation was later relocated to Wythenshawe, while the coaching operation was sold to Selwyns of Runcorn.

Increase in activity in the Warrington area required a new depot to be established at Haydock. The collapse of a Cheshire operator Lofty's of Mickle Trafford saw further growth in the mid-Cheshire area and new Cheshire workings took vehicles as far south as Whitchurch.

In 1997, Arriva acquired the residue of South Lancs Transport following that operator's withdrawal from Chester, and the business was put under the supervision of North Western.

In 1998, some bus operations of Timeline in the North West were purchased along with some vehicles, though the majority went to First Group. Arriva North West manages the bus and coach facilities at the Trafford Centre on behalf of the owners of this striking shopping centre which is located four miles west of Manchester. Arriva branding initially used the identity 'Arriva serving the North West'.

In 1999, the Winsford-based Nova Scotia operation was acquired, its services being integrated into the fleet. In 2000, Arriva acquired MTL, and the bus operations were put under the control of Arriva North West, those operations being branded 'Arriva serving Merseyside' and early in 2002 the head office functions of Arriva Cymru were transferred to Aintree. Upon full integration in the later months, the company was re-titled Arriva North West and Wales.

In August 2005 the vehicles and services of Blue Bus of Bolton were acquired adding 218 employees and eighty-six vehicles to the fleet and taking Arriva into the northern part of the Greater Manchester conurbation. As a result, Arriva almost doubled the buses operating in the Manchester area which had so far covered only the city centre and areas to the south of the city into Cheshire.

Yorkshire Bus Group to Arriva Yorkshire

The West Riding Automobile Company and Yorkshire Woollen District Transport were put under common management by NBC and, when privatisation happened in January 1987, the management team bought both companies. Selby and District was a trading title turned into a separate company by the new owners' Caldaire Holding company. While Caldaire became involved in the North East, the core business in West Yorkshire changed very little but there was steady investment in fleet replacement and upgrade.

There was involvement in the splitting up of National Travel East leaving a residue of operations on National Express contracts, and also competitive operations in Sheffield that led to corresponding competition in Wakefield.

The South Yorkshire Road Transport Company of Pontefract was purchased in July 1994, and maintained a separate trading identity for a time. In March 1995, the Caldaire Group was acquired by British Bus. Jaronda Travel of Selby was acquired in August 1999.

The Arriva identities used were 'Arriva serving Yorkshire' and 'Arriva serving Selby' seeing a merging together of the West Riding and Yorkshire identities for the first time. Arriva Yorkshire partnered with First Leeds in the extension to the East Leeds Guided Bus Corridor along the A64 York Road. This initiative saw both operators together contributing nearly half the scheme cost of around £9.9m with the other half coming from a partnership of Leeds City Council and West Yorkshire PTE.

United, Tees and District, and Teesside Motor Services Ltd became Arriva North East

United Automobile Services Ltd was another NBC subsidiary divided up in preparation for privatisation. In 1986, the northern part of the operating area was hived off into a new company called Northumbria. United continued to trade south of the Tyne, with its head office in Darlington. The operations in Scarborough and Pickering were transferred to a subsidiary of East Yorkshire Motor Services.

In December 1987, United was bought from NBC by Caldaire Holdings, the management buyout vehicle of the West Riding management team. In 1989, the National Express coaching activities of United were sold off to a joint venture company Durham Travel Services, set up by two former United managers with National Express Ltd.

In 1990, United was split into two parts, the Durham and North Yorkshire section continuing to trade as United, the section in Cleveland trading as Tees and District. At this time, the associated businesses of Trimdon Motor Services and Teeside Motor Services were acquired, with the Trimdon business being absorbed into United and the Teeside business continuing.

In the summer of 1992, there was a demerger of the Caldaire Group, with the North East operations passing to the Westcourt Group, and Caldaire North East becoming North East Bus.

In 1994, a new head office and engineering works in Morton Road, Darlington allowed the vacation of the Grange Road site for redevelopment. Also in 1994, the Westcourt Group sold to West Midlands Travel in the November, and North East Bus became part of the National Express Group following the merger with that group in 1995.

Eden Bus Services of Bishop Auckland was acquired in October 1995 and was absorbed into the main operation. National Express Group sold North East Bus to the Cowie Group on the last day of July 1996 and, in October, the Ripon depot operations were sold to Harrogate and District Travel.

Northumbria Motor Services Ltd into Arriva Northumbria

In 1986, the operations of United Auto were split into two parts in preparation for privatisation. The dormant Southern National Omnibus Company Ltd was renamed Northumbria and took over operations in September 1986 with a new head office in Jesmond.

In October 1987, Northumbria was acquired from NBC by its management using Proudmutual as a holding company. Proudmutual also acquired Kentish Bus in March 1988. Other acquisitions included Moor-Dale Coaches and Hunters. In 1994 the Proudmutual group was acquired by British Bus while, at the same time, Moor-Dale Coaches was sold back to former directors.

In the Arriva era, two trading identities were used: 'Arriva serving Northumbria' and 'Arriva serving the North East'.

Crosville Cymru into Arriva Cymru

Crosville Wales Ltd was, until August 1986, the Welsh and Shropshire operations of Crosville Motor Services Ltd based in Chester. In 1986, it was resolved that the Crosville company was too large to be offered for privatisation as a whole, and the then dormant Devon General Omnibus and Touring Company Ltd was revived by NBC in order to take over the assets and business of Crosville in Wales, to be renamed Crosville Wales. The management team of Crosville Wales purchased the company from NBC in December 1987.

In January 1989, the company was bought by National Express Holdings Ltd. In July of that year, it purchased a subsidiary company called Amberline, based at Speke in Liverpool, and added a bus operation to the mainly National Express coach contracts operated.

In July 1991, the National Express group was purchased by a consortium of banks led by Drawlane, as explained earlier. Ultimately, this led to Crosville Wales becoming a full member of the Drawlane Group shortly before its transformation into British Bus plc. In January 1992, the Oswestry depot and its out-station at Abermule were sold to Midland Red North.

Crosville Wales took advantage of second-hand vehicles from other group companies and other operators, building a fleet of Leyland Lynx and National 2s while concurrently buying further new Mercedes minibuses and Dennis Darts.

In 1995, some of the services, but no vehicles, of Alpine Travel were acquired, leading to an operation of certain services as Alpine Bus in a red and white livery. This was superseded by a Shoreline livery of blue, white and yellow, which was phased out and replaced by route branding.

All operations were branded 'Arriva serving Wales/gwansanaethu Cymru', including those of the two acquisitions in 1998. The first was Devaway of Bretton, Chester. This brought a mixed fleet of VRTs, Nationals, and more Lynx and a depot from which to operate Chester area services. The second acquisition was Purple Motors of Bethesda. Further low-floor buses arrived during 1999 to provide the Arriva share of a Quality Partnership Corridor on Deeside jointly provided with First Crosville.

In February 2000 a large batch of low-floor Darts joined the fleet and these displaced the last examples of the Leyland Nationals. These Darts were introduced on low-volume rural services as north Wales authorities chose to use their share of the expanded Rural Bus Grant in improving quality rather than widening availability. Some vehicles were equipped with bike racks.

Clydeside Buses Ltd into Arriva Scotland West Ltd

Clydeside Buses and its predecessors have been serving its core area of Renfrewshire and Inverclyde since 1928. Prior to 1985, the operation had formed the northern section of Western Scottish, part of the Scottish Bus Group (SBG). In preparation for the deregulation of local bus services, Clydeside Scottish assumed responsibility for the Glasgow, Renfrewshire and Inverclyde operations of Western Scottish in 1985. Over the next six years, there was a complex series of reorganisations between Clydeside and Western until, in 1991, Clydeside became the last SBG subsidiary to be privatised when it was purchased by its employees with assistance from Luton and District Transport Group, emerging as Clydeside 2000 plc.

After 1986, there were numerous competitors in the core area and trading proved extremely difficult. When the LDT group sold to British Bus, an offer put to the shareholders of Clydeside was accepted and Clydeside joined British Bus. There was immediate effort to update the fleet against a background of tightening up of enforcement generally in the area. Some of the competitive battles had led to the Traffic Commissioner taking steps to control the number of departures and waiting times in certain town centres.

The development of services saw 'Flagship Routes' introduced to raise quality levels. Additionally, opportunities were taken to acquire various smaller operators in the area such as Ashton Coaches of Greenock, and a significant share in Dart Buses of Paisley. Operations from the Greenock base were restyled as GMS-Greenock Motor Services with a separate livery. McGills Bus Service Ltd of Barrhead was acquired by the group in 1997 and for a time was kept as a separate entity from Clydeside Buses. Clydeside also acquired Bridge Coaches of Paisley which was fully absorbed into Clydeside.

During 2001, the shareholding in Dart Buses was sold to Stagecoach Western and the dormant McGills company used as a vehicle to sell off all remaining Inverclyde operations which ceased trading at the end of June. The redundant depot at Greenock and subsequently former McGill's site at Barrhead were demolished with all operations spread between remaining sites at Inchinnan and Johnstone. In a final move to consolidate the business the remote head office site located in Renfrew was vacated and all employees subsequently relocated within a refurbished facility at Inchinnan depot. The 'Arriva serving Scotland' branding covers all operations.

Arriva acquires Telling Golden Miller

Arriva acquired Heathrow-based Tellings Golden Miller group (TGM) in January 2008. Its group of companies, made up of wholly owned subsidiaries, now operates bus and coach services across England. They include; OFJ Connections, Excel Passenger Logistics, Flight Delay Services, Classic Coaches, Burtons Coaches and Link Line Coaches all of which have kept their identity so that customers can identify with local brands. TGM operates more than 250 vehicles including; front line executive coaches, local buses, and coaches operated on behalf of National Express. TGM operates from bases in the following towns or cities; London Heathrow, Harlesden, Colchester, Cambridge and Newcastle-upon-Tyne.

Expansion into Europe

From its early holdings in Denmark and the Netherlands, Arriva developed a growth strategy across mainland Europe based on acquisitions and contract wins.

Having significant positions in the Czech Republic, Denmark, Germany, Hungary, Italy, the Netherlands, Poland, Portugal, Slovakia, Spain and Sweden, Arriva's mainland Europe division had the highest turnover of the group's three divisions in 2009. On Arriva's acquisition by Deutsche Bahn the group's German operations were divested in 2010.

A 10-year contract to operate bus services in Malta was set to commence in summer 2011.

European growth highlights

September 1997	Unibus Holdings, Denmark
January 1998	Vancom Nederland
December 1998	Veonn & Hanze, Netherlands
March 1999	Bus Danmark
July 1999	Mercancias Ideal Gallego, Spain
September 1999	Transportes Finisterre, Spain
November 2000	Ami-Transportes, Portugal
December 2000	Abilio da Costa Moreira, Portugal
April 2001	Combus, Denmark
January 2002	Autocares Mallorca, Spain
June 2002	Transportes Sul ode Tejo, Portugal
July 2002	SAB Autoservizi, Italy
April 2004	Prignitzer Eisenbahn Gruppe, Germany
October 2004	Regentalbahn, Bavaria, Germany
February 2005	Sippel, Germany
July 2005	SAVDA group, Italy
2006	Verkehrsbetriebe Bils KG, Germany
	Trancentrum Bus s.r.o, Czech Republic
2007	Esfera, Madrid
	Autocares Fray Escoba, Spain
	Bosak, Czech Republic
	Arriva PCC, 50/50 joint venture, Poland
2008	Empresa de Blas y Cia S.L., Spain
	Interbus Invest, Hungary and Slovakia
2009	Interbus Invest, Hungary and Slovakia (remaining 20 per cent)
2010	The group is acquired by Deutsche Bahn, one of the world's leading passenger and logistics service providers

Scandinavia

Arriva Skandinavien provides bus and rail services in Denmark and Sweden. The first acquisition in mainland Europe was Unibus in Denmark, which was acquired in 1997. Unibus operated approximately 8 per cent of the tendered market in Copenhagen and had operations throughout Jutland and Zealand. Founded in 1985, Unibus grew by winning tendered bus operations for the Transport Authority for the Greater Copenhagen Area - HT. Unibus was the biggest coach operator in Copenhagen until in 1995, when the coaching business was sold to Lyngby Turistfart.

This involvement within the Danish bus market led to the acquisition of Bus Danmark (now Arriva Skandinavien) in 1999 and its wholly owned subsidiary Ödakra Buss based in southern Sweden. In April 2000, Arriva Skandinavien acquired the former state owned Company, COMBUS. Part of the company was sold on to Connex (Veolia) but Arriva kept the majority of its regional and provincial bus operations throughout Denmark. During 2001 the first double-deck buses for the Danish fleet were delivered.

The group was the first private company to be awarded a passenger rail franchise under new legislation to privatise the Danish rail industry. In January 2003 it started operating services on eight-year concessions in Jutland. The package consisted of two passenger rail franchises connecting Mid and West Jutland with Aarhus, the second largest town in Denmark. Arriva re-won the Jutland rail contract for a further eight years from 2010 and is the countries top performing rail operator, carrying 5 per cent of all passengers in the country and covering 15 per cent of the national network.

In 2004 Arriva acquired Wulff Bus A/S, a Danish bus operator which had a strong geographical fit with Arriva's existing business in Jutland and Copenhagen. With this acquisition Arriva became Copenhagen's biggest bus operator with a 40 per cent market share. Arriva also completed the acquisition of Veolia Danmark, the second largest operator in the Danish bus market, in 2007. Arriva is now the largest bus operator in Denmark operating around 60 per cent of the market in Copenhagen, and approximately 50 per cent of services outside the capital.

Arriva's Danish operation employs 4,000 people and operates 1,400 buses and forty-seven trains. Arriva first entered the Swedish bus market when it acquired the Danish company Bus Danmark and its wholly owned subsidiary Ödakra Buss based in southern Sweden in 1999. Arriva Sverige (Ödakra Buss) activities focused in the Skåne Län region of southern Sweden and in and around Jönköping. In 2005 a new contract called for a large fleet of MAN buses to operate in the city of Helsingborg.

In 2007 the group began operating train services in Sweden, with a nine-year contract to operate the Pågatåg regional train service in the Skåne region of southern Sweden. In 2009, Arriva expanded its rail operations in Sweden with a new contract operating between Göteborg and Örebo and became the first private entrant into Stockholm in ten years when it began operating 164 buses in the Swedish capital. Arriva also won an eight-year contract to operate sixty-five buses in the Halland region of Southern Sweden from June 2010.

Arriva's Swedish operation employs 1,870 people and operates some 620 buses and forty-six trains.

Following the acquisition of Arriva plc by Deutsche Bahn in 2010, Deutsche Bahn owned Danish bus company Pan Bus came under the management of Arriva Denmark in January 2011. At the same time two DB rail contracts in Sweden, including a joint venture with Swedish national rail operator SJ, were combined with Arriva's Swedish Rail operations.

The Netherlands

Arriva entered the Dutch transport market in 1998 when it acquired two bus companies. It bought Vancom Nederland, the first and to date the only municipal privatisation, and purchased Veonn and Hanze under a part privatisation of the Dutch state-owned transport company Connexxion.

Arriva initiated a joint venture with the state-owned rail operator NS Rail in 1999, combining their trains with Arriva's buses to provide integrated services in the north of the country. The joint venture represented the first rail privatisation in the Netherlands.

Arriva Nederland won two large tenders to operate bus services in central Holland in 2002, the first private operator to win a franchise from the state-owned incumbent. In 2005 Arriva won a fifteen-year rail contract and is now sole provider of regional rail services in provinces of Friesland and Groningen and provides cross-border services into Germany. The company increased its share of the rail passenger sector, with major contract wins in the northern provinces as well as the Dordrecht area, where train services operate alongside its buses.

More recently Arriva began operating the Hoeksche Waard and Goeree Overflakkee bus contract to the south of Rotterdam and the Achterhoek Rivierenland bus and rail tender in Gelderland, Netherlands.

The group is now one of the three largest bus operators in the Netherlands, with approximately 12 per cent of the regional bus market. Arriva's combined businesses in the Netherlands operate 560 buses, fifty-eight trains and employ 1,600 people.

Poland

Arriva and joint venture partners PCC Rail won a three-year contract in 2007 to operate train services in Kujawsko-Pomorskie Voidvodship in north-west Poland. In 2010 Arriva acquired its partner's share and the company, known as Arriva RP, is fully owned by Arriva. In 2010 Arriva RP was awarded a ten-year regional rail contract in the Kujawsko Pomorskie region of Poland extending operations that have been run by Arriva for the past three years and increasing annual kilometres operated by up to fifteen per cent.

Portugal

Arriva entered the Portuguese bus market in 2000 when it acquired AMI Transportes, Joao Carlos Soares and Abilio da Costa Moreira, three family-owned companies running inter-urban services in the north-west of Portugal.

In June 2002 it acquired 51 per cent of Transportes Sul do Tejo (TST) from the Barraqueiro Group and exercised its option to purchase the remaining 49 per cent in September 2003.

TST is the major private operator of scheduled bus and coach services in the growing commuter region to the south of Lisbon, an area of some 600 square miles. It also operates schools and works contracts in the region. Together with Arriva's operations in the north, Arriva Portugal – Transportes LDA, it is one of Portugal's leading bus companies.

In 2006, Arriva acquired 21.5 per cent of Barraqueiro SGPS SA, the leading Portuguese transport operator, with bus and rail operations in and around Lisbon. Arriva acquired a further 10 per cent of Barraqueiro in January 2008 taking its holding to 31.5 per cent (21.5 per cent acquired in 2006).

As part of a consortium including the Barraqueiro, Arriva won a five-year contract to operate and maintain the Metro do Porto, the city of Porto's tram network from April 2010.

Arriva's combined businesses in Portugal employ 3,100 people and operate 1,550 buses.

Italy

Arriva entered the Italian market in July 2002 when it acquired SAB Autoservizi Srl, a bus group with subsidiaries operating in the Lombardy, Liguria and Friuli-Venezia Giulia regions of northern Italy.

SAB and its subsidiary companies operate principally in the Lombardy region of northern Italy, providing urban, inter-urban and airport services in the Bergamo, Brescia and Lecco areas.

The group made further acquisitions in April 2004 when it acquired 49 per cent of Società Autoservizi FVG SpA (SAF) in the Udine area of the Friuli-Venezia Giulia region, and in October 2005, when it acquired 80 per cent of the SADEM operations near Turin. The group increased its stake in Societa Autoservizi, F.V.G S.p.a to 60 per cent in 2005 and acquired the remaining 20 per cent of SADEM in 2008.

SADEM and its subsidiary SAPAV operate in the Piemonte and Valle d'Aosta regions of northern Italy to the west of Arriva's other operations.

In 2006, Arriva acquired a 35 per cent stake in Trieste Trasporti which increased to 40 per cent in 2007 and in the same year entered a joint venture with Ferrovie Nord Milano Group (FNM SpA) and contracted to acquire 49 per cent of Italian bus operator SPT Linea.

Arriva increased its shareholding in Brescia-based SAIA Transporti to 100 per cent in 2008. The initial shareholding was acquired as part of the purchase of the SAB Group of companies in 2002.

Arriva's combined businesses in Italy have 2,500 employees and operate 1,900 buses.

Germany

Arriva entered the German public transport market - the largest in Europe - in 2004, with the acquisition of rail company Prignitzer Eisenbahn Gruppe (PEG) and strengthened its position with further acquisitions, including Regentalbahn based in eastern Bavaria, and contract wins. In 2005 the group entered the German bus market with its acquisition of Sippel and strengthened its position by acquiring Verkehrsbetriebe Bils and Neißeverkehr in 2006 and a majority stake in bus and rail company Osthannoversche Eisenbahnen AG in 2007. By 2009 Arriva had grown its position in the German transport market operating approximately five per cent of the rail market and one per cent of the bus market.

With a series of contract wins and further acquisitions Arriva had established itself as Germany's second largest private rail operator.

In August 2010, Arriva was acquired by German state-owned rail operator Deutsche Bahn, which provides more than two million bus journeys and more than 39,000 train trips every day. As one of the world's leading passenger and logistics service providers DB employs 220,000 people across 130 countries. As a condition of the acquisition of Arriva, the European competition authorities required that Deutsche Bahn sell off Arriva's former operations in Germany. In December 2010 it was announced that Arriva Germany was to be sold to a consortium led by Italy's Ferrovie dello Stato in partnership with Cube Infrastructure.

Czech Republic

Arriva entered the Czech Republic bus market in 2006 with the acquisition of Transcentrum Bus s.r.o, a leading company operating bus services to the north of Prague. Based in Mlada Boleslav, it operates in the Stredocesky region with additional services in the regions of Liberecky and Kralovehradecky.

In 2007 Arriva strengthened its position with the acquisitions of Bosak Bus s.r.o, which operates to the south west of Prague, and Osnado Spol s.r.o, which provides urban, suburban and long-distance services in the north east of Prague.

Hungary and Slovakia

Arriva entered the Hungarian and Slovakian bus markets in July 2008 with the acquisition of 80 per cent of Interbus Invest, the holding company of Eurobus Invest, Hungary's largest private bus operator. In 2009, the group acquired the remaining 20 per cent of Interbus Invest.

Arriva UK Trains

Arriva operates the Arriva Trains Wales/Trenau Arriva Cymru and CrossCountry passenger rail franchises. Arriva was awarded the Welsh rail franchise in 2003 and CrossCountry in 2007.

Arriva Trains Wales/Trenau Arriva Cymru operates interurban, commuter and rural passenger services throughout Wales and the border counties.

The CrossCountry network is the most extensive rail franchise in the UK. Stretching from Aberdeen to Penzance, and from Stansted to Cardiff, it covers around 1,500 route miles and calls at over a hundred and twenty stations.

From 1 January 2011 DB Regio UK, which includes Chiltern Railways, DB Regio Tyne & Wear which operates the Tyne & Wear Metro, and a 50 per cent holding in London Overground Rail Operations Ltd, became part of Arriva's UK Trains division.

For more information on Arriva visit www.arriva.co.uk

ARRIVA SCOTLAND WEST

Arriva Scotland West Ltd, Greenock Road, Inchinnan, PA4 9PG

258	IN	M109RMS	Scania N113 CRL	East Lancs European	N45F	1995		
260	IN	M112RMS	Scania N113 CRL	East Lancs European	N45F	1995		
261	IN	M113RMS	Scania N113 CRL	East Lancs European	N45F	1995		

262-268 — Scania L113 CRL — East Lancs European — N51F — 1995

262	IN	M114RMS	**265**	IN	M117RMS	**267**	IN	M119RMS	**268**	IN	M120RMS
263	IN	M115RMS						

270	JO	L25LSX	Scania N113 CRL	East Lancs European	N51F	1993	Scania demonstrator, 1995
1001	JO	CX55EAA	Mercedes-Benz Citaro O530	Mercedes-Benz	NC42F	2006	Arriva NW& Wales, 2009
1002	JO	CX55EAC	Mercedes-Benz Citaro O530	Mercedes-Benz	NC42F	2006	Arriva NW& Wales, 2009
1003	JO	CX55EAE	Mercedes-Benz Citaro O530	Mercedes-Benz	NC42F	2006	Arriva NW& Wales, 2009

1401-1407 — Dennis Dart SLF 10.2m — Alexander ALX200 — N36F — 1997 — Arriva London, 2003

1401	JO	P962RUL	**1403**	JO	P964RUL	**1405**	JO	P966RUL	**1407**	JO	P968RUL
1402	JO	P963RUL	**1404**	JO	P965RUL	**1406**	JO	P967RUL			

1408	JO	V311NGD	Dennis Dart SLF 10.7m	Plaxton Pointer 2	N43F	1999
1409	JO	V312NGD	Dennis Dart SLF 10.7m	Plaxton Pointer 2	N43F	1999
1410	JO	V313NGD	Dennis Dart SLF 10.7m	Plaxton Pointer 2	N43F	1999

1411-1415 — Dennis Dart SLF — Plaxton Pointer — N35F — 1996

1411	IN	P801RWU	**1413**	JO	P803RWU	**1414**	IN	P804RWU	**1415**	IN	P805RWU
1412	IN	P802RWU						

1416-1425 — Dennis Dart SLF — Alexander ALX200 — N40F — 1997

1416	JO	P806DBS	**1419**	IN	P809DBS	**1421**	IN	P811DBS	**1424**	JO	P814DBS
1417	JO	P807DBS	**1420**	JO	P810DBS	**1423**	JO	P813DBS	**1425**	JO	P815DBS
1418	JO	P808DBS						

Three Mercedes-Benz Citaro O530 buses were transferred from the North West operation are now allocated to Johnston depot for the route connecting Glasgow Airport with Largs. Illustrating the type is 1001, CX55EAA.
Steve Rice

New to Arriva London, 1476, W606VGJ in the Scottish fleet, is seen in Glasgow's Union Street. The Alexander bodywork was converted to single-door and refurbished at the time of the transfer. *Richard Godfrey*

1426-1450

Dennis Dart SLF — Plaxton Pointer — N39F — 1997

1426	IN	P816GMS	1433	IN	P823GMS	1439	JO	P829KES	1445	IN	P835KES
1427	IN	P817GMS	1434	IN	P824GMS	1440	JO	P830KES	1446	JO	P836KES
1428	IN	P818GMS	1435	IN	P825KES	1441	IN	P831KES	1447	JO	P837KES
1429	JO	P819GMS	1436	IN	HIL2148	1442	JO	P832KES	1448	JO	P838KES
1430	JO	P820GMS	1437	IN	P827KES	1443	IN	P833KES	1449	IN	P839KES
1431	IN	P821GMS	1438	IN	P828KES	1444	IN	P834KES	1450	JO	P840KES
1432	IN	P822GMS									

1451-1455

Dennis Dart SLF — Alexander ALX200 — N40F — 1998

1451	JO	R381JYS	1453	JO	R383JYS	1454	JO	R384JYS	1455	JO	R385JYS
1452	JO	R382JYS									

1456-1465

Dennis Dart SLF — Alexander ALX200 — N40F — 1998-99

1456	JO	S860OGB	1459	JO	S863OGB	1462	JO	S866OGB	1464	JO	S868OGB
1457	JO	S861OGB	1460	JO	S864OGB	1463	JO	S867OGB	1465	JO	S869OGB
1458	JO	S862OGB	1461	JO	S865OGB						

1466	JO	P210LKJ	Dennis Dart SLF 10.1m	Plaxton Pointer	N40F	1997	Southern Counties, 2009
1467	JO	P211LKJ	Dennis Dart SLF 10.1m	Plaxton Pointer	N40F	1997	Southern Counties, 2009
1468	JO	P212LKJ	Dennis Dart SLF 10.1m	Plaxton Pointer	N40F	1997	Southern Counties, 2009
1471	JO	V701LWT	Dennis Dart SLF 10.2m	Alexander ALX200	N31F	1999	Arriva London, 2010

1472-1478

Dennis Dart SLF 10.2m — Alexander ALX200 — N27D* — 2000 — Arriva London, 2010

1472	JO	W602VGJ	1474	JO	W604VGJ	1476	JO	W606VGJ	1478	JO	W608VGJ
1473	JO	W603VGJ	1475	JO	W605VGJ	1477	JO	W607VGJ			

1479-1493

Dennis Dart SLF 10.8m — Alexander ALX200 — N33D* — 1999 — Arriva London, 2010

1479	JO	V609LGC	1483	JO	V613LGC	1487	JO	V617LGC	1491	JO	V621LGC
1480	JO	V610LGC	1484	JO	V614LGC	1488	JO	V618LGC	1492	JO	V622LGC
1481	JO	V611LGC	1485	JO	V615LGC	1489	JO	V619LGC	1493	JO	V623LGC
1482	JO	V612LGC	1486	JO	V616LGC	1490	JO	V620LGC			

Arriva Scotland operates three DAF SB120 buses with Wright Cadet bodywork that were new to Arriva North East in 2000. Seen in Glasgow while heading for Barrhead is 1921, W82PRG. *Steve Rice*

1603-1610

1603-1610			Dennis Dart 9.8m			Plaxton Pointer		B40F	1995-96	Arriva London, 2003
1603	u	N681GUM	1606	JO	N672GUM	1608	JO	N677GUM	1610	IN	N685GUM
1605	IN	P822RWU	1607	IN	N675GUM	1609	IN	N683GUM			

1614	IN	N686GUM	Dennis Dart 9.8m	Plaxton Pointer	B40F	1996	Arriva London, 2003
1615	IN	N687GUM	Dennis Dart 9.8m	Plaxton Pointer	B40F	1996	Arriva London, 2003
1619	IN	N689GUM	Dennis Dart 9.8m	Plaxton Pointer	B40F	1996	Arriva London, 2003
1620	IN	N691GUM	Dennis Dart 9.8m	Plaxton Pointer	B40F	1996	Arriva London, 2003
1624	IN	S624KHN	Dennis Dart SLF 10.1m	Plaxton Pointer 2	N39F	1999	
1628	IN	N474MUS	Dennis Dart 9.8m	Northern Counties Paladin	B39F	1995	
1642	JO	S642KHN	Dennis Dart SLF 10.1m	Plaxton Pointer 2	N39F	1999	
1643	IN	S643KHN	Dennis Dart SLF 10.1m	Plaxton Pointer 2	N39F	1999	
1780	JO	N710GUM	Dennis Dart 9m	Plaxton Pointer	B34F	1995	Arriva London, 2003
1781	JO	N711GUM	Dennis Dart 9m	Plaxton Pointer	B34F	1995	Arriva London, 2003
1782	JO	N712GUM	Dennis Dart 9m	Plaxton Pointer	B34F	1995	Arriva London, 2003
1783	JO	P913PWW	Dennis Dart 9m	Plaxton Pointer	B34F	1996	Arriva London, 2003
1784	JO	P914PWW	Dennis Dart 9m	Plaxton Pointer	B34F	1996	Arriva London, 2003
1785	JO	P915PWW	Dennis Dart 9m	Plaxton Pointer	B34F	1996	Arriva London, 2003
1786	IN	N708GUM	Dennis Dart 9m	Plaxton Pointer	B34F	1995	Arriva London, 2003
1787	IN	N709GUM	Dennis Dart 9m	Plaxton Pointer	B34F	1995	Arriva London, 2003
1918	IN	W78PRG	DAF SB120	Wright Cadet	N39F	2000	Arriva NE, 2005
1919	IN	W79PRG	DAF SB120	Wright Cadet	N39F	2000	Arriva NE, 2005
1921	IN	W82PRG	DAF SB120	Wright Cadet	N39F	2000	Arriva NE, 2005
1951	IN	YJ54CKG	VDL Bus SB120	Wrightbus Cadet 2	N30F	2004	
1952	IN	YJ54CKK	VDL Bus SB120	Wrightbus Cadet 2	N30F	2004	

1955-1959

1955-1959			VDL Bus SB120			Plaxton Centro		N40F	2007	
1955	IN	YJ07JSU	1957	IN	YJ07JSX	1958	IN	YJ07JSY	1959	IN	YJ07JSZ
1956	IN	YJ07JSV									

Pictured in Killermont Street, Glasgow in August 2010, DAF SB3000 3001, GSU347, is seen arriving in the city while working the Airport service. The Van Hool bodywork shows an interesting application of the inter-urban colour scheme. *Richard Godfrey*

2001-2010

VDL Bus SB200   Wrightbus Pulsar 2   N44F   2009

2001	IN	YJ09CVH	**2004**	IN	YJ09CUV	**2007**	IN	YJ09CVO	**2009**	IN	YJ09CUW
2002	IN	YJ09CVK	**2005**	IN	YJ09CVM	**2008**	IN	YJ09CVR	**2010**	IN	YJ09CUX
2003	IN	YJ09CVL	**2006**	IN	YJ09CVN						

2011-2014

VDL Bus SB200   Wrightbus Commander   N44F   2004   Arriva Yorkshire, 2010

2011	IN	YJ04HJC	**2012**	IN	YJ04HJD	**2013**	IN	YJ04HJE	**2014**	IN	YJ04HJF
2601	IN	MV02XYJ	Mercedes-Benz Vario O814		Plaxton Beaver 2		B27F		2002		Arriva NW & Wales, 2009
2602	IN	MV02XYK	Mercedes-Benz Vario O814		Plaxton Beaver 2		B27F		2002		Arriva NW & Wales, 2009
2603	IN	MK52XNS	Mercedes-Benz Vario O814		Plaxton Beaver 2		B27F		2002		Arriva NW & Wales, 2009
2801	IN	SF09LOD	Renault Master		IndCar		N15F		2009		
2802	IN	YX09EVG	Volkswagen T5		Bluebird Tucana		N14F		2009		
2803	IN	YX09EVH	Volkswagen T5		Bluebird Tucana		N14F		2009		
3001	JO	GSU347	DAF SB3000		Van Hool Alizée HE		C53F		1994		Arriva The Shires, 2009
3002	JO	WSU476	DAF SB3000		Van Hool Alizée HE		C51F		1994		Arriva The Shires, 2009

4401-4411

Volvo B7RLE   Wrightbus Eclipse Urban   N37F   2007

4401	JO	SF57NPK	**4404**	JO	SJ57DDY	**4407**	JO	SJ57DDU	**4410**	JO	SJ57DDO
4402	JO	SF57NPL	**4405**	JO	SJ57DDX	**4408**	JO	SF57NMO	**4411**	JO	SJ57DDN
4403	JO	SJ57DDZ	**4406**	JO	SJ57DDV	**4409**	JO	SF57NMM			
4531	u	L201TKA	Volvo B6 9.9M		Plaxton Pointer		B38F		1994		Arriva North West & Wales, 2006
4532	u	L210TKA	Volvo B6 9.9M		Plaxton Pointer		B38F		1994		Arriva North West & Wales, 2006
4537	u	L235TKA	Volvo B6 9.9M		Plaxton Pointer		B38F		1994		Arriva North West & Wales, 2006

4665-4670 Scania OmniCity K230 UB Scania N45F 2008

4665	IN	YR58SUH	4667	IN	YR58SUU	4669	IN	YR58SUX	4670	IN	YR58SUY
4666	IN	YR58SUO	4668	IN	YR58SUV						

7264	JO	M169GRY	Scania N113 DRB		East Lancs	B47/33F	1994	Arriva Midlands, 2009
7265	JO	M160GRY	Scania N113 DRB		East Lancs	B47/33F	1994	Arriva Midlands, 2009
7266	JO	M165GRY	Scania N113 DRB		East Lancs	B47/33F	1994	Arriva Midlands, 2009
7267	JO	M831SDA	Scania N113 DRB		East Lancs	BC43/29F	1995	Arriva Midlands, 2009
7268	u	M832SDA	Scania N113 DRB		East Lancs	BC43/29F	1995	Arriva Midlands, 2009
7269	JO	M833SDA	Scania N113 DRB		East Lancs	BC43/29F	1995	Arriva Midlands, 2009
7273	u	L273FVN	Leyland Olympian ON2R50C13Z4	Alexander RH		B45/29F	1993	
7274	u	L274FVN	Leyland Olympian ON2R50C13Z4	Alexander RH		B45/29F	1993	

Previous registrations:

GSU347	M943LYR		V312NGD	V312NGD, WSU476
S869OGB	S869OGB, HIL2148		V313NGD	V313NGD, GSU347
V311NGD	V311NGD, WSU475		WSU476	M947LYR

Allocations:

Inchinnan (Greenock Road) - IN

Mercedes-Benz	2601	2602	2603					
Renault Master	2801							
Volkswagen	2802	2803						
Dart	1605	1607	1609	1610	1614	1615	1619	1620
	1624	1628	1643	1786				
Dart SLF	1411	1412	1414	1415	1419	1421	1426	1427
	1428	1429	1431	1432	1433	1434	1435	1436
	1437	1438	1441	1443	1444	1445	1449	1460
	1466	1628						
SB120	1918	1919	1921	1951	1952	1955	1956	1957
	1958	1959						
SB200	2001	2002	2003	2004	2005	2006	2007	2008
	2009	2010	2011	2012	2013	2014		
Scania sd	258	261	262	263	265	268	4665	4666
	4667	4668	4669	4670				
Citaro	1001	1002	1003					
Scania DD	7269							

Johnstone (Cochranemill Road) - JO

Dart	1780	1781	1782	1783	1784	1785		
Dart SLF	1401	1402	1403	1404	1405	1406	1407	1408
	1409	1410	1413	1416	1417	1418	1420	1423
	1424	1425	1430	1439	1440	1442	1446	1447
	1448	1450	1451	1452	1453	1454	1455	1456
	1457	1458	1459	1460	1461	1462	1463	1464
	1465	1467	1468	1471	1472	1473	1474	1475
	1476	1477	1478	1479	1480	1481	1482	1483
	1484	1485	1486	1487	1488	1489	1490	1491
	1492	1493	1606	1608	1642			
Volvo B7RLE	4401	4402	4403	4404	4405	4406	4407	4408
	4409	4410	4411					
Mercedes Citaro	1001	1002	1003					
Scania DD	7264	7265	7266	7267	7269			

Unallocated and stored - u

Remainder

ARRIVA NORTH EAST

Arriva North East Ltd, Arriva House, Admiral Way, Sunderland, SR3 3XP

1	BH	YJ58FFA	VDL Bus SB200			Plaxton Centro		N45F	2008	
2	DN	YJ58FFB	VDL Bus SB200			Plaxton Centro		N45F	2008	
4	DN	YJ58FFC	VDL Bus SB200			Plaxton Centro		N45F	2008	

261-267

Scania L113 CRL East Lancs European NC51F 1996 Arriva Midlands, 2010

| 261 | SN | N178PUT | 263 | SN | N171PUT | 265 | SN | N174PUT | 267 | DM | N179PUT |
| 262 | SN | N166PUT | 264 | SN | N170PUT | 266 | SN | N432XRC | | | |

271-280

Scania L113 CRL East Lancs European NC45F 1996

271	u	P271VRG	275	u	P275VRG	277	SN	P277VRG	279	SN	P279VRG
272	SN	P272VRG	276	SN	P276VRG	278	u	P278VRG	280	u	P814VTY
274	AS	P274VRG									

281-290

Scania L113 CRL East Lancs European NC45F 1995

281	AS	N281NCN	284	DM	N284NCN	287	DM	N287NCN	289	AS	N289NCN
282	DM	N282NCN	285	u	N285NCN	288	u	N288NCN	290	u	N290NCN
283	DM	N283NCN									

902-923

Optare MetroRider MR15 Optare B31F 1997-98

| 902 | SN | P902DRG | 917 | AS | R917JNL | 919 | AS | R919JNL | 923 | u | R923JNL |
| 915 | AS | R915JNL | 918 | AS | R918JNL | | | | | | |

1201-1205

DAF SB3000 Plaxton Prima Interurban BC51F 1997

| 1201 | NL | R291KRG | 1203 | NL | R293KRG | 1204 | NL | R294KRG | 1205 | NL | R295KRG |
| 1202 | NL | R292KRG | | | | | | | | | |

1206-1214

DAF SB3000 Plaxton Prima Interurban BC51F 1999

1206	NL	V206DJR	1209	DN	V209DJR	1211	AS	V211DJR	1213	DN	V213DJR
1207	RR	V207DJR	1210	AS	V210DJR	1212	AS	V212DJR	1214	NL	V214DJR
1208	DN	V208DJR									

1401	NL	NK53HHX	VDL Bus SB200	Wrightbus Commander	N44F	2003
1402	NL	NK53HHY	VDL Bus SB200	Wrightbus Commander	N44F	2003
1403	NL	NK53HHZ	VDL Bus SB200	Wrightbus Commander	N44F	2003

Corbridge is the location for this view of 1201, R291KRG, a DAF SB3000 with Plaxton Prima Interurban bodywork. All of the vehicles in this 1997 batch are currently based in Newcastle. *Richard Godfrey*

1404-1428 — VDL Bus SB200, Wrightbus Pulsar 2, N44F, 2009

1404	AS	NK09BPF	1411	BH	NK09BRF	1417	BT	NK09EJF	1423	BT	NK09EJY
1405	AS	NK09BPO	1412	BH	NK09BRV	1418	BT	NK09EJG	1424	DN	NK09EJZ
1406	AS	NK09BPU	1413	BH	NK09BRX	1419	BT	NK09EJJ	1425	DN	NK09EKA
1407	AS	NK09BPV	1414	BH	NK09BRZ	1420	BT	NK09EJL	1426	DN	NK09EKB
1408	BH	NK09BPX	1415	BT	NK09EJD	1421	BT	NK09EJV	1427	DN	NK09EKC
1409	BH	NK09BPY	1416	BT	NK09EJE	1422	BT	NK09EJX	1428	DN	NK09EKD
1410	BH	NK09BPZ									

1429-1460 — VDL Bus SB200, Wrightbus Pulsar 2, N44F, 2009-10

1429	RR	NK59DNE	1437	RR	NK10CEV	1445	SN	NK10CFJ	1453	SN	NK10CFX
1430	RR	NK59DNF	1438	RR	NK10CEX	1446	SN	NK10CFL	1454	SN	NK10CFY
1431	RR	NK59DNJ	1439	RR	NK10CEY	1447	SN	NK10CFM	1455	SN	NK10CFZ
1432	RR	NK59DNN	1440	RR	NK10CFA	1448	SN	NK10CFN	1456	SN	NK10CGE
1433	RR	NK10CEJ	1441	SN	NK10CFD	1449	SN	NK10CFO	1457	SN	NK10CGF
1434	RR	NK10CEN	1442	SN	NK10CFE	1450	SN	NK10CFP	1458	SN	NK10CGG
1435	RR	NK10CEO	1443	SN	NK10CFF	1451	SN	NK10CFU	1459	SN	NK10CGO
1436	RR	NK10CEU	1444	SN	NK10CFG	1452	SN	NK10CFV	1460	SN	NK10CGU

1507	u	K507BHN	MAN 11.190	Optare Vecta	B42F	1993	
1526	u	L526FHN	MAN 11.190	Optare Vecta	B42F	1994	
1533	u	L533FHN	MAN 11.190	Optare Vecta	B42F	1994	
1551	u	L551GHN	MAN 11.190	Optare Vecta	B42F	1994	
1558	u	K140RYS	MAN 11.190	Optare Vecta	BC42F	1993	Arriva Midlands North, 1999

1601	DN	L127YVK	Dennis Dart 9m	Northern Counties Paladin	B35F	1994	Arriva Midlands, 2010
1602	DN	L157YVK	Dennis Dart 9m	Northern Counties Paladin	B35F	1994	Arriva Midlands, 2010

1611-1626 — Dennis Dart SLF 10.1m, Plaxton Pointer 2, N39F, 1999

1611	DN	S611KHN	1616	BT	S616KHN	1618	DN	S618KHN	1625	DN	S625KHN
1612	DN	S612KHN	1617	DN	S617KHN	1621	RR	S621KHN	1626	DN	S626KHN
1613	BT	S613KHN									

1635-1640 — Dennis Dart SLF 10.1m, Plaxton Pointer 2, N39F, 1999

1635	RR	S635KHN	1637	BT	S637KHN	1639	DM	S639KHN	1640	DM	S640KHN
1636	BT	S636KHN	1638	DM	S638KHN					

1646-1656 — Dennis Dart SLF 10m, Plaxton Pointer, N34F, 1997, Arriva London, 2007

1646	SN	R421COO	1649	RR	R424COO	1652	u	R427COO	1655	DN	R430COO
1647	SN	R422COO	1650	SN	R425COO	1653	DN	R428COO	1656	DM	R431COO
1648	SN	R423COO	1651	RR	R426COO	1654	DN	R429COO			

1657	u	K582MGT	Dennis Dart 9m	Plaxton Pointer	B34F	1991	Stagecoach, 2007

1658-1669 — Dennis Dart 9.8m, Plaxton Pointer, B40F, 1992-93, Stagecoach, 2007

1658	RR	K709PCN	1661	DN	L735VNL	1664	DN	L738VNL	1667	DN	L741VNL
1659	DN	K717PCN	1662	DN	L736VNL	1665	DN	L739VNL	1668	RR	L748VNL
1660	DN	L729VNL	1663	RR	L737VNL	1666	DN	L740VNL	1669	DN	L759VNL

1670	DN	M770DRG	Dennis Dart 9.8m	Plaxton Pointer	B40F	1994	Stagecoach, 2007

1671-1679 — Dennis Dart 9.8m, Alexander Dash, B36F, 1995-96, Stagecoach, 2007

1671	DN	N301AMC	1674	DN	P615PGP	1676	DN	P617PGP	1678	DN	P637PGP
1673	RR	N305AMC	1675	RR	P616PGP	1677	DN	P634PGP	1679	DN	P638PGP

1680-1684 — Dennis Dart 9.8m, Alexander Dash, B40F, 1996, Stagecoach 2007

1680	DN	P456EEF	1682	DN	P459EEF	1683	DN	P460EEF	1684	DN	P461EEF
1681	DN	P458EEF								

1685	DN	L141YVK	Dennis Dart 9m	Northern Counties Paladin	B35F	1994	Arriva Yorkshire, 2006
1686	SN	J220HGY	Dennis Dart 9m	Plaxton Pointer	B35F	1995	Arriva Yorkshire, 2006
1688	AS	J468OKP	Dennis Dart 9.8m	Plaxton Pointer	B40F	1992	Arriva Yorkshire, 2006
1696	DN	M186YKA	Dennis Dart 9.8m	Plaxton Pointer	B40F	1995	Arriva NW&W, 2009
1697	RR	M186YKA	Dennis Dart 9.8m	Plaxton Pointer	B40F	1995	Arriva NW&W, 2009
1698	AS	M211YKD	Dennis Dart 9.8m	Plaxton Pointer	B40F	1995	Arriva NW&W, 2009
1701	SN	T701RCN	Dennis Dart SLF 8.8m	Plaxton Pointer MPD	N29F	1999	
1702	BH	T702RCN	Dennis Dart SLF 8.8m	Plaxton Pointer MPD	N29F	1999	

Recently delivered to Scotstown depot is 1450, NK10CFP, a VDL Bus SB200 with Wrightbus Pulsar 2 bodywork, a combination that can be found in many of the English operations. This example carries lettering for the 27 series of routes. *Richard Godfrey*

1703-1723

		Dennis Dart SLF 8.8m			Plaxton Pointer MPD		N29F		1999						

1703	DN	V703DNL	1709	u	V709DNL	1714	BH	V714DNL	1719	RR	V719DNL
1704	DN	V612DNL	1710	DN	V710DNL	1715	NL	V715DNL	1720	RR	V720DNL
1705	DN	V705DNL	1711	DN	V711DNL	1716	DN	V716DNL	1721	BH	V721DNL
1706	DN	V706DNL	1712	u	V712DNL	1717	DN	V717DNL	1722	SN	V722DNL
1707	AS	V707DNL	1713	u	V713DNL	1718	SN	V718DNL	1723	NL	V723DNL
1708	DN	V708DNL									

1724-1742

		Dennis Dart SLF 8.8m			Plaxton Pointer MPD		N29F		1999						

1724	BH	V724DNL	1733	BH	V733DNL	1737	RR	V737DNL	1740	BH	V740DNL
1726	BH	V726DNL	1734	SN	V734DNL	1738	RR	V738DNL	1741	BH	V741DNL
1727	SN	V727DNL	1735	DN	V735DNL	1739	RR	V739DNL	1742	BH	V742DNL
1728	BH	V728DNL	1736	RR	V736DNL						

1743-1748

		Dennis Dart SLF 8.8m			Plaxton Pointer MPD		N29F		2000		

1743	WY	V743ECU	1745	DN	V745ECU	1747	DN	V747ECU	1748	WY	V748ECU
1744	WY	V744ECU	1746	DN	V746ECU						

1750-1757

		Dennis Dart SLF 8.8m			Plaxton Pointer MPD		N29F		2000		

1750	NL	W751SBR	1752	NL	W753SBR	1754	AS	W756SBR	1756	SN	W758SBR
1751	NL	W752SBR	1753	SN	W754SBR	1755	SN	W757SBR	1757	WY	W759SBR

1758	NL	NK53HJA	TransBus Dart SLF 8.8m	TransBus Mini Pointer	N29F	2003
1759	NL	NK53VKA	TransBus Dart SLF 8.8m	TransBus Mini Pointer	N29F	2004

1760-1775

		ADL Dart 8.8m			ADL Mini Pointer		NC29F		2005						

1760	NL	NK05GVX	1764	DN	NK05GWC	1768	SN	NK05GWG	1772	DN	NK05GWO
1761	DN	NK05GVY	1765	BH	NK05GWD	1769	SN	NK05GWJ	1773	BH	NK05GWU
1762	NL	NK05GVG	1766	SN	NK05GWE	1770	SN	NK05GWM	1774	BH	NK05GWV
1763	BH	NK05GWA	1767	SN	NK05GWF	1771	SN	NK05GWN	1775	BH	NK05GWW

Supplied in 2000, DAF SB120 1907, W309PPT, now carries the interurban livery on its Wright Cadet body. It is seen in Stockton in August 2010. *Richard Godfrey*

1790	NL	NK55MYR	ADL Dart 8.8m	ADL Mini Pointer	NC29F	2006	
1791	NL	NK55MYS	ADL Dart 8.8m	ADL Mini Pointer	NC29F	2006	
1792	NL	NK55MYT	ADL Dart 8.8m	ADL Mini Pointer	NC29F	2006	
1793	DN	W166PNT	Dennis Dart SLF 8.8m	Plaxton Pointer MPD	N29F	2000	First Stop, Renfrew, 2005
1794	DN	W631RNP	Dennis Dart SLF 8.8m	Plaxton Pointer MPD	N29F	2000	First Stop, Renfrew, 2005
1795	DN	Y258KNB	Dennis Dart SLF 8.8m	Plaxton Pointer MPD	N29F	2001	First Stop, Renfrew, 2005
1796	DN	Y259KNB	Dennis Dart SLF 8.8m	Plaxton Pointer MPD	N29F	2001	First Stop, Renfrew, 2005
1797	DN	Y215BGB	Dennis Dart SLF 8.8m	Plaxton Pointer MPD	N29F	2001	First Stop, Renfrew, 2005
1798	DN	SA52MYT	Dennis Dart SLF 8.8m	Plaxton Pointer MPD	N29F	2003	First Stop, Renfrew, 2005
1799	NL	SF04RHA	TransBus Dart SLF 8.8m	TransBus Mini Pointer	N29F	2004	First Stop, Renfrew, 2005
1800	AS	NK56HKV	ADL Dart 4	ADL Enviro 200	N29F	2006	
1801	AS	NK56HKW	ADL Dart 4	ADL Enviro 200	N29F	2006	

1901-1922 DAF SB120 Wright Cadet N39F 2000

1901	SN	W301PPT	1906	SN	W308PPT	1911	SN	W314PPT	1916	SN	W72PRG	
1902	SN	W302PPT	1907	SN	W309PPT	1912	SN	W315PPT	1917	SN	W76PRG	
1903	SN	W303PPT	1908	SN	W311PPT	1913	SN	W317PPT	1920	SN	W81PRG	
1904	SN	W304PPT	1909	SN	W312PPT	1914	SN	W319PPT	1922	SN	W83PRG	
1905	SN	W307PPT	1910	SN	W313PPT	1915	SN	W69PRG				

1923	AS	YJ57BVB	VDL Bus SB120	Plaxton Centro	N40F	2007	
1924	AS	YJ57BVC	VDL Bus SB120	Plaxton Centro	N40F	2007	
2504	NL	Y294PDN	Optare Solo M920	Optare	N27F	2001	Crystals, Dartford, 2008
2505	NL	Y295PDN	Optare Solo M920	Optare	N27F	2001	Crystals, Dartford, 2008
2627	u	P627FHN	Optare MetroRider MR35	Optare	B25F	1996	
2631	u	P631FHN	Optare MetroRider MR35	Optare	B25F	1996	
2633	AS	P633FHN	Optare MetroRider MR35	Optare	B25F	1997	

2646-2655 Mercedes-Benz Vario O814 Alexander ALX100 B27F 2001

2646	BH	X646WTN	2650	BH	X657WTN	2654	BH	X654WTN	2655	BH	X656WTN
2648	u	X648WTN	2651	BH	X651WTN						

During the past year most of the batch of Mercedes-Benz O405s with Optare Prisma bodywork have moved to Redcar depot. This model was an early attempt by Mercedes to enter the British market and 3019, N519XVN, illustrates the styling. *Richard Godfrey*

2705-2716

Optare MetroRider MR15 — Optare — B31F — 1997-98

2705	AS	R705MHN	2710	AS	R710MHN	2711	AS	R711MHN	2716	AS	R716MHN

2801-2851

Optare Solo M950 — Optare — N31F — 2008

2801	BT	YK08ERO	2814	DM	YK08ETJ	2827	DN	YK08XBG	2840	DN	YK08XBW
2802	BT	YK08ERU	2815	BT	YK08ETL	2828	DN	YK08XBH	2841	DN	YK08XBY
2803	BT	YK08ERV	2816	BT	YK08ETO	2829	DN	YK08XBK	2842	DN	YJ58CAA
2804	BT	YK08ERX	2817	BT	YK08ETR	2830	DN	YK08XBL	2843	DN	YJ58CAE
2805	BT	YK08ERY	2818	BT	YK08ETT	2831	DN	YK08XBM	2844	DN	YJ58CAO
2806	BT	YK08ERZ	2819	BT	YK08ETU	2832	DN	YK08XBN	2845	DN	YJ58CAV
2807	BT	YK08ESU	2820	BT	YK08ETV	2833	DN	YK08XBO	2846	DN	YJ58CAW
2808	DM	YK08ESV	2821	DM	YK08ETX	2834	DN	YK08XBP	2847	DN	YJ58CAX
2809	DM	YK08ESY	2822	DM	YK08ETY	2835	DN	YK08XBR	2848	DN	YJ58CBF
2810	DM	YK08ETA	2823	DM	YK08ETZ	2836	DN	YK08XBS	2849	DN	YJ58CBO
2811	DM	YK08ETD	2824	DN	YK08XBD	2837	NL	YK08XBT	2850	DN	YJ58CBU
2812	DM	YK08ETE	2825	DN	YK08XBE	2838	DN	YK08XBU	2851	DN	YJ58CBV
2813	DM	YK08ETF	2826	DN	YK08XBF	2839	DN	YK08XBV			

2852-2861

Optare Solo SR M950 — Optare — N31F — 2009

2852	BT	YJ59GJK	2855	BT	YJ59GJX	2858	BT	YJ59GKC	2860	BT	YJ59GKE
2853	BT	YJ59GJO	2856	BT	YJ59GJY	2859	BT	YJ59GKD	2861	BT	YJ59GKF
2854	BT	YJ59GJV	2857	BT	YJ59GKA						

3003-3025

Mercedes-Benz O405 — Optare Prisma — B49F — 1995

3003	SN	M303SAJ	3010	RR	N810XHN	3015	RR	N515XVN	3020	SN	N520XVN
3004	RR	M304SAJ	3011	RR	N511XVN	3016	RR	N516XVN	3022	RR	N522XVN
3006	RR	N806XHN	3012	RR	N512XVN	3017	RR	N517XVN	3023	RR	N523XVN
3007	RR	N807XHN	3013	RR	N513XVN	3018	RR	N518XVN	3024	RR	N524XVN
3008	RR	N808XHN	3014	RR	N514XVN	3019	SN	N519XVN	3025	RR	N525XVN
3009	RR	N809XHN									

4001-4007 — DAF SB220 — Plaxton Prestige — N40F — 1998-99 — Go-Ahead North East, 2010

4001	BH	S868ONL	4003	BH	S870ONL	4005	BH	S891ONL	4007	SN	S893ONL
4002	BH	S869ONL	4004	BH	S890ONL	4006	SN	S892ONL			

4015	SN	K415BHN	DAF SB220	Optare Delta	B49F	1993
4022	DM	K422BHN	DAF SB220	Optare Delta	B49F	1993

4023-4058 — DAF SB220 — Plaxton Prestige — N45F — 1998

4023	RR	R423RPY	4033	DN	R433RPY	4041	DN	S341KHN	4050	DN	S350KHN
4024	DN	R424RPY	4034	DN	R434RPY	4042	SN	S342KHN	4051	SN	S351KHN
4025	RR	R425RPY	4035	DM	R435RPY	4043	SN	S343KHN	4052	DN	S352KHN
4026	RR	R426RPY	4036	DM	R436RPY	4044	DN	S344KHN	4053	RR	S353KHN
4027	RR	R427RPY	4037	SN	R437RPY	4045	SN	S345KHN	4054	SN	S354KHN
4030	SN	R430RPY	4038	SN	R438RPY	4046	SN	S346KHN	4056	DN	S356KHN
4031	u	R431RPY	4039	SN	R439RPY	4048	SN	S348KHN	4057	DN	S357KHN
4032	RR	R432RPY	4040	SN	R440RPY	4049	SN	S349KHN	4058	RR	S358KHN

4059	SN	R701KCU	DAF SB220	Northern Counties Paladin	B41F	1997

4060-4073 — DAF SB220 — Plaxton Prestige — N41F — 1998

4060	DM	S702KFT	4064	DM	S706KFT	4068	DM	S710KFT	4071	DM	S713KRG
4061	DN	S703KFT	4065	DM	S707KFT	4069	DM	S711KFT	4072	DM	S714KRG
4062	DM	S704KFT	4066	DM	S708KFT	4070	DM	S712KRG	4073	DM	S715KRG
4063	SN	S705KFT	4067	DM	S709KFT						

4074-4081 — DAF SB220 — Ikarus CitiBus — N43F* — 1999 — *4080-81 are N40F

4074	BH	T74AUA	4076	BH	T76AUA	4078	BH	T79AUA	4080	RR	T81AUA
4075	BH	T75AUA	4077	BH	T78AUA	4079	BH	T83AUA	4081	RR	T82AUA

4082	RR	V653LWT	DAF SB220	Plaxton Prestige	B40F	1999	
4098	DM	P130RWR	DAF SB220	Optare Delta	B44D	1997	Blue Bus, Bolton, 2004
4108	BH	L532EHD	DAF SB220	Ikarus CitiBus	B48F	1994	North Western, 1997

4501-4515 — Volvo B10BLE — Wright Renown — N44F — 1999

4501	NL	V501DFT	4505	NL	V505DFT	4509	NL	V509DFT	4513	NL	V513DFT
4502	AS	V502DFT	4506	NL	V506DFT	4510	NL	V510DFT	4514	NL	V514DFT
4503	AS	V503DFT	4507	NL	V507DFT	4511	NL	V511DFT	4515	NL	V515DFT
4504	AS	V504DFT	4508	NL	V508DFT	4512	NL	V512DFT			

4516-4523 — Volvo B10BLE — Alexander ALX300 — N44F — 2000

4516	AS	W292PPT	4518	AS	W294PPT	4520	NL	W296PPT	4522	NL	W298PPT
4517	AS	W293PPT	4519	NL	W295PPT	4521	BH	W297PPT	4523	NL	W299PPT

4535-4539 — Volvo B10B-58 — Alexander Strider — B51F — 1994-95 — Go-Ahead North East, 2010

4535	AS	L209KEF	4537	AS	L211KEF	4538	AS	L212KEF	4539	AS	N950TVK
4536	u	L210KEF									

4646-4659 — Scania OmniCity CN94UB — Scania — N42F — 2005

4646	DM	NK05GXW	4650	WY	NK05GXD	4654	DM	NK05GXH	4657	DM	NK05GXM
4647	DM	NK05GXA	4651	WY	NK05GXE	4655	WY	NK05GXJ	4658	WY	NK05GXN
4648	WY	NK05GXB	4652	WY	NK05GXF	4656	DM	NK05GXL	4659	WY	NK05GXO
4649	WY	NK05GXC	4653	WY	NK05GXG						

4660-4664 — Scania OmniCity CN230UB — Scania — N41F — 2007

4660	SN	NK07FZC	4662	SN	NK07FZE	4663	DM	NK07FZF	4664	DM	NK07FZG
4661	SN	NK07FZD									

4700-4720 — Temsa Avenue — Temsa — N42F — 2010

4700	RR	YJ59AZB	4706	RR	YJ59BHX	4711	RR	YJ10DHD	4716	RR	YJ10DHN
4701	RR	YJ59BHO	4707	RR	YJ59BHY	4712	RR	YJ10DHF	4717	RR	YJ10DFP
4702	RR	YJ59BHP	4708	RR	YJ59BHZ	4713	RR	YJ10DHG	4718	RR	YJ10DFU
4703	RR	YJ59BHU	4709	RR	YJ59BHC	4714	RR	YJ10DHK	4719	RR	YJ10DFV
4704	RR	YJ59BHV	4710	RR	YJ10DHE	4715	RR	YJ10DHL	4720	RR	YJ10DFW
4705	RR	YJ59BHW									

7203	AS	G529VBB	Leyland Olympian ON2R50C13Z4	Northern Counties	B47/31F	1990	Go-Ahead North East, 2010
7204	AS	G546VBB	Leyland Olympian ON2R50C13Z4	Northern Counties	B47/31F	1990	Go-Ahead North East, 2010
7205	AS	G545VBB	Leyland Olympian ON2R50C13Z4	Northern Counties	B47/31F	1990	Go-Ahead North East, 2010

Arriva Bus and Coach is the dealership that imports Temsa products to Britain. A batch has now entered service with Arriva North East where twenty-one buses operate from Redcar depot. This new model is represented by 4710, YJ10DHE, seen leaving Middlesbrough for Grangetown. *Richard Godfrey*

7252-7258

			Scania N113 DRB		Northern Counties Palatine		B42/29F	1994-95	Arriva London, 2002
7252	NL	L161GYL	7257	DM	N182OYH	7258	NL	N183OYH	

7259-7262

			Scania N113 DRB		East Lancs		B47/33F	1995	Arriva Midlands, 2008
7259	DM	M177GRY	7260	DM	M170GRY	7261	NL	M172GRY	7262	NL	M176GRY

7263-7266

			Scania N113 DRB		East Lancs		B45/33F	1995	Arriva The Shires, 2008
7263	DM	N162VVO	7264	DM	N164VVO	7265	BT	N160VVO	7266	BT	N163VVO
7360	AS	R616MNU		Volvo Olympian	Northern Counties Palatine	B47/29F	1998	Arriva Midlands, 2010	
7361	AS	R619MNU		Volvo Olympian	Northern Counties Palatine	B47/29F	1998	Arriva Midlands, 2010	

7362-7367

			Volvo Olympian		Northern Counties Palatine		B47/29F	1998	Arriva Midlands, 2009
7362	AS	R636MNU	7364	PE	S648KJU	7366	DN	R639MNU	7367	DN	R641MNU
7363	PE	R640MNU	7365	DN	R625MNU					
7368	AS	S646KJU		Volvo Olympian	Northern Counties Palatine	B47/29F	1998	Arriva Midlands, 2010	
7369	AS	S649KJU		Volvo Olympian	Northern Counties Palatine	B47/29F	1998	Arriva Midlands, 2010	

7370-7377

			Volvo Olympian		Northern Counties Palatine II		BC43/27F	1994	
7370	u	M370FTY	7372	u	M372FTY	7374	u	M374FTY	7376	NL	M376FTY
7371	u	M371FTY	7373	u	M373FTY	7375	AS	M375FTY	7377	NL	M377FTY

7410-7420

			Volvo Olympian		Northern Counties Palatine II		B43/29F	1997	
7410	AS	P410CCU	7413	AS	P413CCU	7416	NL	P416CCU	7419	NL	P419CCU
7411	AS	P411CCU	7414	NL	P414CCU	7417	NL	P417CCU	7420	NL	P420CCU
7412	AS	P412CCU	7415	NL	P415CCU	7418	NL	P418CCU		

7421-7426

			Volvo Olympian		East Lancs		B44/30F	1994	Arriva Southern Counties, 1998
7421	NL	M685HPF	7424	u	M688HPF	7425	DM	M689HPF	7426	u	M690HPF

7432-7435 — Dennis Trident — Alexander ALX400 — N51/31F — 2000

7432	NL	W397RBB	7433	NL	W398RBB	7434	NL	W399RBB	7435	NL	W501RBB

7436-7444 — DAF DB250 — East Lancs Lowlander — N44/29F — 2001

7436	AS	Y686EBR	7439	NL	Y689EBR	7441	BT	Y691EBR	7443	AS	Y693EBR
7437	AS	Y687EBR	7440	NL	Y685EBR	7442	AS	Y692EBR	7444	BT	Y694EBR
7438	AS	Y688EBR									

7445	NL	NK05GWX	Volvo B7TL			ADL ALX400		NC45/27F	2005		
7446	NL	NK05GWY	Volvo B7TL			ADL ALX400		NC45/27F	2005		

7447-7452 — DAF DB250 — Northern Counties Palatine 2 — B43/24D — 1998 — Arriva Southern Counties, 2006

7447	BT	R204CKO	7449	BT	R206CKO	7451	BT	R208CKO	7452	BT	R209CKO
7448	BT	R205CKO	7450	BT	R207CKO						

7453-7456 — VDL Bus DB250 — East Lancs Lowlander — NC51/28F — 2007

7453	AS	YJ57BVD	7454	AS	YJ57BVE	7455	AS	YJ57BVF	7456	AS	YJ57BVG

7457	BT	L94HRF	DAF DB250		Optare Spectra	B48/29F	1993	Arriva Midlands, 2009
7458	u	L95HRF	DAF DB250		Optare Spectra	B48/29F	1993	Arriva Midlands, 2009

7501-7513 — ADL Trident 2 — ADL Enviro 400 — NC45/33F — 2007-08

7501	BH	NK57DXX	7505	BH	NK57GWX	7508	AS	NK57GXA	7511	AS	NK57GXD
7502	BH	NK57DXY	7506	AS	NK57GWY	7509	AS	NK57GXB	7512	AS	NK57GXE
7503	BH	NK57DXZ	7507	AS	NK57GWZ	7510	AS	NK57GXC	7513	AS	NK57GXF
7504	BH	NK57DYA									

7514-7521 — ADL Trident 2 — ADL Enviro 400 — NC45/33F — 2009

7514	DN	NK09DFMZ	7516	DN	NK09FNC	7518	DN	NK09FNE	7520	DN	NK09FNG
7515	DN	NK09DFNZ	7517	DN	NK09FND	7519	DN	NK09FNF	7521	DN	NK09FVR

7601-7615 — VDL Bus DB300 — Wrightbus Gemini 2 — N43/28F — 2009

7601	BH	NK59DLO	7605	BH	NK59DLY	7609	BH	NK59DMO	7613	BH	NK59DMY
7602	BH	NK59DLU	7606	BH	NK59DLZ	7610	BH	NK59DMU	7614	BH	NK59DMZ
7603	BH	NK59DLV	7607	BH	NK59DME	7611	BH	NK59DMV	7615	BH	NK59DND
7604	BH	NK59DLX	7608	BH	NK59DMF	7612	BH	NK59DMX			

Ancillary vehicles:

1001-1005 — Volvo B6 9.9M — Plaxton Pointer — TV — 1994 — Arriva North West & Wales, 2006

1001	SN	L219TKA	1003	SN	L232TKA	1004	AS	L244TKA	1005	AS	L225TKA
1002	SN	L220TKA									

9967	u	P618FHN	Optare MetroRider MR35	Optare	B25F	1996	
9968	DN	P621FHN	Optare MetroRider MR35	Optare	B25F	1996	

Previous registrations:

HIL2148	S869OGB	L95HRF	L95HRF, 915DYE
J353BSH	J353BSH, VLT173	UOI772	K141RYS
J354BSH	J354BSH, VLT32,WLT554	WLT954	A954SUL
L94HRF	L94HRF, 49XRF		

Depots and allocations:

Ashington (Lintonville Terrace) - AS

Scania sd	274	281	289					
MetroRider	917	918	919	2633	2705	2710	2711	2716
Volvo B6	1004	1005						
VDL SB3000	1210	1211	1212					
VDL SB200	1404	1405	1406	1407				
Dart	1688	1689						
Dart SLF	1707	1754	1800	1801				
VDL SB120	1923	1924						
Volvo B10BLE	4502	4503	4504	4516	4517	4518		
Volvo B10B	4535	4536	4537	4538	4539			
Olympian	7203	7204	7205	7360	7361	7362	7375	7410
	7411	7412	7413					
DB250	7436	7437	7438	7506	7507	7508	7509	
Trident 2	7506	7507	7508	7509	7510	7511	7512	7513

Belmont (Waddington Street, Durham) - BT

VDL SB200	1415	1416	1417	1418	1419	1420	1421	1422
	1423							
Dart SLF	1613	1616	1636					
Solo	2801	2802	2803	2804	2805	2806	2807	2815
	2816	2817	2818	2819	2820	2852	2853	2854
	2855	2856	2857	2858	2859	2860	2861	
Scania dd	7265	7266						
Olympian	7366	7367						
DAF DB250	7442	7444	7447	7448	7449	7450	7451	7452
	7457	7458						

Blyth (Bridge Street) - BH

SB200	1	1408	1409	1410	1411	1412	1413	1414
	4074	4075	4076	4077	4078	4079	4108	
Dart SLF	1702	1714	1721	1724	1726	1728	1733	1740
	1741	1742	1763	1773	1774	1775		
Mercedes-Benz	2646	2648	2650	2651	2652	2654	2655	
Trident 2	7501	7502	7503	7504	7505			
VDL300	7601	7602	7603	7604	7605	7606	7607	7608
	7609	7610	7611	7612	7613	7614	7615	

Darlington (Faverdale) - DN

Outstation: Barnard Castle

VDL SB3000	1208	1209	1213					
VDL SB200	2	4	1424	1425	1426	1427	1428	
Dart	1601	1602	1659	1660	1661	1662	1664	1665
	1666	1667	1669	1670	1671	1674	1676	1677
	1678	1679	1680	1681	1682	1683	1684	1685
	1696							
Dart SLF	1611	1612	1617	1618	1625	1626	1652	1653
	1654	1655	1703	1704	1705	1706	1708	1709
	1710	1711	1712	1716	1717	1735	1745	1746
	1747	1761	1764	1772	1793	1794	1795	1796
	1797	1798						
Optare Solo	2821	2822	2823	2824	2825	2826	2827	2828
	2829	2830	2831	2832	2833	2834	2835	2836
	2838	2839	2840	2841	2842	2843	2844	2845
	2846	2847	2848	2849	2850	2851		
DAF/VDL SB220	4024	4033	4034	4041	4044	4050	4052	4056
	4057	4061						
Olympian	7364	7364	7365					
Trident 2	7514	7515	7516	7517	7518	7519	7520	7521

Durham (Waddington Street) - DU

Scania SD	267	282	283	284	285	287		
Dart SLF	1638	1639	1640	1656				
Solo	2808	2809	2810	2811	2812	2813	2814	
DAF/VDL SB220	4022	4032	4035	4036	4060	4062	4064	4065
	4066	4067	4068	4069	4070	4071	4072	4073
	4098							
Scania OmniCity	4646	4647	4654	4656	4657	4663	4664	
Scania dd	7259	7260	7263	7264				
Olympian	7425							

Newcastle (Jesmond Road) - NL

VDL SB3000	1201	1202	1203	2204	1205	1206	1214
VDL SB200	1401	1402	1403				
Dart SLF	1715	1723	1750	1751	1752	1758	1759	1760
	1762	1790	1791	1792	1799		
Optare Solo	2504	2505	2837				
Volvo B10BLE	4501	4505	4506	4507	4508	4509	4510	4511
	4512	4513	4514	4515	4519	4520	4521	4522
	4523						
Scania dd	7252	7257	7258	7261	7262		
Olympian	7376	7377	7414	7415	7416	7417	7418	7419
	7420	7421					
Trident	7432	7433	7434	7435			
DAF DB250	7439	7440	7441				
Volvo B7TL	7445	7446					

Redcar (Ennis Road, Dormanstown) - RR

DAF SB300	1207						
VDL SB200	1429	1430	1431	1432	1433	1434	1435	1436
	1437	1438	1439	1440			
Dart	1658	1663	1668	1673	1675	1697	
Dart SLF	1621	1635	1649	1651	1719	1720	1736	1737
	1738	1739					
DAF/VDL SB220	4023	4025	4026	4027	4053	4058	4080	4081
	4082						
Temsa Avenue	4700	4701	4702	4703	4704	4705	4706	4707
	4708	4709	4710	4711	4712	4713	4714	4715
	4716	4717	4718	4719	4720		

Stockton (Boathouse Lane) - SN

Scania	261	262	263	264	265	266	272	276
	277	279					
Volvo B6	1001	1002	1003				
VDL SB200	1441	1442	1443	1444	1445	1446	1447	1448
	1449	1450	1451	1452	1453	1454	1455	1456
	1457	1458	1459	1460			
Dart	1686						
Dart SLF	1646	1647	1648	1650	1701	1718	1722	1727
	1734	1753	1755	1756	1765	1766	1767	1768
	1769	1770	1771				
DAF/VDL SB120	1901	1902	1903	1904	1905	1906	1907	1908
	1909	1910	1911	1912	1913	1914	1915	1916
	1917	1920	1922				
DAF/VDL SB220	4015	4030	4037	4038	4039	4040	4042	4043
	4045	4046	4048	4051	4054	4055	4063	
Scania OmniCity	4660	4661	4662				

Whitby ( ) - WY

Dart SLF	1743	1744	1748	1757			
Scania OmniCity	4648	4649	4650	4651	4652	4653	4655	4658
	4659						

Unallocated or stored - u/w

Remainder

ARRIVA YORKSHIRE

Arriva Yorkshire Ltd; Arriva Yorkshire North Ltd,
24 Barnsley Road, Wakefield, West Yorkshire, WF1 5JX
Arriva Yorkshire West Ltd, Mill Street East, Dewsbury, West Yorkshire, WF12 9AG

11	DY	R10WAL	DAF SB220	Ikarus CitiBus	B49F	1997	K-Line Travel, 2000
13	DY	R69GNW	DAF SB220	Ikarus CitiBus	B49F	1998	K-Line Travel, 2000
29	DY	M819RCP	DAF SB220	Ikarus CitiBus	B49F	1994	K-Line Travel, 2000
53	u	N51FWU	DAF SB220	Ikarus CitiBus	B49F	1995	Arriva Bus & Coach, 2004
54	DY	P202RUM	DAF SB220	Ikarus CitiBus	B49F	1996	Arriva Bus & Coach, 2004
56	DY	N52FWU	DAF SB220	Ikarus CitiBus	B49F	1995	Arriva Bus & Coach, 2004
57	DY	YD02RJO	DAF SB220	Ikarus CitiBus	N44F	2002	Arriva Bus & Coach, 2004
58	DY	YD02RJJ	DAF SB220	Ikarus CitiBus	N44F	2002	Arriva Bus & Coach, 2004

102-109 — Volvo B10BLE — Wright Renown — NC44F — 2000

102	CD	W102EWU	104	CD	W104EWU	107	CD	W107EWU	109	SB	W109EWU
103	CD	W103EWU	106	CD	W106EWU	108	CD	W108EWU			

136	u	L136YVK	Dennis Dart 9m	Northern Counties Paladin	B35F	1994	Arriva Southern Counties, 2001
137	u	L137YVK	Dennis Dart 9m	Northern Counties Paladin	B35F	1994	Arriva Southern Counties, 2001
156	u	K320CVX	Dennis Dart 9m	Plaxton Pointer	B35F	1992	Arriva Southern Counties, 2004
161	u	P326HVX	Dennis Dart 9m	Plaxton Pointer	B34F	1996	
165	SB	W165HBT	Dennis Dart SLF	Alexander ALX200	N40F	2000	
166	SB	W166HBT	Dennis Dart SLF	Alexander ALX200	N40F	2000	
167	SB	TWY7	Dennis Dart SLF	Alexander ALX200	N40F	2000	

170-199 — Dennis Dart SLF — Alexander ALX200 — N40F — 1997

170	SB	P170VUA	179	SB	P179VUA	186	DY	P186VUA	193	DY	P193VUA
171	WF	P171VUA	180	SB	P180VUA	187	DY	P187VUA	194	DY	P194VUA
172	WF	P172VUA	181	SB	P181VUA	188	DY	P188VUA	195	DY	P195VUA
173	WF	P173VUA	182	CD	P182VUA	189	DY	P189VUA	196	DY	P196VUA
175	DY	P175VUA	183	CD	P183VUA	190	DY	P190VUA	197	DY	P197VUA
176	SB	P176VUA	184	CD	P184VUA	191	DY	P191VUA	198	DY	P198VUA
177	SB	P177VUA	185	CD	P185VUA	192	DY	P192VUA	199	DY	P199VUA

200	SB	R103GNW	Dennis Dart SLF	UVG Urbanstar	N40F	1998	Jaronda Travel, Cawood, 1999

Halifax is the location for this view of Dennis Dart 187, P187VUA. The vehicle is seen in the inter-urban livery now being applied to many vehicles in the UK.
Richard Godfrey

201-229

| | | | | | | | | | | Dennis Dart SLF | | Plaxton Pointer MPD | N29F | 2000 |

201	WF	V201PCX	208	WF	V208PCX	215	WF	V215PCX	223	CD	V223PCX

Dennis Dart SLF · Plaxton Pointer MPD · N29F · 2000

201	WF	V201PCX	208	WF	V208PCX	215	WF	V215PCX	223	CD	V223PCX
202	WF	A1YBG	209	WF	V209PCX	216	WF	V216PCX	224	CD	V224PCX
203	WF	V203PCX	210	WF	V210PCX	217	WF	V217PCX	225	WF	V225PCX
204	WF	V204PCX	211	WF	V211PCX	218	WF	V218PCX	226	CD	V226PCX
205	WF	V205PCX	212	WF	V212PCX	219	WF	A4YBG	227	CD	V227PCX
206	WF	V206PCX	213	WF	V213PCX	220	WF	V220PCX	228	CD	V228PCX
207	WF	V207PCX	214	WF	A2YBG	221	WF	V221PCX	229	CD	V229XUB

230	WF	W244SNR	Dennis Dart SLF	Plaxton Pointer MPD	N29F	2000	Arriva Midlands, 2009

260	SB	SN55HTX	ADL Dart 9m	ADL Pointer	N34F	2006	
261	SB	SN55HTY	ADL Dart 9m	ADL Pointer	N34F	2006	
262	SB	SN55HTZ	ADL Dart 9m	ADL Pointer	N34F	2006	

435	WF	P10LPG	DAF SB220	Northern Counties Paladin	B42F	1997	Arriva Bus & Coach, 2004
436	WF	R989FNW	DAF SB220	Northern Counties Paladin	B42F	1997	Arriva Bus & Coach, 2004
437	WF	R985FNW	DAF SB220	Northern Counties Paladin	B42F	1997	Arriva Bus & Coach, 2004
438	WF	R28GNW	DAF SB220	Northern Counties Paladin	B41F	1998	Arriva Bus & Coach, 2004
439	WF	R29GNW	DAF SB220	Northern Counties Paladin	B41F	1998	Arriva Bus & Coach, 2005

440-471

DAF SB220 · Alexander ALX300 · N42F · 1998

440	WF	R440GWY	449	WF	R449KWT	457	WF	R457KWT	465	HE	S465GUB
441	WF	R441KWT	450	CD	R450KWT	458	WF	R458KWT	466	HE	S466GUB
442	WF	R442KWT	451	WF	R451KWT	459	WF	R459KWT	467	HE	S467GUB
443	CD	R443KWT	452	WF	R452KWT	460	HE	R460KWT	468	HE	S468GUB
445	WF	R445KWT	453	WF	R453KWT	461	HE	R461KWT	469	HE	S469GUB
446	WF	R446KWT	454	WF	R454KWT	462	HE	S462GUB	470	HE	S470GUB
447	WF	R447KWT	455	WF	R455KWT	463	HE	S463GUB	471	HE	S471GUB
448	WF	R448KWT	456	WF	R456KWT	464	HE	S464GUB			

472-491

DAF SB220 · Alexander ALX300 · N42F · 1998

472	HE	S472ANW	477	WF	S477ANW	482	CD	S482ANW	487	CD	S487ANW
473	HE	S473ANW	478	WF	S478ANW	483	CD	S483ANW	488	CD	S488ANW
474	WF	S474ANW	479	CD	S479ANW	484	CD	S484ANW	489	WF	S489ANW
475	WF	S475ANW	480	CD	S480ANW	485	CD	S485ANW	490	CD	S490ANW
476	WF	S476ANW	481	CD	S481ANW	486	CD	S486ANW	491	CD	S491ANW

499	WF	YJ04HJG	VDL Bus SB200	Wrightbus Commander	N44F	2004	
621	HE	N621KUA	Volvo Olympian YN2RV18Z4	Northern Counties Palatine II	B43/30F	1996	
622	SB	N622KUA	Volvo Olympian YN2RV18Z4	Northern Counties Palatine II	B43/30F	1996	
623	HE	N623KUA	Volvo Olympian YN2RV18Z4	Northern Counties Palatine II	B43/30F	1996	

624-641

DAF DB250 · Optare Spectra · B48/29F · 1999

624	WF	T624EUB	629	WF	T629EUB	634	WF	T634EUB	638	WF	T638EUB
625	WF	T625EUB	630	WF	T630EUB	635	WF	T635EUB	639	WF	T639EUB
626	WF	T626EUB	631	WF	T631EUB	636	WF	T636EUB	640	WF	V640KVH
627	WF	T627EUB	632	WF	T632EUB	637	WF	T637EUB	641	WF	V641KVH
628	WF	T628EUB	633	WF	T633EUB						

651-674

Volvo B7L · Alexander ALX400 · N47/28F · 2000

651	SB	W651CWX	657	CD	W657CWX	663	CD	W663CWX	669	CD	W669CWX
652	CD	W652CWX	658	CD	W658CWX	664	CD	W664CWX	671	CD	W671CWX
653	SB	W653CWX	659	CD	W659CWX	665	CD	W665CWX	672	CD	W672CWX
654	HE	W654CWX	661	CD	W661CWX	667	CD	W667CWX	673	CD	W673CWX
656	SB	W656CWX	662	CD	W662CWX	668	CD	W668CWX	674	CD	W674CWX

675-696

Volvo B7L · Plaxton President · N47/28F · 2001

675	SB	X675YUG	681	SB	X681YUG	686	SB	X686YUG	692	HE	X692YUG
676	SB	X676YUG	682	SB	X682YUG	687	HE	X687YUG	693	HE	X693YUG
677	SB	X677YUG	683	SB	X683YUG	688	HE	X688YUG	694	HE	X694YUG
678	SB	X678YUG	684	SB	X684YUG	689	HE	X689YUG	695	HE	X695YUG
679	SB	X679YUG	685	SB	X685YUG	691	HE	X691YUG	696	HE	X696YUG

700-723

DAF DB250 · Optare Spectra · N47/27F · 2002

700	WF	YD02PXW	706	WF	YG52CFE	712	CD	YG52CFN	718	HE	YD02PYU
701	WF	YD02PXX	707	WF	YG52CFF	713	CD	YG52CFO	719	HE	YD02PYV
702	WF	YD02PXY	708	CD	YG52CFJ	714	CD	YG52CFP	720	HE	YD02PYW
703	WF	YD02PXZ	709	CD	YG52CFK	715	CD	YG52CFU	721	HE	YD02PYX
704	WF	YG52CFA	710	CD	YG52CFL	716	HE	YG52CFV	722	HE	YD02PYY
705	WF	YG52CFD	711	CD	YG52CFM	717	HE	YG52CFX	723	HE	YD02PYZ

Thirteen Optare Tempo X1100s were placed in service with Arriva Yorkshire in 2009. These are built at the nearby works in Cross Gates, Leeds. The first of the batch, 1300, YJ09EYA, is seen in Castleford where the type is based. *John Young*

1050-1066

ADL Dart 4			ADL Enviro 200			N38F		2009			
1050	DY	YJ09CSU	1055	DY	YJ09CUA	1059	DY	YJ09CUK	1063	DY	YJ09CVB
1051	DY	YJ09CTV	1056	DY	YJ09CUC	1060	DY	YJ09CUO	1064	DY	YJ09CVC
1052	DY	YJ09CTX	1057	DY	YJ09CUG	1061	DY	YJ09CUY	1065	DY	YJ09CVD
1053	DY	YJ09CTY	1058	DY	YJ09CUH	1062	DY	YJ09CVA	1066	DY	YJ09CVE
1054	DY	YJ09CTZ									

1100-1112

Volvo B7RLE			Wrighbus Eclipse Urban			N44F		2008			
1100	HE	YJ08DVA	1104	HE	YJ08DVG	1107	HE	YJ08DVN	1110	HE	YJ08DVR
1101	HE	YJ08DVB	1105	HE	YJ08DVH	1108	HE	YJ08DVO	1111	HE	YJ08DVT
1102	HE	YJ08DVC	1106	HE	YJ08DVK	1109	HE	YJ08DVP	1112	HE	YJ08DVU
1103	HE	YJ08DVF									

1300-1312

Optare Tempo X1100			Optare			N43F		2009			
1300	CD	YJ09EYA	1304	CD	YJ09EYG	1307	CD	YJ09EYL	1310	CD	YJ09EYP
1301	CD	YJ09EYB	1305	CD	YJ09EYH	1308	CD	YJ09EYM	1311	CD	YJ09EYR
1302	CD	YJ09EYC	1306	CD	YJ09EYK	1309	CD	YJ09EYO	1312	CD	YJ09EYS
1303	CD	YJ09ETF									

1401-1408

VDL Bus SB200			Wrightbus Commander			N44F		2006			
1400	WF	YJ56JYE	1403	WF	YJ56JYH	1405	WF	YJ56JYL	1407	WF	YJ56JYO
1401	WF	YJ56JYF	1404	WF	YJ56JYK	1406	WF	YJ56JYN	1408	WF	YJ56JYP
1402	WF	YJ56JYG									

1409-1415

VDL Bus SB200			Wrightbus Pulsar			N44F		2007			
1409	DY	YJ57BVT	1411	DY	YJ57BVV	1413	DY	YJ57BVX	1415	DY	YJ57BVZ
1410	DY	YJ57BVU	1412	DY	YJ57BVW	1414	DY	YJ57BVY			

1450-1453

VDL Bus SB200			Wrightbus Pulsar 2			N44F		2009			
1450	WF	YJ59BUH	1451	WF	YJ59BRY	1452	WF	YJ59BRZ	1453	WF	YJ59BSO

One of the last batches of Plaxton President bodies was built on Volvo B7Ls, the low-floor model from Volvo. Seen in Selby is 677, X677YUG, which dates from 2001. *Dave Heath*

1500-1507

VDL Bus DB300   Wrighbus Eclipse Gemini 2   N43/28F   2009

| 1500 | SB | YJ59BTO | 1502 | SB | YJ59BTV | 1504 | SB | YJ59BTY | 1506 | SB | YJ59BUA |
| 1501 | SB | YJ59BTU | 1503 | SB | YJ59BTX | 1505 | SB | YJ59BTZ | 1507 | SB | YJ59BUE |

1600-1613

VDL Bus DB250   East Lancs Lowlander   N47/27F   2006

1600	DY	YJ06WLX	1604	DY	YJ06WMD	1608	DY	YJ06WMK	1611	DY	YJ06WWX
1601	DY	YJ06WLZ	1605	DY	YJ06WME	1609	DY	YJ06WML	1612	DY	YJ06WWY
1602	DY	YJ06WMA	1606	DY	YJ06WMF	1610	DY	YJ06WWV	1613	DY	YJ06WWZ
1603	DY	YJ06WMC	1607	DY	YJ06WMG						

1800-1815

Volvo B9TL   Darwen Olympus   N51/30F   2008

1800	WA	YJ57BEO	1804	WA	YJ08EEB	1808	WA	YJ08EEM	1812	WA	YJ08EES
1801	WA	YJ57BEU	1805	WA	YJ08EEF	1809	WA	YJ08EEN	1813	WA	YJ08EET
1802	WA	YJ08ECY	1806	WA	YJ08EEG	1810	WA	YJ08EEP	1814	WA	YJ08EEU
1803	WA	YJ08EEW	1807	WA	YJ08EEH	1811	WA	YJ08EER	1815	WA	YJ08EEV

1900-1913

ADL Trident 2   ADL Enviro 400   N47/33F   2008

1900	HE	YJ58FHA	1904	HE	YJ58FHE	1908	HE	YJ58FHJ	1911	HE	YJ58FHN
1901	HE	YJ58FHB	1905	HE	YJ58FHF	1909	HE	YJ58FHL	1912	HE	YJ58FHO
1902	HE	YJ58FHC	1906	HE	YJ58FHG	1910	HE	YJ58FHM	1913	HE	YJ58FHP
1903	HE	YJ58FHD	1907	HE	YJ58FHH						

Ancillary vehicles:

T401	CDt	K401HWW	Volvo B10B	Alexander Strider	B51F	1993
T402	HEt	K402HWW	Volvo B10B	Alexander Strider	B51F	1993
T403	WFt	K403HWW	Volvo B10B	Alexander Strider	B51F	1993

Previous registrations:

A1YBG	V202PCX		P10LPG	P10LPG, 99D73675
A2YBG	V214PCX		TWY7	W167HBT
A4YBG	V219PCX			

Huddersfield is the home to all fourteen Enviro 400-bodied Alexander Dennis Trident 2s in the Arriva Yorkshire fleet. Illustrating the type is 1906, YJ58FHG. *Richard Godfrey*

Depots and Allocations:

Castleford (Wheldon Road) - CD

Dart SLF	182	183	184	185	223	224	226
	227	228	229				
Volvo B10BLE	108						
DAF/VDL SB200	443	450	479	480	481	482	483	484
	485	486	487	488	490	491		
Optare Tempo	1300	1301	1302	1303	1304	1305	1306	1307
	1308	1309	1310	1311	1312			
Volvo B7TL	652	657	658	659	661	662	663	664
	665	667	668	669	671	672	673	674
DAF/VDL DB250	708	709	710	711	712	713	714	715
Ancillary	*T401*							

Dewsbury (Mill Street East) - DY

Dart	175	186	187	189	190	191	192	193
	194	195	196	197	198	199	1050	1051
	1052	1053	1054	1055	1056	1057	1058	1059
	1060	1061	1062	1063	1064	1065	1066	
DAF/VDL SB220	11	13	29	53	54	56	57	58
	1409	1410	1411	1412	1413	1414	1415	
DB250	1600	1601	1602	1603	1604	1605	1606	1607
	1608	1609	1610	1611	1612	1613		

Heckmondwike (Beck Lane) - HE

DAF/VDL SB220	460	461	462	465	466	467	468	469
	470	471	472					
Volvo B7RLE	1100	1101	1102	1103	1104	1105	1106	1107
	1108	1109	1110	1111	1112			
Olympian	621	623						
Volvo B7TL	654	687	688	689	691	692	693	694
	695	696						
DAF/VDL DB250	716	717	718	719	720	721	722	723
Trident 2	1900	1901	1902	1903	1904	1905	1906	1907
	1908	1909	1910	1911	1912	1913		

Ancillary   *T402*

Selby (Cowie Drive, Ousegate) - SB

Dart SLF	165	166	167	170	176	177	179	180
	181	200	260	261	262			
Volvo B10BLE	109							
Olympian	512	513	514	616	622			
Volvo B7L	651	653	656	675	676	677	678	679
	681	682	683	684	685	686		
VDL SB300	1500	1501	1502	1503	1504	1505	1506	1507

Wakefield (Belle Isle, Barnsley Road) - WF

Dart SLF	161	171	172	173	201	202	203	204
	205	206	207	208	209	210	211	212
	213	214	215	216	217	218	219	220
	221	225	230					
DAF/VDL SB120	1400	1401	1402	1403	1404	1405	1406	1407
	1408							
Volvo B10B	411							
DAF/VDL SB220	435	436	437	438	439	440	441	442
	443	445	446	447	448	449	451	452
	453	454	455	456	457	458	459	473
	474	475	476	477	478	489	495	496
	497	498	499					
VDL SB200	1400	1401	1402	1403	1404	1405	1406	1407
	1408	1409	1410	1411	1412	1413	1414	1415
	1450	1451	1452	1453				
DAF/VDL DB250	624	625	626	627	628	629	630	631
	632	633	634	635	636	637	638	639
	640	641	700	701	702	703	704	705
	706							
Volvo B9TL	1800	1801	1802	1803	1804	1805	1806	1807
	1808	1809	1810	1811	1812	1813	1814	1815

Ancillary   *T403*

Unallocated or stored - u/w

Remainder

ARRIVA NORTH WEST & WALES

Arriva North West Ltd, Arriva Merseyside Ltd,
Arriva Cymru Ltd, Arriva Manchester Ltd, Arriva Liverpool Ltd,
73 Ormskirk Road, Aintree, Liverpool, L9 5AE

623	CH	YJ06ATK	Optare Solo M850		Optare			N23F	2006		*Operated for Flintshire CC*
624	CH	YJ56ATK	Optare Solo M710 SE		Optare			N23F	2006		*Operated for Flintshire CC*
625	CH	YN07EHZ	Optare Solo M710 SL		Optare			N19F	2007		*Operated for Flintshire CC*

660-672

			Optare Solo M880			Optare			N28F		2007-08			
660	MA	CX57CYO	663	MA	CX57CYT	667	MA	CX57CYW	670	MA	CX57CZA
661	MA	CX57CYP	664	MA	CX57CYU	668	MA	CX57CYX	671	CH	CX58ETY
662	MA	CX57CYS	665	MA	CX57CYV	669	MA	CX57CYY	672	CH	CX58ETZ

673	CH	CX58EUA	Optare Solo M950 SL		Optare		N32F	2008	
674	CH	CX58EUB	Optare Solo M950 SL		Optare		N32F	2008	
675	CH	CX58EUA	Optare Solo M950 SL		Optare		N32F	2008	

676-680

			Optare Solo M880 SL			Optare			N28F		2008-09			
676	WY	CX58FYU	678	WY	CX58FYW	679	WY	CX58FYY	680	WY	CX58FYZ
677	WY	CX58FYV									

681-697

			Optare Solo M950 sl			Optare			N32F		2009			
681	BG	CX09BFM	686	BG	CX09BFV	690	BG	CX09BGF	694	AB	CX09BGV
682	BG	CX09BFN	687	BG	CX09BFY	691	BG	CX09BGK	695	AB	CX09BGY
683	BG	CX09BFO	688	BG	CX09BFZ	692	BG	CX09BGO	696	RH	CX09BGZ
684	BG	CX09BFP	689	BG	CX09BGE	693	BG	CX09BGU	697	RH	CX09BHA
685	BG	CX09BFU									

801	AB	R546ABA	Dennis Dart SLF 8.8m		Plaxton Pointer MPD		N28F	1997

802-809

			Dennis Dart SLF 8.8m			Plaxton Pointer MPD			N25F		1998			
802	AB	S872SNB	804	LJ	S874SNB	806	WX	S876SNB	808	WX	S878SNB
803	WX	S873SNB	805	WX	S875SNB	807	WX	S877SNB	809	WX	S879SNB

Local services in Aberystwyth were revised in late June 2010 and are now marketed under the AHA slogan (Ar Hyd Aber which means "All Round Aber"). Clearly displaying its Rugby Legend name, Optare Solo 695, CX09BGY, is seen at the Ynyslas terminus of route 4. *Tom Johnson*

Seen with Conway Castle in the background, Mini Pointer Dart 812, T64JBA, which joined the North West fleet with the operations of Nova Scotia of Winsford. This model has been used extensively in the fleet, especially along the North Wales coast. *John Young*

810-813

| | | | | | | | Dennis Dart SLF 8.8m | Plaxton Pointer MPD | N29F | 1999 | Nova Scotia, Winsford, 2000 |

810	WX	T62JBA	811	WX	T63JBA	812	LJ	T64JBA	813	WX	T65JBA

814-820

Dennis Dart SLF 8.8m — Plaxton Pointer MPD — N27F — 1999

814	LJ	T564JJC	816	LJ	T566JJC	818	LJ	T568JJC	820	AB	T570JJC
815	LJ	T565JJC	817	LJ	T567JJC	819	LJ	T569JJC			

821-852

Dennis Dart SLF 8.8m — Plaxton Pointer MPD — N27F — 2000-01

821	LJ	W269NFF	831	WX	X271RFF	841	AB	Y541UJC	847	RH	Y547UJC
822	LJ	W394OJC	832	AB	X272RFF	842	AB	Y542UJC	848	WX	Y548UJC
823	AB	V553ECC	833	BG	X273RFF	843	RH	Y543UJC	849	WX	Y549UJC
824	AB	V554ECC	834	LJ	X274RFF	844	RH	Y544UJC	851	WX	Y551UJC
826	AB	V556ECC	838	WX	Y538VFF	846	RH	Y546UJC	852	WX	Y552UJC
827	BG	V557ECC	839	WX	Y539VFF						

856-859

Dennis Dart SLF 8.8m — Plaxton Pointer MPD — N29F — 1999 — Arriva Midlands North, 2003

856	WI	T526AOB	857	WI	T527AOB	858	WI	T528AOB	859	WI	T529AOB

860-886

Dennis Dart SLF 8.8m — Plaxton Pointer MPD — N29F — 2000-01

860	WI	X209JOF	865	WI	X215JOF	869	WI	X32KON	878	WI	Y38TDA
861	WI	X211JOF	866	WI	X216JOF	872	WI	Y32TDA	879	WI	Y39TDA
862	WI	X212JOF	867	WI	X217JOF	876	WI	Y36TDA	882	WI	Y42TDA
863	WI	X213JOF	868	WI	X218JOF	877	WI	Y37TDA	886	WI	Y46TDA
864	LJ	X214JOF									

890	BN	T10BLU	Dennis Dart SLF	Plaxton Pointer MPD	N29F	2002	Blue Bus, Bolton, 2005
891	WY	T11BLU	Dennis Dart SLF	Plaxton Pointer MPD	N29F	2002	Blue Bus, Bolton, 2005
892	WY	W12LUE	Dennis Dart SLF	Plaxton Pointer MPD	N29F	2002	Blue Bus, Bolton, 2005
893	WY	X13LUE	Dennis Dart SLF	Plaxton Pointer MPD	N29F	2002	Blue Bus, Bolton, 2005
894	WY	X14LUE	Dennis Dart SLF	Plaxton Pointer MPD	N29F	2002	Blue Bus, Bolton, 2005

Many East Lancs-bodied Darts were supplied during the time East Lancs was in the same group of companies as Arriva's predecessor, Drawlane. The type is now leaving the fleets, so 1263, N263CKA, is one of the few still operating from Wythenshawe depot. It is seen in Urmston. *John Young*

1035-1040

Scania L113 CRL   East Lancs Flyte   B47F   1996

1035	SP	P135GND	1037	SP	P137GND	1039	SP	P139GND	1040	SP	P140GND
1036	SP	P136GND	1038	SP	P138GND			

1035	SP	P135GND	1037	SP	P137GND	1039	SP	P139GND	1040	SP	P140GND
1036	SP	P136GND	1038	SP	P138GND						

1041-1061

Scania L113 CRL   Northern Counties Paladin   B47F   1997

1041	JS	P41MVU	1047	RU	R47XVM	1052	JS	P52MVU	1057	JS	R57XVM
1042	RU	P42MVU	1048	RU	R48XVM	1053	JS	P53MVU	1058	JS	P58MVU
1043	JS	P43MVU	1049	RU	P49MVU	1054	JS	R54XVM	1059	JS	R59XVM
1044	RU	P244NBA	1050	JS	P250NBA	1055	JS	R255WRJ	1060	JS	P260NBA
1045	RU	P45MVU	1051	JS	R51XVM	1056	JS	P56MVU	1061	JS	P61MVU
1046	RU	P46MVU									

1130	u	N707GUM	Dennis Dart 9m		Plaxton Pointer	B34F	1995	Arriva London, 2001
1157	u	M157WKA	Dennis Dart 9.8m		East Lancs	B40F	1995	
1216	BD	M216YKD	Dennis Dart 9.8m		Plaxton Pointer	B40F	1995	

1247-1264

Dennis Dart 9.8m   East Lancs   B40F   1995

1247	WY	N247CKA	1253	u	N253CKA	1259	u	N259CKA	1262	u	N262CKA
1250	u	N250CKA	1255	u	N255CKA	1260	u	N260CKA	1263	WY	N263CKA
1252	WI	N252CKA	1256	WY	N256CKA	1261	u	N261CKA	1264	u	N264CKA

1300	u	P3SLT	Dennis Dart 9.8m	Plaxton Pointer	B40F	1996	South Lancashire, 1997
1312	WX	N706GUM	Dennis Dart 9m	Plaxton Pointer	B34F	1996	Arriva London, 2005
1313	WX	N703GUM	Dennis Dart 9m	Plaxton Pointer	B34F	1996	Arriva London, 2005
1333	u	P833RWU	Dennis Dart 9.8m	Plaxton Pointer	B40F	1996	Arriva London, 2003
1340	u	M160SKR	Dennis Dart 9m	Plaxton Pointer	B35F	1995	Arriva Southern Counties, 1999
1341	u	M161SKR	Dennis Dart 9m	Plaxton Pointer	B35F	1995	Arriva Southern Counties, 1999
1796	u	N24FWU	DAF SB220	Northern Counties Paladin	B49F	1995	West Coast Motors, 1996
1942	u	N212TPK	Dennis Lance 11m	East Lancs	B49F	1996	Arriva London, 2001
1943	u	N213TPK	Dennis Lance 11m	East Lancs	B49F	1996	Arriva London, 2001

2001-2005

Scania L113 CRL   Wright Axcess-CitroÁnlow   N42F   1996

2001	JS	N101YVU	2003	JS	N103YVU	2004	JS	N104YVU	2005	JS	N105YVU
2002	GL	M2SLT									

2006-2034 — Scania L113 CRL — Wright Axcess-ultralow — N43F — 1996

2006	GL	N106DWM	2014	JS	N114DWM	2021	JS	N121DWM	2028	GL	N128DWM
2007	JS	N107DWM	2015	JS	N115DWM	2022	JS	N122DWM	2029	JS	N129DWM
2008	GL	N108DWM	2016	JS	N116DWM	2023	JS	N123DWM	2030	GL	N130DWM
2009	GL	N109DWM	2017	JS	N117DWM	2024	JS	N124DWM	2031	GL	N131DWM
2010	GL	N110DWM	2018	JS	N118DWM	2025	GL	N125DWM	2032	GL	N132DWM
2011	GL	N211DWM	2019	JS	N119DWM	2026	GL	N126DWM	2033	GL	N133DWM
2013	JS	N113DWM	2020	JS	N120DWM	2027	JS	N127DWM	2034	GL	N134DWM

2061	SP	CX05EOV	Scania OmniCity CN94UB	Scania	N34F	2005
2062	SP	CX05EOW	Scania OmniCity CN94UB	Scania	N34F	2005
2063	SP	CX05EOY	Scania OmniCity CN94UB	Scania	N34F	2005

2101-2109 — Dennis Dart SLF 10.1m — Plaxton Pointer 2 — N39F — 1997 — Arriva North East, 2003

2101	JS	R601MHN	2104	WX	R604MHN	2106	WX	R606MHN	2108	AB	R608MHN
2102	JS	R602MHN	2105	WX	R685MHN	2107	WX	R607MHN	2109	BD	R609MHN
2103	WI	R603MHN									

2110-2134 — Dennis Dart SLF 10.1m — Plaxton Pointer 2 — N39F — 1999 — Arriva North East, 2005-06

2110	CH	S610KHN	2122	CH	S622KHN	2129	CH	S629KHN	2132	WX	S632KHN
2114	BD	S614KHN	2123	BD	S623KHN	2130	CH	S630KHN	2133	WX	S633KHN
2119	BD	S619KHN	2127	JS	S627KHN	2131	BG	S631KHN	2134	BG	S634KHN
2120	CH	S620KHN	2128	CH	S628KHN						

2141-2144 — ADL Dart 4 — ADL Enviro 200 — N38F — 2008

2141	SO	CX08DJJ	2142	SO	CX08DJK	2143	SO	CX08DJO	2144	SO	CX08DJU

2201-2262 — Dennis Dart SLF 10.1m — Plaxton Pointer 2 — N36F — 2000-01

2201	GL	X201ANC	2217	BO	X217ANC	2234	BO	X234ANC	2248	MA	X248HJA
2202	GL	X202ANC	2218	BO	X218ANC	2235	BO	X235ANC	2249	MA	X249HJA
2203	GL	X203ANC	2219	BO	X219ANC	2236	BO	X236ANC	2251	MA	X251HJA
2204	GL	X204ANC	2221	BO	X221ANC	2237	BO	X237ANC	2252	MA	X252HJA
2207	GL	X207ANC	2223	BO	X223ANC	2238	MA	X238ANC	2253	MA	X253HJA
2208	GL	X208ANC	2224	BO	X224ANC	2239	MA	X239ANC	2254	MA	X254HJA
2209	JS	X209ANC	2226	BO	X226ANC	2241	MA	X241ANC	2256	MA	X256HJA
2211	JS	X211ANC	2227	BO	X227ANC	2242	MA	X242ANC	2257	CH	X257HJA
2212	JS	X212ANC	2228	BO	X228ANC	2243	MA	X243HJA	2258	CH	X258HJA
2213	JS	X213ANC	2229	BO	X229ANC	2244	MA	X244HJA	2259	WY	X259HJA
2214	JS	X214ANC	2231	BO	X231ANC	2246	MA	X246HJA	2261	WY	X261OBN
2215	BO	X215ANC	2232	BO	X232ANC	2247	MA	X247HJA	2262	WY	X262OBN
2216	BO	X216ANC	2233	BO	X233ANC						

2263-2272 — Dennis Dart SLF 10.2m — Alexander ALX200 — N40F — 2000-01

2263	BO	X263OBN	2266	BO	X266OBN	2268	BO	X268OBN	2271	WY	X271OBN
2264	BO	X264OBN	2267	BO	X267OBN	2269	WY	X269OBN	2272	BO	X272OBN
2265	BO	X265OBN									

2273	LJ	S558MCC	Dennis Dart SLF 10.2m	Alexander ALX200	N40F	1998
2274	LJ	S559MCC	Dennis Dart SLF 10.2m	Alexander ALX200	N40F	1998

2276-2279 — Dennis Dart SLF 10.2m — Alexander ALX200 — N36F — 1997 — Arriva London, 2002-03

2276	LJ	P953RUL	2277	LJ	P959RUL	2278	LJ	P960RUL	2279	LJ	P961RUL

2280-2284 — Dennis Dart SLF 10.1m — Plaxton Pointer — N40F — 1996 — Arriva Southern Counties, 2004

2280	BD	P180LKL	2282	BD	P182LKL	2283	BD	P183LKL	2284	BD	P214LKJ

2285-2288 — Dennis Dart SLF 10.1m — Plaxton Pointer — N39F — 1996 — Arriva Southern Counties, 2004

2285	BD	P419HVX	2286	SO	P420HVX	2287	SO	P422HVX	2288	SO	P430HVX

2291-2294 — Dennis Dart SPD 11.3m — Plaxton Super Pointer — N41F — 1996

2291	SO	S248UVR	2292	SO	S249UVR	2293	SO	S250UVR	2294	SO	S251UVR

2296-2300 — Dennis Dart SLF 10.1m — Plaxton Pointer — N34F — 1997 — Arriva London, 2003

2296	RH	R416COO	2298	RH	R418COO	2299	RH	R419COO	2300	RH	R420COO
2297	RH	R417COO									

2301	WX	R301PCW	Dennis Dart SLF 10.1m	Plaxton Pointer 2	N39F	1998

The holiday town of Llandudno, situated on the North Wales coast is the location for this view of 2343, V573DJC, one of the Dennis Darts added to the fleet at the turn of the millennium. A recent repaint has seen the application of the new colours. *Richard Hughes*

2302-2313   Dennis Dart SLF 10.2m   Alexander ALX200   N40F   1998

2302	WY	R302CVU	**2305**	WY	R305CVU	**2309**	WY	R309CVU	**2312** WY R312CVU
2303	WY	R303CVU	**2306**	WY	R606FBU	**2310**	WY	R310CVU	**2313** WY R313CVU
2304	WY	R304CVU	**2308**	WY	R308CVU	**2311**	WY	R311CVU	

2314-2324   Dennis Dart SLF 10.1m   Plaxton Pointer 2   N36F   1999

2314	BO	T314PNB	**2317**	BO	T317PNB	**2320**	BO	T320PNB	**2323** BO T323PNB
2315	BO	T315PNB	**2318**	BO	T318PNB	**2321**	BO	T821PNB	**2324** BO T324PNB
2316	BO	T316PNB	**2319**	BO	T319PNB	**2322**	BO	T322PNB	

2325	u	R521UCC	Dennis Dart SLF 10.1m	Plaxton Pointer	N39F	1997
2326	u	R522UCC	Dennis Dart SLF 10.1m	Plaxton Pointer	N39F	1997
2328	CH	S848RJC	Dennis Dart SLF 10.1m	Plaxton Pointer 2	N39F	1998	Ieuan Williams, Deiniolen, 1999
2330	BG	T560JJC	Dennis Dart SLF 10.1m	Plaxton Pointer 2	N39F	1999
2331	BG	T561JJC	Dennis Dart SLF 10.1m	Plaxton Pointer 2	N39F	1999
2332	AB	T562JJC	Dennis Dart SLF 10.1m	Plaxton Pointer 2	N39F	1999

2341-2361   Dennis Dart SLF 10.1m   Plaxton Pointer 2   N39F*   1999-2000   *2341/2 are N33F

2341	CH	V571DJC	**2347**	RH	V577DJC	**2352**	RH	V582DJC	**2357** CH V587DJC
2342	CH	V572DJC	**2348**	CH	V578DJC	**2353**	RH	V583DJC	**2358** CH V588DJC
2343	BG	V573DJC	**2349**	RH	V579DJC	**2354**	RH	V584DJC	**2359** CH V580ECC
2344	BG	V574DJC	**2350**	RH	V580DJC	**2355**	CH	V585DJC	**2360** CH V590DJC
2345	RH	V575DJC	**2351**	RH	V581DJC	**2356**	CH	V586DJC	**2361** CH V591DJC
2346	BG	V576DJC							

2400	MA	R91GNW	DAF SB220		Plaxton Prestige	N40F	1998	Blue Bus, Bolton, 2005
2401	SP	R151GNW	DAF SB220		Plaxton Prestige	N38F	1998	Arriva London, 1999
2402	SP	R152GNW	DAF SB220		Plaxton Prestige	N38F	1998	Arriva London, 1999
2403	SP	R153GNW	DAF SB220		Plaxton Prestige	N38F	1998	Arriva London, 1999

2404-2415   DAF SB220   Alexander ALX300   N42F   2000

2404	BD	V404ENC	**2407**	SP	V407ENC	**2410**	SP	V410ENC	**2413** SP V413ENC
2405	SP	V405ENC	**2408**	SP	V408ENC	**2411**	BD	V411ENC	**2414** BD V414ENC
2406	SP	V406ENC	**2409**	BD	V409ENC	**2412**	BD	V412ENC	**2415** SP V415ENC

2416-2449 DAF SB120 — Wright Cadet — N39F — 2000-01

2416	SP	X416AJA	2426	SP	X426AJA	2434	SP	X434HJA	2442	BD	X442HJA
2417	SP	X417AJA	2427	BD	X427AJA	2435	BD	X435HJA	2443	BD	X443HJA
2418	SP	X418AJA	2428	BD	X428HJA	2436	BD	X436HJA	2445	BD	X445HJA
2419	SP	X419AJA	2429	BD	X429HJA	2437	BD	X437HJA	2446	BD	X446HJA
2421	SP	X421AJA	2431	SP	X431HJA	2438	BD	X438HJA	2447	BD	X447HJA
2422	SP	X422AJA	2432	SP	X432HJA	2439	BD	X439HJA	2448	BD	X448HJA
2423	SP	X423AJA	2433	SP	X433HJA	2441	BD	X441HJA	2449	BD	X449HJA
2424	SP	X424AJA									

2450	BN	V33BLU	DAF SB220		East Lancs Myllennium	N42F	1999	Blue Bus, Bolton, 2005

2451-2474 DAF SB220 — East Lancs Myllennium — N44F — 2001

2451	BD	Y451KBU	2457	BD	Y457KBU	2463	SP	Y463KNF	2469	SP	Y469KNF
2452	BD	Y452KBU	2458	BD	Y458KBU	2464	BN	Y464KNF	2470	SP	Y733KNF
2453	BD	Y453KBU	2459	BD	Y459KBU	2465	SP	Y465KNF	2471	SP	Y471KNF
2454	BN	Y454KBU	2460	BD	Y243KBU	2466	SP	Y466KNF	2472	SP	Y472KNF
2455	BD	Y241KBU	2461	BD	Y461KNF	2467	SP	Y467KNF	2473	SP	Y473KNF
2456	BD	Y242KBU	2462	SP	Y462KNF	2468	SP	Y468KNF	2474	BN	Y744KNF

2475	SP	T917KKM	DAF SB220	Plaxton Prestige	N39F	1999	Arriva Southern Counties, 2004
2476	SP	T920KKM	DAF SB220	Plaxton Prestige	N39F	1999	Arriva Southern Counties, 2004
2477	SP	T922KKM	DAF SB220	Plaxton Prestige	N39F	1999	Arriva Southern Counties, 2004
2479	SP	X782NWX	DAF SB120	Wright Cadet	N39F	1999	Selwyns, Runcorn, 2005

2480-2485 VDL Bus SB120 — Wrightbus Cadet 2 — N39F — 2004

2480	BG	CX04AXW	2482	BG	CX04AXZ	2484	BG	CX04AYB	2485	BG	CX04AYC
2481	BG	CX04AXY	2483	BG	CX04AYA						

2489-2503 VDL Bus SB120 — Wrightbus Cadet 2 — N39F — 2004

2489	JS	CX54DKD	2493	JS	CX54DKK	2497	WI	CX54DKU	2501	WI	CX54DLF
2490	JS	CX54DKE	2494	JS	CX54DKL	2498	WI	CX54DKV	2502	WI	CX54DLJ
2491	JS	CX54DKF	2495	JS	CX54DKN	2499	WI	CX54DKY	2503	WI	CX54DLK
2492	JS	CX54DKJ	2496	JS	CX54DKO	2500	WI	CX54DLD			

2504-2513 VDL Bus SB200 — Wrightbus Commander — NC43F — 2005

2504	AB	CX54EPJ	2507	AB	CX54EPN	2510	AB	CX05AAF	2512	AB	CX05AAK
2505	BG	CX54EPK	2508	AB	CX54EPO	2511	AB	CX05AAJ	2513	WX	CX05AAN
2506	AB	CX54EPL	2509	AB	CX05AAE						

2514-2555 VDL Bus SB120 — Wrightbus Cadet 2 — N39F — 2005

2514	RU	DK55FWY	2525	RU	DK55FXL	2536	RU	DK55FXZ	2546	RU	DK55FYL
2515	RU	DK55FWZ	2526	RU	DK55FXM	2537	RU	DK55FYA	2547	RU	DK55FYM
2516	RU	DK55FXA	2527	RU	DK55FXO	2538	RU	DK55FYB	2548	RU	DK55FYN
2517	SP	DK55FXB	2528	RU	DK55FXR	2539	RU	DK55FYC	2549	SP	DK55FYO
2518	SP	DK55FXC	2529	RU	DK55FXS	2540	RU	DK55FYD	2550	SP	DK55FYP
2519	SP	DK55FXD	2530	RU	DK55FXT	2541	RU	DK55FYE	2551	SP	DK55FYR
2520	SP	DK55FXE	2531	RU	DK55FXU	2542	RU	DK55FYF	2552	RU	DK55FYS
2521	RU	DK55FXF	2532	RU	DK55FXV	2543	RU	DK55FYG	2553	RU	DK55FYT
2522	RU	DK55FXG	2533	RU	DK55FXW	2544	SP	DK55FYH	2554	RU	DK55FYV
2523	RU	DK55FXH	2534	RU	DK55FXX	2545	RU	DK55FYJ	2555	RU	DK55FYW
2524	RU	DK55FXJ	2535	RU	DK55FXY						

2556	BN	Y20BLU	DAF SB120	Wrightbus Cadet	N36F	2001	Blue Bus, Bolton, 2005
2557	BN	Y21BLU	DAF SB120	Wrightbus Cadet	N36F	2001	Blue Bus, Bolton, 2005
2558	BN	MM02ZVH	DAF SB120	Wrightbus Cadet	N39F	2002	Blue Bus, Bolton, 2005
2559	BN	MM02ZVJ	DAF SB120	Wrightbus Cadet	N39F	2002	Blue Bus, Bolton, 2005
2560	BN	V34ENC	DAF SB220	Ikarus Citibus 481	N42F	1999	Blue Bus, Bolton, 2005
2561	BN	V35ENC	DAF SB220	Ikarus Citibus 481	N42F	1999	Blue Bus, Bolton, 2005
2562	BN	W174CDN	DAF SB220	Ikarus Citibus 481	N42F	2000	Blue Bus, Bolton, 2005
2563	BN	Y36KNB	DAF SB220	Ikarus Polaris	N42F	2001	Blue Bus, Bolton, 2005
2564	BN	Y37KNB	DAF SB220	Ikarus Polaris	N42F	2001	Blue Bus, Bolton, 2005
2565	BN	Y38KNB	DAF SB220	Ikarus Polaris	N42F	2001	Blue Bus, Bolton, 2005
2566	MA	MK52XNN	DAF SB220	Ikarus Polaris	N44F	2002	Blue Bus, Bolton, 2005
2567	MA	MK52XNO	DAF SB220	Ikarus Polaris	N44F	2002	Blue Bus, Bolton, 2005
2568	MA	MK52XNP	DAF SB220	Ikarus Polaris	N44F	2002	Blue Bus, Bolton, 2005
2569	MA	MK52XNR	DAF SB220	Ikarus Polaris	N44F	2002	Blue Bus, Bolton, 2005

2570-2573 VDL Bus SB120 — Wrightbus Cadet 2 — N39F — 2006

2570	CH	CX06BGU	2571	CH	CX06BGV	2572	CH	CX06BGY	2573	CH	CX06BGZ

Arriving in Rhyl bus station on the principal route that links Llandudno with Rhyl is 2655, CX07CUJ, a VDL Bus SB200 with Wrightbus Pulsar bodywork. The allocation of odd-numbered buses to Llandudno depot to facilitate garage identification more easily by route inspectors will be noted. In 2011 several vehicles will be seen in traditional Crosville livery to mark the 100th anniversary of the company name. *Tom Johnson*

2574-2607

VDL Bus SB200   Wrightbus Commander 2   N44F   2006

2574	GL	CX06BHA	2583	SP	CX06BHP	2592	SP	CX06BJK	2600	SP	CX06BKE
2575	GL	CX06BHD	2584	SP	CX06BHU	2593	SP	CX06BJO	2601	SP	CX06BKF
2576	GL	CX06BHE	2585	SP	CX06BHV	2594	SP	CX06BJU	2602	SP	CX06BKG
2577	GL	CX06BHF	2586	SP	CX06BHW	2595	SP	CX06BJV	2603	SP	CX06BKJ
2578	GL	CX06BHJ	2587	SP	CX06BHY	2596	SP	CX06BJY	2604	SP	CX06BKK
2579	GL	CX06BHK	2588	SP	CX06BHZ	2597	SP	CX06BJZ	2605	SP	CX06BKL
2580	SP	CX06BHL	2589	SP	CX06BJE	2598	SP	CX06BKA	2606	SP	CX06BKN
2581	SP	CX06BHN	2590	SP	CX06BJF	2599	SP	CX06BKD	2607	SP	CX06BKO
2582	SP	CX06BHO	2591	SP	CX06BJJ						

2608-2619

VDL Bus SB120   Plaxton Centro   N40F   2006

2608	WI	CX56CDY	2611	WI	CX56CEF	2614	WI	CX56CEN	2617	WI	CX56CEV
2609	WI	CX56CDZ	2612	WI	CX56CEJ	2615	WI	CX56CEO	2618	WI	CX56CEY
2610	WI	CX56CEA	2613	WI	CX56CEK	2616	WI	CX56CEU	2619	WI	CX56CFA

2620	LJ	CX07COJ	VDL Bus SB200		Wrightbus Pulsar	N44F	2007

2621-2641

VDL Bus SB120   Wrightbus Cadet 2   N44F   2007

2621	BN	CX07COU	2627	BN	CX07CPU	2632	AB	CX07CRJ	2637	CH	CX07CSF
2622	BN	CX07CPE	2628	BN	CX07CPV	2633	CH	CX07CRK	2638	CH	CX07
2623	BN	CX07CPF	2629	CH	CX07CPY	2634	CH	CX07CRU	2639	AB	CX07CSU
2624	SO	CX07CPK	2630	CH	CX07CPZ	2635	CH	CX07CRV	2640	AB	CX07CSV
2625	BN	CX07CPN	2631	CH	CX07CRF	2636	CH	CX07CRZ	2641	AB	CX07CSY
2626	BN	CX07CPO									

2642-2662

VDL Bus SB200   Wrightbus Pulsar   N44F   2007

2642	RH	CX07CSZ	2648	RH	CX07CTV	2653	LJ	CX07CUG	2658	RH	CX07CUV
2643	LJ	CX07CTE	2649	LJ	CX07CTY	2654	RH	CX07CUH	2659	LJ	CX07CUW
2644	RH	CX07CTF	2650	AB	CX07CTZ	2655	LJ	CX07CUJ	2660	RH	CX07CUY
2645	LJ	CX07CTK	2651	LJ	CX07CUA	2656	RH	CX07CUK	2661	LJ	CX07CVA
2646	RH	CX07CTO	2652	RH	CX07CUC	2657	LJ	CX07CUU	2662	RH	CX07CVB
2647	LJ	CX07CTU									

2663-2700 — VDL Bus SB200 — Wrightbus Pulsar — N44F — 2008

2663	GL	CX58EUD	2673	GL	CX58EUP	2683	BN	CX58EVD	2692	JS	CX58EWE
2664	GL	CX58EUE	2674	GL	CX58EUR	2684	BN	CX58EVF	2693	JS	CX58EWF
2665	GL	CX58EUF	2675	GL	CX58EUT	2685	BN	CX58EVG	2694	JS	CX58EWG
2666	GL	CX58EUH	2676	BN	CX58EUU	2686	BN	CX58EVH	2695	JS	CX58EWH
2667	GL	CX58EUJ	2677	BN	CX58EUV	2687	BN	CX58EVJ	2696	JS	CX58EWJ
2668	GL	CX58EUK	2678	BN	CX58EUW	2688	BN	CX58EVK	2697	JS	CX58EWK
2669	GL	CX58EUL	2679	BN	CX58EUY	2689	JS	CX58EWB	2698	JS	CX58EWL
2670	GL	CX58EUM	2680	BN	CX58EUZ	2690	JS	CX58EWC	2699	JS	CX58EWM
2671	GL	CX58EUN	2681	BN	CX58EVB	2691	JS	CX58EWD	2700	JS	CX58EWN
2672	GL	CX58EUO	2682	BN	CX58EVC						

2701-2730 — Volvo B10BLE — Wrightbus Renown — N44F — 2001

2701	JS	X701DBT	2709	JS	X709DBT	2717	SP	Y717KNF	2724	SO	Y724KNF
2702	JS	X702DBT	2710	JS	X956DBT	2718	SP	Y718KNF	2725	SO	Y475KNF
2703	JS	X703DBT	2711	JS	Y711KNF	2719	SP	Y719KNF	2726	SO	Y726KNF
2704	JS	X704DBT	2712	JS	Y712KNF	2720	SP	Y457KNF	2727	SO	Y727KNF
2705	JS	X705DBT	2713	JS	Y713KNF	2721	SP	Y721KNF	2728	SO	Y728KNF
2706	JS	X706DBT	2714	JS	Y714KNF	2722	SO	Y722KNF	2729	JS	Y729KNF
2707	JS	X707DBT	2715	JS	Y715KNF	2723	SO	Y723KNF	2730	JS	Y458KNF
2708	JS	X708DBT	2716	SP	Y716KNF						

2732	BN	V22BLU	Volvo B10BLE	Wright Renown	N42F	1999	Blue Bus, Bolton, 2005
2733	BN	X23BLU	Volvo B10BLE	Wright Renown	N42F	2000	Blue Bus, Bolton, 2005

2740-2749 — ADL E300 — ADL Enviro 300 — N45F — 2008

2740	MA	CX58EVL	2743	MA	CX58EVR	2746	MA	CX58EVV	2748	MA	CX58EVY
2741	MA	CX58EVN	2744	MA	CX58EVT	2747	MA	CX58EVW	2749	MA	CX58EWA
2742	MA	CX58EVP	2745	MA	CX58EVU						

2793-2799 — Volvo B7RLE — Wrightbus Eclipse Urban — N44F — 2004-07 — KMP, 2008

2793	BG	CX04HRN	2795	BG	CX04HRP	2797	BG	CX55FAF	2799	BG	CX57BZO
2794	BG	CX04HRR	2796	BG	CX05JVD	2798	BG	CX55FAJ			

2800	BN	Y22CJW	Volvo B7L	Wrightbus Eclipse	N41F	2001

2801-2822 — Volvo B6BLE — Wright Crusader 2 — N39F — 2000

2801	SO	X801AJA	2806	MA	X806AJA	2812	MA	X812AJA	2817	SO	X817AJA
2802	SO	X802AJA	2807	MA	X807AJA	2813	SO	X813AJA	2818	SO	X818AJA
2803	SO	X803AJA	2808	MA	X808AJA	2814	SO	X814AJA	2819	SO	X819AJA
2804	SO	X804AJA	2809	MA	X809AJA	2815	SO	X815AJA	2821	SO	X821AJA
2805	MA	X805AJA	2811	MA	X811AJA	2816	SO	X816AJA	2822	SO	X822AJA

2825	u	T222MTB	MAN 18.220	Alexander ALX300	N42F	1999	Blue Bus, Bolton, 2005

2826-2829 — MAN 14.220 — East Lancs Myllennium — N39F — 2002 — Blue Bus, Bolton, 2005

2826	BN	MF52LYY	2827	BN	MF52LYZ	2828	BN	MF52LZA	2829	BN	MF52LZB

2860-2867 — Optare Tempo X1130 — Optare — N41F — 2005-06 — *operated for Ceredigion*

2860	AB	YJ55BKG	2862	AB	YJ55BKL	2864	AB	YJ55BKN	2866	AB	YJ55BKV
2861	AB	YJ55BKK	2863	AB	YJ55BKN	2865	AB	YJ55BKU	2867	AB	YJ06YRY

2868	AB	YJ06YRZ	Optare Tempo X1200	Optare	NC42F	2006	*operated for Ceredigion*
2869	AB	YJ06YRO	Optare Tempo X1200	Optare	NC42F	2006	*operated for Ceredigion*
2870	AB	YJ55BJE	Optare Tempo X1200	Optare	NC41F	2005	*operated for Ceredigion*
2871	AB	YJ55BJF	Optare Tempo X1200	Optare	NC41F	2005	*operated for Ceredigion*
2872	AB	YJ55BJK	Optare Tempo X1200	Optare	NC41F	2005	*operated for Ceredigion*

2900-2929 — VDL Bus SB200 — Wrightbus Pulsar 2 — N44F — 2008

2900	GL	CX58EWO	2908	WX	CX58EWY	2916	BO	CX58EXH	2923	BO	CX58EZE
2901	GL	CX58EWP	2909	WX	CX58EWZ	2917	BO	CX58EXJ	2924	BO	CX58EZF
2902	GL	CX58EWR	2910	WX	CX58EXA	2918	BO	CX58EXK	2925	BO	CX58EZG
2903	GL	CX58EWS	2911	WX	CX58EXB	2919	BO	CX58EXL	2926	BO	CX58EZH
2904	GL	CX58EWT	2912	WX	CX58EXC	2920	BO	CX58EZA	2927	BO	CX58EZJ
2905	GL	CX58EWU	2913	WX	CX58EXE	2921	BO	CX58EZB	2928	BO	CX58EZK
2906	WX	CX58EWV	2914	WX	CX58EXF	2922	BO	CX58EZC	2929	BO	CX58EZL
2907	WX	CX58EWW	2915	LJ	CX58EXG						

Since the last edition of this book further Optare Tempo buses owned by Ceredigion have been allocated to Arriva. One of the latest arrivals transferred from another operator is 2871, YJ55BJF, seen here leaving Carmarthen bus station. *Richard Godfrey*

2930-2999   VDL Bus SB200   Wrightbus Pulsar 2   N44F   2009

2930	WY	MX09EKK	2948	RU	MX09LXT	2966	JS	MX09OOU	2983	JS	MX09OPO		
2931	WY	MX09EKL	2949	RU	MX09LXU	2967	JS	MX09OOV	2984	JS	MX59JYY		
2932	WY	MX09EKM	2950	RU	MX09LXV	2968	JS	MX09OOW	2985	JS	MX59JYZ		
2933	WY	MX09EKN	2951	RU	MX09LXW	2969	JS	MX09OOY	2986	JS	MX59JZA		
2934	WY	MX09EKO	2952	RU	MX09LXY	2970	JS	MX09OPA	2987	JS	MX59JZC		
2935	WY	MX09EKP	2953	RU	MX09LXZ	2971	JS	MX09OPB	2988	JS	MX59JZD		
2936	WY	MX09EKR	2954	GL	MX09JHH	2972	JS	MX09OPC	2989	JS	MX59JZE		
2937	WY	MX09EKT	2955	GL	MX09JHK	2973	JS	MX09OPD	2990	JS	MX59JZF		
2938	WY	MX09EKU	2956	GL	MX09JHL	2974	JS	MX09OPE	2991	JS	MX59JZC		
2939	WY	MX09EKW	2957	GL	MX09JHO	2975	JS	MX09OPF	2992	JS	MX59JZH		
2940	WY	MX09EKY	2958	GL	MX09JHU	2976	JS	MX09OPG	2993	JS	MX59JZJ		
2941	BO	MX09LYA	2959	GL	MX09JHV	2977	JS	MX09OPH	2994	GL	MX59FHB		
2942	BO	MX09LYC	2960	GL	MX09JHY	2978	JS	MX09OPJ	2995	BN	MX59FGD		
2943	BO	MX09LYD	2961	GL	MX09JHZ	2979	JS	MX09OPK	2996	MA	MX59FGE		
2944	BO	MX09LYF	2962	GL	MX09JJE	2980	JS	MX09OPL	2997	MA	MX59FGF		
2945	BO	MX09LYG	2963	GL	MX09JJF	2981	JS	MX09OPM	2998	MA	MX59FGG		
2946	BO	MX09LYH	2964	GL	MX09JTY	2982	JS	MX09OPN	2999	MA	MX59FGJ		
2947	BO	MX09LYJ	2965	JS	MX09OOJ								

3000-3022   VDL Bus SB200   Wrightbus Pulsar 2   N44F   2009

3000	BD	MX59AAE	3006	BD	MX59AAU	3012	GL	MX59ABN	3018	BO	MX59FFW
3001	BD	MX59AAF	3007	BD	MX59AAV	3013	GL	MX59FFR	3019	BO	MX59FFX
3002	BD	MX59AAJ	3008	BD	MX59AAY	3014	GL	MX59FFS	3020	BO	MX59FFZ
3003	BD	MX59AAK	3009	BD	MX59AAZ	3015	BO	MX59FFT	3021	BO	MX59FGA
3004	BD	MX59AAN	3010	BD	MX59ABF	3016	BO	MX59FFU	3022	BO	MX59FGB
3005	BD	MX59AAO	3011	BD	MX59ABK	3017	BO	MX59FFV			

Southport depot recently received fourteen new VDL SB200s fitted with Wrightbus Pulsar 2 bodywork. Several are lettered for the service south into Liverpool, including 3033, MX10BZS, seen in the seaside resort.
Norman Price

3023-3061

VDL Bus SB200 — Wrightbus Pulsar 2 — N44F — 2009

3023	SK	MX59JJE	3033	SP	MX10BZS	3043	SP	MX10CZG	3053	GL	MX10DBY
3024	SK	MX59JJF	3034	SP	MX10BZT	3044	SP	MX10CZH	3054	GL	MX10DBZ
3025	SK	MX59JJK	3035	SP	MX10BZU	3045	SP	MX10CZJ	3055	GL	MX10DCE
3026	SK	MX59JJL	3036	SP	MX10BZV	3046	SP	MX10CZK	3056	GL	MX10DCF
3027	SK	MX59JJO	3037	SP	MX10BZW	3047	SK	MX10DAA	3057	GL	MX10DCO
3028	SK	MX59JJU	3038	SP	MX10BZY	3048	SK	MX10DAO	3058	GL	MX10DCU
3029	SK	MX59JJV	3039	SP	MX10CZC	3049	GL	MX10DAU	3059	GL	MX10DCV
3030	GL	MX59JJY	3040	SP	MX10CZD	3050	GL	MX10DBO	3060	GL	MX10DCY
3031	GL	MX59JJZ	3041	SP	MX10CZE	3051	GL	MX10DBU	3061	GL	MX10DCZ
3032	GL	MX59JKZ	3042	SP	MX10CZF	3052	GL	MX10DBV			

3271-3308

Volvo Olympian YN2RV18Z4 — Northern Counties Palatine II B47/30F — 1995-96

3271	SP	N271CKB	3281	SP	N281CKB	3290	SK	N290CKB	3299	BD	N299CKB
3272	SK	N272CKB	3282	SP	N282CKB	3291	BD	N291CKB	3301	BD	N301CKB
3273	SK	N273CKB	3283	SK	N283CKB	3292	BD	N292CKB	3302	BD	N302CKB
3274	SK	N274CKB	3284	SK	N284CKB	3293	BD	N293CKB	3303	BD	N303CLV
3275	SK	N275CKB	3285	SK	N285CKB	3294	BD	N294CKB	3304	BD	N304CLV
3276	SP	N276CKB	3286	SK	N286CKB	3295	BD	N295CKB	3305	BD	N305CLV
3277	SP	N277CKB	3287	SK	N287CKB	3296	BD	N296CKB	3306	BD	N306CLV
3278	SP	N278CKB	3288	SK	N288CKB	3297	BD	N297CKB	3307	BD	N307CLV
3279	SP	N279CKB	3289	SK	N289CKB	3298	BD	N298CKB	3308	BD	N308CLV

3309-3337

Volvo Olympian YN2RV18Z4 — Northern Counties Palatine II B47/30F — 1998

3309	BO	R309WVR	3315	BO	R315WVR	3326	SP	R326WVR	3332	SP	R332WVR
3310	BO	R310WVR	3317	SP	R317WVR	3327	SP	R327WVR	3334	SP	R334WVR
3311	BO	R311WVR	3319	BO	R319WVR	3329	SP	R329WVR	3335	SP	R335WVR
3312	BO	R312WVR	3321	SP	R321WVR	3330	SP	R330WVR	3336	BO	R336WVR
3313	BO	R313WVR	3322	SP	R322WVR	3331	SP	R331WVR	3337	BO	R337WVR
3314	BO	R314WVR	3324	BO	R324WVR						

The 2011 Arriva Bus Handbook

An unusual body style for Arriva is the East Lancs Pyoneer. One of only four operated, 3364, R44BLU is seen in school service in Leyland. All four were new to Blue Bus of Bolton. *Richard Godfrey*

3343-3349

		Volvo Olympian			Northern Counties Palatine	B47/29F	1998		
3343	BN	R233AEY	3345	AB	R235AEY	3347	WX	R237AEY	3349	WI	R239AEY
3344	WI	R234AEY	3346	WI	R236AEY	3348	WI	R238AEY		

3350-3354

		Volvo Olympian YN2RV18Z4			Northern Counties Palatine	B47/30F	1996	Arriva Southern Counties, 2004
3350	WI	N705TPK	3352	WI	N707TPK	3353	WI	N708TPK	3354	WI	N709TPK
3351	WI	N706TPK					

3355-3360

		Volvo Olympian			Northern Counties Palatine	B45/30F	1997	Arriva Southern Counties, 2004
3355	BG	P938MKL	3357	BG	P940MKL	3359	BG	P942MKL	3360	WI	P943MKL
3356	BG	P939MKL	3358	BG	P941MKL					

3362	BN	T42PVM	Volvo Olympian	East Lancs Pyoneer	B47/30F	1999	Blue Bus, Bolton, 2005
3363	BN	S43BLU	Volvo Olympian	East Lancs Pyoneer	B47/30F	1998	Blue Bus, Bolton, 2005
3364	BN	R44BLU	Volvo Olympian	East Lancs Pyoneer	BC45/30F	1998	Blue Bus, Bolton, 2005
3365	BN	S45BLU	Volvo Olympian	East Lancs Pyoneer	B47/30F	1998	Blue Bus, Bolton, 2005

3601-3613

		DAF DB250			Northern Counties Palatine II	B47/30F	1995	Arriva London, 2001
3601	BN	N601DWY	3605	BN	N605DWY	3610	BN	N610DWY	3612	BN	N612DWY
3602	BN	N602DWY	3607	BN	N607DWY	3611	BN	N611DWY	3613	BN	N613DWY
3603	BN	N603DWY	3608	u	N608DWY					

3614-3618

		DAF DB250			Northern Counties Palatine II	B43/28F	1998	Arriva London/SC, 2003/04
3614	BN	R213CKO	3616	SP	R201CKO	3617	SP	R202CKO	3618	SP	R203CKO
3615	SP	V715LWT						

3837	u	N716TPK	Dennis Dominator DDA2006	East Lancs	B45/31F	1996	
3980	SO	GKA449L	Leyland Atlantean AN68/1R	Alexander AL	O43/32F	1973	
3984	RH	E224WBG	Leyland Olympian ONCL10/1RZ	Alexander RL	O43/30F	1988	
3987	RH	E227WBG	Leyland Olympian ONCL10/1RZ	Alexander RL	O43/30F	1988	
3992	LJ	YMB512W	Bristol VRT/SL3/6LXB	Eastern Coach Works	O43/31F	1981	Crosville, 1986
3995	RH	G35HKY	Scania N113 DRB	Northern Counties	O47/33F	1990	Arriva Fox County, 2002
3996	LJ	D170FYM	Leyland Olympian ONLXB/1RH	Eastern Coach Works	O42/30F	1986	Arriva Midlands, 2007
3997	LJ	D171FYM	Leyland Olympian ONLXB/1RH	Eastern Coach Works	O42/30F	1986	Arriva Midlands, 2007
3998	LJ	C212GTU	Leyland Olympian ONLXB/1R	Eastern Coach Works	O42/27F	1985	Crosville, 1986
3999	RH	D242FYM	Leyland Olympian ONLXB/1RH	Eastern Coach Works	O42/30F	1986	Arriva Midlands, 2007
4000	BD	Y46ABA	Dennis Trident	Plaxton President	N47/28F	2001	Blue Bus, Bolton, 2005
4001	BD	Y47ABA	Dennis Trident	Plaxton President	N47/28F	2001	Blue Bus, Bolton, 2005
4002	BD	Y48ABA	Dennis Trident	Plaxton President	N47/28F	2001	Blue Bus, Bolton, 2005

4012-4020

DAF DB250 10.6m • Alexander ALX400 • N45/23F • 1999 • Arriva London, 2010

4012	MA	S202JUA	4015	MA	S205JUA	4017	MA	S207JUA	4019 MA S209JUA
4013	MA	S203JUA	4016	MA	S206JUA	4018	MA	S208JUA	4020 MA S210JUA
4014	MA	S204JUA							

4025-4031

DAF DB250 10.6m • Alexander ALX400 • N45/23F • 1999 • Arriva London, 2006

4025	SP	S265JUA	4027	SP	S267JUA	4029	SP	S269JUA	4031 SP S271JUA
4026	SP	S266JUA	4028	SP	S268JUA	4030	SP	S270JUA	

4056-4065

DAF DB250 10.6m • Alexander ALX400 • N45/23F • 1999 • Arriva London, 2010

4056	SK	T296FGN	4059	SK	T299FGN	4062	SK	T302FGN	4064 SK T304FGN
4057	SK	T297FGN	4060	MA	T300FGN	4063	SK	T303FGN	4065 SK T305FGN
4058	SK	T298FGN	4061	SK	T301FGN				

4073-4091

DAF DB250 10.6m • Alexander ALX400 • N45/23F • 1999 • Arriva London, 2011

4073	u	S243JUA	4078	u	S248JUA	4083	u	S252JUA	4090 u S260JUA
4074	u	S244JUA	4079	u	S249JUA	4089	u	S259JUA	4091 u S261UA
4076	u	S246JUA	4082	u	S252JUA				

4100-4129

Volvo B7TL • ADL ALX400 • BC45/27F • 2006

4100	SP	CX55EAF	4108	SP	CX55EAY	4116	SP	CX06EAM	4123 SP CX06EBD
4101	SP	CX55EAG	4109	SP	CX55EBA	4117	SP	CX06EAO	4124 SP CX06EBF
4102	SP	CX55EAJ	4110	SP	CX55EBC	4118	SP	CX06EAP	4125 SP CX06EBG
4103	SP	CX55EAK	4111	SP	CX55EBD	4119	SP	CX06EAW	4126 SP CX06EBJ
4104	SP	CX55EAM	4112	SP	CX55EBF	4120	SP	CX06EAY	4127 SP CX06EBK
4105	SP	CX55EAO	4113	SP	CX55EBG	4121	SP	CX06EBA	4128 SP CX06EBL
4106	SP	CX55EAP	4114	SP	CX55EBJ	4122	SP	CX06EBC	4129 SP CX06EBM
4107	SP	CX55EAW	4115	SP	CX06EAK				

4400-4434

ADL Trident 2 • ADL Enviro 400 • BC47/33F • 2008-09

4400	BD	CX58FZM	4409	BD	CX58FZW	4418	BD	CX58GBU	4427 BO MX09LXJ
4401	BD	CX58FZN	4410	BD	CX58FZY	4419	BD	CX58GBV	4428 BO MX09LXK
4402	BD	CX58FZO	4411	BD	CX58FZZ	4420	BD	CX58GBY	4429 BO MX09LXL
4403	BD	CX58FZP	4412	BD	CX58GAA	4421	BD	CX58GBZ	4430 BO MX09LXM
4404	BD	CX58FZR	4413	BD	CX58GAO	4422	BD	CX58GCF	4431 BO MX09LXN
4405	BD	CX58FZS	4414	BD	CX58GAU	4423	BO	MX09LXE	4432 BO MX09LXO
4406	BD	CX58FZT	4415	BD	CX58GBE	4424	BO	MX09LXF	4433 BO MX09LXR
4407	BD	CX58FZU	4416	BD	CX58GBF	4425	BO	MX09LXG	4434 BO MX09LXS
4408	BD	CX58FZV	4417	BD	CX58GBO	4426	BO	MX09LXH	

5301-5320

Scania L113 CRL • Wright Axcess-ultralow • N40F • 1996

5301	GL	P301HEM	5307	GL	P307HEM	5312	GL	P312HEM	5317 GL P317HEM
5302	GL	P302HEM	5308	GL	P308HEM	5313	GL	P313HEM	5318 GL P318HEM
5303	GL	P303HEM	5309	GL	P309HEM	5314	GL	P314HEM	5319 GL P319HEM
5305	GL	P305HEM	5310	GL	P310HEM	5315	GL	P315HEM	5320 GL P320HEM
5306	GL	P306HEM	5311	GL	P311HEM	5316	GL	P316HEM	

6001-6020

Mercedes-Benz Citaro O530G • AB49T • 2004 • Arriva London, 2011

6001	u	BX04MWW	6006	u	BX04MXC	6013	u	BX04MXL	6017 u BX04MXR
6002	u	BX04MWY	6007	u	BX04MXD	6014	u	BX04MXM	6018 u BX04MXS
6003	u	BX04MWZ	6008	u	BX04MXE	6015	u	BX04MXN	6019 u BX04MXT
6004	u	BX04MXA	6010	u	BX04MXH	6016	u	BX04MXP	6020 u BX04MXU
6005	u	BX04MXB	6011	u	BX04MXJ				

6527	u	M527WHF	Volvo B10B	Wright Endurance	BC49F	1994
6532	u	M532WHF	Volvo B10B	Wright Endurance	BC49F	1994
6536	u	M536WHF	Volvo B10B	Wright Endurance	BC49F	1994

6558-6623

Volvo B10B • Wright Endurance • BC49F • 1994-96

6558	u	M558WTJ	6581	GL	N581CKA	6593	u	N593CKA	6610 u N610CKA
6561	u	M561WTJ	6582	GL	N582CKA	6595	u	N595CKA	6611 u N611CKA
6569	AB	M569YEM	6583	GL	N583CKA	6599	GL	N599CKA	6612 u N612CKA
6571	AB	M571YEM	6584	GL	N584CKA	6603	GL	N603CKA	6615 GL N615CKA
6572	u	M572YEM	6585	GL	N585CKA	6604	GL	N604CKA	6616 u N616CKA
6573	u	M573YEM	6587	GL	N587CKA	6606	GL	N606CKA	6619 u N619CKA
6575	GL	M575YEM	6589	GL	N589CKA	6607	u	N607CKA	6621 u N621CKA
6578	GL	N578CKA	6591	u	N591CKA	6608	u	N608CKA	6622 u N622CKA
6579	GL	N579CKA	6592	GL	N592CKA	6609	u	N609CKA	6623 GL N623CKA
6580	GL	N580CKA							

New to Merseyside were sixty-four Dennis Darts with Marshall Capital bodywork. Pictured in Wigan, 7632, V632DVU, illustrates the new livery on this body style as it heads north to Ormskirk. *Richard Godfrey*

7531-7545

Dennis Dart SLF 9.8m — Plaxton Pointer — N38F — 1996-97

7531	WX	N531DWM	7535	RH	P535MBU	7539	RH	P539MBU	7543	BD	P543MBU
7532	WX	N532DWM	7536	CH	P536MBU	7540	RH	P540MBU	7544	JS	P544MBU
7533	RH	P533MBU	7537	CH	P537MBU	7541	BG	P541MBU	7545	BN	P545MBU
7534	RH	P534MBU	7538	CH	P538MBU	7542	BG	P542MBU			

7547-7571

Dennis Dart SLF 9.8m — Plaxton Pointer — N38F — 1998

7547	BD	R547ABA	7553	WX	R553ABA	7560	LJ	R560ABA	7567	JS	R567ABA
7548	SH	R548ABA	7554	BD	R554ABA	7561	RU	R561ABA	7568	GL	R568ABA
7549	SH	R549ABA	7556	BD	R556ABA	7562	RH	R562ABA	7569	u	R569ABA
7550	WX	R550ABA	7557	BD	R557ABA	7563	CH	R563ABA	7570	JS	R570ABA
7551	BD	R551ABA	7558	RU	R558ABA	7564	RH	R564ABA	7571	JS	R571ABA
7552	BN	R552ABA	7559	LJ	R559ABA	7565	AB	R565ABA			

7612-7623

Dennis Dart SLF 10.5m — Marshall Capital — N38F — 1999

7612	WI	T612PNC	7615	WY	T615PNC	7618	WX	T618PNC	7621	SK	T621PNC
7613	SK	T613PNC	7616	WY	T616PNC	7619	GL	T619PNC	7622	BN	T622PNC
7614	WI	T614PNC	7617	SK	T617PNC	7620	WI	T620PNC	7623	LJ	T623PNC

7624-7676

Dennis Dart SLF 10.5m — Marshall Capital — N38F — 1999-2000

7624	WI	V624DBN	7637	SP	V637DVU	7650	SK	V650DVU	7663	BO	V663DVU
7625	LJ	V625DVU	7638	SK	V638DVU	7651	SO	V651DVU	7664	GL	V664DVU
7626	BO	V626DVU	7639	SK	V639DVU	7652	SO	V652DVU	7665	GL	V665DVU
7627	WI	V627DVU	7640	u	V640DVU	7653	SO	V653DVU	7667	BO	V667DVU
7628	WI	V628DVU	7641	LJ	V641DVU	7654	SO	V654DVU	7668	GL	V668DVU
7629	LJ	V629DVU	7642	JS	V642DVU	7655	BD	V655DVU	7669	SK	V669DVU
7630	LJ	V630DVU	7643	SK	V643DVU	7656	SO	V656DVU	7670	GL	V670DVU
7631	GL	V631DVU	7644	WI	V644DVU	7657	GL	V657DVU	7671	GL	V671DVU
7632	SK	V632DVU	7645	JS	V645DVU	7658	GL	V658DVU	7672	GL	V672DVU
7633	SK	V633DVU	7646	SK	V646DVU	7659	BO	V659DVU	7673	WI	V673DVU
7634	SK	V634DVU	7647	WI	V647DVU	7660	SK	V660DVU	7674	SK	V674DVU
7635	SK	V635DVU	7648	SK	V648DVU	7661	SK	V661DVU	7675	JS	V675DVU
7636	SK	V636DVU	7649	SK	V649DVU	7662	BO	V662DVU	7676	SP	V676DVU

Ancillary vehicles:

8175	u	K27EWC	Leyland Lynx LX2R11C15Z4R	Leyland Lynx 2	TV	1992	Colchester, 1994
8201	SP	L301TEM	Volvo B10B	Alexander Strider	TV	1994	
8202	SP	L302TEM	Volvo B10B	Alexander Strider	TV	1994	
8203	MA	L303TEM	Volvo B10B	Alexander Strider	TV	1994	
8204	GL	M109XKC	Volvo B10B	Northern Counties Paladin	TV	1993	Liverbus, 1995
8205	WX	M110XKC	Volvo B10B	Northern Counties Paladin	TV	1993	Liverbus, 1995
8206	BD	M112XKC	Volvo B10B	Northern Counties Paladin	TV	1993	Liverbus, 1995
8207	BO	M113XKC	Volvo B10B	Northern Counties Paladin	TV	1993	Liverbus, 1995
8212	SK	L502TKA	Volvo B10B	Wright Endurance	TV	1994	
8214	SP	M514WHF	Volvo B10B	Wright Endurance	TV	1994	
8215	CH	L505TKA	Volvo B10B	Wright Endurance	TV	1994	
8218	JS	L508TKA	Volvo B10B	Wright Endurance	TV	1994	
8219	BO	M519WHF	Volvo B10B	Wright Endurance	TV	1994	
8223	RU	M523WHF	Volvo B10B	Wright Endurance	TV	1994	
8229	BD	M429UNW	Volvo B10B	Alexander Strider	TV	1994	Arriva Midlands, 2009
8230	JS	M530WHF	Volvo B10B	Wright Endurance	TV	1994	
8232	BN	M532WHF	Volvo B10B	Wright Endurance	TV	1994	
8245	GL	N605CKA	Volvo B10B	Wright Endurance	TV	1996	

Previous registrations:

CX04HRN	L77KMP	R91GNW	R91GNW, R33GNW
CX04HRP	L777KMP	T10BLU	MF51TVV
CX04HRR	N777KMP	T11BLU	MF51TVW
CX05JVD	M7KMP	V580ECC	V589DJC
CX55FAE	A7KMP	W12LUE	MF51TVX
CX55FAJ	K7KMP	X13LUE	MF51TVY
CX57BZO	N77KMP	X14LUE	MV02XYH
M2SLT	N102YVU		

Depots and Allocations:

Aberystwyth (Park Avenue) - AB

Outstations: Dolgellau, Lampeter and New Quay

Solo	694	695						
Dart	801	802	820	823	824	826	832	834
	841	842	2108	2325	2332	7565		
Volvo B10B	6569	6571						
DAF/VDL SB200	2504	2506	2507	2508	2509	2510	2511	2512
Optare Tempo	2860	2861	2862	2863	2864	2865	2866	2867
	2868	2869	2870	2871				
Olympian	3345	3347						

Bangor (Llandegai Industrial Estate) - BG

Outstations: Amlwch, Holyhead and Pwllheli

Optare Solo	681	682	683	684	685	686	687	688
	689	690	691	692	693			
Dart	827	833	2131	2134	2330	2331	2343	2344
	2346	7541	7542					
DAF/VDL SB120	2480	2481	2482	2483	2484	2485		
VDL Bus SB200	2505							
Volvo B7RLE	2793	2794	2795	2796	2797	2798	2799	
Olympian	3355	3356	3357	3358				

Birkenhead (Laird Street) - BD

Dart	2114	2119	2123	2280	2282	2283	2284	2285
	7543	7547	7551	7635	7642			
	7554	7556	7557					
DAF/VDL SB120	2427	2428	2429	2435	2436	2437	2438	2439
	2441	2442	2443	2445	2446	2447	2448	2449
DAF/VDL SB220	2404	2409	2411	2412	2414	2451	2452	2453
	2455	2456	2457	2458	2459	2460	2461	
VDL Bus SB200	3000	3001	3002	3003	3004	3005	3006	3007
	3008	3009	3010	3011				
Olympian	3292	3293	3294	3295	3296	3297	3298	3299
	3301	3302	3303	3304	3305	3306	3307	3308
Trident	4000	4001	4002					
Trident 2	4400	4401	4402	4403	4404	4405	4406	4407
	4408	4409	4410	4411	4412	4413	4414	4415
	4416	4417	4418	4419	4420	4421	4422	
Ancillary	*8206*	*8229*						

Bolton (Folds Road) - BN

Dart	890	2254	7545	7552	7622			
DAF/VDL SB120	2556	2557	2558	2559				
DAF/VDL SB220	2450	2454	2464	2474	2560	2561	2562	2565
VDL Bus SB200	2566	2621	2622	2623	2625	2626	2627	2628
	2676	2677	2678	2679	2680	2681	2682	2683
	2684	2685	2686	2687	2688	2995		
MAN	2825	2826	2827	2828	2829			
Volvo B10BLE	2732	2733						
Volvo B7L	2800							
Volvo Olympian	3343	3362	3363	3364	3365			
DAF DB250	3601	3602	3603	3605	3607	3610	3611	3612
	3613	3614						
Ancillary	*8232*							

Bootle (Hawthorne Road) - BO

Dart	2215	2216	2217	2218	2219	2221	2223	2224
	2226	2227	2228	2229	2231	2232	2233	2234
	2235	2236	2237	2263	2264	2265	2266	2267
	2268	2272	2314	2315	2316	2317	2318	2319
	2320	2321	2322	2323	2324	7568	7626	7659
	7662	7663	7667					
DAF/VDL SB120	2517	2518	2519	2638				
VDL SB200	2916	2917	2918	2919	2920	2921	2922	2923
	2924	2925	2926	2927	2928	2929	2941	2942
	2943	2944	2945	2946	2947	3015	3016	3017
	3018	3019	3020	3021	3022			
Olympian	3309	3310	3311	3312	3313	3314	3315	3319
	3324	3336	3337					
Trident 2	4423	4424	4425	4426	4427	4428	4429	4430
	4431	4432	4433	4434				
Ancillary	*8207*	*8219*						

Chester (Manor Lane, Hawarden) - CH

Solo	623	624	625	671	672	673	674	675
Dart	2110	2120	2122	2128	2129	2130	2257	2258
	2328	2341	2342	2348	2355	2356	2357	2358
	2359	2360	2361	7536	7537	7538	7563	
DAF/VDL SB120	2570	2571	2572	2573	2629	2630	2631	
	2633	2634	2635	2636	2637	2639	2641	
Ancillary	*8215*							

Liverpool (Green Lane) - GL

Dart	2201	2202	2203	2204	2207	2208	7619	7631
	7657	7658	7664	7665	7668	7670	7671	7672
Volvo B10B	6575	6578	6579	6580	6581	6582	6584	6585
	6587	6589	6592	6599	6603	6604	6606	6611
	6615	6622	6623					
Scania L113	2002	2006	2008	2009	2010	2011	2025	2026
	2028	2030	2031	2032	2033	2034	5301	5302
	5303	5305	5306	5307	5308	5309	5310	5311
	5312	5313	5314	5315	5316	5317	5318	5319
	5320							
VDL Bus SB200	2574	2575	2576	2577	2663	2664	2665	2666
	2667	2668	2669	2670	2671	2672	2673	2674
	2675	2900	2901	2902	2903	2904	2905	2954
	2955	2956	2957	2958	2959	2960	2961	2962
	2963	2964	2994	3012	3013	3014	3029	3030
	3031	3032	3049	3050	3051	3052	3053	3054
	3055	3056	3057	3058	3059	3060	3061	
Ancillary	*8204*	*8245*						

Liverpool (Shaw Road, Speke) - SP

DAF/VDL SB120	2416	2417	2418	2419	2421	2422	2423	2424
	2425	2426	2431	2432	2433	2434	2479	2520
	2544	2549	2550	2551	2633	2634	2639	
Scania L113	1035	1036	1037	1038	1039	1040		
Volvo B10B	2716	2717	2718	2719	2720	2721		
DAF/VDL SB220	2401	2402	2403	2405	2406	2407	2408	2410
	2413	2415	2462	2463	2465	2466	2467	2468
	2469	2470	2471	2472	2473	2475	2476	2477
VDL Bus SB200	2578	2579	2580	2581	2582	2583	2584	2585
	2586	2587	2588	2589	2590	2591	2592	2593
	2594	2595	2596	2597	2598	2599	2600	2601
	2602	2603	2604	2605	2606	2607		
OmniCity	2061	2062	2063					
DB250	3615	3616	3617	3618	4025	4026	4027	4028
	4029	4030	4031					
Olympian	3271	3277	3278	3279	3281	3282	3317	3321
	3322	3326	3327	3329	3330	3331	3332	3334
	3335							
Volvo B7TL	4100	4101	4102	4103	4104	4105	4106	4107
	4108	4109	4110	4111	4112	4113	4114	4115
	4116	4117	4118	4119	4120	4121	4122	4123
	4124	4125	4126	4127	4128	4129		
Ancillary	*8201*	*8202*						

An interesting selection of buses is used on the open-top services that operate along the North Wales coast. The top of the Great Orme proves the background to former Merseyside Atlantean 3980, GKA449L. This recently refurbished bus is the only example of the Leyland Atlantean model still operating with Arriva. *John Young*

Llandudno Junction (Glan-y-mor Road) - LJ

Dart	804	812	814	815	816	817	818	819
	821	822	834	864	2273	2274	2276	2277
	2278	2279	2326	7559	7560	7625	7629	7630
VDL Bus SB200	2620	2643	2645	2647	2649	2651	2653	2655
	2657	2659	2661					
VRT open-top	3992							
Olympian	3996	3997	3998					

Manchester (St Andrew's Square, Piccadilly) - MA

Optare Solo	660	661	662	663	664	665	667	668
	669	670						
Dart	2238	2239	2241	2242	2243	2244	2246	2247
	2248	2249	2251	2252	2253			
DAF/VDL SB220	2400	2564	2565	2566	2567	2568	2569	
Enviro 300	2740	2741	2742	2743	2744	2745	2746	2747
	2748							
VDL SB200	2996	2997	2998	2999				
DB250	4012	4013	4014	4015	4016	4017	4018	4019
	4020	4024						
Ancillary	8203							

Rhyl (Ffynnongroew Road) - RH

Optare Solo	696	697						
Dart	843	844	846	847	2296	2297	2298	2299
	2300	2341	2345	2347	2349	2350	2351	2352
	2353	2354	7533	7534	7535	7539	7540	7562
	7564							
VDL Bus SB200	2642	2644	2646	2648	2650	2652	2654	2656
	2658	2660	2662					
Olympian open-top	3984	3987	3999					
Scania open-top	3995							

Runcorn (Beechwood) - RU

Dart	7558	7561						
DAF/VDL SB120	2514	2515	2516	2521	2522	2523	2524	2525
	2526	2527	2528	2529	2530	2531	2532	2533
	2534	2535	2536	2537	2538	2539	2540	2541
	2542	2543	2545	2546	2547	2548	2552	2553
	2554	2555						
VDL Bus SB200	2948	2949	2950	2951	2952	2953		
Scania sd	1042	1044	1045	1046	1047	1048	1049	
Ancillary	*8223*							

St Helens (Jackson Street) - JS

Dart	2100	2102	2127	2211	2209	2212	2213	2214
	7544	7548	7549	7567	7570	7571	7661	
Volvo B6	2805	2806	2807	2808	2809	2811	2812	
SB120	2489	2490	2491	2492	2493	2494	2495	2496
Scania sd	1041	1043	1050	1051	1052	1053	1054	1055
	1056	1057	1058	1059	1060	1061	2001	2003
	2004	2005	2007	2013	2014	2015	2016	2017
	2018	2019	2020	2021	2022	2023	2027	2029
Volvo B10BLE	2701	2702	2703	2704	2705	2706	2707	2708
	2709	2710	2711	2712	2713	2714	2715	2729
	2730							
VDL Bus SB200	2689	2690	2691	2692	2693	2694	2695	2696
	2697	2698	2699	2700	2965	2966	2967	2968
	2969	2970	2971	2972	2973	2974	2975	2976
	2977	2978	2979	2980	2981	2982	2983	2984
	2985	2986	2987	2988	2989	2990	2991	2992
	2993							
Ancillary	*8218*							

Skelmersdale (Neverstitch Road) - SK

Dart	7613	7617	7621	7632	7633	7634	7636	7637
	7638	7639	7641	7643	7645	7646	7648	7649
	7650	7660	7661	7665	7669	7674		
DAF SB250	4056	4057	4058	4059	4061	4062	4063	4064
	4065							
VDL SB200	3023	3024	3025	3026	3027	3028	3047	3048
Olympian	3272	3273	3274	3275	3276	3283	3284	3285
	3286	3287	3288	3289	3290			
Ancillary	*8212*							

Southport (Cobden Road) - SO

Dart	2286	2287	2288	2291	2292	2293	2294	7568
	7637	7651	7652	7653	7654	7655	7656	7676
Volvo B6	2801	2802	2803	2804	2813	2814	2815	2816
	2817	2818	2819	2821	2822			
Dart 4	2141	2142	2143	2144				
Volvo B10BLE	2722	2723	2724	2725	2726	2727	2728	
VDL Bus SB200	2624	3033	3034	3035	3036	3037	3038	3039
	3040	3041	3042	3043	3044	3045	3046	
Open-top	3980							

Ancillary   *8217*

Winsford (Winsford Industrial Estate) - WI

Outstation: Macclesfield

Dart	1249	1250						
Dart SLF	856	857	858	859	860	861	862	863
	865	866	867	868	869	872	876	877
	878	879	882	886	2103	7612	7614	7620
	7627	7628	7640	7644	7647	7673		
SB120	2497	2498	2499	2500	2501	2502	2503	2608
	2609	2610	2611	2612	2613	2614	2615	2616
	2617	2618	2619					
Olympian	3344	3346	3348	3349	3350	3351	3352	3353
	3354	3360						

Wrexham (Berse Road, Caego) - WX

Dart SLF	803	805	806	807	808	809	810	811
	813	831	838	839	848	849	851	852
	2104	2105	2106	2107	2132	2133	2301	7531
	7532	7550	7553					
SB200	2513	2906	2907	2908	2909	2910	2911	2912
	2914							

Ancillary   *8205*

Wythenshawe (Greeba Road) - WY

Optare Solo	676	677	678	679	680			
Dart SLF	891	892	893	894	2256	2259	2261	2262
	2269	2271	2302	2303	2304	2305	2306	2308
	2309	2310	2311	2312	2313	7615	7616	
Dart	1245	1247	1248	1253	1255	1256	1262	1263
VDL Bus SB200	2930	2931	2932	2933	2934	2935	2936	2937
	2938	2939	2940					

Unallocated/stored - u

remainder

ARRIVA MIDLANDS

Arriva Midlands North Ltd; Arriva Derby Ltd;
Wardle Transport; Stevensons of Uttoxeter Ltd;
Arriva Fox County Ltd, 852 Melton Road, Thurmaston, Leicester, LE4 8BT

1321	SM	W216JND	Mercedes-Benz 312D	Concept	M12	2000	Wardle Transport, 2010
1351	SM	KY51SXD	Mercedes-Benz 311D	Mercedes-Benz	M4	2001	Wardle Transport, 2010
1404	SM	SF04RGY	Mercedes-Benz Sprinter 413cdi	Onyx	M16	2004	Wardle Transport, 2010
1406	SM	VU06KFA	Mercedes-Benz Sprinter 413cdi	Onyx	M16	2006	Wardle Transport, 2010
1421	SM	OEZ2159	Mercedes-Benz Sprinter 411cdi	Stanway	M12	2001	Wardle Transport, 2010
1423	SM	ELZ2362	Mercedes-Benz Sprinter 411cdi	Minibus Options	M16	2000	Wardle Transport, 2010
1424	SM	RUI2486	Mercedes-Benz Sprinter 411cdi	Mercedes-Benz	M16	2002	Wardle Transport, 2010
1434	SM	FCZ3413	Mercedes-Benz Sprinter 416cdi	Mercedes-Benz	M16	2000	Wardle Transport, 2010
1439	SM	OUI3925	Mercedes-Benz Sprinter 413cdi	Concept	M16	2001	Wardle Transport, 2010
1450	SM	BV51ENL	Mercedes-Benz Sprinter 413cdi	Excel	M16	2002	Wardle Transport, 2010
1451	SM	YX53CYZ	Mercedes-Benz Sprinter 413cdi	Onyx	M5	2003	Wardle Transport, 2010
1452	SM	YK54AWH	Mercedes-Benz Sprinter 411cdi	Oughtred & Harrison	M16	2005	Wardle Transport, 2010
1453	SM	YK54AWJ	Mercedes-Benz Sprinter 411cdi	Oughtred & Harrison	M16	2005	Wardle Transport, 2010
1454	SM	YX55BGY	Mercedes-Benz Sprinter 413cdi	Onyx	M16	2005	Wardle Transport, 2010
1455	SM	HX55EZF	Mercedes-Benz Sprinter 416cdi	Driveline	M16	2005	Wardle Transport, 2010
1456	SM	YX56DJD	Mercedes-Benz Sprinter 416cdi	Yorkshire Conversions	M16	2006	Wardle Transport, 2010
1457	SM	YX56DJE	Mercedes-Benz Sprinter 416cdi	Yorkshire Conversions	M16	2006	Wardle Transport, 2010
1460	SM	PCZ6034	Mercedes-Benz Sprinter 413cdi	Onyx	M16	2001	Wardle Transport, 2010
1485	SM	REZ8516	Mercedes-Benz Sprinter 411cdi	Mercedes-Benz	M5	2002	Wardle Transport, 2010
1495	SM	NEZ9506	Mercedes-Benz Sprinter 411cdi	Mercedes-Benz	M12	2002	Wardle Transport, 2010
1498	SM	OKZ9847	Mercedes-Benz 410D	Mellor	M16	1999	Wardle Transport, 2010
1517	SM	P175UAD	Mercedes-Benz 508D	UVG	M5	1996	Wardle Transport, 2010
1623	SM	IJZ2331	Mercedes-Benz 612D	Mellor	B16F	1998	Wardle Transport, 2010
1626	SM	S268JUG	Mercedes-Benz 614D	UVG	B14F	1998	Wardle Transport, 2010
1647	SM	W478EUB	Mercedes-Benz 614D	Oughtred & Harrison	B13F	2000	Wardle Transport, 2010
1648	SM	W482EUB	Mercedes-Benz 614D	Oughtred & Harrison	B10F	2000	Wardle Transport, 2010
1649	SM	W483EUB	Mercedes-Benz 614D	Oughtred & Harrison	B13F	2000	Wardle Transport, 2010
1688	SM	IHZ8821	Mercedes-Benz 614D	Excel	C16F	2001	Wardle Transport, 2010
2011	SM	M113BMR	Dennis Dart 9.8m	Plaxton Pointer	B40F	1994	Wardle Transport, 2010
2024	TF	P824RWU	Dennis Dart 9.8m	Plaxton Pointer	B40F	1996	Arriva London, 2001
2027	u	N674GUM	Dennis Dart 9.8m	Plaxton Pointer	B40F	1995	Arriva London, 2002
2033	u	M803MOJ	Dennis Dart 9.8m	Marshall C37	B40F	1994	
2034	BT	M804MOJ	Dennis Dart 9.8m	Marshall (2001)	B35F	1994	
2035	u	P835RWU	Dennis Dart 9.8m	Plaxton Pointer	B40F	1996	Arriva London, 2001
2036	CK	P836RWU	Dennis Dart 9.8m	Plaxton Pointer	B40F	1996	Arriva London, 2001
2037	SD	P837RWU	Dennis Dart 9.8m	Plaxton Pointer	B40F	1996	Arriva London, 2001
2038	BT	M100PHA	Dennis Dart 9.8m	Marshall C37	BC40F	1995	Arriva Southern Counties, 1999

Telford's modern town centre is the location for East Lancs Spryte-bodied Dennis Dart 2366, N249VPH, which was new to the Guildford and West Surrey operation in 1996.
Richard Godfrey

Like many of the operations mid-life vehicles have been transferred from London. One of the batch of Darts with Plaxton Pointer bodywork, 2050, P850PWW, is seen in Wolverhampton. The type is now being used more frequently as reserve buses. *Richard Godfrey*

2039-2055

| | | | Dennis Dart 9.8m | | Plaxton Pointer | B40F | 1996 | Arriva London, 2001-02 |

2039	u	P839RWU	2043	u	P843PWW	2048	u	P848PWW	2052	SD	P852PWW
2040	SD	P840PWW	2045	CK	P845PWW	2049	CK	P849PWW	2053	CK	P853PWW
2041	SD	P841PWW	2046	CK	P846PWW	2050	CK	P850PWW	2054	CK	P854PWW
2042	CK	P842PWW	2047	CK	P847PWW	2051	SY	P851PWW	2055	CK	P855PWW

2060	u	M20MPS	Dennis Dart 9.8m	Marshall C37	B40F	1994	Arriva Southern Counties, 1999
2089	CK	N689GUM	Dennis Dart 9.8m	Plaxton Pointer	B40F	1995	Arriva London, 2002
2090	u	N690GUM	Dennis Dart 9.8m	Plaxton Pointer	B40F	1995	Arriva London, 2002
2096	TF	N806EHA	Dennis Dart 9.8m	East Lancs	B40F	1995	
2097	u	N807EHA	Dennis Dart 9.8m	East Lancs	B40F	1995	

2130-2138

| | | | Dennis Dart SLF 8.8m | | Plaxton Pointer MPD | N29F | 2000 | Arriva London, 2009 |

2130	LE	V423DGT	2133	CV	V426DGT	2135	LE	V428DGT	2137	CV	V430DGT
2131	LE	V424DGT	2134	CV	V427DGT	2136	CV	V429DGT	2138	CV	V431DGT
2132	LE	V425DGT									

2200	BT	R929RAU	Dennis Dart SLF 10.1m	Plaxton Pointer 2	B41F	1997	Trent Buses, Derby, 2007

2201-2206

| | | | Dennis Dart SLF 10.1m | | Plaxton Pointer | N39F | 1997 | |

2201	CV	P201HRY	2203	CV	P203HRY	2205	CV	P205HRY	2206	CV	P206HRY
2202	BT	P202HRY	2204	CV	P204HRY						

2207	BT	S207DTO	Dennis Dart SLF 10.1m	Plaxton Pointer 2	N39F	1998	
2208	CV	S208DTO	Dennis Dart SLF 10.1m	Plaxton Pointer 2	N39F	1998	

2209-2212

| | | | TransBus Dart SLF 8.8m | | TransBus Mini Pointer | N29F | 2003 | |

2209	LE	SN03LGC	2210	DE	SN03LGD	2211	LE	SN03LGE	2212	DE	SN03LGF

2214	LE	P954RUL	Dennis Dart SLF 10.2m	Alexander ALX200	N36F	1997	Arriva London, 2002
2215	BT	R45VJF	Dennis Dart SLF 10.2m	Alexander ALX200	N40F	1997	
2216	BT	R46VJF	Dennis Dart SLF 10.2m	Alexander ALX200	N40F	1997	

2217-2224

| | | | Dennis Dart SLF 9.8m | | Plaxton Pointer 2 | N33F | 1999 | |

2217	DE	T47WUT	2219	CK	T49JJF	2222	DE	T52JJF	2224	DE	T54JJF
2218	DE	T48WUT	2221	SD	T51JJF	2223	DE	T53JJF			

2226-2238
Dennis Dart SLF 10.2m — Alexander ALX200 — N40F — 2000

2226	DE	W226SNR	2229	DE	W229SNR	2233	DE	W233SNR	2236	DE	W236SNR
2227	DE	W227SNR	2231	DE	W231SNR	2234	DE	W234SNR	2237	DE	W237SNR
2228	DE	W228SNR	2232	DE	W232SNR	2235	DE	W235SNR	2238	DE	W238SNR

2239-2251
Dennis Dart SLF 8.8m — Plaxton Pointer MPD — N29F — 2000

2239	TF	W239SNR	2243	BT	W243SNR	2247	SY	W247SNR	2249	CK	W249SNR
2241	SY	W241SNR	2246	CK	W246SNR	2248	SY	W248SNR	2251	SY	W251SNR
2242	BT	W242SNR									

2252	DE	X252HBC	Dennis Dart SLF 10.2m	Alexander ALX200	N40F	2000	

2253-2267
Dennis Dart SLF 8.8m — Plaxton Pointer MPD — N29F — 2001

2253	WG	Y253YBC	2258	WG	Y258YBC	2262	LE	Y262YBC	2265	LE	Y265YBC
2254	WG	Y254YBC	2259	WG	Y259YBC	2263	LE	Y263YBC	2266	LE	Y266YBC
2256	WG	Y256YBC	2261	WG	Y261YBC	2264	LE	Y264YBC	2267	LE	Y267YBC
2257	WG	Y257YBC									

2268-2275
Dennis Dart SLF 8.8m — Plaxton Pointer MPD — N29F — 2002

2268	LE	SK52MLE	2270	LE	SK52MLJ	2272	LE	SK52MLN	2274	TF	FK52MML
2269	LE	SK52MLF	2271	LE	SK52MLL	2273	TF	SK52MLO	2275	TF	FL52MML

2276-2280
TransBus Dart SLF 8.8m — TransBus Mini Pointer — N29F — 2003

2276	CK	SN53ESG	2277	CK	SN53ESO	2279	TF	SN03LDV	2280	TF	SN03LDX

2281-2288
Dennis Dart SLF 8.8m — Plaxton Pointer MPD — N29F — 1999

2281	SD	V201KDA	2283	SD	V203KDA	2285	SD	V205KDA	2287	CK	V207KDA
2282	SD	V202KDA	2284	SD	V204KDA	2286	CK	V206KDA	2288	BT	V208KDA

2289-2297
Dennis Dart SLF 8.8m — Plaxton Pointer MPD — N29F — 2001-02

2289	CK	BU51KWJ	2292	CK	BU51KWL	2294	CK	Y184TUK	2296	SY	BF52NZO
2290	CK	BU51KWN	2293	CK	BU51KWK	2295	OS	BF52NZN	2297	OS	BF52NZP
2291	CK	BU51KWM									

2299	BT	T61JBA	Dennis Dart SLF 10.6m	Marshall Capital	N37F	1999	Arriva North West, 2000

2301-2305
Dennis Dart SLF 10.6m — Plaxton Pointer — N37F — 1996

2301	CK	N301ENX	2303	SY	N303ENX	2304	SY	N304ENX	2305	SY	N305ENX
2302	SY	N302ENX									

2306-2310
Dennis Dart SLF 10.6m — Plaxton Pointer — NC37F — 1996

2306	SD	P306FEA	2308	SY	P308FEA	2309	SY	P309FEA	2310	SY	P310FEA
2307	SY	P307FEA									

2311-2314
Dennis Dart SLF 10.6m — East Lancs Spryte — N41F — 1996

2311	SD	P311FEA	2312	SD	P312FEA	2313	SD	P313FEA	2314	SD	P314FEA

2316-2327
Dennis Dart SLF 10.6m — Plaxton Pointer — NC39F — 1997

2316	BT	P316FEA	2319	BT	P319HOJ	2322	BT	P322HOJ	2325	CV	P325HOJ
2317	BT	P317FEA	2320	BT	P320HOJ	2323	CK	P323HOJ	2326	BT	P326HOJ
2318	CK	P318FEA	2321	BT	P321HOJ	2324	BT	P324HOJ	2327	BT	P327HOJ

2329-2344
Dennis Dart SLF 10.6m — Plaxton Pointer 2 — NC39F — 1997-98

2329	CK	R329TJW	2334	SD	R334TJW	2338	SD	R338TJW	2342	SY	R342TJW
2330	SD	R330TJW	2335	SD	R335TJW	2339	LE	R339TJW	2343	SY	R343TJW
2331	SD	R331TJW	2336	SD	R336TJW	2340	LE	R340TJW	2344	CK	R344TJW
2332	SD	R332TJW	2337	SD	R337TJW	2341	LE	R341TJW			

2345-2353
Dennis Dart SLF 10.6m — Plaxton Pointer 2 — NC44F — 1999

2345	SY	S345YOG	2348	OS	S348YOG	2350	CK	S350YOG	2352	OS	S352YOG
2346	OS	S346YOG	2349	OS	S349YOG	2351	CK	S351YOG	2353	OS	S353YOG
2347	OS	S347YOG									

2354-2358
Dennis Dart SLF 10.2m — Alexander ALX200 — N36F — 1997 — Arriva London, 2002

2354	LE	P952RUL	2356	LE	P956RUL	2357	LE	P957RUL	2358	LE	P958RUL
2355	LE	P955RUL									

In 2009 several low-floor Darts were acquired and these displaced older examples of the model. UVG Citistar bodywork is carried by 2394, R561UOT, which was new to Marchwood Motorways in Southampton. It is seen in Wolverhampton while operating to its home base in Cannock. *Richard Godfrey*

2359-2366

| | | | | | | | | Dennis Dart SLF 9.5m | East Lancs Spryte | N31F | 1996 | Arriva Southern Counties, 2002 |

2359	SY	N238VPH	2361	TF	N241VPH	2363	CK	N243VPH	2365	TF	N248VPH
2360	SD	N240VPH	2362	SY	N242VPH	2364	SD	N244VPH	2366	TF	N249VPH

2367-2379

ADL Dart 10.7m   ADL Pointer   N41F*   2004-05   *2371-7 are NC41F

2367	OS	FJ54OTN	2371	SD	FJ55BWA	2374	SD	FJ55BWD	2377	SD	FJ55BWG
2368	OS	FJ54OTP	2372	SD	FJ55BWB	2375	SD	FJ55BWE	2378	OS	FJ55BVT
2369	OS	FJ54OTT	2373	SD	FJ55BWC	2376	SD	FJ55BWF	2379	OS	FJ55BVU
2370	OS	FJ54OTR									

2380	CK	PSU969	Dennis Dart SLF		UVG CitiStar	N40F	1998	Chase Coaches, Burntwood, 2007
2381	CK	PSU988	Dennis Dart SLF		UVG CitiStar	N40F	1998	Chase Coaches, Burntwood, 2007
2382	CK	PSU989	Dennis Dart SLF		UVG CitiStar	N40F	1998	Chase Coaches, Burntwood, 2007
2390	BT	V338MBV	Dennis Dart SLF 10.5m		East Lancs Spryte	N33F	1999	Tellings-Golden Miller, 2009
2391	BT	V337MBV	Dennis Dart SLF 10.5m		East Lancs Spryte	N33F	1999	Tellings-Golden Miller, 2009
2392	BT	R920RAU	Dennis Dart SLF		Plaxton Pointer 2	N40F	1997	Trent Barton, 2009
2393	CK	P81MOR	Dennis Dart SLF		UVG CitiStar	N38F	1997	Ensign Bus, 2009
2394	CK	R561UOT	Dennis Dart SLF		UVG CitiStar	N43F	1997	Ensign Bus, 2009
2395	BT	P82MOR	Dennis Dart SLF		UVG CitiStar	N37F	1997	Ensign Bus, 2009
2396	LE	R503MOT	Dennis Dart SLF		UVG CitiStar	N37F	1997	Ensign Bus, 2009
2397	BT	R504MOT	Dennis Dart SLF		UVG CitiStar	N34F	1997	Ensign Bus, 2009
2398	LE	R505MOT	Dennis Dart SLF		UVG CitiStar	N37F	1997	Ensign Bus, 2009
2400	BT	P174VUA	Dennis Dart SLF		Alexander ALX200	N40F	1997	Arriva Yorkshire, 2009
2401	LE	P514CVO	Dennis Dart SLF		East Lancs Spryte	N44F	1996	City of Nottingham, 2009
2402	SM	DG52TYP	Dennis Dart SLF 8.8m		Plaxton Pointer MPD	N29F	2002	*Operated on behalf of Stoke City*
2403	SM	DG52TYS	Dennis Dart SLF 8.8m		Plaxton Pointer MPD	N29F	2002	*Operated on behalf of Stoke City*
2404	SM	DG52TYT	Dennis Dart SLF 8.8m		Plaxton Pointer MPD	N29F	2002	*Operated on behalf of Stoke City*
2405	SM	DG52TYU	Dennis Dart SLF 8.8m		Plaxton Pointer MPD	N29F	2002	*Operated on behalf of Stoke City*
2406	SM	DA51XTC	Dennis Dart SLF 8.8m		Plaxton Pointer MPD	N29F	2002	*Operated on behalf of Stoke City*
2407	SM	DA51XTE	Dennis Dart SLF 8.8m		Plaxton Pointer MPD	N29F	2002	*Operated on behalf of Stoke City*
2408	SM	DA51XTD	Dennis Dart SLF 8.8m		Plaxton Pointer MPD	N29F	2002	*Operated on behalf of Stoke City*

Now part of the Bridgnorth allocation, SB120 2721, Y361UON, was allocated to Oswestry depot when photographed. The shorter DAF product has been used on many services within Shropshire. *Richard Godfrey*

2409	SM	XIL8793	Dennis Dart SLF 10.7m	Plaxton Pointer	N36F	1998	Wardle Transport, 2010
2410	SM	S2WMS	Dennis Dart SLF 10.7m	Plaxton Pointer 2	N39F	1999	Wardle Transport, 2010
2411	SM	R704MEW	Dennis Dart SLF 9.3m	Marshall Capital	N32F	1998	Wardle Transport, 2010

2613-2642

Volvo B6BLE — Wright Crusader 2 — N40F — 1999-2000

2613	TH	V213KDA	2621	TH	V221KDA	2629	TH	V229KDA	2636	TF	V236KDA
2614	TH	V214KDA	2622	TH	V212KDA	2630	TF	V230KDA	2637	TF	V237KDA
2615	TH	V215KDA	2623	TH	V223KDA	2631	TH	V231KDA	2638	TF	V238KDA
2616	TH	V216KDA	2624	TH	V224KDA	2632	TF	V232KDA	2639	TF	V239KDA
2617	TH	V217KDA	2625	TH	V225KDA	2633	TF	V233KDA	2640	TH	V210KDA
2618	TH	V218KDA	2626	TH	V226KDA	2634	TF	V234KDA	2641	TH	V211KDA
2619	TH	V219KDA	2627	TH	V227KDA	2635	TF	V235KDA	2642	TH	V209KDA
2620	TH	V220KDA	2628	TH	V228KDA						

2701	CK	YJ54CKE	DAF SB120 9.4m	Wrightbus Cadet	N30F	2004
2702	CK	YJ54CKF	DAF SB120 9.4m	Wrightbus Cadet	N30F	2004

2703-2707

DAF SB120 10.8m — Wrightbus Cadet — N39F — 2002

2703	SY	BU02URX	2705	SY	BU02URZ	2706	SY	BU02USB	2707	SY	BU02USC
2704	SY	BU02URY									

2708-2727

DAF SB120 10.8m — Wrightbus Cadet — N39F — 2001

2708	SY	Y348UON	2715	TF	Y365UON	2720	TF	Y347UON	2724	TF	Y364UON
2711	TF	Y351UON	2716	TF	Y356UON	2721	BR	Y361UON	2725	SY	Y346UON
2712	TF	Y352UON	2717	TF	Y357UON	2722	SY	Y362UON	2726	TF	Y366UON
2713	TF	Y353UON	2718	TF	Y358UON	2723	SY	Y363UON	2727	TF	Y367UON
2714	TF	Y354UON	2719	TF	Y349UON						

2728-2736

DAF SB120 10.8m — Wrightbus Cadet — N39F — 2002-03

2728	BR	BF52OAG	2731	SD	BU03HRD	2733	BR	BU03HRF	2735	CK	BU03HRJ
2729	BR	BF52NZM	2732	SD	BU03HRE	2734	TF	BU03HRG	2736	CK	BU03HRK
2730	BR	BU03HRC									

Two recent developments in the Midlands fleet have been the acquisition of Wardle Transport and the impending replacement of Shrewsbury's Park and Ride fleet with ten Optare Versa buses. Both are covered by this picture of 2963, WT58SOT, pictured in Hanley. This purchase takes the Arriva operation further north within Staffordshire. *Richard Godfrey*

2737	OS	CX04EHZ	DAF SB120 10.8m	Wrightbus Cadet	N39F	2004	Arriva North West & Wales, 2004
2738	TF	X781NWX	DAF SB120 9.4m	Wrightbus Cadet	N30F	2001	Arriva North West & Wales, 2005
2739	TF	X783NWX	DAF SB120 9.4m	Wrightbus Cadet	N30F	2001	Arriva North West & Wales, 2005
2740	OS	CX04EHV	DAF SB120 10.8m	Wrightbus Cadet	N39F	2004	Arriva North West & Wales, 2006
2741	OS	CX04EHW	DAF SB120 10.8m	Wrightbus Cadet	N39F	2004	Arriva North West & Wales, 2006
2742	OS	CX04EHY	DAF SB120 10.8m	Wrightbus Cadet	N39F	2004	Arriva North West & Wales, 2006
2900	SY	YJ57EKA	Optare Solo M880	Optare	N29F	2007	
2901	SY	YJ57EKB	Optare Solo M880	Optare	N29F	2007	
2902	BR	YJ57EKC	Optare Solo M880	Optare	N29F	2007	
2903	SY	YJ57EKD	Optare Solo M920	Optare	N34F	2007	
2904	BR	YJ07VRU	Optare Solo M850	Optare	N29F	2007	Optare demonstrator, 2008

2905-2922

| | | | Optare Solo SR M890 | | Optare | | N26F | 2008-09 |

2905	DE	YJ58CCA	2910	DE	YJ58CCN	2915	DE	YJ09MLO	2919	DE	YJ09MLZ
2906	DE	YJ58CCD	2911	DE	YJ58CCO	2916	DE	YJ09MLV	2920	DE	YJ09MMA
2907	DE	YJ58CCE	2912	DE	YJ58CCU	2917	DE	YJ09MLX	2921	DE	YJ09MME
2908	DE	YJ58CCF	2913	DE	YJ09MLL	2918	DE	YJ09MLY	2922	DE	YJ09MMF
2909	DE	YJ58CCK	2914	DE	YJ09MLN						

2923-2930

| | | | Optare Solo M920 | | Optare | | N31F | 2009 |

2923	LE	YJ09MJE	2925	LE	YJ09MJK	2927	LE	YJ09MJX	2929	LE	YJ09OUA
2924	LE	YJ09MJF	2926	LE	YJ09MJV	2928	LE	YJ09MJY	2930	LE	YJ09OUB

2931	SM	BU54ALL	Optare Solo M780	Optare	N23F	2004	*Operated on behalf of Stoke City*
2932	SM	YJ54BSY	Optare Solo M780 SL	Optare	N23F	2004	*Operated on behalf of Stoke City*
2933	SM	YJ54BSZ	Optare Solo M780 SL	Optare	N23F	2004	*Operated on behalf of Stoke City*
2934	SM	YJ05JXP	Optare Solo M850	Optare	N27F	2005	*Operated on behalf of Stoke City*
2961	SM	WT08BUS	Optare Versa V1100	Optare	N38F	2008	*Operated on behalf of Stoke City*
2962	SM	WT58BUS	Optare Versa V1100	Optare	N38F	2008	*Operated on behalf of Stoke City*
2963	SM	WT58SOT	Optare Versa V1100	Optare	N38F	2008	*Operated on behalf of Stoke City*

2964-2973

| | | | Optare Versa V1100 | | Optare | | N39F | On order |

2964	SY	YJ60LUA	2967	SY	YJ60LUE	2970	SY	YJ60LUL	2972	SY	YJ60LUP
2965	SY	YJ60LUB	2968	SY	YJ60LUF	2971	SY	YJ60LUO	2973	SY	YJ60LUR
2966	SY	YJ60LUC	2969	SY	YJ60LUH						

2974-2995 — Optare Versa V1100 — Optare — N39F* — 2009 — *2985-7 are N35F

2974	TF	YJ09MKM	2980	TF	YJ09MKX	2986	BT	YJ09LBL	2991	SY	YJ09MKE
2975	TF	YJ09MKN	2981	TF	YJ09MKZ	2987	BT	YJ09LBN	2992	OS	YJ09MKF
2976	TF	YJ09MKO	2982	BR	YJ09MLE	2988	SY	YJ09OTW	2993	OS	YJ09MKG
2977	TF	YJ09MKP	2983	BR	YJ09MLF	2989	SY	YJ09MKC	2994	SY	YJ09MKK
2978	TF	YJ09MKU	2984	BR	YJ09MLK	2990	SY	YJ09MKD	2995	OS	YJ09MKL
2979	TF	YJ09MKV	2985	BT	YJ09LBK						

2996	SY	YJ58PHX	Optare Versa V1100	Optare	N38F	2008	
2997	BR	YJ57EKE	Optare Versa V1100	Optare	N35F	2007	
3153	SM	FY03WZV	Mercedes-Benz Sprinter 413cdi	Ferqui	C16F	2003	Wardle Transport, 2010
3154	SM	UKZ5466	Mercedes-Benz Vario 0814	Plaxton Cheetah	C33F	2001	Wardle Transport, 2010
3292	SM	HKZ9240	Bova Futura FHD 12.340	Bova	C53F	2000	Wardle Transport, 2010
3310	TF	H81DVM	Volvo Citybus B10M-50	Alexander Q	B55F	1991	Timeline, Leigh, 1998
3390	SM	T20CCH	Volvo B10M-62	Berkhof Excellence	C50F	1999	Wardle Transport, 2010
3391	SM	CJZ9115	Volvo B10M-62	Jonckheere Mistral	C50F	1995	Wardle Transport, 2010
3393	SM	B20SEM	Volvo B9M	Jonckheere Mistral	C43F	1996	Wardle Transport, 2010

3415-3429 — Scania L113 CRL — Plaxton Paladin — NC45F* — 1998 — *3415-19 are NC47F

3415	CK	R415TJW	3419	CK	R419TJW	3423	CK	R423TJW	3427	SY	R427TJW
3416	TH	R416TJW	3420	CK	R420TJW	3424	BT	R424TJW	3428	SY	R428TJW
3417	TH	R417TJW	3421	CK	R421TJW	3425	SY	R425TJW	3429	CK	R429TJW
3418	SY	R418TJW	3422	u	R422TJW	3426	SY	R426TJW			

3468	u	N168PUT	Scania L113 CRL	East Lancs European	NC51F	1996
3473	u	N173PUT	Scania L113 CRL	East Lancs European	NC51F	1996
3489	TH	N429XRC	Scania L113 CRL	East Lancs European	N51F	1996
3491	TF	N431XRC	Scania L113 CRL	East Lancs European	N51F	1996

3501-3504 — Scania N113 CRL — East Lancs European — BC42F — 1995

3501	SY	M401EFD	3502	SY	M402EFD	3503	SY	M403EFD	3504	SY	M404EFD

3550	TH	YN56NNA	Scania OmniCity CN230 UD	Scania	N36F	2007
3551	TH	YN56NNB	Scania OmniCity CN230 UD	Scania	N36F	2007

3552-3566 — Scania OmniCity CN230 UB — Scania — N41F — 2008

3552	DE	YR59SRO	3556	DE	YR59SRY	3560	DE	YR59SSO	3564	DE	YR59SSZ
3553	DE	YR59SRU	3557	DE	YR59SRZ	3561	DE	YR59SSU	3565	DE	YR59STX
3554	DE	YR59SRV	3558	DE	YR59SSJ	3562	DE	YR59SSV	3566	DE	YR59STY
3555	DE	YR59SRX	3559	DE	YR59SSK	3563	DE	YR59SSX			

3567-3577 — Scania OmniCity CN230 UB — Scania — N42F — 2009

3567	DE	YT09ZBL	3570	DE	YT09ZBP	3573	DE	YT09ZBV	3576	DE	YT09ZBY
3568	DE	YT09ZBN	3571	DE	YT09ZBR	3574	DE	YT09ZBW	3577	DE	YT09ZBZ
3569	DE	YT09ZBO	3572	DE	YT09ZBU	3575	DE	YT09ZBX			

3578	WG	YN58RCF	Scania OmniCity CN94 UB	Scania	N42F	2005	Rotala, 2009
3579	WG	YN05HCG	Scania OmniCity CN94 UB	Scania	N42F	2005	Rotala, 2009
3580	TH	YN04AHA	Scania OmniCity CN94 UB	Scania	N41F	2004	Rotala, 2009

3601-3612 — Volvo B10BLE — Alexander ALX300 — N44F — 2000

3601	CK	V601DBC	3604	CV	V604DBC	3607	CV	V607DBC	3610	CK	V610DBC
3602	CK	V602DBC	3605	CV	V605DBC	3608	CV	V608DBC	3611	CV	V611DBC
3603	CK	V603DBC	3606	CV	V606DBC	3609	CK	V609DBC	3612	CV	V612DBC

3701-3704 — DAF SB200 — Wrightbus Commander — N44F — 2003

3701	CK	FD52GGO	3702	CK	FD52GGP	3703	CK	FD52GGU	3704	CK	FD52GGV

3705-3718 — DAF SB200 — Wrightbus Commander — N44F — 2002

3705	BT	BF52NZR	3709	BT	BF52NZV	3713	BT	BF52NZZ	3716	TF	BF52OAC
3706	BT	BF52NZS	3710	BT	BF52NZW	3714	BT	BF52OAA	3717	TF	BF52OAD
3707	BT	BF52NZT	3711	BT	BF52NZX	3715	TF	BF52OAB	3718	TF	BF52OAE
3708	BT	BF52NZU	3712	BT	BF52NZY						

3719-3726 — VDL Bus SB200 — Wrightbus Commander — N44F — 2006

3719	WG	FJ06ZTE	3721	WG	FJ06ZTG	3723	LE	FJ06ZTK	3725	LE	FJ06ZTM
3720	WG	FJ06ZTF	3722	WG	FJ06ZTH	3724	LE	FJ06ZTL	3726	LE	FJ06ZTN

The frequent Wrekin service 44 was provided with a fleet of new Wrightbus Commander vehicles in 2002. These were replaced with the latest version of the Wrightbus/VDL combination during 2009. Branded with the Wrekin Connect logo, 3748, YJ59BVL, is seen returning to Leegomery where the principal hospital is situated.
Richard Godfrey

3727-3731

VDL Bus SB200 — Wrightbus Pulsar — N44F — 2007

3727	CK	YJ57BUA	3729	CK	YJ57BPZ	3730	CK	YJ57BRF	3731	CK	YJ57BRV
3728	CK	YJ57BUE									

3732-3739

VDL Bus SB200 — Plaxton Centro — N44F — 2007

3732	LE	YJ57AZD	3734	LE	YJ57AZG	3736	LE	YJ57AZN	3738	SD	YJ57AZP
3733	LE	YJ57AZF	3735	LE	YJ57AZL	3737	SD	YJ57AZO	3739	SD	YJ57AZR

3740	SD	YJ57AZT	VDL Bus SB200	Wrightbus Commander	N44F	2007
3741	SD	YJ57AZU	VDL Bus SB200	Wrightbus Commander	N44F	2007

3742-3755

VDL Bus SB200 — Wrightbus Pulsar 2 — N44F — 2009

3742	TF	YJ59BVA	3746	TF	YJ59BVH	3750	TF	YJ59BVN	3753	TF	YJ59BUU
3743	TF	YJ59BVB	3747	TF	YJ59BVK	3751	TF	YJ59BUO	3754	TF	YJ59BUV
3744	TF	YJ59BVF	3748	TF	YJ59BVL	3752	TF	YJ59BUP	3755	TF	YJ59BUW
3745	TF	YJ59BVG	3749	TF	YJ59BVM						

3800-3812

Scania OmniLink K230 — Scania — NC45F — 2008

3800	TH	YN08HZK	3804	TH	YN08HZR	3807	TH	YN08HZU	3810	WG	YN08HZX
3801	TH	YN08HZL	3805	TH	YN08HZS	3808	WG	YN08HZV	3811	WG	YN08HZY
3802	TH	YN08HZM	3806	TH	YN08HZT	3809	WG	YN08HZW	3812	WG	YN08HZZ
3803	TH	YN08HZP									

3900-3913

Volvo B7RLE — Wrightbus Eclipse Urban — N45F — 2008

3900	LE	FY58HYH	3904	LE	FY58HYN	3908	LE	FY58HYS	3911	LE	FY58HYV
3901	LE	FY58HYK	3905	LE	FY58HYO	3909	LE	FY58HYT	3912	LE	FY58HYW
3902	LE	FY58HYL	3906	LE	FY58HYP	3910	LE	FY58HYU	3913	LE	FY58HYX
3903	LE	FY58HYM	3907	LE	FY58HYR						

4001-4014 — Volvo B7TL — Wrightbus Eclipse Gemini — N41/29F — 2006

4001	WG	FJ06ZPX	4005	WG	FJ06ZRL	4009	WG	FJ56OBG	4012	WG	FJ56OBL
4002	WG	FJ06ZPW	4006	WG	FJ56OBC	4010	WG	FJ56OBH	4013	WG	FJ56OBM
4003	WG	FJ06ZPV	4007	WG	FJ56OBE	4011	WG	FJ56OBK	4014	WG	FJ56OBN
4004	WG	FJ56OBD	4008	WG	FG56OBF						

4200-4207 — Volvo B9TL — Wrightbus Eclipse Gemini — N43/29F — 2008

4200	TH	FJ08LVL	4202	TH	FJ08LVN	4204	TH	FJ08LVP	4206	TH	FJ08LVS
4201	TH	FJ08LVM	4203	TH	FJ08LVO	4205	TH	FJ08LVR	4207	TH	FJ08LVT

4208-4224 — Volvo B9TL — Wrightbus Eclipse Gemini — N43/27F — 2008

4208	DE	FJ58KXF	4213	DE	FJ58KXM	4217	DE	FJ58KXR	4221	DE	FJ58KXV
4209	DE	FJ58KXG	4214	DE	FJ58KXN	4218	DE	FJ58KXS	4222	DE	FJ58KXW
4210	DE	FJ58KXH	4215	DE	FJ58KXO	4219	DE	FJ58KXT	4223	DE	FJ58KXX
4211	DE	FJ58KXK	4216	DE	FJ58KXP	4220	DE	FJ58KXU	4224	DE	FJ58KXY
4212	DE	FJ58KXL									

4511	SM	MNZ1138	Leyland Olympian ONCL10/1RZ	Alexander RL		B43/30F	1988	Wardle Transport, 2010
4545	SM	K345OFM	Leyland Olympian ON3R42C18Z4	Alexander RH		BC49/37F	1993	Wardle Transport, 2010
4546	SM	K346OFM	Leyland Olympian ON3R42C18Z4	Alexander RH		BC49/37F	1993	Wardle Transport, 2010
4547	SM	K347OFM	Leyland Olympian ON3R42C18Z4	Alexander RH		BC49/37F	1993	Wardle Transport, 2010
4597	SM	VEZ9715	Leyland Olympian ON2R50C13Z4	Northern Counties		B47/27D	1990	Wardle Transport, 2010
4607	SM	P607CAY	Volvo Olympian YN2RV18Z4	Northern Counties Palatine		B47/29F	1996	Wardle Transport, 2010

4614-4638 — Volvo Olympian — Northern Counties Palatine — B47/29F — 1996-98

4614	CV	R614MNU	4617	LE	R617MNU	4621	CV	R621MNU	4624	WG	R624MNU
4615	CV	R615MNU	4618	u	R618MNU	4622	CV	R622MNU	4638	WG	R638MNU
4616	WG	R616MNU	4620	CV	R620MNU						

4644-4652 — Volvo Olympian — Northern Counties Palatine — B47/29F — 1998

4644	WG	S644KJU	4645	u	S645KJU	4650	BT	S650KJU	4652	BT	S652KJU

4687	SM	WBZ8737	Volvo Olympian	East Lancs	B49/35F	1996	Wardle Transport, 2010
4692	SM	VLZ9237	Volvo Olympian	East Lancs	B49/35F	1998	Wardle Transport, 2010

4701-4716 — DAF DB250 — East Lancs Lowlander — N44/29F — 2001

4701	WG	Y701XJF	4705	WG	Y705XJF	4709	WG	Y709XJF	4714	WG	FE51YWM
4702	WG	Y702XJF	4706	WG	Y706XJF	4711	WG	FE51YWJ	4715	WG	FE51WSU
4703	WG	Y703XJF	4707	WG	Y707XJF	4712	WG	FE51YWK	4716	WG	FE51WSV
4704	WG	Y704XJF	4708	WG	FE51YWH	4713	WG	FE51YWL			

4717-4733 — DAF DB250 — East Lancs Lowlander — N44/29F — 2002

4717	WG	FD02UKB	4722	WG	FN52XBG	4726	WG	PN52XBF	4730	WG	FD02UKR
4718	WG	FD02UKC	4723	WG	FD02UKJ	4727	WG	FD02UKN	4731	WG	FD02UKS
4719	WG	FD02UKE	4724	WG	FD02UKK	4728	WG	FD02UKO	4732	WG	FD02UKT
4720	WG	PN52XBH	4725	WG	FD02UKL	4729	WG	FD02UKP	4733	WG	FD02UKU
4721	WG	FD02UKG									

4734-4745 — DAF DB250 — East Lancs Lowlander — N44/29F — 2003

4734	WG	PN52XRJ	4737	WG	PN52XRM	4740	WG	PN52XRR	4743	WG	PN52XRU
4735	WG	PN52XRK	4738	WG	PN52XRO	4741	WG	PN52XRS	4744	WG	PN52XRV
4736	WG	PN52XRL	4739	WG	PN52XRP	4742	WG	PN52XRT	4745	WG	PN52XRW

4746-4777 — DAF DB250 — Wrightbus Pulsar Gemini — N44/29F — 2006

4746	CV	FJ06ZTO	4754	CV	FJ06ZSZ	4762	LE	FJ06ZSK	4770	LE	FJ06ZRP
4747	CV	FJ06ZTP	4755	CV	FJ06ZTB	4763	LE	FJ06ZSL	4771	LE	FJ56KFC
4748	CV	FJ06ZST	4756	CV	FJ06ZTC	4764	LE	FJ06ZSN	4772	LE	FJ56KFD
4749	CV	FJ06ZSU	4757	LE	FJ06ZTD	4765	LE	FJ06ZSO	4773	LE	FJ56KFE
4750	CV	FJ06ZSV	4758	LE	FJ06ZSD	4766	LE	FJ06ZSP	4774	LE	FJ56KFF
4751	CV	FJ06ZSW	4759	LE	FJ06ZSE	4767	LE	FJ56KFA	4775	LE	FJ56KFG
4752	CV	FJ06ZSX	4760	LE	FJ06ZSF	4768	LE	FJ06ZRN	4776	LE	FJ56KFK
4753	CV	FJ06ZSY	4761	LE	FJ06ZSG	4769	LE	FJ06ZRO	4777	LE	FJ56KFL

4891-4898 — Dennis Trident 10.5m — Alexander ALX400 4.2m — N51/22D — 1999 — Wardle Transport, 2010

4891	LE	T691KPU	4895	LE	T695KPU	4896	LE	T696KPU	4898	LE	T698KPU

5000-5004 — Mercedes-Benz Citaro O530G — AB49T — 2004

5000	LE	BX04MYG	5002	LE	BX04MXK	5003	LE	BX04MYA	5004	LE	BX04MXH
5001	LE	BX04MXG									

A large number of the articulated buses purchased for London operations are now seeking new homes following a political change within the English capital's governance. Five are now operating from Leicester depot where they are used on the university services. 5003, BX04MYA, is shown. *Mark Lyons*

6000-6006

			Optare Solo M850		Optare			N24F	2003		*Operated for Shropshire CC*
6000	SY	BU03HRL	**6002**	SY	BU03HPX	**6004**	SY	BU03HPZ	**6006**	u	FJ04PFX	
6001	SY	BU03HPV	**6003**	SY	BU03HPY	**6005**	SY	BU03HRA				

6007	BR	FN04AFJ	Optare Solo M920	Optare	N33F	2004	*Operated for Shropshire CC*
6008	SY	FJ54OTV	Optare Solo M850	Optare	N29F	2004	*Operated for Shropshire CC*
6009	SY	FJ54OTW	Optare Solo M850	Optare	N29F	2004	*Operated for Shropshire CC*
6010	SY	FJ54OTX	Optare Solo M920	Optare	N30F	2004	*Operated for Shropshire CC*

Ancillary vehicles:

9507	DE	K102OHF	Volvo B10B	Northern Counties Paladin	TV	1995	Arriva North West & Wales, 2007
9516	LE	K108OHF	Volvo B10B	Northern Counties Paladin	TV	1995	Arriva North West & Wales, 2007
9517	CK	K107OHF	Volvo B10B	Northern Counties Paladin	TV	1995	Arriva North West & Wales, 2007
9520	DE	K103OHF	Volvo B10B	Northern Counties Paladin	TV	1995	Arriva North West & Wales, 2007
9521	TF	K105OHF	Volvo B10B	Northern Counties Paladin	TV	1995	Arriva North West & Wales, 2007
9522	LE	K101OHF	Volvo B10B	Northern Counties Paladin	TV	1995	Arriva North West & Wales, 2007
9525	LE	M422UNW	Volvo B10B	Alexander Strider	TV	1994	Arriva Yorkshire, 2009
9526	CK	M430UNW	Volvo B10B	Alexander Strider	TV	1994	Arriva Yorkshire, 2009
9530	u	M421UNW	Volvo B10B	Alexander Strider	TV	1994	Arriva Yorkshire, 2009

Previous registrations:

CJZ9115	M10TGM	OKZ9847	T160RWK
EEZ2362	X798ULG	OUI3925	Y181KNE
HKZ9240	W197EJO	PSU969	S407JUA
IHZ8821	Y668RVY	PSU988	S406JUA
IJZ2331	R876DCA	PSU989	S402JUA
K345OFM	FS7207(HK)	REZ8516	DG52WJU
K346OFM	FS3214(HK)	RUI2486	LV02ODW
K347OFM	FS6695(HK)	UKZ5466	Y477TSU
MNZ1138	E219WBG	VEZ9715	G516VBB
NEZ9506	DG52WJY	VLZ9237	R468RRA
OCZ6034	DK51LTU	WBZ8737	P490CVO
OEZ2159	Y569HPK	XIL8793	S309MKH

Depots and Allocations:

Bridgnorth - BR

Optare Solo	2902	2904	6007		
Optare Versa	2982	2983	2984	2997	
DAF SB120	2721	2728	2729	2730	2733

Burton-on-Trent (Wetmore Road) - BT

Dart	2034	2038						
Dart SLF	2200	2202	2207	2215	2216	2242	2243	2288
	2299	2316	2317	2319	2320	2321	2322	2324
	2326	2327	2390	2391	2392	2395	2397	2400
Optare Versa	2985	2986	2987					
Scania L113	3424							
VDL SB200	3705	3706	3707	3708	3709	3710	3711	3712
	3713	3714						
Olympian	4650	4652						

Cannock (Delta Way) - CK

Dart	2036	2042	2045	2046	2047	2050	2053	2055
	209							
Dart SLF	2219	2246	2249	2276	2277	2286	2287	2289
	2290	2291	2292	2293	2294	2301	2323	2329
	2344	2350	2351	2363	2380	2381	2382	2393
	2394							
DAF/VDL SB120	2701	2702	2735	2736				
Scania L113	3415	3419	3420	3421	3423	3429		
Volvo B10BLE	3601	3602	3603	3609	3610			
VDL Bus SB200	3701	3702	3703	3704	3727	3728	3729	3730
	3731							
Ancillary	*9517*	*9526*						

Coalville (Ashby Road) - CV

Dart SLF	2133	2134	2136	3137	2201	2203	2204	2205
	2206	2208	2325					
Volvo B10BLE	3604	3605	3607	3608	3611	3612		
Olympian	4614	4615	4620	4621	4622			
VDL DB250	4746	4747	4748	4749	4750	4751	4752	4753
	4754	4755	4756					

Derby (Ascot Drive) - DE

Solo	2905	2906	2907	2908	2909	2910	2911	2912
	2913	2914	2915	2916	2917	2918	2919	2920
	2921	2922						
Dart SLF	2210	2212	2217	2218	2222	2223	2224	2226
	2227	2228	2229	2231	2232	2233	2234	2235
	2236	2237	2238	2252				
Scania OmniCity	3552	3553	3554	3555	3556	3557	3558	3559
	3560	3561	3562	3563	3564	3565	3566	3567
	3568	3569	3570	3571	3572	3573	3574	3575
	3576	3577						
Volvo B9TI	4208	4209	4210	4211	4212	4213	4214	4215
	4216	4217	4218	4219	4220	4221	4222	4223
	4224							
Ancillary	*9507*	*9520*	*9521*					

Leicester (Melton Road, Thurmaston) - LE

Optare Solo	2923	2924	2925	2926	2927	2928	2929	2930
Dart	2041	2054						
Dart SLF	2130	2131	2132	2209	2214	2262	2263	2264
	2265	2266	2267	2268	2269	2270	2271	2272
	23339	2340	2341	2342	2343	2354	2355	2356
	2357	2358	2396	2398	2401			
VDL SB200	3723	3724	3725	3726	3732	3733	3734	3735
	3736							
Volvo B7RLE	3900	3901	3902	3903	3904	3905	3906	3907
	3908	3909	3910	3911	3912	3913		
VDL DB250	4757	4758	4759	4760	4761	4762	4763	4764
	4765	4766	4767	4768	4769	4770	4771	4772
	4773	4774	4775	4776	4777			
Ancillary	*9516*	*9522*	*9525*					

Oswestry (Salop Road) - OS

Optare Solo	2903							
Dart	2295	2297	2346	2347	2348	2349	2352	2353
	2367	2368	2369	2370	2378	2379		
Optare Versa	2992	2993	2995					
VDL Bus SB120	2737	2740	2741	2742				

Shrewsbury (Spring Gardens) - SY

Solo	2904	6000	6001	6002	6003	6004	6005	6008
	6009	6010						
Versa	2988	2989	2990	2991	2994	2996		
Dart	2051							
Dart SLF	2241	2247	2248	2251	2296	2302	2303	2304
	2305	2307	2308	2309	2310	2345	2359	2362
DAF/VDL SB120	2703	2704	2705	2706	2707	2708	2722	2723
	2725							
Scania L113	3418	3425	3426	3427	3428			
Scania N113	3501	3502	3503	3504				

Stafford (Dorrington Park Industrial Estate, Common Road) - SD

Dart	2037	2041	2052	2138	2221			
Dart SLF	2281	2282	2283	2284	2285	2306	2311	2312
	2313	2314	2330	2331	2332	2334	2335	2336
	2337	2338	2360	2364	2371	2372	2373	2374
	2375	2376	2377					
DAF/VDL SB120	2731	2732						
VDL Bus SB200	3737	3738	3739	3740	3741			

Stoke-on-Trent (Ford Green Road, Smallthorne, ST6 1NT) - SD

Mercedes-Benz	1321	1351	1404	1406	1421	1423	1424	1434
	1439	1450	1451	1452	1453	1454	1455	1456
	1457	1460	1485	1495	1498	1517	1623	1626
	1647`	1648	1649	1688	3153	3154		
Optare Solo	2931	2932	2933	2934				
Dart	2011							
Dart SLF	2402	2403	2404	2405	2406	2407	2408	2409
	2410	2411						

Optare Versa	2961	2962	2963					
Bova coach	3292							
Volvo B10M coach	3390	3391	3393					
Olympian	4511	4545	4546	4547	4597	4607	4687	4692
Trident	4891	4895	4896	4897				

Tamworth (Aldergate) - TH

Volvo B6	2613	2614	2615	2616	2617	2618	2619	2620
	2621	2622	2623	2624	2625	2626	2627	2628
	2629	2631	2640	2641	2642			
Scania L113	3416	3417	3489					
Scania OmniCity	3550	3551						
Scania OmniLink	3800	3801	3802	3803	3804	3805	3806	3807
Volvo B9TL	4200	4201	4202	4203	4204	4205	4206	4207

Telford (Charlton Street, Wellington, TF1 3) - TF

Dart	2024	2096						
Dart SLF	2239	2273	2274	2275	2279	2280	2361	2365
	2366							
Volvo B6	2630	2631	2632	2633	2634	2635	2636	2637
	2638	2639						
DAF/VDL SB120	2711	2712	2713	2714	2715	2716	2717	2718
	2719	2720	2724	2726	2727	2734	2738	2739
Optare Versa	2974	2975	2976	2977	2978	2979	2980	2981
Volvo B10M	3310							
Scania L113	3491							
DAF/VDL SB200	3716	3717	3718	3742	3743	3744	3745	3746
	3747	3748	3749	3750	3751	3752	3753	3754
	3755							

Ancillary	*9521*

Wigston (Station Street, South Wigston) - WG

Dart	2253	2254	2256	2257	2258	2259	2261	
DAF/VDL SB200	3719	3720	3721	3722				
Scania OmniCity	3578	3579						
Scania OmniLink	3808	3809	3810	3811	3812			
Olympian	4617	4624	4638	4644	4651			
Volvo B7TL	4001	4002	4003	4004	4005	4006	4007	4008
	4009	4010	4011	4012	4013	4014		
VDL DB250	4701	4702	4703	4704	4705	4706	4707	4708
	4709	4711	4712	4713	4714	4715	4716	4717
	4718	4719	4720	4721	4722	4723	4724	4725
	4726	4727	4728	4729	4730	4731	4732	4733
	4734	4735	4736	4737	4738	4739	4740	4741
	4742	4743	4744	4745				

Unallocated, stored and withdrawn - u

Remainder

ARRIVA THE SHIRES & ESSEX

Arriva The Shires Ltd; Arriva East Herts & Essex Ltd
487 Dunstable Road, Luton, LU4 8DS

| 417 | MK | FJ07TKA | Scania K340 EB4 | | Caetano Levanté | C49FT | 2007 | |

418-424			Scania K340 EB4		Caetano Levanté		C49FT	2008	
418	MK	FJ08DXG	**420**	MK	FJ08DXL	**422**	MK	FJ08DXO	**424**	MK	FJ08DXR
419	MK	FJ08DXK	**421**	MK	FJ08DXM	**423**	MK	FJ08DXP			

442	AY	Y42HBT	Optare Solo M850	Optare	N23F	2001	*Op'd for Buckinghamshire CC*
446	AY	Y46HBT	Optare Solo M850	Optare	N23F	2001	*Op'd for Buckinghamshire CC*
447	AY	Y47HBT	Optare Solo M850	Optare	N23F	2001	*Op'd for Buckinghamshire CC*
2128	LU	N908ETM	Mercedes-Benz 709D	Plaxton Beaver	B27F	1995	
2132	LU	N912ETM	Mercedes-Benz 709D	Plaxton Beaver	B27F	1995	
2133	LU	N913ETM	Mercedes-Benz 709D	Plaxton Beaver	B27F	1995	
2180	HH	R180VBM	Mercedes-Benz Vario O810	Plaxton Beaver 2	B27F	1997	
2249	HH	R759DUB	Mercedes-Benz Vario O810	Plaxton Beaver 2	B27F	1997	Arriva Yorkshire, 1999-2003
2401	HW	YJ57EKF	Optare Versa V1110	Optare	N38F	2007	
2402	HW	YJ57EKG	Optare Versa V1110	Optare	N38F	2007	

2403-2407			Optare Versa V1110		Optare		N34F	2008	
2403	WA	YJ58PFU	**2405**	WA	YJ58PFX	**2406**	HA	YJ58PFY	**2407**	HA	YJ58PFZ
2404	WA	YJ58PFV						

2418-2423			Optare Solo M850		Optare		N31F	1999	MK Metro, 2005
2418	MK	T405ENV	**2420**	MK	T407ENV	**2422**	MK	T409ENV	**2423**	MK	T410ENV
2419	MK	T406ENV	**2421**	MK	T408ENV			

2424-2430			Optare Solo M850		Optare		N31F	1999-2001 MK Metro, 2005
2424	MK	V412UNH	**2427**	MK	W415KNH	**2429**	MK	T45KAW	**2430**	MK	X351AUX
2425	MK	V413UNH	**2428**	MK	W416KNH			

Arriva The Shires operates seven Optare Versa buses. Pictured in Puckeridge is 2403, YJ58PFU, which is based at Watford. *Richard Godfrey*

2431-2434

2431-2434		Optare Solo M920		Optare		N35F	1999	MK Metro, 2005	

| 2431 | MK | S401ERP | 2432 | MK | S402ERP | 2433 | S403ERP | 2434 | S404ERP |

2435	MK	S903DUB	Optare Solo M920	Optare	N33F	1998	MK Metro, 2005
2436	MK	X417BBD	Optare Solo M920	Optare	N35F	2000	MK Metro, 2005
2437	MK	X418BBD	Optare Solo M920	Optare	N35F	2000	MK Metro, 2005
2438	MK	X419BBD	Optare Solo M920	Optare	N35F	2000	MK Metro, 2005
2439	MK	V82EVU	Optare Solo M920	Optare	N37F	1999	MK Metro, 2005
2440	MK	MK02BUS	Optare Solo M920	Optare	N33F	2002	MK Metro, 2005
2441	MK	KJ02JXT	Optare Solo M920	Optare	N33F	2002	MK Metro, 2005
2442	MK	W681DDN	Optare Solo M920	Optare	N33F	2000	MK Metro, 2005
2443	MK	YN53SVG	Optare Solo M920	Optare	N33F	2003	MK Metro, 2005
2444	MK	YN04LXM	Optare Solo M920	Optare	N33F	2004	MK Metro, 2005
2445	MK	YN03NEF	Optare Solo M920	Optare	N31F	2003	MK Metro, 2005
2446	MK	YN03NCF	Optare Solo M920	Optare	N31F	2003	MK Metro, 2005
2447	MK	YJ05JXU	Optare Solo M1020	Optare	N37F	2005	MK Metro, 2005
2448	MK	YJ05JXV	Optare Solo M1020	Optare	N37F	2005	MK Metro, 2005
2449	MK	YJ55YGV	Optare Solo M1020	Optare	N37F	2005	MK Metro, 2005
2450	MK	YJ55YGW	Optare Solo M1020	Optare	N37F	2005	MK Metro, 2005
2451	MK	YJ08XDK	Optare Solo M950	Optare	N33F	2008	
2452	MK	YJ58PKA	Optare Solo M950	Optare	N33F	2008	

2453-2456

2453-2456		Optare Solo M880		Optare	N33F	2006	

| 2453 | HA | YJ06FXS | 2454 | HA | YJ06FXT | 2455 | HA | YJ06FXU | 2456 | HA | YJ06FXV |

2457-2460

2457-2460		Optare Solo M880		Optare	N29F	2004	

| 2457 | HA | KE04PZF | 2458 | HA | KE04PZG | 2459 | HA | KE04OSU | 2460 | HA | KE04OSV |

2461-2467

2461-2467		Optare Solo M880		Optare	N29F	2005	

| 2461 | HH | KE55FDG | 2463 | WR | KE55KPG | 2465 | HA | KE55KTJ | 2467 | HA | KE55KTC |
| 2462 | HH | KE55FDF | 2464 | WR | KE55KPJ | 2466 | HA | KE55KTD | | | |

2468-2472

2468-2472		Optare Solo M780SL		Optare	N25F	2006	

| 2468 | WD | YJ06YRP | 2470 | WD | YJ06YRS | 2471 | WD | YJ06YRT | 2472 | WD | YJ06YRU |
| 2469 | WD | YJ06YRR | | | | | | | | | |

2473	HA	YJ56ATY	Optare Solo M880	Optare	N33F	2006	
2474	HA	YJ56ATZ	Optare Solo M880	Optare	N33F	2006	

2475-2492

2475-2492		Optare Solo M950		Optare	N33F	2007	

2475	WD	YJ07VPW	2480	WD	YJ07VRE	2485	WR	YJ07BEU	2489	SV	YJ57EJL
2476	WD	YJ07VPX	2482	HH	YJ07VRF	2486	WR	YJ57EJF	2490	WR	YJ57EJN
2477	WD	YJ07VPY	2483	WR	YJ07BCZ	2487	WR	YJ57EJG	2491	MK	YK07BGE
2478	WD	YJ07VRC	2484	WR	YJ07BEO	2488	WR	YJ57EJK	2492	WD	YK07BGF
2479	WD	YJ07VRD									

2493	SV	YJ57EJD	Optare Solo M880	Optare	N28F	2008	
2494	SV	YJ57EJE	Optare Solo M880	Optare	N28F	2008	
2495	MK	YJ57XWH	Optare Solo M950	Optare	N33F	2008	
2496	HW	YK57FHH	Optare Solo M950	Optare	N33F	2008	
2497	HW	YK57FHJ	Optare Solo M950	Optare	N33F	2008	

2498-2508

2498-2508		Optare Solo M950		Optare	N33F	2008	

2498	MK	YJ58PKC	2501	MK	YJ58PKF	2504	MK	YJ58PKO	2507	MK	YJ58PKX
2499	MK	YJ58PKD	2502	MK	YJ58PKK	2505	MK	YJ58PKU	2508	WD	YJ58VCG
2500	MK	YJ58PKE	2503	MK	YJ58PKN	2506	MK	YJ58PKV			

2509	MK	YJ09OTY	Optare Solo M880 SL	Optare	N32F	2009	
2510	MK	YJ09OTZ	Optare Solo M880 SL	Optare	N32F	2009	
2511	HA	CE52UWW	Optare Solo M850	Optare	N27F	2002	Veolia, 2010
3002	HH	V392KVY	Optare Excel L1150	Optare	N45F	1999	Claribel, Birmingham, 2006
3003	HH	V393KVY	Optare Excel L1150	Optare	N45F	1999	Claribel, Birmingham, 2006
3085	SV	KE53KBO	TransBus Dart 8.8m	TransBus Mini Pointer	N29F	2003	Sovereign, Stevenage, 2005
3086	SV	KE53KBP	TransBus Dart 8.8m	TransBus Mini Pointer	N29F	2003	Sovereign, Stevenage, 2005

3147-3163

3147-3163		Scania L113 CRL		East Lancs European	N51F*	1995	*3152-63 are NC47F

3147	LU	N697EUR	3152	AY	N702EUR	3155	AY	N705EUR	3162	AY	N712EUR
3148	AY	N698EUR	3153	AY	N703EUR	3156	HW	N706EUR	3163	HW	N713EUR
3149	AY	N699EUR	3154	AY	N704EUR	3160	AY	N710EUR			

Amersham is the location of this view of Northern Counties-bodied Scania 3201, R201RBM. It is based at High Wycombe where it is one of ten Scania single-deck buses at that town's depot. *Richard Godfrey*

3143-3149

Scania L113 CRL — East Lancs European — N51F — 1995

| 3143 | HH | N693EUR | 3146 | HW | N696EUR | 3148 | LU | N698EUR | 3149 | LU | N699EUR |
| 3144 | MK | N694EUR | 3147 | HH | N697EUR | | | | | | |

3151-3166

Scania L113 CRL — East Lancs European — NC47F — 1995

3152	AY	N702EUR	3157	AY	N707EUR	3161	HW	N711EUR	3164	AY	N714EUR
3154	AY	N704EUR	3158	HW	N708EUR	3162	HW	N712EUR	3165	LU	N715EUR
3155	AY	N705EUR	3159	AY	N709EUR	3163	HW	N713EUR	3166	AY	N716EUR
3156	AY	N706EUR									

3167	LU	N28KGS	Scania L113 CRL	East Lancs European	N51F	1996
3168	LU	N29KGS	Scania L113 CRL	East Lancs European	N51F	1996
3170	LU	N32KGS	Scania L113 CRL	East Lancs European	N51F	1996
3171	HH	P671OPP	Dennis Dart SLF	East Lancs Flyte	N41F	1996
3172	u	P672OPP	Dennis Dart SLF	East Lancs Flyte	N41F	1996
3173	HH	P673OPP	Dennis Dart SLF	East Lancs Flyte	N41F	1996
3174	u	P674OPP	Dennis Dart SLF	East Lancs Flyte	N41F	1996

3175-3190

Dennis Dart SLF — Plaxton Pointer — N39F* — 1997 — *3175-8 are N41F

3175	HH	P175SRO	3179	u	P179SRO	3183	WD	P183SRO	3187	WD	P187SRO
3176	HH	P176SRO	3180	u	P180SRO	3184	WD	P184SRO	3188	WD	P188SRO
3177	HH	P177SRO	3181	HW	P181SRO	3185	WD	P185SRO	3189	WD	P189SRO
3178	HW	P178SRO	3182	WD	P182SRO	3186	u	P186SRO	3190	HH	P190SRO

3191-3205

Scania L113 CRL — Northern Counties Paladin — N51F* — 1997 — *3196-9, 3201-5 are NC47F

3191	LU	R191RBM	3195	LU	R195RBM	3199	LU	R199RBM	3203	HW	R203RBM
3192	LU	R192RBM	3196	AY	R196RBM	3201	HW	R201RBM	3204	u	R204RBM
3193	LU	R193RBM	3197	AY	R197RBM	3202	MK	R202RBM	3205	HW	R205RBM
3194	LU	R194RBM	3198	LU	R198RBM						

3207-3215

Dennis Dart SLF — Plaxton Pointer — N31F — 1997-98

| 3207 | HH | R207GMJ | 3209 | HH | R209GMJ | 3212 | MK | R212GMJ | 3214 | HW | R214GMJ |
| 3208 | HW | R208GMJ | 3210 | HW | R210GMJ | 3213 | HW | R213GMJ | 3215 | HH | R215GMJ |

3216-3229 Dennis Dart SLF — Plaxton Pointer 2 — N39F* — 1998-98 — *seating varies

3216	HW	S216XPP	3220	WD	S317JUA	3224	WD	S307JUA	3227	SV	T827NMJ
3217	HW	S217XPP	3221	WD	S318JUA	3225	WD	V422DGT	3228	HH	T828NMJ
3218	WD	S315JUA	3222	WD	S316JUA	3226	HW	V421DGT	3229	HA	T829NMJ
3219	SV	T219NMJ	3223	WD	S308JUA						

3230-3239 Dennis Dart SLF — Plaxton Pointer MPD — N29F — 1999-2000

3230	HA	V230HBH	3233	HH	V233HBH	3236	HH	V236HBH	3238	HH	V238HBH
3231	HA	V231HBH	3234	HH	V234HBH	3237	HH	V237HBH	3239	HH	V239HBH
3232	HH	V232HBH	3235	HH	V235HBH						

3240	HW	P601RGS	Volvo B6LE	Wright Crusader	NC38F	1997	Sovereign, Stevenage, 2005
3241	HA	R602WMJ	Volvo B6LE	Wright Crusader	NC38F	1998	Sovereign, Stevenage, 2005
3245	HW	R603WMJ	Volvo B6LE	Wright Crusader	NC38F	1998	Sovereign, Stevenage, 2005
3248	HW	R604WMJ	Volvo B6LE	Wright Crusader	NC38F	1998	Sovereign, Stevenage, 2005
3249	HA	R605WMJ	Volvo B6LE	Wright Crusader	NC38F	1998	Sovereign, Stevenage, 2005

3250-3260 Volvo B6BLE — Wright Crusader 2 — N40F* — 1999 — *3258-60 are N33D

3250	HA	V250HBH	3253	HA	V253HBH	3256	HA	V256HBH	3259	WD	V259HBH
3251	HA	V251HBH	3254	HA	V254HBH	3257	HA	V257HBH	3260	WD	V260HBH
3252	u	V252HBH	3255	HA	V255HBH	3258	WD	V258HBH			

3261-3268 Volvo B10BLE — Wright Renown — N44F — 1999

3261	LU	V261HBH	3263	LU	V263HBH	3265	LU	V265HBH	3267	LU	V267HBH
3262	LU	V262HBH	3264	LU	V264HBH	3266	LU	V266HBH	3268	LU	V268HBH

3269	AY	T495KGB	DAF SB220	Plaxton Prestige	N42F	1999	

3270-3276 DAF SB220 LPG — Plaxton Prestige — N39F — 1999

3270	HH	V270HBH	3272	HH	V272HBH	3274	u	V274HBH	3276	u	V276HBH
3271	HH	V271HBH	3273	WD	V273HBH	3275	WD	V275HBH			

3277	HH	T491KGB	DAF SB220 LPG	Plaxton Prestige	N42F	1999	Arriva Scotland West, 2000
3278	WD	T492KGB	DAF SB220 LPG	Plaxton Prestige	N42F	1999	Arriva Scotland West, 2000
3279	WD	T495KGB	DAF SB220 LPG	Plaxton Prestige	N42F	1999	Arriva Scotland West, 2000

3280-3297 Dennis Dart SLF — Plaxton Pointer MPD — N29F — 1999-2000

3280	LU	V280HBH	3285	LU	V285HBH	3290	LU	V290HBH	3294	MK	V294HBH
3281	WA	V281HBH	3286	LU	V286HBH	3291	LU	V291HBH	3295	HA	X295MBH
3282	WA	V282HBH	3287	LU	V287HBH	3292	LU	V292HBH	3296	HY	X296MBH
3283	LU	V283HBH	3288	LU	V288HBH	3293	SV	V293HBH	3297	HY	X297MBH
3284	LU	V284HBH	3289	LU	V289HBH						

3298	HW	R607WMJ	Volvo B6LE	Wright Crusader	NC38F	1998	Sovereign, Stevenage, 2005
3299	HW	R608WMJ	Volvo B6LE	Wright Crusader	NC38F	1998	Sovereign, Stevenage, 2005
3300	SV	R524TWR	Volvo B10BLE	Wright Renown	BC47F	1998	Sovereign, Stevenage, 2005

3301-3310 Volvo B10BLE — Wright Renown — NC47F — 2000 — Sovereign, Stevenage, 2005

3301	SV	W128XRO	3304	SV	W132XRO	3307	SV	W136XRO	3309	SV	W138XRO
3302	SV	W129XRO	3306	SV	W134XRO	3308	SV	W137XRO	3310	SV	W139XRO
3303	SV	W131XRO									

3311-3314 Volvo B10BLE — Wright Renown — NC47F — 2002 — Sovereign, Stevenage, 2005

3311	SV	PN02HVS	3312	SV	PN02HVL	3313	SV	PN02HVM	3314	SV	PN02HVO

3322	SV	PN02HVR	Volvo B10BLE	Wright Renown	NC47F	2002	Sovereign, Stevenage, 2005
3323	SV	PN02HVP	Volvo B10BLE	Wright Renown	NC47F	2002	Sovereign, Stevenage, 2005
3342	t	L602EKM	Volvo B6-9.9M	Plaxton Pointer	TV	1994	
3371	u	K321CVX	Dennis Dart 9m	Plaxton Pointer	B35F	1992	
3372	u	K322CVX	Dennis Dart 9m	Plaxton Pointer	B35F	1992	
3379	WD	P186LKJ	Dennis Dart SLF 10.1m	Plaxton Pointer	N40F	1996	Arriva Southern Counties, 2010
3380	WD	P204LKJ	Dennis Dart SLF 10.1m	Plaxton Pointer	N40F	1997	Arriva Southern Counties, 2010
3381	WA	P330HVX	Dennis Dart 9m	Plaxton Pointer	B34F	1996	Arriva Southern Counties, 2010
3382	HA	P324HVX	Dennis Dart 9m	Plaxton Pointer	B34F	1996	Arriva Southern Counties, 2010
3386	SV	P256FPK	Dennis Dart SLF	Plaxton Pointer	N39F	1997	

3401-3406 VDL Bus SB200 — Plaxton Centro — N45F — 2007

3401	WD	YJ57BWA	3403	WD	YJ57BWC	3405	WD	YJ57BWE	3406	WD	YJ57BWF
3402	WD	YJ57BWB	3404	WD	YJ57BWD						

Route 100 links Aylesbury with Milton Keynes. Pictured with additional lettering for the route is 3447, R207VPU, a SB220 with Plaxton Prestige bodywork. *Colin Lloyd*

3407-3412
VDL Bus SB200 · Wrightbus Pulsar · N44F · 2009

3407	SV	KX09KDJ	3409	SV	KX09KDN	3411	SV	KX09KDU	3412	SV	KX09KDV
3408	SV	KX09KDK	3410	SV	KX09KDO						

3413	HW	P833HVX	Dennis Dart 9m	Plaxton Pointer	B34F	1996
3414	HA	P334HVX	Dennis Dart 9m	Plaxton Pointer	B34F	1996
3416	HA	R416HVX	Dennis Dart SLF	Wright Crusader	N41F	1998
3417	HA	R417HVX	Dennis Dart SLF	Wright Crusader	N41F	1998
3418	HA	R418HVX	Dennis Dart SLF	Wright Crusader	N41F	1998
3435	HA	R165GNW	Dennis Dart SLF	Wright Crusader	N36F	1997
3439	HA	R169GNW	Dennis Dart SLF	Wright Crusader	N36F	1997
3440	HA	R170GNW	Dennis Dart SLF	Wright Crusader	N36F	1997

3441-3449
DAF SB220 · Plaxton Prestige · NC37F · 1997

3441	LU	R201VPU	3445	AY	R205VPU	3447	AY	R207VPU	3449	LU	R209VPU
3444	AY	R204VPU	3446	AY	R206VPU	3448	AY	R208VPU			

3452-3459
Volvo B10BLE · Alexander ALX300 · N44F · 2000

3452	HW	W452XKX	3454	HW	W454XKX	3458	SV	W458XKX	3459	SV	W459XKX
3453	HW	W453XKX	3457	SV	W457XKX						

3482-3498
Dennis Dart SLF · Plaxton Pointer MPD · N39F · 2000

3482	HW	W482YGS	3486	AY	W486YGS	3491	SV	W491YGS	3495	MK	W495YGS
3483	HW	W483YGS	3487	AY	W487YGS	3492	AY	W492YGS	3496	MK	W496YGS
3484	AY	W484YGS	3488	LU	W488YGS	3493	SV	W493YGS	3497	AY	W497YGS
3485	AY	W485YGS	3489	LU	W489YGS	3494	SV	W494YGS	3498	SV	W498YGS

3500	HH	KE51PSZ	Dennis Dart SLF 8.8m	Alexander Pointer MPD	N28F	2001
3501	HH	KE51PTO	Dennis Dart SLF 8.8m	Alexander Pointer MPD	N28F	2001
3502	WD	KE51PTU	Dennis Dart SLF 8.8m	Alexander Pointer MPD	N28F	2001
3509	AY	KE51PTX	Dennis Dart SLF 8.8m	Alexander Pointer MPD	N28F	2001
3510	MK	V897DNB	Dennis Dart SLF 11.3m	Plaxton Pointer SPD	N41F	1999	MK Metro, 2006
3520	MK	R809WJA	Dennis Dart SLF 10.1m	UVG UrbanStar	N38F	1997	MK Metro, 2006

One of seventeen new Alexander Denis Enviro 300 buses supplied for services in Stevenage is The Shires' 3557 KX09GYG, seen at Leverstock Green. *Richard Godfrey*

3521-3524

Dennis Dart SLF 10.7m — Plaxton Pointer — N43F — 1998 — MK Metro, 2006

3521	MK	HDZ2611	3522	MK	HDZ2607	3523	MK	HDZ2605	3524	MK	HDZ2604

3525	MK	W986WDS	Dennis Dart SLF 10.7m	Caetano Compass	N43F	2000	MK Metro, 2006
3526	MK	HX51LSO	Dennis Dart SLF 10.7m	Caetano Compass	N45F	2001	MK Metro, 2006
3527	MK	W3CTS	Dennis Dart SLF 10.7m	Caetano Compass	N44F	2000	MK Metro, 2006

3528-3536

Dennis Dart SLF 10.7 — Caetano Compass — N42F — 1999 — MK Metro, 2006

3528	MK	NDZ7935	3530	MK	NDZ7919	3534	MK	T408LGP	3536	MK	T424LGP
3529	MK	NDZ7933	3532	MK	NDZ4521	3535	MK	T425LGP			

3537	MK	HDZ2606	Dennis Dart 9.8m	UVG UrbanStar	N44F	1997	MK Metro, 2006

3550-3578

ADL E300 — ADL Enviro 300 — N45F — 2009

3550	SV	KX09GXZ	3558	SV	KX09GYH	3565	SV	KX09GYS	3572	MK	KX09GZA
3551	SV	KX09GYA	3559	SV	KX09GYJ	3566	SV	KX09GYT	3573	MK	KX09GZB
3552	SV	KX09GYB	3560	SV	KX09GYK	3567	HH	KX09GYU	3574	MK	KX09GZC
3553	SV	KX09GYC	3561	SV	KX09GYN	3568	HH	KX09GYV	3575	MK	KX09GZD
3554	SV	KX09GYD	3562	SV	KX09GYO	3569	HH	KX09GYW	3576	MK	KX09GZE
3555	SV	KX09GYE	3563	SV	KX09GYP	3570	MK	KX09GYY	3577	MK	KX09GXW
3556	SV	KX09GYF	3564	SV	KX09GYR	3571	MK	KX09GYZ	3578	MK	KX09GXY
3557	SV	KX09GYG									

3601-3619

Scania L94 UB — Wrightbus Solar — N43F — 2005

3601	LU	KE55CTV	3606	LU	KE55CTK	3611	LU	KE55GWC	3616	LU	KE55CVL
3602	LU	KE55CTU	3607	LU	KE55CTF	3612	LU	KE55CVG	3617	LU	KE55CVM
3603	LU	KE55FBY	3608	LU	KE55GVY	3613	LU	KE55CVH	3618	LU	KE55GXR
3604	LU	KE55FBX	3609	LU	KE55GVZ	3614	LU	KE55CVJ	3619	LU	KE55CVA
3605	LU	KE55CTO	3610	LU	KE55GWA	3615	LU	KE55CVK			

3621-3628

Scania L94 UB — Wrightbus Solar — N43F — 2006

3621	MK	YN55PZY	3623	MK	YN06JXJ	3625	MK	YN06JXL	3627	MK	YN06JXO
3622	MK	YN55PZZ	3624	MK	YN06JXK	3626	MK	YN06JXM	3628	MK	YN06JXP

Arriva The Shires operates Transport for London (TfL) route 303 using VDL SB120s and these are painted in London colours. Illustrating the type is 3712, YE06HRC, seen in Edgware. *Richard Godfrey*

3640	MK	KX59ACJ	Scania OmniCity CN230UB	Scania	N41F	2009
3641	MK	KX59ACO	Scania OmniCity CN230UB	Scania	N41F	2009
3701	HW	KE55CKU	VDL Bus SB120 9.4m	Wrightbus Cadet 2	N35F	2005
3702	HW	KE55CKO	VDL Bus SB120 9.4m	Wrightbus Cadet 2	N35F	2005
3703	HW	KE55CKP	VDL Bus SB120 9.4m	Wrightbus Cadet 2	N35F	2005

3704-3710

VDL Bus SB120 10.8m — Wrightbus Cadet 2 — N28D — 2006

3704	WD	YJ06LFE	**3706**	WD	YJ06LFG	**3708**	WD	YJ06LFK	**3710**	WD	YJ06LDK
3705	WD	YJ06LFF	**3707**	WD	YJ06LFH	**3709**	WD	YJ06LFL			

3711-3728

VDL Bus SB120 10.8m — Wrightbus Cadet 2 — N39F — 2006

3711	WD	YE06HRA	**3716**	WD	YE06HRJ	**3721**	WD	YE06HPK	**3725**	WD	YE06HPP
3712	WD	YE06HRC	**3717**	WD	YE06HPA	**3722**	WD	YE06HPL	**3726**	WD	YE06HPU
3713	WD	YE06HRD	**3718**	WD	YE06HPC	**3723**	WD	YE06HPN	**3727**	WD	YE06HNT
3714	WD	YE06HRF	**3719**	WD	YE06HPF	**3724**	WD	YE06HPO	**3728**	WD	YE06HNU
3715	WD	YE06HRG	**3720**	WD	YE06HPJ						

3729	MK	KX54AVE	VDL Bus SB120 10.8m	Wrightbus Cadet 2	N39F	2004	MK Metro, 2006
3730	MK	KX54AVD	VDL Bus SB120 10.8m	Wrightbus Cadet 2	N39F	2004	MK Metro, 2006
3731	MK	YG52CMU	VDL Bus SB120 10.8m	Wrightbus Cadet 2	N39F	2002	MK Metro, 2006

3732-3738

VDL Bus SB120 10.8m — Wrightbus Cadet 2 — N39F — 2007

3732	MK	YJ07JVU	**3734**	MK	YJ07JVW	**3736**	MK	YJ07JVY	**3738**	MK	YJ07JVF
3733	MK	YJ07JVV	**3735**	MK	YJ07JVX	**3737**	MK	YJ07JVZ			

3804	WD	SN56AXG	ADL Dart 4	ADL Enviro 200	N28D	2007	
3805	WD	SN56AXH	ADL Dart 4	ADL Enviro 200	N28D	2007	
3806	SV	KC03PGE	TransBus Dart 10.1m	TransBus Pointer	N37F	2003	Sovereign, Stevenage, 2005
3807	SV	KC03PGF	TransBus Dart 10.1m	TransBus Pointer	N37F	2003	Sovereign, Stevenage, 2005
3808	SV	SN54GPK	ADL Dart 10.1m	ADL Pointer	N37F	2004	Sovereign, Stevenage, 2005
3809	SV	SN54GPO	ADL Dart 10.1m	ADL Pointer	N37F	2004	Sovereign, Stevenage, 2005
3810	SV	SN54GPU	ADL Dart 10.1m	ADL Pointer	N37F	2004	Sovereign, Stevenage, 2005

3821-3827

Dennis Dart SLF — Plaxton Pointer 2 — N36F — 1996 — Wycombe Bus, 2000

3821	HW	N521MJO	**3823**	AY	N523MJO	**3825**	HW	P525YJO	**3827**	HW	P527YJO
3822	HW	N522MJO	**3824**	HW	N524MJO	**3826**	HW	P526YJO			

The Green Line name continues to be seen on express services from the Home Counties into central London. Allocated to route 724 and bearing appropriate lettering, Mercedes-Benz 3908, BU06HSN, is seen heading for Terminal 5 at Heathrow Airport. *Dave Heath*

3828	HA	KE03UKK	TransBus Dart 8.8m		TransBus Mini Pointer	N29F	2003		
3829	AY	KE53NFG	TransBus Dart 8.8m		TransBus Mini Pointer	N29F	2003		
3830	WR	KE04CZF	VDL Bus SB120		Wrightbus Cadet	N35F	2004		
3831	WR	KE04CZG	VDL Bus SB120		Wrightbus Cadet	N35F	2004		
3832	WR	KE04CZH	VDL Bus SB120		Wrightbus Cadet	N35F	2004		

3835-3839
TransBus Dart 8.8m — TransBus Mini Pointer — N29F — 2003-04

3835	HH	KE53NFD	3837	HW	KE53NEU	3838	HW	KE53NFA	3839	HW	KE53NFC
3836	HH	KE53NFF							

3842	u	N622FJO	Volvo B10B	Plaxton Verde	B51F	1996	Wycombe Bus, 2000
3843	u	N623FJO	Volvo B10B	Plaxton Verde	B51F	1996	Wycombe Bus, 2000
3844	u	N624FJO	Volvo B10B	Plaxton Verde	B51F	1996	Wycombe Bus, 2000

3849-3852
Volvo B10B — Wright Endurance — BC49F — 1997 — Sovereign, Stevenage, 2005

3849	HW	R369TWR	3850	HW	R370TWR	3851	HW	R371TWR	3852	HW	R372TWR

3856-3867
Volvo B7RLE — Wrightbus Eclipse Urban — N43F — 2005

3856	HA	KE54LNR	3859	HA	KE54LPJ	3862	HW	KE05FMV	3865	HW	KE05FMP
3857	HA	KE54LPC	3860	HA	KE54HHF	3863	HW	KE05GOH	3866	HW	KE05FMO
3858	HA	KE54LPF	3861	HW	KE05FMX	3864	HW	KE05FMU	3867	HW	KE05FMM

3868-3874
Volvo B7RLE — Wrightbus Eclipse Urban — N45F* — 2007 — *3873/4 are N44F

3868	SV	KE07EVX	3870	SV	KE07EWA	3872	SV	KE07EWC	3874	HA	KE57EPC
3869	SV	KE07EVY	3871	SV	KE07EWB	3873	HA	KE57EPA			

3890	AY	LF02PVA	Volvo B7L	Wrightbus Eclipse	N41F	2002	*On loan from Arriva Bus & Coach*

3901-3909
Mercedes-Benz Citaro O530 — Mercedes-Benz — NC40F — 2006

3901	WR	BU06HSD	3904	WR	BU06HSG	3906	WR	BU06HSK	3908	HA	BU06HSN
3902	WR	BU06HSE	3905	WR	BU06HSJ	3907	HA	BU06HSL	3909	HA	BU06HSO
3903	WR	BU06HSF								

The latest frontal treatment to the Mercedes-Benz Citaro can be seen by comparing this view with the earlier model on the facing page. Milton Keynes is the location for this picture of 3927, BG59FCX, one of five delivered in 2011 for the town. *Richard Godfrey*

3910-3924

Mercedes-Benz Citaro O530   Mercedes-Benz   NC42F*   2008   *3910 is NC39F

3910	HA	BV58URL	3914	WD	BV58MLK	3918	WD	BV58MKP	3922	AY	BV58URP
3911	WD	BV58MLE	3915	WD	BV58MKO	3919	AY	BV58URM	3923	AY	BV58URR
3912	WD	BV58MLF	3916	WD	BV58MLL	3920	AY	BV58URN	3924	AY	BV58URS
3913	WD	BV58MLJ	3917	WD	BV58MLN	3921	AY	BV58URO			

3925-3929

Mercedes-Benz Citaro O530   Mercedes-Benz   NC42F   2010

3925	MK	BG59FCU	3927	MK	BG59FCX	3928	MK	BG59FCY	3929	MK	BG59FCZ
3926	MK	BG59FCV								

4044	t	R909BKO	DAF SB3000		Plaxton Première ère 320	C53F	1998	Arriva Southern Counties, 2006

4047-4055

DAF SB3000   Plaxton Prima Interurban   C53F   1997

4047	HH	R447SKX	4049	HH	R449SKX	4051	HH	R451SKX	4053	HH	R453SKX
4048	HH	R448SKX	4050	HH	R450SKX	4052	HH	R452SKX	4055	HH	R455SKX

4060	t	M948LYR	DAF SB3000	Van Hool Alizée HE	C53F	1995	London North East, 1998
4061	t	M949LYR	DAF SB3000	Van Hool Alizée HE	C53F	1995	London North East, 1998
4064	t	P201RWR	DAF DE33WSSB3000	Van Hool Alizée	C51FT	1997	First Edinburgh, 2001

4065-4069

VDL Bus SB4000   Van Hool T9 Alizée   C55F   2005

4065	SV	YJ55WSW	4067	SV	YJ55WSX	4068	SV	YJ55WSY	4069	SV	YJ55WSZ
4066	SV	YJ55WSV								

4070	MK	YJ03PFX	DAF SB4000	Van Hool T9 Alizée	C49FT	2003	Arriva Midlands, 2010
4071	MK	YJ53VFY	DAF SB4000	Van Hool T9 Alizée	C49FT	2003	Arriva Midlands, 2010
4072	MK	YJ04BKF	VDL Bus SB4000	Van Hool T9 Alizée	C49FT	2004	Arriva Midlands, 2010
4073	MK	YJ54CPE	VDL Bus SB4000	Van Hool T9 Alizée	C49FT	2004	Arriva Midlands, 2010
4074	MK	YJ54CPF	VDL Bus SB4000	Van Hool T9 Alizée	C49FT	2004	Arriva Midlands, 2010
4075	MK	YJ05PVT	VDL Bus SB4000	Van Hool T9 Alizée	C49FT	2005	Arriva Midlands, 2010
4101	MK	FJ07TKC	Scania K340 EB	Caetano Levante	C49FT	2007	
4102	MK	FJ07TKE	Scania K340 EB	Caetano Levante	C49FT	2007	
4103	MK	FJ07TKF	Scania K340 EB	Caetano Levante	C49FT	2007	

Easybus livery is carried on Van Hool Acron 4385, YJ58FFV, one of twenty integral coaches used on Luton airport services. The additional door for a wheelchair lift will be noted. *Dave Heath*

4104-4109
Scania K340 EB | Caetano Levante | C49FT | 2006 | Arriva Midlands, 2010

4104	MK	FJ56PCX	**4106**	MK	FJ56PCZ	**4108**	MK	FJ56PDO	**4109**	MK	FJ56OBP
4105	MK	FJ56PCY	**4107**	MK	FJ56PDK					

4352	t	M52AWW	Scania K113 CRB	Van Hool Alizée	C51F	1995	Arriva Yorkshire (W), 1999

4359-4369
DAF SB3000 | Plaxton Prima Interurban | C53F | 2000

4359	HH	W359XKX	**4363**	AY	W363XKX	**4365**	LU	W365XKX	**4368**	AYV	W368XKX
4361	AY	W361XKX	**4364**	HH	W364XKX	**4367**	AY	W367XKX	**4369**	HH	W369XKX
4362	AY	W362XKX								

4372-4387
Van Hool Acron T917 | Van Hool | C63F | 2008-09

4372	LU	YJ58FJN	**4376**	LU	YJ58FJV	**4380**	LU	YJ58FKA	**4384**	LU	YJ58FJA
4373	LU	YJ58FJO	**4377**	LU	YJ58FJX	**4381**	LU	YJ58FHX	**4385**	LU	YJ58FFV
4374	LU	YJ58FJP	**4378**	LU	YJ58FJY	**4382**	LU	YJ58FHY	**4386**	LU	YJ58FFW
4375	LU	YJ58FJU	**4379**	LU	YJ58FJZ	**4383**	LU	YJ58FHZ	**4387**	LU	YJ09CXL

4426	HW	S426MCC	DAF SB220	Plaxton Prestige	N42F	1999	Arriva North West, 2003
4427	WD	S427MCC	DAF SB220	Plaxton Prestige	N42F	1999	Arriva North West, 2003
4428	WD	S428MCC	DAF SB220	Plaxton Prestige	N42F	1999	Arriva Southern Counties, 2005
4429	HW	S429MCC	DAF SB220	Plaxton Prestige	N42F	1999	Arriva North West, 2003
4490	HW	T490KGB	DAF SB220	Plaxton Prestige	N42F	1999	Arriva Scotland, 2002
4491	HW	T494KGB	DAF SB220	Plaxton Prestige	N42F	1999	Arriva Scotland, 2002

4514-4518
DAF SB120 9.4m | Wrightbus Cadet | N35F | 2002

4514	WD	KE51PVF	**4516**	SV	KE51PVK	**4517**	SV	KL52CWJ	**4518**	SV	KL52CWK
4515	WD	KE51PVZ								

4519-4525
VDL Bus SB120 9.4m | Wrightbus Cadet | N35F | 2003

4519	SV	KE03OUN	**4521**	WR	KE03OUS	**4523**	HH	KE03OUK	**4525**	SV	KE03OUM
4520	SV	KE03OUP	**4522**	WR	KE03OUU	**4524**	HH	KE03OUL			

The 2011 Arriva Bus Handbook

One of twelve Dennis Tridents with Alexander bodywork, 5433, W433XKX, is seen in Cheshunt in September 2010. A further five of this type were transferred from Southern Counties in 2005. *Richard Godfrey*

5084-5094

			Leyland Olympian ONCL10/1RZ			Alexander RL		B47/32F*	1988	*5091 is BC47/29F
5084	LU	F634LMJ	5087	LU	F637LMJ	5093	LU	F643LMJ	5094	LU	F644LMJ
5086	LU	F636LMJ	5091	LU	F641LMJ					

5095-5107

			Leyland Olympian ON2R50C13Z4			Alexander RL		B47/32F	1989-90	*seating varies
5095	LU	G645UPP	5099	AY	G649UPP	5102	AY	G652UPP	5105	LU	G655UPP
5096	LU	G646UPP	5100	AY	G650UPP	5103	MK	G653UPP	5106	LU	G656UPP
5097	AY	G647UPP	5101	AY	G651UPP	5104	AY	G654UPP	5107	LU	G657UPP
5098	LU	G648UPP								

5120	u	G290UMJ	Leyland Olympian ONCL10/1RZ	Leyland	B47/31F	1989	London Country NW, 1990
5121	u	G291UMJ	Leyland Olympian ONCL10/1RZ	Leyland	B47/31F	1989	London Country NW, 1990
5127	MK	H197GRO	Leyland Olympian ON2R50C13Z4	Leyland	B47/31F	1991	
5132	HW	H202GRO	Leyland Olympian ON2R50C13Z4	Leyland	B47/31F	1991	
5135	LU	G132YWC	Leyland Olympian ONCL10/2RZ	Northern Counties	B49/33F	1989	London Country NW, 1990

5136-5145

			Volvo Olympian YN2RV18Z4			Northern Counties Palatine		B47/30F	1996	
5136	AY	N36JPP	5139	LU	N39JPP	5142	LU	N42JPP	5144	AY	N35JPP
5137	LU	N37JPP	5140	LU	N46JPP	5143	LU	N43JPP	5145	AY	N45JPP
5138	LU	N38JPP	5141	HW	N41JPP					

5146-5161

			Volvo Olympian			Northern Counties Palatine II		BC39/29F	1998	
5146	WD	S146KNK	5150	WD	S150KNK	5154	WD	S154KNK	5159	AY	S159KNK
5147	HW	S147KNK	5151	HW	S151KNK	5156	AY	S156KNK	5160	AY	S160KNK
5148	HW	S148KNK	5152	HH	S152KNK	5157	AY	S157KNK	5161	AY	S161KNK
5149	HH	S149KNK	5153	HW	S153KNK	5158	AY	S158KNK			

5421-5433

			Dennis Trident			Alexander ALX400		N47/31F	2000	
5421	AY	W421XKX	5424	WR	W424XKX	5427	WR	W427XKX	5431	AY	W431XKX
5422	AY	W422XKX	5425	WR	W425XKX	5428	WR	W428XKX	5432	AY	W432XKX
5423	WR	W423XKX	5426	WR	W426XKX	5429	WR	W429XKX	5433	WR	W433XKX

5434-5440

			ADL Trident 2			ADL Enviro 400			N47/33F	2008	
5434	AY	SN58EOF	5436	HH	SN58EOH	5438	HH	SN58EOK	5440	HH	SN58EOO
5435	AY	SN58EOG	5437	HH	SN58EOJ	5439	HH	SN58EOM			

5442-5447

			Dennis Trident			Alexander ALX400			N47/31F	2000	Arriva Southern Counties, 2005
5442	WR	W442XKX	5445	WR	W445XKX	5446	WR	W446XKX	5447	WR	W447XKX
5443	WR	W443XKX									

5452-5458

			ADL Trident 2			ADL Enviro 400			N47/33F	2008	
5452	AY	SN58ENX	5454	AY	SN58EOA	5456	AY	SN58EOC	5458	AY	SN58EOE
5453	AY	SN58ENY	5455	AY	SN58EOB	5457	AY	SN58EOD			

5831	LU	G231VWL	Leyland Olympian ON2R50G16Z4	Alexander RH	B47/29F	1990	Wycombe Bus, 2000
5835	LU	G235VWL	Leyland Olympian ON2R50G16Z4	Alexander RH	B47/29F	1990	Wycombe Bus, 2000

6000-6024

			DAF DB250			Alexander ALX400			N45/20D	2002-03	
6000	WD	KL52CWN	6007	WD	KL52CWW	6013	WD	KL52CXE	6019	WD	KL52CXM
6001	WD	KL52CWO	6008	WD	KL52CWZ	6014	WD	KL52CXF	6020	WD	KL52CXN
6002	WD	KL52CWP	6009	WD	KL52CXA	6015	WD	KL52CXG	6021	WD	KL52CXO
6003	WD	KL52CWR	6010	WD	KL52CXB	6016	WD	KL52CXH	6022	WD	KL52CXP
6004	WD	KL52CWT	6011	WD	KL52CXC	6017	WD	KL52CXJ	6023	WD	KL52CXR
6005	WD	KL52CWU	6012	WD	KL52CXD	6018	WD	KL52CXK	6024	WD	KL52CXS
6006	WD	KL52CWV									

6025	WD	YJ54CFG	VDL Bus DB250	Alexander ALX400	N45/20D	2005

6026-6036

			VDL Bus DB250 10.2m			Wrightbus Pulsar Gemini			N43/21D	2006	
6026	WD	YJ55WPO	6029	WD	YJ55WOC	6032	WD	YJ55WOM	6035	WD	YJ55WOV
6027	WD	YJ55WOA	6030	WD	YJ55WOD	6033	WD	YJ55WOR	6036	WD	YJ55WOX
6028	WD	YJ55WOB	6031	WD	YJ55WOH	6034	WD	YJ55WOU			

6037	WD	Y521UGC	DAF DB250 10.2m	Alexander ALX400	N43/20D	2001	Arriva London, 2006
6039	WD	Y531UGC	DAF DB250 10.2m	Alexander ALX400	N43/20D	2001	Arriva London, 2008
6040	WD	S236JUA	DAF DB250 10.6m	Alexander ALX400	N45/21D	1998	Arriva London, 2010
6041	WD	LJ05GLY	VDL Bus DB250 10.3m	Wrightbus Pulsar Gemini	N43/22D	2005	Arriva London, 2010
6100	WD	KX59AEE	VDL Bus DB300 Hybrid	Wrightbus Gemini 2	N41/24D	2009	
6101	WD	KX59AEF	VDL Bus DB300 Hybrid	Wrightbus Gemini 2	N41/24D	2009	

Previous registration:

J64BJN	J9BUS

Depots and allocations:

Aylesbury (Smeaton Close, Brunel Park) - AY

Outstation - Leighton Buzzard

Optare Solo	442	446	447					
Dart	3296	3297	3484	3485	3486	3487	3492	3497
	3509	3829						
Scania L113	3152	3154	3155	3156	3157	3166	3196	3197
DAF/VDL SB220	3269	3444	3445	3447	3448			
Volvo B7L	3890							
MB Citaro	3919	3920	3921	3922	3923	3924		
DAF Coach	4361	4362	4363	4367	4368			
Olympian	5097	5099	5100	5101	5102	5104	5136	5144
	5145	5156	5157	5158	5159	5160	5161	
Trident	5421	5422	5431	5432	5434	5435	5436	5437
	5438	5439	5440	5452	5453			

The latest double-deck buses for The Shires fleet are fourteen Trident 2s with Enviro 400 bodywork which are divided between Aylesbury and Hemel Hempstead. Seen in the latter town is 5457, SN58EOD, which carries lettering for route 320. *Dave Heath*

Harlow (Fourth Avenue) - HA

Outstation - Langston Road, Debden

Optare Solo	2453	2454	2455	2456	2457	2458	2459	2460
	2465	2466	2467	2473	2474	2511		
Optare Versa	2406	2407						
Dart	3218	3229	3230	3231	3295	3382	3414	3416
	3417	3435	3439	3440	3483	3828		
Volvo B6	3241	3249	3250	3251	3253	3254	3255	3256
	3257							
Volvo B7RLE	3856	3857	3858	3859	3860	3873	3874	
MB Citaro	3907	3908	3909	3910				

Hemel Hempstead (Whiteleaf Road) - HH

Mercedes-Benz	2180	2249						
Optare Solo	2461	2462	2482					
Optare Excel	3002	3003						
Dart	3171	3173	3175	3176	3177	3190	3207	3209
	3215	3228	3232	3233	3234	3235	3236	3237
	3238	3239	3370	3500	3501	3835	3836	
DAF/VDL SB120	4523	4524						
DAF/VDL SB220	3270	3271	3272	3277				
Enviro 300	3567	3568	3569					
SB3000	4047	4048	4049	4050	4051	4052	4053	4055
	4359	4364	4369					
Olympian	5149	5152						
Trident	5454	5455	5456	5457	5458			

High Wycombe (Lincoln Road) - HW

Outstation: Old Amersham

Optare Solo	2496	2497						
Optare Versa	2401	2402						
Volvo B6	3240	3245	3248	3298	3299			
Dart	3178	3181	3214	3216	3217	3226	3413	3482
	3821	3822	3824	3825	3826	3827	3837	3838
	3839							
Scania sd	3143	3146	3147	3158	3161	3162	3163	3201
	3203	3205						
Volvo B10BLE	3452	3454						
DAF/VDL SB120	3701	3702	3703					
Volvo B10B	3849	3850	3851	3852				
Volvo B7RLE	3861	3862	3863	3864	3865	3866	3867	
DAF/VDL SB220	4429	4490	4491					
Olympian	5141	5147	5148	5150	5151	5153	5162	

Luton (Dunstable Road) - LU

Mercedes-Benz	2128	2132	2133					
Dart	3280	3283	3284	3285	3286	3287	3288	3289
	3290	3291	3292	3488	3489			
Scania L113	3148	3149	3165	3167	3168	3170	3191	3192
	3193	3194	3195	3198	3199			
Scania L94	3601	3602	3603	3604	3605	3606	3607	3608
	3609	3610	3611	3612	3613	3614	3615	3616
	3617	3618	3619					
DAF/VDL SB220	3441	3449						
Volvo B10BLE	3261	3262	3263	3264	3265	3266	3268	
Van Hool T917	4372	4373	4374	4375	4376	4377	4378	4379
	4380	4381	4382	4383	4384	4385	4386	4387
Olympian	5084	5086	5087	5091	5093	5094	5095	5096
	5098	5105	5106	5107	5135	5137	5138	5139
	5140	5142	5143	5831	5835			

Stevenage (Babbage Road and Norton Green Road) - SV

Optare Solo	2489	2493	2494					
Dart	3085	3086	3219	3227	3293	3386	3491	3493
	3494	3498	3806	3807	3808	3809	3810	
Enviro 300	3550	3551	3552	3553	3554	3555	3556	3557
	3558	3559	3560	3561	3562	3563	3564	3565
	3566							
Volvo B10BLE	3300	3301	3302	3303	3304	3306	3307	3308
	3309	3310	3311	3312	3313	3314	3322	3323
	3457	3458	3459					
VDL Bus SB200	3407	3408	3409	3410	3411	3412		
Volvo B7RLE	3868	3869	3870	3871	3872			
DAF/VDL SB4000	4065	4066	4067	4068	4069			
DAF/VDL SB120	4516	4517	4518	4519	4520	4525		

Ware (Marsh Lane) - WR

Outstation - Pindar Road, Hoddesden

Optare Solo	2463	2464	2483	2484	2485	2486	2487	2488
Optare Versa	2403	2404	2405					
Dart	3281	3282	3381					
DAF/VDL SB120	3830	3831	3832	4521	4522			
MB Citaro	3901	3902	3903	3904	3905	3906		
Trident	5423	5424	5425	5426	5427	5428	5429	5433
	5442	5443	5445	5446	5447			

Watford (St Albans Road, Garston) - WD

Optare Solo	2468	2469	2470	2471	2472	2475	2476	2477
	2478	2479	2480	2492	2508			
Dart	3182	3183	3184	3185	3187	3188	3189	3218
	3220	3221	3222	3223	3225	3280	3502	3804
	3805							
Volvo B6	3258	3260						
DAF/VDL SB120	3704	3705	3706	3707	3708	3709	3710	3711
	3712	3713	3714	3715	3716	3717	3718	3719
	3720	3721	3722	3723	3724	3725	3726	3727
	3728	4514	4515					
DAF/VDL SB220	3273	3274	3275	3278	3279	4427	4428	
Mercedes-Benz Citaro	3911	3912	3913	3914	3915	3916	3917	3918
VDL Bus SB200	3401	3402	3403	3404	3405	3406	4427	4428
Trident	5448							
DB250	6000	6001	6002	6003	6004	6005	6006	6007
	6008	6009	6010	6011	6012	6013	6014	6015
	6016	6017	6018	6019	6020	6021	6022	6023
	6024	6025	6026	6027	6028	6029	6030	6031
	6032	6033	6034	6035	6036	6037	6039	6040
	6041							
DB300	6100	6101						

Wolverton (Arden Park, Old Wolverton Road, Wolverton, Milton Keynes) - MK

Optare Solo	2418	2419	2420	2421	2422	2423	2424	2425
	2427	2428	2429	2430	2431	2432	2434	2435
	2436	2437	2438	2439	2440	2441	2442	2443
	2444	2445	2446	2447	2448	2449	2450	2451
	2452	2491	2495	2498	2499	2500	2501	2502
	2503	2504	2505	2506	2507	2508	2509	2510
Dart	3212	3294	3495	3496				
	3510	3520	3521	3522	3523	3524	3525	
	3526	3527	3528	3529	3530	3532	3534	
	3535	3536	3537					
DAF/VDL SB120	3729	3730	3731	3732	3733	3734	3735	3736
	3737	3738						
Scania L94	3621	3622	3623	3624	3625	3626	3627	3628
Enviro 300	3570	3571	3572	3573	3574	3575	3576	3577
	3578							
Mercedes-Benz Citaro	3925	3926	3927	3928	3929			
Scania coach	410	418	419	420	421	422	423	424
	4101	4102	4103	4104	4105	4106	4108	4109
Olympian	5103	5127						

Unallocated, stored and withdrawn - u

Remainder

ARRIVA LONDON

Arriva London North Ltd, 16 Watsons Road, Wood Green, London, N22 7TZ
Arriva London South Ltd, Croydon Bus Garage, Brighton Road, South Croydon, CR2 6EL

ADL61-81

Dennis Dart SLF 9.4m | Alexander ALX200 | N23D | 2000 | Arriva The Shires, 2005

61	CN	W461XKX	66	EC	W466XKX	72	EC	W472XKX	77	EC	W477XKX
62	CN	W462XKX	67	EC	W467XKX	73	EC	W473XKX	78	EC	W478XKX
63	CN	W463XKX	68	EC	W468XKX	74	EC	W474XKX	79	EC	W479XKX
64	CN	W464XKX	69	EC	W469XKX	75	EC	W475XKX	81	EC	W481XKX
65	CN	W465XKX	71	EC	W471XKX	76	EC	W476XKX			

ADL969-983

Dennis Dart SLF 10.2m | Alexander ALX200 | N27D | 1998

969	DX	S169JUA	973	DX	S173JUA	977	DX	S177JUA	981	DX	S181JUA
970	DX	S170JUA	974	DX	S174JUA	978	DX	S178JUA	982	DX	S182JUA
971	DX	S171JUA	975	EC	S175JUA	979	DX	S179JUA	983	DX	S183JUA
972	DX	S172JUA	976	DX	S176JUA	980	DX	S180JUA			

DDL6	CNt	S306JUA	Dennis Dart SLF 10.1m	Plaxton Pointer 2	N26D	1998	

DLA11-64

DAF DB250 10.6m | Alexander ALX400 | N45/19D* | 1998-99 | *seating varies

11	WN	S211JUA	22	CNt	S322JUA	33	Wt	S233JUA	50	BN	S250JUA
12	WN	S212JUA	23	Et	S223JUA	34	CNt	S234JUA	51	SF	S251JUA
13	WN	S213JUA	24	CNt	S224JUA	35	Et	S235JUA	54	SF	S254JUA
14	WN	S214JUA	25	Et	S225JUA	37	Et	S237JUA	55	SF	S255JUA
15	WN	S215JUA	26	CNt	S226JUA	38	BN	S238JUA	56	CNt	S256JUA
16	WN	S216JUA	27	CNt	S227JUA	39	SF	S239JUA	57	EC	S257JUA
17	WN	S217JUA	28	CNt	S228JUA	40	w	S240JUA	58	EC	S258JUA
18	WN	S218JUA	29	CNt	S229JUA	42	w	S242JUA	62	SF	S262JUA
19	WN	S219JUA	30	CNt	S230JUA	45	SF	S245JUA	63	TH	S263JUA
20	WN	S220JUA	31	CNt	S231JUA	47	WN	S247JUA	64	TH	S264JUA
21	Et	S221JUA	32	Et	S232JUA						

DLA72-92

DAF DB250 10.6m | Alexander ALX400 | N45/19D | 1999

72	SF	S272JUA	78	E	S278JUA	83	E	S283JUA	88	w	S288JUA
73	E	S273JUA	79	E	S279JUA	84	E	S284JUA	89	DX	S289JUA
74	E	S274JUA	80	E	S280JUA	85	E	S285JUA	90	DX	S290JUA
75	E	S275JUA	81	E	S281JUA	86	DX	S286JUA	91	E	S291JUA
76	E	S276JUA	82	E	S282JUA	87	w	S287JUA	92	E	S292JUA
77	E	S277JUA									

DLA93-125

DAF DB250 10.6m | Alexander ALX400 | N45/17D* | 1999 | *seating varies

93	E	T293FGN	109	E	T309FGN	115	E	T315FGN	121	E	T421GGO
94	E	T294FGN	110	E	T310FGN	116	E	T316FGN	122	E	T322FGN
95	E	T295FGN	111	E	T311FGN	117	E	T317FGN	123	E	T323FGN
106	E	T306FGN	112	E	T312FGN	118	E	T318FGN	124	E	T324FGN
107	E	T307FGN	113	E	T313FGN	119	E	T319FGN	125	E	T325FGN
108	E	T308FGN	114	E	T314FGN	120	E	T320FGN			

Several of the early DAF DB250s with Alexander bodywork are currently being transferred to the North West and Wales fleet. In so doing they are being converted to single door and being refurbished. Turnpike Lane is the location for this view of DLA204, W404VGJ, which is allocated to Tottenham depot. *Colin Lloyd*

DLA126-189

DAF DB250 10.2m   Alexander ALX400   N43/18D*   1999-2000 *seating varies

126	E	V326DGT	142	N	V342DGT	158	N	V358DGT	174	N	W374VGJ
127	E	V327DGT	143	N	V343DGT	159	E	V359DGT	175	TC	W432WGJ
128	E	V628LGC	144	N	V344DGT	160	E	V660LGC	176	TC	W376VGJ
129	E	V329DGT	145	N	V345DGT	161	E	V361DGT	177	TC	W377VGJ
130	E	V330DGT	146	N	V346DGT	162	E	V362DGT	178	TC	W378VGJ
131	E	V331DGT	147	N	V347DGT	163	E	V363DGT	179	TC	W379VGJ
132	TC	V332DGT	148	N	V348DGT	164	E	V364DGT	180	TC	W433WGJ
133	TC	V633LGC	149	N	V349DGT	165	E	V365DGT	181	TC	W381VGJ
134	w	V334DGT	150	E	V650LGC	166	N	V366VGJ	182	TC	W382VGJ
135	TC	V335DGT	151	E	V351DGT	167	N	V367VGJ	183	TC	W383VGJ
136	N	V336DGT	152	E	V352DGT	168	N	V368VGJ	184	TC	W384VGJ
137	N	V337DGT	153	E	V353DGT	169	N	V369VGJ	185	TC	W385VGJ
138	N	V338DGT	154	N	V354DGT	170	N	W431WGJ	186	TC	W386VGJ
139	N	V339DGT	155	N	V355DGT	171	N	W371VGJ	187	TC	W387VGJ
140	E	V640LGC	156	N	V356DGT	172	N	W372VGJ	188	TC	W388VGJ
141	E	V341DGT	157	N	V357DGT	173	N	W373VGJ	189	TC	W389VGJ

DLA190-223

DAF DB250 10.2m   Alexander ALX400   N43/18D*   2000   *seating varies

190	AR	W434WGJ	199	AR	W399VGJ	208	BN	W408VGJ	216	TC	X416FGP
191	AR	W391VGJ	200	AR	W435WGJ	209	BN	W409VGJ	217	TC	X417FGP
192	AR	W392VGJ	201	AR	W401VGJ	210	AR	W438WGJ	218	TC	X418FGP
193	AR	W393VGJ	202	AR	W402VGJ	211	AR	W411VGJ	219	TC	X419FGP
194	AR	W394VGJ	203	AR	W403VGJ	212	BN	W412VGJ	220	TC	X501GGO
195	AR	W395VGJ	204	AR	W404VGJ	213	BN	W413VGJ	221	TC	X421FGP
196	AR	W396VGJ	205	BN	W436WGJ	214	AR	W414VGJ	222	TC	X422FGP
197	AR	W397VGJ	206	BN	W437WGJ	215	TC	X415FGP	223	TH	X423FGP
198	AR	W398VGJ	207	BN	W407VGJ						

DLA224-256

DAF DB250 10.2m — Alexander ALX400 — N43/19D* — 2000-01 — *seating varies

224	TC	X424FGP	233	AR	X433FGP	241	AR	X441FGP	249	AR	X449FGP
225	AR	X425FGP	234	AR	X434FGP	242	AR	X442FGP	250	TC	X506GGO
226	AR	X426FGP	235	AR	X435FGP	243	AR	X443FGP	251	TC	X451FGP
227	AR	X427FGP	236	BN	X436FGP	244	AR	X504GGO	252	TC	X452FGP
228	AR	X428FGP	237	AR	X437FGP	245	AR	X445FGP	253	TC	X453FGP
229	AR	X429FGP	238	AR	X438FGP	246	AR	X446FGP	254	TC	X454FGP
230	AR	X502GGO	239	AR	X439FGP	247	AR	X447FGP	255	TC	X507GGO
231	AR	X431FGP	240	AR	X503GGO	248	AR	X448FGP	256	TC	X508GGO
232	AR	X432FGP									

DLA270-319

DAF DB250 10.2m — Alexander ALX400 — N43/19D* — 2000-01 — *seating varies

270	BN	Y452UGC	283	AR	Y483UGC	296	AR	Y496UGC	308	EC	Y508UGC
271	BN	Y471UGC	~~284~~	~~AR~~	~~Y484UGC~~	297	AR	Y497UGC	309	EC	Y509UGC
272	AR	Y472UGC	285	AR	Y485UGC	298	AR	Y498UGC	310	EC	Y527UGC
273	AR	Y473UGC	286	AR	Y486UGC	299	EC	Y499UGC	311	BN	Y511UGC
274	AR	Y474UGC	287	AR	Y487UGC	300	EC	Y524UGC	312	BN	Y512UGC
275	AR	Y475UGC	288	AR	Y488UGC	301	EC	Y501UGC	313	BN	Y513UGC
276	AR	Y476UGC	289	AR	Y489UGC	302	EC	Y502UGC	314	BN	Y514UGC
277	AR	Y477UGC	290	BN	Y523UGC	303	EC	Y503UGC	315	BN	Y529UGC
278	AR	Y478UGC	291	AR	Y491UGC	304	EC	Y504UGC	316	BN	Y516UGC
279	AR	Y479UGC	292	AR	Y492UGC	305	EC	Y526UGC	317	BN	Y517UGC
280	AR	Y522UGC	293	AR	Y493UGC	306	EC	Y506UGC	318	BN	Y518UGC
281	AR	Y481UGC	294	AR	Y494UGC	307	EC	Y507UGC	319	BN	Y519UGC
282	AR	Y482UGC	295	AR	Y495UGC						

DLA322-336

DAF DB250 10.2m — TransBus ALX400 — N45/20D — 2003

322	TH	LG52DAO	326	TH	LG52DBV	330	TH	LG52DCF	334	TH	LG52DCX
323	TH	LG52DAU	327	TH	LG52DBY	331	TH	LG52DCO	335	TH	LG52DCY
324	TH	LG52DBO	328	TH	LG52DBZ	332	TH	LG52DCU	336	TH	LG52DCZ
325	TH	LG52DBU	329	TH	LG52DCE	333	TH	LG52DCV			

DLA337-389

DAF DB250 10.2m — TransBus ALX400 — N45/20D* — 2003 — *338 is N45/19D

337	TH	LJ03MFX	351	EC	LJ03MKZ	364	EC	LJ03MKL	377	TH	LJ03MTK
338	TH	LJ03MFY	352	EC	LJ03MLE	365	EC	LJ03MWE	378	TH	LJ03MTU
339	TH	LJ03MFZ	353	EC	LJ03MLF	366	EC	LJ03MWF	379	TH	LJ03MTV
340	TH	LJ03MGE	354	EC	LJ03MLK	367	EC	LJ03MWG	380	TH	LJ03MTY
341	TH	LJ03MGU	355	EC	LJ03MJX	368	EC	LJ03MWK	381	TH	LJ03MTZ
342	TH	LJ03MGV	356	EC	LJ03MJY	369	u	LJ03MWL	382	TH	LJ03MUA
343	TH	LJ03MDV	357	EC	LJ03MKA	370	EC	LJ03MUY	383	TH	LJ03MUB
344	TH	LJ03MDX	358	EC	LJ03MKC	371	TH	LJ03MVC	384	TH	LJ03MYU
345	TH	LJ03MDY	359	EC	LJ03MKD	372	TH	LJ03MVD	385	TH	LJ03MYV
346	TH	LJ03MDZ	360	EC	LJ03MKE	373	TH	LJ03MVE	386	TH	LJ03MYX
347	TH	LJ03MEU	361	EC	LJ03MKF	374	TH	LJ03MSY	387	TH	LJ03MYY
348	EC	LJ03MKU	362	EC	LJ03MKG	375	TH	LJ03MTE	388	TH	LJ03MYZ
349	EC	LJ03MKV	363	EC	LJ03MKK	376	TH	LJ03MTF	389	TH	LJ03MZD
350	EC	LJ03MKX									

DLP15-20

DAF DB250 10.6m — Plaxton President — N45/19D — 1999

15	E	T215XBV	17	E	T217XBV	19	u	T219XBV	20	E	T220XBV
16	E	T216XBV	18	E	T218XBV						

DLP40-75

DAF DB250 10.6m — Plaxton President — N45/21D — 2001

40	AD	Y532UGC	49	AD	Y549UGC	58	AD	LJ51DKF	67	WN	LJ51DLD
41	AD	Y541UGC	50	AD	LJ51DJU	59	AD	LJ51DKK	68	AD	LJ51DLF
42	AD	Y542UGC	51	AD	LJ51DJV	60	AD	LJ51DKL	69	WN	LJ51DLK
43	AD	Y543UGC	52	AD	LJ51DJX	61	AD	LJ51DKN	70	WN	LJ51DLN
44	AD	Y544UGC	53	AD	LJ51DJY	62	AD	LJ51DKO	71	AD	LJ51DLU
45	AD	Y533UGC	54	AD	LJ51DJZ	63	AD	LJ51DKU	72	WN	LJ51DLV
46	AD	Y546UGC	55	AD	LJ51DKA	64	WN	LJ51DKV	73	AD	LJ51DLX
47	AD	Y547UGC	56	AD	LJ51DKD	65	AD	LJ51DKX	74	AD	LJ51DLY
48	AD	Y548UGC	57	AD	LJ51DKE	66	AD	LJ51DKY	75	AD	LJ51DLZ

DLP76-90

DAF DB250 10.2m — TransBus President — N43/19D* — 2002 — *seating varies

76	E	LJ51OSX	80	E	LJ51ORC	84	E	LJ51ORK	88	E	LF02PKD
77	E	LJ51OSY	81	E	LJ51ORF	85	E	LJ51ORL	89	E	LF02PKE
78	E	LJ51OSZ	82	E	LJ51ORG	86	E	LF02PKA	90	E	LF02PKJ
79	E	LJ51ORA	83	E	LJ51ORH	87	E	LF02PKC			

Along with deliveries from Alexander the DB250s were also bodied with President bodywork that were built at the former Northern Counties facility in Wigan. Initial Presidents carried the Plaxton name while later models used TransBus. DLP108, LF52UPR, is seen operating route 279 at Edmonton. *Richard Godfrey*

DLP91-110

DAF DB250 10.6m   TransBus President   N45/19D*   2002   *seating varies

91	E	LF52URS	96	EC	LF52URX	101	EC	LF52URG	106	E	LF52URM
92	E	LF52URT	97	EC	LF52URB	102	EC	LF52URH	107	E	LF52UPP
93	E	LF52URU	98	EC	LF52URC	103	EC	LF52URJ	108	E	LF52UPR
94	E	LF52URV	99	EC	LF52URD	104	EC	LF52URK	109	E	LF52UPS
95	EC	LF52URW	100	EC	LF52URE	105	E	LF52URL	110	E	LF52UPT

DW1-50

DAF DB250 10.3m   Wrightbus Pulsar Gemini   N43/21D   2003

1	TC	801DYE	14	TC	LJ03MWC	27	TC	LJ53BGK	39	CN	LJ53NHF
2	TC	LJ03MWN	15	TC	LJ03MWD	28	TC	LJ53BGO	40	CN	LJ53NHG
3	TC	LJ03MWP	16	TC	LJ03MVF	29	TC	LJ53BGU	41	CN	LJ53NHH
4	TC	LJ03MWU	17	TC	LJ03MVG	30	TC	LJ53NHV	42	CN	LJ53NHK
5	TC	LJ03MWV	18	TC	LJ53NHT	31	TC	LJ53NHX	43	CN	LJ53NHL
6	TC	LJ03MVT	19	TC	WLT719	32	TC	LJ53NHY	44	CN	VLT244
7	TC	WLT807	20	TC	LJ53BFP	33	TC	LJ53NHZ	45	CN	LJ53NHN
8	TC	LJ03MVV	21	TC	LJ53BFU	34	TC	734DYE	46	CN	LJ53NHO
9	TC	LJ03MVW	22	TC	822DYE	35	TC	LJ53NJF	47	CN	LJ53NHP
10	TC	LJ03MVX	23	TC	LJ53BFX	36	TC	LJ53NJK	48	CN	WLT348
11	TC	LJ03MVY	24	TC	LJ53BFY	37	TC	LJ53NJN	49	CN	LJ53NGU
12	TC	LJ03MVZ	25	TC	725DYE	38	CN	LJ53NHE	50	CN	LJ53NGV
13	TC	LJ03MWA	26	TC	LJ53BGF						

Working route 59 along Aldwych, DW85, carries former Routemaster plate WLT385. *Colin Lloyd*

DW51-93

VDL Bus DB250 10.3m   Wrightbus Pulsar Gemini   N43/22D   2004

51	CN	LJ04LDX	62	BN	LJ04LDC	73	BN	LJ04LGK	84	BN	LJ04LFX
52	CN	LJ04LDY	63	BN	LJ04LDD	74	BN	LJ04LGL	85	BN	WLT385
53	CN	LJ04LDZ	64	BN	WLT664	75	BN	LJ04LGN	86	BN	LJ04LFZ
54	CN	LJ04LEF	65	BN	LJ04LDF	76	BN	WLT676	87	BN	LJ04LGA
55	BN	LJ04LEU	66	BN	LJ04LDK	77	BN	LJ04LGV	88	BN	LJ04LGC
56	BN	656DYE	67	BN	LJ04LDL	78	BN	LJ04LGW	89	BN	LJ04LGD
57	BN	LJ04LFB	68	BN	LJ04LDN	79	BN	LJ04LGX	90	BN	LJ04LGE
58	BN	LJ04LFD	69	BN	LJ04LDU	80	BN	LJ04LGY	91	BN	LJ04LFG
59	BN	LJ04LFE	70	BN	WLT970	81	BN	LJ04LFU	92	BN	LJ04LFH
60	BN	LJ04LFF	71	BN	LJ04LGF	82	BN	LJ04LFV	93	BN	LJ04LFK
61	BN	LJ04LDA	72	BN	LJ04LGG	83	BN	LJ04LFW			

DW94-102

VDL Bus DB250 10.3m   Wrightbus Pulsar Gemini   N43/22D   2004

94	CN	LJ54BFP	97	CN	WLT997	99	CN	LJ54BFZ	101	CN	LJ54BGF
95	CN	VLT295	98	CN	LJ54BFY	100	CN	LJ54BGE	102	CN	LJ54BGK
96	CN	LJ54BFV									

DW103-133

VDL Bus DB250 10.3m   Wrightbus Pulsar Gemini   N43/22D   2005

103	BN	LJ05BJV	111	BN	LJ05BHP	119	BN	LJ05BHP	127	BN	LJ05BNL
104	BN	LJ05BJX	112	BN	LJ05BHU	120	BN	LJ05BMZ	128	BN	LJ05GKX
105	BN	LJ05BJY	113	BN	LJ05BHV	121	BN	LJ05BNA	129	BN	LJ05GKY
106	BN	LJ05BJZ	114	BN	LJ05BHW	122	BN	LJ05BNB	130	BN	LJ05GKZ
107	BN	LJ05BKA	115	BN	LJ05BHX	123	BN	LJ05BND	131	BN	LJ05GLF
108	BN	LJ05BHL	116	BN	LJ05BHY	124	BN	LJ05BNE	132	BN	LJ05GLK
109	BN	LJ05BHN	117	BN	LJ05BHZ	125	BN	LJ05BNF	133	BN	LJ05GLV
110	BN	LJ05BHO	118	BN	LJ05BMV	126	BN	LJ05BNK			

Also on route 59, this time at Waterloo, is DW284, LJ59LWM. Comparison with the picture on the previous page will show the variations between the initial Gemini and the Gemini 2 body styling. *Dave Heath*

DW201-262

VDL Bus DB300 10.4m   Wrightbus Pulsar Gemini 2   N41/24D   2009

201	CT	LJ09KRO	217	CT	LJ09STX	233	CT	LJ59AEC	248	CT	LJ59AAO
202	CT	LJ09SUO	218	CT	LJ09STZ	234	CT	LJ59AED	249	CT	LJ59AAU
203	CT	LJ09SUU	219	CT	LJ09SUA	235	CT	LJ59AEE	250	CT	LJ59AAV
204	CT	LJ09SUV	220	CT	LJ09SUF	236	CT	LJ59AEF	251	CT	LJ59AAX
205	CT	LJ09SUX	221	CT	LJ09SUH	237	CT	LJ59AEG	252	CT	LJ59AAY
206	CT	LJ09SUY	222	CT	LJ59AAO	238	CT	LJ59AEK	253	CT	LJ59AAZ
207	CT	LJ09SVA	223	CT	LJ59AAU	239	CT	LJ59AEL	254	CT	LJ59GVC
208	CT	LJ09SVC	224	CT	LJ59AET	240	CT	LJ59AEM	255	CT	LJ59GVE
209	CT	LJ09SVD	225	CT	LJ59AEU	241	CT	LJ59AEN	256	CT	LJ59GVF
210	CT	LJ09SVE	226	CT	LJ59AEV	242	CT	LJ59ACU	257	CT	LJ59GVG
211	CT	LJ09SVF	227	CT	LJ59AEW	243	CT	LJ59ACV	258	CT	LJ59GVK
212	CT	LJ09SSO	228	CT	LJ59AEX	244	CT	LJ59ACX	259	CT	LJ59GTF
213	CT	LJ09SSU	229	CT	LJ59AEY	245	CT	LJ59AAF	260	CT	LJ59GTU
214	CT	LJ09SSV	230	CT	LJ59AEZ	246	CT	LJ59AAK	261	CT	361CLT
215	CT	LJ09SSX	231	CT	LJ59AEA	247	CT	LJ59AAN	262	CT	LJ59GUA
216	CT	LJ09SSZ	232	CT	LJ59AEB						

DW263-295

VDL Bus DB300 10.4m   Wrightbus Pulsar Gemini 2   N41/24D   2009-10

263	CT	LJ59LXU	272	CT	LJ59LWV	280	BN	LJ59LWG	288	BN	LJ59LWR
264	CT	LJ59LXV	273	CT	LJ59LWW	281	BN	LJ59LWH	289	BN	LJ59LVH
265	CT	LJ59LXW	274	CT	LJ59LWX	282	BN	LJ59LWK	290	BN	LJ59LVV
266	CT	LJ59LXX	275	CT	LJ59LWY	283	BN	LJ59LWL	291	BN	LJ59LVW
267	CT	LJ59LXY	276	CT	LJ59LWZ	284	BN	LJ59LWM	292	BN	LJ59LVX
268	CT	LJ59LXZ	277	CT	LJ59LXA	285	BN	LJ59LWN	293	BN	LJ59LVY
269	CT	LJ59LWS	278	CT	LJ59LXB	286	BN	LJ59LWO	294	BN	LJ59LVZ
270	CT	LJ59LWT	279	CT	LJ59LWF	287	BN	LJ59LWP	295	BN	LJ59LWA
271	CT	LJ59LWU									

DW296-365

VDL Bus DB300 10.4m — Wrightbus Pulsar Gemini 2 — N41/24D — 2010 and on order

296	BN	LJ10CUH	314	AR	LJ10CVA	332	AR	LJ60AYR	349	-	LJ
297	BN	LJ10CUK	315	AR	LJ10CVB	333	AR	LJ60AYS	350	-	LJ
298	AR	LJ10CVE	316	AR	LJ10CVC	334	AR	LJ60AYT	351	-	LJ
299	AR	LJ10CVF	317	AR	LJ10CVD	335	AR	LJ60AYU	352	-	LJ
300	AR	LJ10CVG	318	AR	LJ60AXX	336	AR	LJ60AWW	353	-	LJ
301	AR	LJ10CVH	319	AR	LJ60AXY	337	AR	LJ60AWX	354	-	LJ
302	AR	LJ10CVK	320	AR	LJ60AXZ	338	-	LJ	355	-	LJ
303	AR	LJ10CVL	321	AR	LJ60AYA	339	-	LJ	356	-	LJ
304	AR	LJ10CVM	322	AR	LJ60AYB	340	-	LJ	357	-	LJ
305	AR	LJ10CVN	323	AR	LJ60AYC	341	-	LJ	358	-	LJ
306	AR	LJ10CVO	324	AR	LJ60AYD	342	-	LJ	359	-	LJ
307	AR	LJ10CVP	325	AR	LJ60AYE	343	-	LJ	360	-	LJ
308	AR	LJ10CUO	326	AR	LJ60AYH	344	-	LJ	361	-	LJ
309	AR	LJ10CUU	327	AR	LJ60AYK	345	-	LJ	362	-	LJ
310	AR	LJ10CUV	328	AR	LJ60AYM	346	-	LJ	363	-	LJ
311	AR	LJ10CUW	329	AR	LJ60AYN	347	-	LJ	364	-	LJ
312	AR	LJ10CUX	330	AR	LJ60AYO	348	-	LJ	365	-	LJ
313	AR	LJ10CUY	331	AR	LJ60AYP						

DWL1-22

DAF SB120 10.2mAEC — Wrightbus Cadet — N27D* — 2001 — *seating varies

1	TH	Y801DGT	7	TH	LJ51DDK	13	E	LJ51DDX	18	EC	LJ51DFC
2	TH	Y802DGT	8	TH	LJ51DDL	14	E	LJ51DDY	19	TH	LJ51DFD
3	TH	Y803DGT	9	TH	LJ51DDN	15	TH	LJ51DDZ	20	TH	LJ51DFE
4	TH	Y804DGT	10	EC	LJ51DDO	16	TH	LJ51DEU	21	EC	LJ51DFF
5	TH	Y805DGT	11	TH	LJ51DDU	17	TH	LJ51DFA	22	EC	LJ51DFG
6	TH	Y806DGT	12	TH	LJ51DDV						

DWL23-29

DAF SB120 10.8m — Wrightbus Cadet — N30D — 2002

23	E	LF02PLU	25	E	LF02PLX	27	E	LF02PMO	29	E	LF02PMV
24	E	LF02PLV	26	E	LF02PLZ						

DWL30-55

DAF SB120 10.2m — Wrightbus Cadet — N26D* — 2002 — *seating varies

30	CNt	LF02PMX	37	Et	LF02PNO	44	Et	LF52UTB	50	Et	LF52UOB
31	CNt	LF02PMY	38	Et	LF02PNU	45	EC	LF52UNW	51	EC	LF52UOC
32	CNt	LF02PNE	39	Et	LF02PNV	46	EC	LF52UNX	52	WN	LF52UOD
33	CNt	LF02PNJ	40	Et	LF02PNX	47	EC	LF52UNY	53	WN	LF52UOE
34	CNt	LF02PNK	41	Et	LF02PNY	48	EC	LF52UNZ	54	WN	LF52USZ
35	Et	LF02PNL	42	EC	LF02POA	49	EC	LF52UOA	55	WN	LF52UTA
36	Et	LF02PNN	43	EC	LF02POH						

DWL56-67

DAF SB120 10.2m — Wrightbus Cadet — N26D* — 2003 — *seating varies

56	WN	LJ03MUW	59	CN	LJ03MZG	62	CN	LJ03MYH	65	CN	LJ03MYM
57	WN	LJ03MZE	60	CN	LJ03MZL	63	CN	LJ03MYK	66	CN	LJ53NGX
58	CN	LJ03MZF	61	CN	LJ03MYG	64	CN	LJ03MYL	67	CN	LJ53NGY

DWS1-18

DAF SB120 9.4m — Wrightbus Cadet2 — N26D — 2003

1	CN	LJ53NGZ	6	CN	LJ53NFT	11	CN	LJ53NFZ	15	CN	LJ53NGN
2	CN	LJ53NHA	7	CN	LJ53NFU	12	CN	LJ53NGE	16	CN	LJ53NFE
3	CN	LJ53NHB	8	CN	LJ53NFV	13	CN	LJ53NGF	17	CN	LJ53NFF
4	CN	LJ53NHC	9	CN	LJ53NFX	14	CN	LJ53NGG	18	CN	LJ53NFG
5	CN	LJ53NHD	10	CN	LJ53NFY						

EN1-13

ADL Dart 4 8.9m — ADL Enviro200 — N26F — 2008

1	LV	LJ57USS	5	LV	LJ57USW	8	LV	LJ57USZ	11	LV	LJ57UTC
2	LV	LJ57UST	6	LV	LJ57USX	9	LV	LJ57UTA	12	LV	LJ57UTE
3	LV	LJ57USU	7	LV	LJ57USY	10	LV	LJ57UTB	13	LV	LJ57UTF
4	LV	LJ57USV									

ENL1-9

ADL Dart 4 10.2m — ADL Enviro200 — N29D — 2007

1	TC	LJ07ECW	4	TC	LJ07ECZ	6	TC	LJ07EDF	8	TC	LJ07EBP
2	TC	LJ07ECX	5	TC	LJ07EDC	7	TC	LJ07EBO	9	TC	LJ07EBU
3	TC	LJ07ECY									

ENL10-48

ADL Dart 4   10.2m   ADL Enviro200   N29D   2008-09

10	E	LJ58AVT	20	E	LJ58AVE	30	WN	LJ09KPR	40	WN	LJ09KOX
11	E	LJ58AVU	21	TC	LJ58AUV	31	WN	LJ09KPT	41	WN	LJ09KPA
12	E	LJ58AVV	22	TC	LJ58AUW	32	WN	LJ09KPU	42	WN	LJ09KPE
13	E	LJ58AVX	23	TC	LJ58AUX	33	WN	LJ09KPV	43	WN	LJ09KPF
14	E	LJ58AVY	24	TC	LJ58AUY	34	WN	LJ09KPX	44	WN	LJ09KPG
15	E	LJ58AVZ	25	TC	LJ58AVB	35	WN	LJ09KPY	45	WN	LJ09KPK
16	E	LJ58AWA	26	TC	LJ58AVC	36	WN	LJ09KPZ	46	WN	LJ09KPL
17	E	LJ58AWC	27	TC	LJ58AVD	37	WN	LJ09KRD	47	WN	LJ09KPN
18	E	LJ58AWF	28	TC	LJ58AUC	38	WN	LJ09KRE	48	WN	LJ09KPO
19	E	LJ58AWG	29	TC	LJ58AUE	39	WN	LJ09KRF			

ENL49-74

ADL Dart 4   10.2m   ADL Enviro200   N29D   2010

49	DX	LJ10CSF	56	DX	LJ10CSX	63	DX	LJ60AYF	69	DX	LJ60AYN
50	DX	LJ10CSO	57	DX	LJ10CSY	64	DX	LJ60AYG	70	DX	LJ60AYO
51	DX	LJ10CSU	58	DX	LJ10CSZ	65	DX	LJ60AYH	71	DX	LJ60AYP
52	DX	LJ59LVL	59	DX	LJ10CTE	66	DX	LJ60AYK	72	DX	LJ60AYS
53	DX	LJ59LVM	60	DX	LJ10CTF	67	DX	LJ60AYL	73	DX	LJ60AXV
54	DX	LJ59LVN	61	DX	LJ10CTK	68	DX	LJ60AYM	74	DX	LJ60AXW
55	DX	LJ10CSV	62	DX	LJ60ATY						

ENS1-14

ADL Dart 4   9.3m   ADL Enviro200   N24D   2007

1	AE	LJ07EDK	4	AE	LJ07EDR	9	AE	LJ07EEA	12	AE	LJ07ECN
2	AE	LJ07EDL	5	AE	LJ07EDU	10	AE	LJ07EEB	13	AE	LJ07ECT
3	AE	LJ07EDO	6	AE	LJ07EDV	11	AE	LJ07ECF	14	AE	LJ07ECU
4	AE	LJ07EDP	7	AE	LJ07EDX						

HV1-6

Volvo B5L Hybrid   10.4m   Wrightbus Gemini 2   N39/21D   2009

1	WN	LJ09KRU	3	WN	LJ09KOH	5	WN	LJ09KOV	6	WN	LJ09KOW
2	WN	LJ09KOE	4	WN	LJ09KOU						

HV7-26

Volvo B5L Hybrid   10.4m   Wrightbus Gemini 2   N39/21D   2010

7	AR	LJ60AWY	12	AR	LJ60AXD	17	AR	LJ60AWH	22	AR	LJ60AWR
8	AR	LJ60AWZ	13	AR	LJ60AXF	18	AR	LJ60AWM	23	AR	LJ60AWU
9	AR	LJ60AXA	14	AR	LJ60AXG	19	AR	LJ60AWN	24	AR	LJ60AWV
10	AR	LJ60AXB	15	AR	LJ60AWF	20	AR	LJ60AWO	25	AR	LJ60JGY
11	AR	LJ60AXC	16	AR	LJ60AWG	21	AR	LJ60AWP	26	AR	LJ60JGZ

HW1-5

Wrightbus/VDL DB250   Wrightbus Gemini   N41/24D   2009

1	WN	LJ09KRG	3	WN	LJ58AVK	4	WN	LJ09KRK	5	WN	LJ09KRN
2	WN	LJ58AVG									

Many of the earlier Darts operating with Arriva London have been replaced with Enviro 200s. Based on the Alexander Dennis Dart 4 chassis, the model is supplied in a variety of lengths. 10.2metre long ENL15, LJ58AVZ, is seen at Waltham Cross.
Dave Heath

MA22-76   Mercedes-Benz Citaro O530G   AB49T   2004

22	EC	BX04MXW	39	u	BX04NEJ	53	LV	BX04MYZ	65	LV	BX04NCU			
26	EC	BX04MYB	42	LV	BX04MYJ	54	w	BX04MZD	66	LV	BX04NCV			
27	u	BX04MYC	43	LV	BX04MYK	55	LV	BX04MZE	67	LV	BX04NCY			
28	EC	BX04MYD	44	EC	BX04MYL	56	LV	BX04MZG	68	LV	BX04NCZ			
29	EC	BX04MYF	45	LV	BX04MYM	57	LV	BX04MZJ	69	LV	BX04NDC			
30	EC	BX04MYY	46	LV	BX04MYN	58	LV	BX04MZL	70	LV	BX04NDE			
31	EC	BX04MYZ	47	LV	BX04MYR	59	LV	BX04MZN	71	LV	BX04NDF			
34	LV	BX04NDU	48	LV	BX04MYS	60	LV	BX04NBK	72	LV	BX04NDJ			
35	EC	BX04NDV	49	LV	BX04MYT	61	LV	BX04NBL	73	LV	BX04NDK			
36	u	BX04NDY	50	LV	BX04MYU	62	LV	BX04NCF	74	LV	BX04NDL			
37	EC	BX04NDZ	51	LV	BX04MYV	63	LV	BX04NCJ	75	LV	BX04NDN			
38	EC	BX04NEF	52	LV	BX04MYW	64	LV	BX04NCN	76	LV	BX04NEN			

MA77-157   Mercedes-Benz Citaro O530G   AB49T   2005

77	LV	BX05UWV	98	EC	398CLT	118	w	BX55FVU	138	w	BX55FWZ
78	LV	BX05UWW	99	w	BX55FUW	119	w	319CLT	139	w	BX55FXB
79	LV	BX05UWY	100	w	BX55FUY	120	w	BX55FVW	140	EC	BX55FXC
80	LV	BX05UWZ	101	w	BX55FVA	121	w	BX55FVY	141	EC	BX55FXE
81	LV	BU05VFE	102	w	BX55FVB				142	EC	BX55FXF
82	LV	BU05VFF	103	w	BX55FVC	123	w	BX55FWG	143	EC	BX55FXG
83	LV	BX05UXC	104	w	BX55FVD	124	w	BX55FWH	144	EC	BX55FXH
84	LV	BU05VFG	105	w	BX55FVF	125	w	BX55FWJ	145	w	BX55FXJ
85	LV	185CLT	106	w	BX55FVG	126	w	BX55FWK	146	w	BX55FXK
86	LV	BU05VFH	107	w	BX55FVH	127	w	BX55FWL	147	w	BX55FXL
87	LV	BU05VFJ	108	w	BX55FVJ	128	w	BX55FWM	148	w	BX55FXM
88	LV	BX05UXD	109	w	BX55FVK	129	w	BX55FWN	149	w	BX55FXO
89	LV	BX55FWA	110	w	BX55FVL	130	w	BX55FWP	150	w	BX55FXP
90	LV	BX55FWB	111	w	BX55FVM	131	w	BX55FWR	151	w	BX55FXR
91	EC	BX55FUH	112	w	BX55FVN	132	w	BX55FWS	152	w	BX55FXS
92	EC	BX55FUJ	113	w	BX55FVQ	133	w	BX55FWT	153	w	BX55FXT
93	LV	593CLT	114	w	BX55FVP	134	w	BX55FWU	154	w	BX55FXU
94	EC	BX55FUO	115	w	BX55FVR	135	w	BX55FWV	155	w	BX55FXV
95	EC	BX55FUP	116	w	BX55FVS	136	w	BX55FWW	156	w	BX55FXW
96	EC	BX55FUT	117	w	BX55FVT	137	EC	BX55FWY	157	w	BX55FXY
97	EC	BX55FUU									

The days of the articulated Mercedes-Benz Citaro buses in London have been cut short by politics. Many of the buses are being prepared for the new Arriva operations that commence in Malta in July 2011 (shown as 'w' above) while others are heading for English operations in Leicester and Runcorn. Pictured in April 2010, MA154 BX55FXU, was seen passing through Finsbury Park. It will shortly arrive in Malta. *Dave Heath*

One of many Mini Pointer Darts operated by Arriva London, PDL61, LJ51DCO, is seen in Ilford on route 462.
Colin Lloyd

PDL12-18

Dennis Dart SLF 8.8m		Plaxton Pointer MPD		N26F		2000					
12	AR	V432DGT	14	AR	V434DGT	16	AR	W136VGJ	18	AR	W138VGJ
13	AR	V433DGT	15	AR	V435DGT	17	AR	W137VGJ			

PDL19-38

Dennis Dart SLF 10.7m		Plaxton Pointer 2		N31D		2000					
19	TH	X519GGO	24	AE	X524GGO	29	DX	X529GGO	34	DX	X534GGO
20	TH	X471GGO	25	AE	X475GGO	30	DX	X481GGO	35	AE	X485GGO
21	TH	X521GGO	26	AE	X526GGO	31	DX	X531GGO	36	DX	X536GGO
22	TH	X522GGO	27	DX	X527GGO	32	AE	X532GGO	37	DX	X537GGO
23	AE	X523GGO	28	DX	X478GGO	33	AE	X533GGO	38	AE	X538GGO

PDL39-49

Dennis Dart SLF 8.8m		Plaxton Pointer MPD		N23F*		2001		*seating varies			
39	AR	X239PGT	42	AR	X242PGT	45	AR	X546GGO	48	AR	X248PGT
40	AR	X541GGO	43	AR	X243PGT	46	AR	X246PGT	49	AR	X249PGT
41	AR	X241PGT	44	AR	X244PGT	47	AR	X247PGT			

PDL50-69

Dennis Dart SLF 8.8m		Plaxton Pointer MPD		N23F*		2001		*seating varies			
50	AR	LJ51DAA	55	DX	LJ51DBV	60	DX	LJ51DCF	65	E	LJ51DCY
51	AR	LJ51DAO	56	DX	LJ51DBX	61	DX	LJ51DCO	66	E	LJ51DCZ
52	DX	LJ51DAU	57	DX	LJ51DBY	62	E	LJ51DCU	67	E	LJ51DDA
53	DX	LJ51DBO	58	DX	LJ51DBZ	63	LV	LJ51DCV	68	E	LJ51DDE
54	DX	LJ51DBU	59	DX	LJ51DCE	64	E	LJ51DCX	69	LV	LJ51DDF

PDL70-94

TransBus Dart 8.8m		TransBus Mini Pointer		N29F*		2002		*seating varies			
70	EC	LF02PTZ	77	EC	LF52UON	83	LV	LF52URZ	89	EC	LF52USJ
71	EC	LF52UOG	78	EC	LF52UOO	84	EC	LF52USB	90	EC	LF52USL
72	EC	LF52UOH	79	EC	LF52UOP	85	EC	LF52USC	91	EC	LF52URN
73	EC	LF52UOJ	80	EC	LF52UOR	86	EC	LF52USD	92	EC	LF52URO
74	EC	LF52UOK	81	EC	LF52UNV	87	EC	LF52USG	93	EC	LF52URP
75	EC	LF52UOL	82	EC	LF52URY	88	EC	LF52USH	94	EC	LF52URR
76	EC	LF52UOM									

Alexander Dennis Trident 2s made their appearance in the Arriva London fleet during 2008 and feature ADL's Enviro 400 body. Working route 466 is T56, LJ08CYK. *Mark Doggett*

PDL95-116

				ADL Dart 9.3m			ADL Pointer			N27D	2005		
95	EC	LJ54BCX	101	EC	LJ54BBF	107	EC	LJ54LHG	112	EC	LJ54LHN
96	EC	LJ54BAA	102	EC	LJ54BBK	108	EC	LJ54LHH	113	EC	LJ54LHO
97	EC	LJ54BAO	103	EC	LJ54BBN	109	EC	LJ54LHK	114	EC	LJ54LHP
98	CN	LJ54BAU	104	EC	LJ54BBO	110	EC	LJ54LHL	115	CT	LJ54LHR
99	EC	LJ54BAV	105	EC	LJ54BBU	111	EC	LJ54LHM	116	CT	LJ54LGV
100	EC	LJ54BBE	106	EC	LJ54LHF						

PDL117-123

				ADL Dart 10.1m			ADL Pointer			N29D	2005		
117	TC	LJ05GOP	119	TC	LJ05GOX	121	TC	LJ05GPK	123	TC	LJ05GPU
118	TC	LJ05GOU	120	TC	LJ05GPF	122	TC	LJ05GPO			

PDL124-136

				ADL Dart 9.3m			ADL Pointer			N24D	2006		
124	CN	LJ56APZ	128	CN	LJ56ARX	131	CN	LJ56ASU	134	CN	LJ56AOW
125	CN	LJ56ARF	129	CN	LJ56ARZ	132	CN	LJ56ASV	135	CN	LJ56AOX
126	CN	LJ56ARO	130	CN	LJ56ASO	133	CN	LJ56ASX	136	CN	LJ56AOY
127	CN	LJ56ARU									

T1-65

				ADL Trident 2 10.1m			ADL Enviro 400			N41/26D	2008		
1	AD	LJ08CVS	18	DX	LJ08CVO	34	AD	LJ08CTZ	50	TC	LJ08CTO
2	AD	LJ08CVT	19	DX	519CLT	35	AD	LJ08CUA	51	TC	LJ08CYC
3	AD	LJ08CVU	20	DX	LJ08CVR	36	AD	LJ08CUE	52	TC	LJ08CYE
4	AD	LJ08CVV	21	DX	LJ08CUU	37	AD	LJ08CUG	53	TC	LJ08CYF
5	AD	205CLT	22	DX	LJ08CUV	38	AD	LJ08CUH	54	TC	LJ08CYG
6	AD	LJ08CVX	23	DX	LJ08CUW	39	AD	LJ08CUK	55	TC	LJ08CYH
7	AD	LJ08CVY	24	DX	324CLT	40	AD	LJ08CUO	56	TC	LJ08CYK
8	AD	LJ08CVZ	25	DX	LJ08CUY	41	AD	LJ08CSO	57	TC	LJ08CYL
9	AD	LJ08CWA	26	DX	LJ08CVA	42	AD	LJ08CSU	58	TC	LJ08CYO
10	AD	LJ08CWC	27	AD	LJ08CVB	43	AD	LJ08CSV	59	TC	LJ08CYP
11	AD	LJ08CVF	28	AD	LJ08CVC	44	AD	LJ08CSX	60	TC	LJ05CYS
12	DX	LJ08CVG	29	AD	LJ08CVD	45	AD	LJ08CSY	61	TC	LJ08CXR
13	DX	LJ08CVH	30	AD	330CLT	46	AD	LJ08CSZ	62	TC	LJ08CXS
14	DX	LJ08CVK	31	AD	LJ08CTV	47	AD	LJ08CTE	63	TC	LJ08CXT
15	DX	LJ08CVL	32	AD	LJ08CTX	48	TC	LJ08CTF	64	TC	LJ08CXU
16	DX	LJ08CVM	33	AD	LJ08CTY	49	TC	LJ08CTK	65	TC	LJ08CXV
17	DX	217CLT									

Newly into service T187, LJ60ATF, is seen operating route 150 in Ilford. Current orders take the number of this model in the fleet to 200. *Dave Heath*

T66-83

	ADL Trident 2 10.1m		ADL Enviro 400		N41/26D	2009	

66	CT	LJ59ACY	71	CT	LJ59ADZ	76	CT	LJ59ABO	80	CT	LJ59ABZ
67	CT	LJ59ACZ	72	CT	LJ59AEA	77	CT	LJ59ABU	81	CT	LJ59ACF
68	CT	LJ59ADO	73	CT	LJ59ABF	78	CT	LJ59ABV	82	CT	LJ59ACO
69	CT	LJ59ADV	74	CT	LJ59ABK	79	CT	LJ59ABX	83	CT	LJ59AAE
70	CT	70CLT	75	CT	LJ59ABN						

T84-117

	ADL Trident 2 10.1m		ADL Enviro 400		N41/26D	2009-10	

84	N	LJ59LZD	93	N	593CLT	102	N	LJ59LZB	110	N	LJ59LYK
85	N	185CLT	94	N	LJ59LYT	103	N	LJ59LZC	111	N	LJ59LYO
86	N	LJ59LZF	95	N	LJ59LYU	104	N	LJ59LYA	112	N	LJ59LYP
87	N	LJ59LZG	96	N	LJ59LYV	105	N	LJ59LYC	113	N	LJ59LYS
88	N	LJ59LZH	97	N	LJ59LYW	106	N	LJ59LYD	114	N	LJ59LXP
89	N	LJ59LZK	98	N	398CLT	107	N	LJ59LYF	115	N	LJ59LXR
90	N	LJ59LZL	99	N	LJ59LYY	108	N	LJ59LYG	116	N	LJ59LXS
91	N	LJ59LZM	100	N	LJ59LYZ	109	N	LJ59LYH	117	N	LJ59LXT
92	N	LJ59LZN	101	N	LJ59LZA						

T118-144

	ADL Trident 2 10.1m		ADL Enviro 400		N41/26D	2010	

118	TC	LJ10HVO	125	TH	LJ10HVE	132	TH	LJ10HUA	139	TH	LJ10HUY
119	TC	LJ10HVP	126	TH	LJ10HVF	133	TH	LJ10HUB	140	TH	LJ10HUZ
120	TC	LJ10HVR	127	TH	LJ10HVG	134	TH	LJ10HUK	141	TH	LJ10HTT
121	TC	LJ10HVA	128	TH	LJ10HVH	135	TH	LJ10HUO	142	TH	LJ10HTU
122	TH	LJ10HVB	129	TH	LJ10HVK	136	TH	LJ10HUP	143	TH	LJ10HTV
123	TH	LJ10HVC	130	TH	LJ10HVL	137	TH	LJ10HUU	144	TH	LJ10HTX
124	TH	LJ10HVD	131	TH	LJ10HTZ	138	TH	LJ10HUV			

T145-193

	ADL Trident 2 10.1m		ADL Enviro 400		N41/26D	2010	

145	LV	LJ60AVR	158	LV	LJ60AWF	170	AE	LJ60AUV	182	DX	LJ60AUL
146	LV	LJ60AVT	159	LV	LJ60AWG	171	AE	LJ60AUW	183	DX	LJ60AUM
147	LV	LJ60AVU	160	LV	LJ60AWK	172	AE	LJ60AUX	184	DX	LJ60AUN
148	LV	LJ60AVV	161	LV	LJ60AWL	173	AE	LJ60AUY	185	DX	LJ60ASX
149	LV	LJ60AVW	162	LV	LJ60AWN	174	AE	LJ60AVB	186	DX	LJ60ASZ
150	LV	LJ60AVX	163	LV	LJ60AWO	175	AE	LJ60ATZ	187	DX	LJ60ATF
151	LV	LJ60AVY	164	LV	LJ60AWP	176	AE	LJ60AUA	188	DX	LJ60ATK
152	LV	LJ60AVZ	165	LV	LJ60AUO	177	AE	LJ60AUC	189	DX	LJ60ATN
153	LV	LJ60AWA	166	LV	LJ60AUP	178	AE	LJ60AUE	190	DX	LJ60ATO
154	LV	LJ60AWB	167	LV	LJ60AUR	179	AE	LJ60AUF	191	DX	LJ60ATU
155	LV	LJ60AWC	168	LV	LJ60AUT	180	DX	LJ60AUH	192	DX	LJ60ATV
156	LV	LJ60AWD	169	AE	LJ60AUU	181	DX	LJ60AUK	193	DX	LJ60ATX
157	LV	LJ60AWE									

VLA1-55 Volvo B7TL 10.6m TransBus ALX400 4.4m N49/22D 2003

1	N	LJ03MYP	15	N	LJ03MXH	29	N	LJ53BDO	43	N	LJ53BCV
2	N	LJ03MYR	16	N	LJ03MXK	30	N	LJ53BDU	44	N	LJ53BCX
3	N	LJ03MYS	17	N	LJ03MXL	31	N	LJ53BDV	45	N	LJ53BCY
4	N	LJ03MYT	18	N	LJ03MXM	32	N	LJ53BDX	46	N	LJ53BAA
5	N	LJ03MXV	19	N	LJ03MXN	33	N	LJ53BDY	47	N	LJ53BAO
6	N	LJ03MXW	20	N	LJ03MXP	34	N	LJ53BDZ	48	N	LJ53BAU
7	N	LJ03MXX	21	N	LJ53BFK	35	N	LJ53BEO	49	N	LJ53BAV
8	N	LJ03MXY	22	N	LJ53BFL	36	N	LJ53BBV	50	N	LJ53BBE
9	N	LJ03MXZ	23	N	LJ53BFM	37	N	LJ53BBX	51	N	LJ53BBF
10	N	LJ03MYA	24	N	LJ53BFN	38	N	LJ53BBZ	52	N	LJ53BBK
11	N	LJ03MYB	25	N	LJ53BFO	39	N	LJ53BCF	53	N	LJ53BBN
12	N	LJ03MYC	26	N	LJ53BCZ	40	N	LJ53BCK	54	N	LJ53BBO
13	N	LJ03MYD	27	N	LJ53BDE	41	N	LJ53BCO	55	N	LJ53BBU
14	N	LJ03MYF	28	N	LJ53BDF	42	N	LJ53BCU			

VLA56-69 Volvo B7TL 10.6m TransBus ALX400 4.4m N49/22D 2004 *operated by The Original Tour*

56	WD	LJ04LFL	60	WD	LJ04LFR	64	WD	LJ04YWT	67	WD	LJ04YWW
57	WD	LJ04LFM	61	WD	LJ04LFS	65	WD	LJ04YWU	68	WD	LJ04YWX
58	WD	LJ04LFN	62	WD	LJ04LFT	66	WD	LJ04YWV	69	WD	LJ04YWY
59	WD	LJ04LFP	63	WD	LJ04YWS						

VLA70-73 Volvo B7TL 10.6m TransBus ALX400 4.4m N49/22D 2004

70	N	LJ04YWZ	71	N	LJ04YXA	72	N	LJ04YXB	73	N	LJ04YWE

VLA74-128 Volvo B7TL 10.1m ADL ALX400 N45/19D 2004-05

74	AR	LJ54BGO	88	AR	LJ54BDF	102	AR	LJ54BCU	116	N	LJ54BKG
75	AR	LJ54BEO	89	AR	LJ54BDO	103	AR	LJ54BCV	117	N	LJ54BKK
76	AR	LJ54BEU	90	AR	LJ54BDU	104	N	LJ05BKY	118	N	LJ54BKL
77	AR	LJ54BFA	91	AR	LJ54BDV	105	N	LJ05BKZ	119	N	LJ54BKN
78	AR	LJ54BFE	92	AR	LJ54BDX	106	N	LJ05BLF	120	N	LJ54BKO
79	AR	LJ54BFF	93	AR	LJ54BDY	107	N	LJ05BLK	121	N	LJ54BKU
80	AR	LJ54BFK	94	AR	LJ54BDZ	108	N	LJ05BLN	122	BN	LJ54BKV
81	AR	LJ54BFL	95	AR	LJ54BBV	109	N	LJ05BLV	123	BN	LJ54BKX
82	AR	LJ54BFM	96	AR	LJ54BBX	110	N	LJ05BLX	124	BN	LJ54BJE
83	AR	LJ54BFN	97	AR	LJ54BBZ	111	N	LJ05BLY	125	BN	LJ54BJF
84	AR	LJ54BFO	98	AR	LJ54BCE	112	N	LJ05BMO	126	BN	LJ54BJK
85	AR	LJ54BCY	99	AR	LJ54BCF	113	N	LJ05BMU	127	BN	LJ54BJO
86	AR	LJ54BCZ	100	AR	LJ54BCK	114	N	LJ05BKD	128	BN	LJ54BJU
87	AR	LJ54BDE	101	AR	LJ54BCO	115	N	LJ05BKF			

VLA129-143 Volvo B7TL 10.1m ADL ALX400 N45/19D 2005

129	DX	LJ05GLZ	133	DX	LJ05GPY	137	DX	LJ05GRU	141	DX	LJ05GSU
130	DX	LJ05GME	134	DX	LJ05GPZ	138	DX	LJ05GRX	142	DX	LJ55BTE
131	DX	LJ05GMF	135	DX	LJ05GRF	139	DX	LJ05GRZ	143	DX	LJ55BTF
132	DX	LJ05GPX	136	DX	LJ05GRK	140	DX	LJ05GSO			

VLA144-179 Volvo B7TL 10.1m ADL ALX400 N45/19D 2005

144	BN	LJ55BTO	153	BN	LJ55BRV	162	BN	LJ55BUP	171	BN	LJ55BUZ
145	BN	LJ55BTU	154	BN	LJ55BRX	163	BN	LJ55BUR	172	BN	LJ55BVD
146	BN	LJ55BTV	155	BN	LJ55BRZ	164	BN	LJ55BUS	173	BN	LJ55BVE
147	BN	LJ55BTX	156	BN	LJ55BSO	165	BN	LJ55BUT	174	BN	LJ55BVF
148	BN	LJ55BTY	157	BN	LJ55BSU	166	BN	LJ55BUU	175	BN	LJ55BVG
149	BN	LJ55BTZ	158	BN	LJ55BSV	167	BN	LJ55BUV	176	BN	LJ55BVH
150	BN	LJ55BUA	159	BN	LJ55BSX	168	BN	LJ55BUW	177	BN	LJ55BVK
151	BN	LJ55BUE	160	BN	LJ55BSY	169	BN	LJ55BUX	178	BN	LJ55BVL
152	BN	LJ55BPZ	161	BN	LJ55BSZ	170	BN	LJ55BUY	179	BN	LJ55BVM

Volvo has been one of the suppliers of chassis to Arriva London through its initial low-floor model, the B7TL. Bodywork on these has been divided between Alexander and Wrightbus. Pictured operating route 141 is VLW55, LF02PSY, from the 2002 order. *Dave Heath*

VLW1-41

		Volvo B7TL 10.1m				Wrightbus Eclipse Gemini		N41/21D*	2001-02	*seating varies		

1	WN	Y581UGC	12	WN	VLT12	22	WN	LJ51DGY	32	WN	VLT32
2	WN	Y102TGH	13	WN	LJ51DFX	23	WN	LJ51DGZ	33	WN	LJ51DHO
3	WN	LJ51DJF	14	WN	LJ51DFY	24	WN	LJ51DHA	34	WN	LJ51DHP
4	WN	LJ51DJK	15	WN	LJ51DFZ	25	WN	LJ51DHC	35	WN	LJ51DHV
5	WN	LJ51DJO	16	WN	LJ51DGE	26	WN	LJ51DHD	36	WN	LJ51DHX
6	WN	LJ51DFK	17	WN	LJ51DGF	27	WN	VLT27	37	WN	LJ51DHY
7	WN	LJ51DFL	18	WN	LJ51DGO	28	WN	LJ51DHF	38	WN	LJ51DHZ
8	WN	LJ51DFN	19	WN	LJ51DGU	29	WN	LJ51DHG	39	WN	LJ51DJD
9	WN	LJ51DFO	20	WN	LJ51DGV	30	WN	LJ51DHK	40	WN	LJ51DJE
10	WN	LJ51DFP	21	WN	LJ51DGX	31	WN	LJ51DHL	41	WN	LJ51OSK
11	WN	LJ51DFU									

VLW42-104

		Volvo B7TL 10.1m				Wrightbus Eclipse Gemini		N41/21D*	2002-03	*seating varies		

42	WN	LF02PKO	58	WN	LF02PTU	74	WN	LF52UTM	90	CT	LF52URA
43	WN	LF02PKU	59	WN	LF02PTX	75	WN	LF52USM	91	CT	LF52UPD
44	WN	LF02PKV	60	WN	LF02PTY	76	WN	LF52USN	92	CT	WLT892
45	WN	LF02PKX	61	WN	LF02PVE	77	WN	LF52USO	93	CT	LF52UPG
46	WN	LF02PKY	62	WN	LF02PVJ	78	WN	LF52USS	94	CT	LF52UPH
47	WN	VLT47	63	WN	LF02PVK	79	WN	LF52UST	95	CT	WLT895
48	WN	LF02PLJ	64	WN	LF02PVL	80	WN	LF52USU	96	CT	LF52UPK
49	WN	LF02PLN	65	WN	LF02PVN	81	WN	LF52USV	97	AR	WLT897
50	WN	LF02PLO	66	WN	LF02PVO	82	WN	LF52USW	98	AR	LF52UPM
51	WN	WLT751	67	WN	LF52UTC	83	WN	LF52USX	99	AR	LG52DDA
52	WN	LF02PSO	68	WN	LF52UTE	84	WN	LF52USY	100	AR	LG52DDE
53	WN	LF02PSU	69	WN	LF52USE	85	WN	LF52UPV	101	AR	LG52DDF
54	WN	WLT554	70	WN	LF52UTG	86	CT	LF52UPW	102	AR	LG52DDJ
55	WN	LF02PSY	71	WN	LF52UTH	87	CT	LF52UPX	103	E	LG52DDK
56	WN	LF02PSZ	72	WN	WLT372	88	CT	WLT888	104	E	LG52DDL
57	WN	LF02PTO	73	WN	LF52UTL	89	CT	LF52UPZ			

VLW105-179

Volvo B7TL 10.1m Wrightbus Eclipse Gemini N41/21D* 2002-03 *seating varies

No		Reg	No		Reg	No		Reg	No		Reg
105	DX	LJ03MHU	124	AE	LF52UOX	143	SF	LG03MFA	162	SF	LG03MRX
106	DX	LJ03MHV	125	AR	LF52UOY	144	SF	LG03MFE	163	SF	LG03MRY
107	DX	LJ03MHX	126	AE	LF52UPA	145	SF	LG03MFF	164	SF	LG03MSU
108	DX	LJ03MHY	127	AE	LF52UPB	146	SF	LG03MFK	165	SF	LG03MSV
109	DX	LJ03MHZ	128	AE	LF52UPC	147	SF	LG03MBF	166	SF	LG03MSX
110	DX	LJ03MJE	129	AE	LG52DAA	148	SF	LG03MBU	167	SF	LG03MMU
111	DX	LJ03MJF	130	AE	LJ03MGZ	149	SF	LG03MBV	168	SF	LG03MMV
112	DX	LJ03MJK	131	AE	LJ03MHA	150	SF	LG03MBX	169	SF	LG03MMX
113	DX	LJ03MJU	132	AE	LJ03MHE	151	SF	LG03MBY	170	SF	LG03MOA
114	DX	LJ03MJV	133	AE	LJ03MHF	152	SF	LG03MDE	171	SF	LG03MOF
115	DX	LJ03MGX	134	AE	LJ03MHK	153	SF	LG03MDF	172	SF	LG03MOV
116	DX	LJ03MGY	135	AE	LJ03MHL	154	SF	LG03MDN	173	SF	VLT173
117	E	LF52UPN	136	AE	LJ03MHM	155	SF	LG03MDN	174	SF	LG03MPF
118	E	LF52UPO	137	AE	LJ03MHN	156	SF	LG03MDU	175	SF	LG03MPU
119	E	LF52UOS	138	SF	LJ03MFN	157	SF	LG03MPX	176	SF	LG03MPV
120	E	LF52UOT	139	SF	LJ03MFP	158	SF	LG03MPY	177	SF	LG03MLL
121	E	LF52UOU	140	SF	LJ03MFU	159	SF	LG03MPZ	178	SF	LG03MLN
122	AE	LF52UOV	141	SF	LJ03MFV	160	SF	LG03MRU	179	SF	LG03MLV
123	E	LF52UOW	142	SF	LG03MEV	161	SF	LG03MRV			

VLW180-199

Volvo B7TL 10.6m Wrightbus Eclipse Gemini N45/24D 2003

No		Reg	No		Reg	No		Reg	No		Reg
180	SF	LJ03MLX	185	SF	LJ03MMF	190	SF	LJ03MXR	195	SF	LJ53BEU
181	SF	LJ03MLY	186	SF	LJ03MMK	191	SF	LJ03MXS	196	SF	LJ53BEY
182	SF	LJ03MLZ	187	SF	LJ03MKM	192	SF	LJ03MXT	197	SF	LJ53BFA
183	SF	LJ03MMA	188	SF	LJ03MKN	193	SF	LJ03MXU	198	SF	LJ53BFE
184	SF	LJ03MME	189	SF	LJ03MYN	194	SF	LJ03MWX	199	SF	LJ53BFF

Special event vehicles:

RM5	N	VLT5	AEC Routemaster R2RH	Park Royal		B36/28R	1959
RM6	N	VLT6	AEC Routemaster R2RH	Park Royal		B36/28R	1959
RML901	u	WLT901	AEC Routemaster R2RH/1	Park Royal		B40/32R	1963
RM1124	u	VYJ806	AEC Routemaster R2RH	Park Royal		B36/28R	1965
RMC1453	SF	453CLT	AEC Routemaster R2RH	Park Royal		B36/28R	1962
RMC1464	N	464CLT	AEC Routemaster R2RH	Park Royal		O36/28R	1962
RM2217	N	CUV217C	AEC Routemaster R2RH	Park Royal		B36/28R	1965
RML2355	u	CUV335C	AEC Routemaster R2RH/1	Park Royal		B40/32R	1965

Previous registrations:

70CLT	BX04NDE	T324FGN	T324FGN, 99D53451
185CLT	BU05VFD	T325FGN	T325FGN, 99D53440
205CLT	LJ08CVW	V423DGT	V435DGT
217CLT	LJ08CVN	V435DGT	V423DGT
319CLT	BX55FVV	VLT12	LJ51DFV
324CLT	LJ08CUX	VLT27	LJ51DHE
330CLT	LJ08CVE	VLT32	LJ51DHN
361CLT	BX04NBL	VLT47	LF02PKZ
398CLT	BX55FUV	VLT173	LJ03MPE
480CLT	BX05UWZ	VLT244	LJ53NHM
519CLT	LJ08CVP	VLT295	LJ54BFU
593CLT	BX55FUM	VYJ806	124CLT
656DYE	LJ04LFA	WLT348	LJ53NGO
725DYE	LJ53BGE	WLT372	LF52UTJ
734DYE	LJ53NJE	WLT385	LJ04LFY
801DYE	LJ03MWM	WLT531	--
822DYE	LJ53BFV	WLT554	LF02PSX
BX04MXB	BX04MXB, 205CLT	WLT664	LJ04LDE
BX04MXR	BX04MXR, 217CLT	WLT676	from new
BX04MXT	BX04MXT, 519CLT	WLT719	LJ53NHU
BX04MXZ	BX04MXZ, 324CLT	WLT751	LF02PRZ
BX04MYY	BX04MYY, 330CLT	WLT807	LJ03MVU
BX05UWZ	BX05UWZ, 430CLT	WLT888	LF52VPY
BX55FWH	BX55FWH, 124CLT	WLT892	LF52UPE
LF52USE	LF52USE, VLT25	WLT895	LF52UPJ
LJ03MMX	LJ03MMX, VLT25	WLT897	LF52UPL
LJ53MHX	LJ53MHX, WLT531	WLT970	LJ04LDV
		WLT997	LJ54BFX

Depots and allocations:

Barking (Ripple Road, IG11 0ST) - DX

Dart	PDL27	PDL28	PDL29	PDL30	PDL31	PDL34	PDL36	PDL37
	PDL52	PDL53	PDL54	PDL55	PDL56	PDL57	PDL58	PDL59
	PDL60	PDL61						
Dart 4	ENL49	ENL50	ENL51	ENL52	ENL53	ENL54	ENL55	ENL56
	ENL57	ENL58	ENL59	ENL60	ENL61	ENL62	ENL63	ENL64
	ENL65	ENL66	ENL67	ENL68	ENL69	ENL70	ENL71	ENL72
	ENL73	ENL74						
Volvo B7TL	VLA129	VLA130	VLA131	VLA132	VLA133	VLA134	VLA135	VLA136
	VLA137	VLA138	VLA139	VLA140	VLA141	VLA142	VLA143	VLW105
	VLW106	VLW107	VLW108	VLW109	VLW110	VLW111	VLW112	VLW113
	VLW114	VLW115	VLW116					
DB250	DLA88	DLA89	DLA90					
Trident 2/Enviro 400	T12	T13	T14	T15	T16	T17	T18	T19
	T20	T21	T22	T23	T24	T25	T26	T180
	T181	T182	T183	T184	T185	T186	T187	T188
	T189	T190	T191	T192	T193			

Brixton (Streatham Hill, SW2 4TB) - BN

Outstation: Battersea - BA

DB250	DLA38	DLA50	DLA205	DLA206	DLA207	DLA208	DLA209	DLA212
	DLA213	DLA236	DAL270	DLA271	DLA290	DLA311	DLA312	DLA313
	DLA314	DLA315	DLA316	DLA317	DLA318	DLA319	DW55	DW56
	DW57	DW58	DW59	DW60	DW61	DW62	DW63	DW64
	DW65	DW66	DW67	DW68	DW69	DW70	DW71	DW72
	DW73	DW74	DW75	DW76	DW77	DW78	DW79	DW80
	DW81	DW82	DW83	DW84	DW85	DW86	DW87	DW88
	DW89	DW90	DW91	DW92	DW93	DW102	DW103	DW104
	DW105	DW106	DW107	DW108	DW109	DW110	DW111	DW112
	DW113	DW114	DW115	DW116	DW117	DW118	DW119	DW120
	DW121	DW122	DW123	DW124	DW125	DW126	DW127	DW128
	DW129	DW130	DW131	DW132	DW133	DW280	DW281	DW282
	DW283	DW284	DW285	DW286	DW287	DW288	DW289	DW290
	DW291	DW292	DW293	DW294	DW295	DW296	DW297	
Volvo B7TL	VLA122	VLA123	VLA124	VLA125	VLA126	VLA127	VLA128	VLA144
	VLA145	VLA146	VLA147	VLA148	VLA149	VLA150	VLA151	VLA152
	VLA153	VLA154	VLA155	VLA156	VLA157	VLA158	VLA159	VLA160
	VLA161	VLA162	VLA163	VLA164	VLA165	VLA166	VLA167	VLA168
	VLA169	VLA170	VLA171	VLA172	VLA173	VLA174	VLA175	VLA176
	VLA177	VLA178	VLA179					

Cambridge Heath (Ash Grove, E8 4RH) - AE

Dart	ADL969	ADL970	ADL971	ADL972	ADL974	ADL975	ADL976	ADL977
	ADL978	ADL979	ADL980	ADL981	ADL982	ADL983	PDL23	PDL24
	PDL25	PDL26	PDL32	PDL33	PDL35	PDL38		
Trident 2	T169	T170	T171	T172	T173	T174	T175	T176
	T177	T178	T179					
Volvo B7TL	VLA122	VLA124	VLA126	VLA127	VLA128	VLA129	VLA130	VLA131
	VLA132	VLA133	VLA134	VLA135	VLA136	VLA137		

Clapton (Bohemia Place, Mare Street, E8 1DU) - CT

Dart	PDL115	PDL116						
Enviro200	ENS1	ENS2	ENS3	ENS4	ENS5	ENS6	ENS7	ENS8
	ENS9	ENS10	ENS11	ENS12	ENS13	ENS14		
DB250	DW201	DW202	DW203	DW204	DW205	DW206	DW207	DW208
	DW209	DW210	DW211	DW212	DW213	DW214	DW215	DW216
	DW217	DW218	DW219	DW220	DW221	DW222	DW223	DW224
	DW225	DW226	DW227	DW228	DW229	DW230	DW231	DW232
	DW233	DW234	DW235	DW236	DW237	DW238	DW239	DW240
	DW241	DW242	DW243	DW244	DW245	DW246	DW247	DW248
	DW249	DW250	DW251	DW252	DW253	DW254	DW255	DW256
	DW257	DW258	DW259	DW260	DW261	DW262	DW263	DW264
	DW265	DW266	DW267	DW268	DW269	DW270	DW271	DW272
	DW273	DW274	DW275	DW276	DW277	DW278	DW279	
Trident 2	T66	T67	T68	T69	T70	T71	T72	T73
	T74	T75	T76	T77	T78	T79	T80	T81
	T82							
Volvo B7TL	VLW86	VLW87	VLW88	VLW89	VLW90	VLW91	VLW92	VLW93
	VLW94	VLW95	VLW96					

Croydon (Beddington Farm Road, CR40 4XB) - CN

Dart	ADL61	ADL62	ADL63	ADL64	ADL65	PDL98	PDL124	PDL125
	PDL126	PDL127	PDL128	PDL129	PDL130	PDL131	PDL132	PDL133
	PDL134	PDL135	PDL136					
SB120	DWL58	DWL59	DWL60	DWL61	DWL62	DWL63	DWL64	DWL65
	DWL66	DWL67	DWS1	DWS2	DWS3	DWS4	DWS5	DWS6
	DWS7	DWS8	DWS9	DWS10	DWS11	DWS12	DWS13	DWS14
	DWS15	DWS16	DWS17	DWS18				
DB250	DW38	DW39	DW40	DW41	DW42	DW43	DW44	DW45
	DW46	DW47	DW48	DW49	DW50	DW51	DW52	DW53
	DW54	DW94	DW95	DW96	DW97	DW98	DW99	DW100
	DW101							
Ancillary	DDL6	DLA22	DLA24	DLA26	DLA27	DLA28	DLA29	DLA30
	DLA31	DLA34	DLA45	DLA56	DWL30	DWL31	DWL32	DWL33
	DWL34							

Croydon (Brighton Road, South Croydon) - TC

Dart	PDL117	PDL118	PDL119	PDL120	PDL121	PDL122	PDL123	
Dart 4 / Enviro200	ENL1	ENL2	ENL3	ENL4	ENL5	ENL6	ENL7	ENL8
	ENL9	ENL21	ENL22	ENL23	ENL24	ENL25	ENL26	ENL27
	ENL28	ENL29						
DB250	DLA132	DLA133	DLA135	DLA175	DLA176	DLA177	DLA178	DLA179
	DLA180	DLA181	DLA182	DLA183	DLA184	DLA185	DLA186	DLA187
	DLA188	DLA189	DLA215	DLA216	DLA217	DLA218	DLA219	DLA220
	DLA221	DLA222	DLA223	DLA224	DLA250	DLA251	DLA252	DLA253
	DLA254	DLA255	DLA256	DW1	DW2	DW3	DW4	DW5
	DW6	DW7	DW8	DW9	DW10	DW11	DW12	DW13
	DW14	DW15	DW16	DW17	DW18	DW19	DW20	DW21
	DW22	DW23	DW24	DW25	DW26	DW27	DW28	DW29
	DW30	DW31	DW32	DW33	DW34	DW35	DW36	DW37
Trident 2 / Enviro 400	T48	T49	T50	T51	T52	T53	T54	T55
	T56	T57	T58	T59	T60	T61	T62	T63
	T64	T65	T118	T119	T120	T121		

Edmonton (Towpath Road, Stonehill Business Park, N18 3QX) - EC

Dart	ADL66	ADL67	ADL68	ADL69	ADL71	ADL72	ADL73	ADL74
	ADL75	ADL76	ADL77	ADL78	ADL79	ADL81	ADL973	PDL70
	PDL71	PDL72	PDL73	PDL74	PDL75	PDL76	PDL77	PDL78
	PDL79	PDL80	PDL81	PDL82	PDL83	PDL84	PDL85	PDL86
	PDL87	PDL88	PDL89	PDL90	PDL91	PDL92	PDL93	PDL94
	PDL95	PDL96	PDL97	PDL98	PDL99	PDL100	PDL101	PDL102
	PDL103	PDL104	PDL105	PDL106	PDL107	PDL108	PDL109	PDL110
	PDL111	PDL112	PDL113	PDL114				
SB120	DWL10	DWL18	DWL20	DWL21	DWL22	DWL42	DWL43	DWL45
	DWL46	DWL47	DWL48	DWL49	DWL51			
Citaro G	MA22	MA26	MA28	MA29	MA30	MA31	MA35	MA37
	MA38	MA44	MA91	MA92	MA95	MA96	MA97	MA98
	MA137	MA140	MA141	MA142	MA143	MA144		
DB250	DLA57	DLA58	DLA299	DLA300	DLA301	DLA302	DLA303	DLA304
	DLA305	DLA306	DLA307	DLA308	DLA309	DLA310	DLA348	DLA349
	DLA350	DLA351	DLA352	DLA353	DLA354	DLA355	DLA356	DLA357
	DLA358	DLA359	DLA360	DLA361	DLA362	DLA363	DLA364	DLA365
	DLA366	DLA367	DLA368	DLA369	DLA370			

Enfield (Southbury Road, Ponders End, EN3 4HX) - E

Dart	PDL62	PDL64	PDL65	PDL66	PDL67	PDL68		
SB120	DWL13	DWL14	DWL23	DLW24	DWL25	DWL26	DWL27	DWL29
	DWL35	DWL36	DWL37	DWL38	DWL39	DWL40	DWL41	DWL44
	DWL50							
Dart 4 / Enviro 200	ENL10	ENL11	ENL12	ENL13	ENL14	ENL15	ENL16	ENL17
	ENL18	ENL19	ENL20					
DB250	DLA1	DLA21	DLA23	DLA25	DLA32	DLA33	DLA35	DLA37
	DLA78	DLA79	DLA80	DLA81	DLA82	DLA83	DLA84	DLA85
	DLA91	DLA92	DLA93	DLA94	DLA95	DLA106	DLA107	DLA108
	DLA109	DLA110	DLA111	DLA112	DLA113	DLA114	DLA115	DLA116
	DLA117	DLA118	DLA119	DLA120	DLA121	DLA122	DLA123	DLA124
	DLA125	DLA126	DLA127	DLA128	DLA130	DLA131	DLA140	DLA141
	DLA150	DLA151	DLA152	DLA153	DLA159	DLA160	DLA161	DLA162
	DLA165	DLP15	DLP16	DLP17	DLP18	DLP20	DLP76	DLP77
	DLP78	DLP79	DLP80	DLP81	DLP82	DLP83	DLP84	DLP85
	DLP86	DLP87	DLP88	DLP89	DLP90	DLP91	DLP92	DLP93
	DLP94	DLP95	DLP96	DLP97	DLP98	DLP99	DLP100	DLP101
	DLP102	DLP103	DLP104	DLP105	DLP106	DLP107	DLP108	DLP109
	DLP110							
Volvo B7TL	VLW103	VLW104	VLW117	VLW118	VLW119	VLW120	VLW121	VLW123

Lea Valley (Leeside Road, Edmonton, N17 0SH) - LV

Dart	PDL63	PDL69						
Dart 4/Enviro 200	EN1	EN2	EN3	EN4	EN5	EN6	EN7	EN8
	EN9	EN10	EN11	EN12	EN13			
Citaro G	MA34	MA42	MA43	MA45	MA46	MA47	MA48	MA49
	MA50	MA51	MA52	MA53	MA55	MA56	MA57	MA58
	MA59	MA60	MA61	MA62	MA63	MA64	MA65	MA66
	MA67	MA68	MA69	MA70	MA71	MA72	MA74	MA75
	MA76	MA77	MA78	MA79	MA80	MA81	MA82	MA83
	MA84	MA85	MA86	MA87	MA88	MA89	MA90	MA93
Trident 2	T145	T146	T147	T148	T149	T150	T151	T152
	T153	T154	T155	T156	T157	T158	T159	T160
	T161	T162	T163	T164	T165	T166	T167	T168

Norwood (Ernest Avenue, West Norwood, SE27 0HN) - N

Routemaster	RM5	RM6	RMC1464	RML2217	RML2355			
DB250	DLA136	DLA137	DLA138	DLA139	DAL142	DLA143	DLA144	DLA145
	DLA146	DLA147	DLA148	DLA149	DLA154	DLA155	DLA156	DLA157
	DAL158	DLA166	DLA167	DLA168	DLA169	DLA170	DLA171	DLA172
	DLA173	DLA174						
Volvo B7TL	VLA1	VLA2	VLA3	VLA4	VLA5	VLA6	VLA7	VLA8
	VLA9	VLA10	VLA11	VLA12	VLA13	VLA14	VLA15	VLA16
	VLA17	VLA18	VLA19	VLA20	VLA21	VLA22	VLA23	VLA24
	VLA25	VLA26	VLA27	VLA28	VLA29	VLA30	VLA31	VLA32
	VLA33	VLA34	VLA35	VLA36	VLA37	VLA38	VLA39	VLA40
	VLA41	VLA42	VLA43	VLA44	VLA45	VLA46	VLA47	VLA48
	VLA49	VLA50	VLA51	VLA52	VLA53	VLA54	VLA55	VLA70
	VLA71	VLA72	VLA73	VLA104	VLA105	VLA106	VLA107	VLA108
	VLA109	VLA110	VLA111	VLA112	VLA113	VLA114	VLA115	VLA116
	VLA117	VLA118	VLA119	VLA120				
Trident 2	T84	T85	T86	T87	T88	T89	T90	T91
	T92	T93	T94	T95	T96	T97	T98	T99
	T100	T101	T102	T103	T104	T105	T106	T107
	T108	T109	T110	T111	T112	T113	T114	T115
	T116	T117						

Palmers Green (Regents Avenue, N13 5UR) - AD

DB250	DLP40	DLP41	DLP42	DLP43	DLP44	DLP45	DLP46	DLP47
	DLP48	DLP49	DLP50	DLP51	DLP52	DLP53	DLP54	DLP55
	DLP56	DLP57	DLP58	DLP59	DLP60	DLP61	DLP62	DLP63
	DLP65	DLP66	DLP68	DLP71	DLP73	DLP74	DLP75	
Trident 2	T1	T2	T3	T4	T5	T6	T7	T8
	T9	T10	T11	T27	T28	T29	T30	T31
	T32	T33	T34	T35	T36	T37	T38	T39
	T40	T41	T42	T43	T44	T45	T46	T47

Stamford Hill (Rookwood Road, N16 6SS) - SF

DB250	DLA39	DLA51	DLA54	DLA55	DLA62	DLA72		
	DLA103	DLA105						
Routemaster	RML901	RMC1453						
Volvo B7TL	VLW138	VLW139	VLW140	VLW141	VLW142	VLW143	VLW144	VLW145
	VLW146	VLW147	VLW148	VLW149	VLW150	VLW151	VLW152	VLW153
	VLW154	VLW155	VLW156	VLW157	VLW158	VLW159	VLW160	VLW161
	VLW162	VLW163	VLW164	VLW165	VLW166	VLW167	VLW168	VLW170
	VLW171	VLW174	VLW176	VLW177	VLW178	VLW179	VLW180	VLW181
	VLW183	VLW184	VLW185	VLW187	VLW188	VLW189	VLW190	VLW191
	VLW192	VLW193	VLW194	VLW195	VLW196	VLW197	VLW199	

Thornton Heath (London Road, CR7 6AU) - TH

Dart	PDL19	PDL20	PDL21	PDL22				
SB120	DWL1	DWL2	DWL3	DWL4	DWL5	DWL6	DWL7	DWL8
	DWL9	DWL11	DWL12	DWL15	DWL16	DWL17	DWL19	
DB250	DLA63	DLA64	DLA322	DLA323	DLA324	DLA325	DLA326	DLA327
	DLA328	DLA329	DLA330	DLA331	DLA332	DLA333	DLA334	DLA335
	DLA336	DLA337	DLA338	DLA339	DLA340	DLA341	DLA342	DLA343
	DLA344	DLA345	DLA246	DLA347	DLA371	DLA371	DLA372	DLA373
	DLA374	DLA375	DLA376	DLA377	DLA378	DLA379	DLA380	DLA381
	DLA382	DLA383	DLA384	DLA385	DLA386	DLA387	DLA388	DLA389
Trident 2	T122	T123	T124	T125	T126	T127	T128	T129
	T130	T131	T132	T133	T134	T135	T136	T137
	T138	T139	T140	T141	T142	T143	T144	

Tottenham (Philip Lane, N17 0XR) - AR

Dart	PDL12	PDL13	PDL14	PDL15	PDL16	PDL17	PDL18	PDL39
	PDL40	PDL41	PDL42	PDL43	PDL44	PDL45	PDL46	PDL47
	PDL48	PDL49	PDL50	PDL51				
DB250	DLA163	DLA164	DLA190	DLA191	DLA192	DLA193	DLA194	DLA195
	DLA196	DLA197	DLA198	DLA199	DLA202	DLA203	DLA204	DLA210
	DLA211	DLA214	DLA225	DLA226	DLA227	DLA228	DLA229	DLA230
	DLA231	DLA232	DLA233	DLA234	DLA235	DLA237	DLA238	DLA239
	DLA240	DLA241	DLA242	DLA243	DLA244	DLA245	DLA246	DLA247
	DLA248	DLA249	DLA273	DLA274	DLA275	DLA277	DLA278	DLA279
	DLA280	DLA281	DLA282	DLA283	DLA284	DLA285	DLA286	DLA287
	DLA288	DLA289	DLA291	DLA292	DLA293	~~DLA294~~	DLA295	DLA296
	DLA297	DLA298	DW298	DW299	DW300	DW301	DW302	DW303
	DW304	DW305	DW306	DW307	DW308	DW309	DW310	DW311
	DW312	DW313	DW314	DW315	DW316	DW317	DW318	DW319
	DW320	DW321	DW322	DW323	DW324	DW325	DW326	DW327
	DW328	DW329	DW330	DW331	DW332	DW333	DW334	DW335
	DW336							
Hybrid	HV7	HV8	HV9	HV10	HV11	HV12	HV13	HV14
	HV15	HV16	HV17	HV18	HV19	HV20	HV21	HV22
	HV23							
Volvo B7TL	VLA74	VLA75	VLA76	VLA77	VLA78	VLA79	VLA80	VLA81
	VLA82	VLA83	VLA84	VLA85	VLA86	VLA87	VLA88	VLA89
	VLA90	VLA91	VLA92	VLA93	VLA94	VLA95	VLA96	VLA97
	VLA98	VLA99	VLA100	VLA101	VLA102	VLA103	VLW97	VLW98
	VLW99	VLW100	VLW101	VLW102				

Wood Green (High Road) - WN

SB120	DWL52	DWL53	DWL54	DWL55	DWL56	DWL57		
Dart 4 / Enviro 200	ENL30	ENL31	ENL32	ENL33	ENL34	ENL35	ENL36	ENL37
	ENL38	ENL39	ENL40	ENL41	ENL42	ENL43	ENL44	ENL45
	ENL46	ENL47	ENL48					
DB250	DLA11	DLA12	DLA13	DLA14	DLA15	DLA16	DLA17	DLA18
	DLA19	DLA20	DLA47	DLP64	DLP67	DLP69	DLP70	DLP72
Volvo B5L Hybrid	HV1	HV2	HV3	HV4	HV5	HV6		
Wrightbus Hybrid	HW1	HW2	HW3	HW4	HW5			
Volvo B7TL	VLW1	VLW2	VLW3	VLW4	VLW5	VLW6	VLW7	VLW8
	VLW9	VLW10	VLW11	VLW12	VLW13	VLW14	VLW15	VLW16
	VLW17	VLW18	VLW19	VLW20	VLW21	VLW22	VLW23	VLW24
	VLW25	VLW26	VLW27	VLW28	VLW29	VLW30	VLW31	VLW32
	VLW33	VLW34	VLW35	VLW36	VLW37	VLW38	VLW39	VLW40
	VLW41	VLW42	VLW43	VLW44	VLW45	VLW46	VLW47	VLW48
	VLW49	VLW50	VLW51	VLW52	VLW53	VLW54	VLW55	VLW56
	VLW57	VLW58	VLW59	VLW60	VLW61	VLW62	VLW63	VLW64
	VLW65	VLW66	VLW67	VLW68	VLW69	VLW70	VLW71	VLW72
	VLW73	VLW74	VLW75	VLW76	VLW77	VLW78	VLW79	VLW80
	VLW81	VLW82	VLW83	VLW84	VLW85			

Unallocated - u/w

remainder

ARRIVA - THE ORIGINAL TOUR

The Original Tour Ltd, Jews Road, Wandsworth, SW18 1TB

EMB763 D553YNO	MCW Metrobus DR115/4	MCW		P065/31D	1987	New World FirstBus, 2001
EMB764 E964JAR	MCW Metrobus DR115/4	MCW		P065/31D	1987	New World FirstBus, 2001
EMB765 E965JAR	MCW Metrobus DR115/4	MCW		P065/31D	1987	New World FirstBus, 2001
EMB766 E766JAR	MCW Metrobus DR115/4	MCW		P065/31D	1987	New World FirstBus, 2001
EMB767 E767JAR	MCW Metrobus DR115/4	MCW		P065/31D	1987	New World FirstBus, 2001
EMB768 E768JAR	MCW Metrobus DR115/4	MCW		P065/31D	1987	New World FirstBus, 2001
EMB769 E769JAR	MCW Metrobus DR115/4	MCW		P065/31D	1987	New World FirstBus, 2001
EMB770 E770JAR	MCW Metrobus DR115/4	MCW		P065/31D	1987	New World FirstBus, 2001
EMB771 E771JAR	MCW Metrobus DR115/4	MCW		P065/31D	1987	New World FirstBus, 2001
EMB772 E772JAR	MCW Metrobus DR115/4	MCW		P065/31D	1987	New World FirstBus, 2001
EMB773 E773JAR	MCW Metrobus DR115/4	MCW		P065/31D	1987	New World FirstBus, 2001
EMB774 E774JAR	MCW Metrobus DR115/4	MCW		P065/31D	1987	New World FirstBus, 2001
EMB775 D675YNO	MCW Metrobus DR115/4	MCW		P065/31D	1987	New World FirstBus, 2001
EMB776 UAR776Y	MCW Metrobus DR115/3	MCW		059/33D	1984	City Sightseeing, Aus., 2004
EMB777 A735WEV	MCW Metrobus DR115/3	MCW		059/33D	1984	City Sightseeing, Aus., 2004
EMB778 A737WEV	MCW Metrobus DR115/3	MCW		059/33D	1984	City Sightseeing, Aus., 2004
EMB779 MXT179	MCW Metrobus DR115/3	MCW		059/33D	1984	City Sightseeing, Aus., 2004
EMB780 A755WEV	MCW Metrobus DR115/3	MCW		059/33D	1983	New World FirstBus, 2004
EMB781 A750WEV	MCW Metrobus DR115/3	MCW		059/33D	1983	New World FirstBus, 2004
EMB782 A749WEV	MCW Metrobus DR115/3	MCW		059/33D	1983	New World FirstBus, 2004
EMB783 UAR247Y	MCW Metrobus DR115/3	MCW		059/33D	1987	New World FirstBus, 2004
EMB784 UAR250Y	MCW Metrobus DR115/3	MCW		059/33D	1987	New World FirstBus, 2004
EMB785 NKJ785	MCW Metrobus DR115/3	MCW		059/33D	1987	New World FirstBus, 2004

DLP201-214	DAF DB250 10.6m	Plaxton President		O45/21F	1999	Arriva London, 2006

201	WD	201KYD	**205**	WD	T205XBV	**209**	WD	T209XBV	**212**	WD	T212XBV
202	WD	T202XBV	**206**	WD	T206XBV	**210**	WD	T210XBV	**213**	WD	T213XBV
203	WD	T203XBV	**207**	WD	T207XBV	**211**	WD	T211XBV	**214**	WD	T214XBV
204	WD	T204XBV	**208**	WD	T208XBV					

Arriva operates The Original Tour open-top services in London using a mix of converted London buses and new purpose-built vehicles.
Retaining its London number is DLP207, T207XBV, seen at London Bridge.
Dave Heath

Gaining popularity across Europe is the Ayats open-top double-deck bus. Ten operate on The Original Tour represented by VLY608, LX05KOA, seen at St Paul's Churchyard. *Richard Godfrey*

OA315-352

		Leyland Olympian			Alexander RH			PO43/25D* 1992			Arriva London, 2003-05

321-32/8-40 are CO43/25D; 350-2 are B43/25D

315	WD	J315BSH	325	WD	J325BSH	335	WD	J335BSH	344	WD	J344BSH
316	WD	J316BSH	326	WD	J326BSH	336	WD	J336BSH	345	WD	J345BSH
317	WD	J317BSH	327	WD	J327BSH	337	WD	J337BSH	346	WD	J346BSH
318	WD	J318BSH	328	WD	J328BSH	338	WD	J338BSH	347	WD	J347BSH
319	WD	J319BSH	329	WD	J329BSH	339	WD	J339BSH	348	WD	J348BSH
320	WD	J320BSH	330	WD	J330BSH	340	WD	J340BSH	349	WD	J349BSH
321	WD	J321BSH	331	WD	J331BSH	341	WD	J341BSH	350	WD	J350BSH
322	WD	J322BSH	332	WD	J332BSH	342	WD	J342BSH	351	WD	J351BSH
323	WD	J323BSH	333	WD	J433BSH	343	WD	J343BSH	352	WD	J352BSH
324	WD	J324BSH	334	WD	J334BSH						

VLY601-610

		Volvo B7L 10.6m			Ayats Bravo City			051/24F	2005		

601	WD	LX05GDV	604	WD	LX05GEJ	607	WD	LX05KNZ	609	WD	EU05DVW
602	WD	LX05GDY	605	WD	LX05HRO	608	WD	LX05KOA	610	WD	EU05DVX
603	WD	LX05GDZ	606	WD	LX05HSC						

VLE611-620

		Volvo B9TL 10.9m			East Lancs Visionaire			PO49/31F	2007		

611	WD	LJ07XEN	614	WD	LJ07XER	617	WD	LJ07XEU	619	WD	LJ07XEW
612	WD	LJ07XEO	615	WD	LJ07XES	618	WD	LJ07XEV	620	WD	LJ07UDD
613	WD	LJ07XEP	616	WD	LJ07XET						

Ancillary vehicle:

MB1152 B152WUL	MCW Metrobus DR101/17	MCW		TV	1983	Arriva London, 1999

Previous registrations:

201KYD	V601LGC	E770JAR	DU8506 (HK)
A735WEV	CZ9920(HK)	E771JAR	DT9187 (HK)
A737WEV	DA2952(HK)	E772JAR	DV2896 (HK)
A749WEV	-	E773JAR	DU3481 (HK)
A750WEV	-	E964JAR	DT4549 (HK)
A755WEV	-	E965JAR	DV4883 (HK)
D553YNO	DV471 (HK)	MXT179	- (HK), UAR773Y
D675YNO	DV3433(HK)	NKJ785	- (HK), UAR772Y
E767JAR	DU3460 (HK)	UAR247Y	CZ2554(HK)
E768JAR	DU8346 (HK)	UAR250Y	CZ664(HK)
E769JAR	DT7256 (HK)	UAR776Y	

Depot: Jews Road, Wandsworth (WD)

ARRIVA SOUTHERN COUNTIES

Arriva Southern Counties Ltd, Arriva West Sussex Ltd,
Arriva Kent Thameside Ltd; Arriva Kent & Sussex Ltd; New Enterprise Ltd
Arriva Medway Towns Ltd; Arriva Guildford & West Surrey Ltd;
Arriva Southend Ltd
Invicta House, Armstrong Road, Maidstone, Kent, ME15 6TX

1110	GU	X653WTN	Mercedes-Benz Vario 0814	Alexander ALX100	B27F	2001	Arriva North East, 2010	
1111	GU	R798DUB	Mercedes-Benz Vario 0814	Alexander ALX100	B27F	1998	Arriva North East, 2010	

1118-1122
Mercedes-Benz Vario 0810 — Plaxton Beaver 2 — B27F — 1998

1118	TO	R118TKO	**1120**	SR	R120TKO	**1121**	SR	R121TKO	**1122**	NF	R122TKO
1119	GI	R119TKO						

1172	SR	R942VPU	Mercedes-Benz Vario 0810	Plaxton Beaver 2	B27F	1998		
1186	GU	R186DNM	Mercedes-Benz Vario 0810	Plaxton Beaver 2	B27F	1997		
1190	TO	P481DPE	Mercedes-Benz 711D	Plaxton Beaver 2	B27F	1997		

1501-1506
Optare Solo SR M960* — Optare — N32F — 2008-09 — *1504-6 are SR M890s

1501	TW	YJ58CDZ	**1503**	TW	YJ58CEF	**1505**	NF	YJ09MMO	**1506**	NF	YJ09MMU
1502	TW	YJ58CEA	**1504**	NF	YJ09MMK			

1507	GU	YJ57EJN	Optare Solo M950	Optare	N33F	2007	Arriva The Shires, 2010	
1508	GU	YN03NCF	Optare Solo M920	Optare	N31F	2003	Arriva The Shires, 2010	

1601-1605
Dennis Dart SLF — Plaxton Pointer MPD — N29F — 2000

1601	TW	W601YKN	**1603**	TW	W603YKN	**1604**	TW	W604YKN	**1605**	TW	W605YKN
1602	TW	W602YKN						

1606-1617
TransBus Dart 8.8m — TransBus Mini Pointer — N29F — 2004

1606	GU	GN04UCW	**1609**	SE	GN04UCZ	**1612**	GI	GN04UDE	**1615**	GI	GN04UDJ
1607	GU	GN04UCX	**1610**	GI	GN04UDB	**1613**	GI	GN04UDG	**1616**	GI	GN04UDK
1608	SE	GN04UCY	**1611**	GI	GN04UDD	**1614**	GI	GN04UDH	**1617**	GI	GN04UDL

1618-1623
ADL Dart 8.8m — ADL Mini Pointer — N29F — 2005

1618	NF	GN05ANU	**1620**	NF	GN05ANX	**1622**	NF	GN05AOB	**1623**	NF	GN05AOC
1619	NF	GN05ANV	**1621**	NF	GN05AOA			

1624-1636
ADL Dart 8.8m — ADL Mini Pointer — N23F — 2006-07

1624	DA	SN06BPE	**1628**	DA	SN06BPV	**1631**	DA	SN06BPZ	**1634**	SR	GN06EBF
1625	DA	SN06BPF	**1629**	DA	SN06BPX	**1632**	DA	SN06BRF	**1635**	SR	GN06EBG
1626	DA	SN06BPK	**1630**	DA	SN06BPY	**1633**	SR	GN06EBB	**1636**	SR	GN06EBH
1627	DA	SN06BPU						

1637-1649
ADL Dart 4 — ADL Enviro 200 — N26F — 2007

1637	TW	GN57BNX	**1641**	TW	GN57BOH	**1644**	DA	GN57BPK	**1647**	DA	GN57BPV
1638	TW	GN57BNY	**1642**	TW	GN57BOJ	**1645**	DA	GN57BPO	**1648**	DA	GN57BPX
1639	TW	GN57BNZ	**1643**	DA	GN57BPF	**1646**	DA	GN57BPU	**1649**	DA	GN57BPY
1640	TW	GN57BOF						

2000	TO	GB03TGM	Setra S415 HD	Setra	C49FT	2003	Arriva TGM, 2008	
2852	TO	NM02DYA	Volvo B10M-62	Caetano Enigma	C49FT	2002	Arriva TGM, 2008	
2853	TO	YN54WDE	Volvo B7R	Plaxton Profile	C53F	2004	OFJ Connections, 2008	
2854	TO	YN54OCY	Volvo B7R	Plaxton Profile	C53F	2004	OFJ Connections, 2008	
2855	TO	YN53VBX	TransBus Javelin	Plaxton Profile	C53F	2004	OFJ Connections, 2008	
2856	TO	UK04TGM	Volvo B12B	Caetano Levante	C49FT	2004	Arriva TGM, 2010	
2857	TO	YN53OYW	Scania K114	Irizar PB	C49FT	2004	Arriva TGM, 2010	
2889	TO	R456SKX	DAF SB3000	Plaxton Prima Interurban	C53F	1997	Arriva The Shires, 2009	
2894	TO	W183CDN	DAF SB3000	Van Hool T9 Alizée	C52F	2000		
2895	TO	SCZ9651	DAF SB3000	Van Hool T9 Alizée	C49F	1999	Eirebus, Dublin, 2003	
2896	TO	SCZ9652	DAF SB3000	Van Hool T9 Alizée	C49F	1999	Eirebus, Dublin, 2003	
2898	TO	W198CDN	DAF SB3000	Ikarus Blue Danube 396	C53F	2000		

The shortest version of the Enviro 200 is 9.9metre long. One of six allocated to Tunbridge Wells is 1642, GN57BOJ, seen here on route 281. *Mark Doggett*

2903-2908

DAF SB3000 — Plaxton Première 320 — C53F — 1998

2903	TO	R903BKO	2905	TO	R905BKO	2907	TO	R907BKO	2908	TO	R908BKO
2904	TO	R904BKO	2906	TO	R906BKO						

3021-3024

Dennis Lance 11m — East Lancs — N49F — 1996

3021	SE	N221TPK	3022	SE	N322TPK	3024	GU	N224TPK

3025-3036

Dennis Dart SLF — Plaxton Pointer 2 — N35F — 1996 — North Western (Beeline), 1998

3025	GU	N225TPK	3028	GU	N228TPK	3031	GU	N231TPK	3035	GU	N235TPK
3026	GU	N226TPK	3029	SR	N229TPK	3033	GU	N233TPK	3036	GU	N236TPK
3027	SR	N227TPK	3030	GU	N230TPK						

3037	GI	N237VPH	Dennis Dart SLF	East Lancs Spryte	N31F	1996
3038	GI	N245VPH	Dennis Dart SLF	East Lancs Spryte	N31F	1996
3039	TO	N239VPH	Dennis Dart SLF	East Lancs Spryte	N31F	1996
3046	TW	N246VPH	Dennis Dart SLF	East Lancs Spryte	N31F	1996
3047	TW	N247VPH	Dennis Dart SLF	East Lancs Spryte	N31F	1996
3050	GI	P250APM	Dennis Dart SLF	East Lancs Spryte	N31F	1996
3051	GI	P251APM	Dennis Dart SLF	East Lancs Spryte	N31F	1996
3053	GI	P253APM	Dennis Dart SLF	East Lancs Spryte	N31F	1997
3054	GI	P254APM	Dennis Dart SLF	East Lancs Spryte	N31F	1997
3055	TO	P255APM	Dennis Dart SLF	East Lancs Spryte	N31F	1997

3070-3096

Dennis Dart SLF — Plaxton Pointer — N39F — 1997

3070	GI	P270FPK	3076	GI	P276FPK	3089	TW	P289FPK	3093	GU	P293FPK
3071	GI	P271FPK	3077	GI	P277FPK	3090	GU	P290FPK	3094	GU	P294FPK
3072	GI	P272FPK	3084	SR	P284FPK	3091	GU	P291FPK	3095	GU	P295FPK
3073	GI	P273FPK	3086	GU	P286FPK	3092	GU	P292FPK	3096	u	P296FPK
3075	GI	P275FPK	3088	GU	P288FPK						

3097-3102

Dennis Dart SLF — Plaxton Pointer 2 — N39F — 1997

3097	GU	R297CMV	3099	GU	R299CMV	3101	GU	R301CMV	3102	GU	R302CMV
3098	GU	R298CMV	3100	GU	R310CMV						

Originally from a batch of thirteen, several of which are now in the Midlands, 3046, N246VPH, illustrates the East Lancs Spryte body as applied to the Dennis Dart. It was pictured in its new interurban colours at Otford during August 2010. *Richard Godfrey*

3109	GU	T109LKK	Dennis Dart SLF 9m	Plaxton Pointer 2	N39F	1999	
3110	GU	T110LKK	Dennis Dart SLF 9m	Plaxton Pointer 2	N39F	1999	
3111	NF	N523MJO	Dennis Dart SLF 9m	Plaxton Pointer 2	N36F	1996	Arriva The Shires, 2009
3112	GU	NDZ7926	Dennis Dart SLF 9m	Plaxton Pointer 2	N36F	1996	Arriva The Shires, 2009
3113	GU	NDZ7918	Dennis Dart SLF 9m	Plaxton Pointer 2	N36F	1996	Arriva The Shires, 2009
3114	NF	R206GMJ	Dennis Dart SLF	Plaxton Pointer	N31F	1997	Arriva The Shires, 2010
3115	NF	R211GMJ	Dennis Dart SLF	Plaxton Pointer	N31F	1997	Arriva The Shires, 2010
3172	SE	N234TPK	Dennis Dart SLF 9m	Plaxton Pointer	N35F	1996	

3176-3191
Dennis Dart SLF 10.1m   Plaxton Pointer   N40F   1996

3176	SR	P176LKL	3181	SE	P181LKL	3187	GU	P187LKJ	3190	GI	P190LKJ
3177	ME	P177LKL	3184	SR	P184LKL	3188	GI	P188LKJ	3191	GI	P191LKJ
3178	GI	P178LKL	3185	TW	P185LKL	3189	GI	P189LKJ			

3192-3247
Dennis Dart SLF 10.1m   Plaxton Pointer   N40F   1997

3192	TW	P192LKJ	3206	TW	P206LKJ	3224	GI	P224MKL	3236	GI	P236MKN
3193	TW	P193LKJ	3207	ME	P207LKJ	3225	GI	P225MKL	3237	GI	P237MKN
3194	ME	P194LKJ	3208	ME	P208LKJ	3226	GI	P226MKL	3238	GI	P238MKN
3195	ME	P195LKJ	3209	ME	P209LKJ	3227	GI	P227MKL	3239	GI	P239MKN
3196	TW	P196LKJ	3213	GU	P213LKJ	3228	GI	P228MKL	3240	GI	P240MKN
3197	NF	P197LKJ	3215	ME	P215LKJ	3229	GI	P229MKL	3241	GI	P241MKN
3198	GI	P198LKJ	3216	SR	P216LKL	3230	GI	P230MKL	3242	GI	P242MKN
3199	SR	P199LKJ	3218	TW	P218MKL	3231	GI	P231MKL	3243	GI	P243MKN
3201	SR	P201LKJ	3219	GI	P219MKL	3232	GI	P232MKL	3244	GI	P244MKN
3202	ME	P202LKJ	3220	GI	P220MKL	3233	GI	P233MKN	3245	GI	P245MKN
3203	ME	P203LKJ	3221	GI	P221MKL	3234	GI	P234MKN	3246	GI	P246MKN
3205	ME	P205LKJ	3223	GI	P223MKL	3235	GI	P235MKN	3247	NF	P247MKN

| 3249 | ME | P279FPK | Dennis Dart SLF 10.1m | Plaxton Pointer 2 | N40F | 1997 | |

3250-3259
Scania L113 CRL   Wright Axcess-ultralow   N43F   1995

3250	SE	N250BKK	3253	SE	N253BKK	3256	SE	N256BKK	3258	SE	N258BKK
3251	SE	N251BKK	3254	SE	N254BKK	3257	SE	N257BKK	3259	SE	N259BKK
3252	SE	N252BKK	3255	SE	N255BKK						

London red livery has been applied to Dart 3265, R265EKO, seen here on route 402 in Sevenoaks. Production of the Pointer body moved to Alexander's Falkirk plant in 1999, although the Plaxton badge continued to be applied. *Richard Godfrey*

3261-3272   Dennis Dart SLF 10.1m   Plaxton Pointer 2   N39F   1998

3261	NF	R261EKO	3264	TW	R264EKO	3267	NF	R267EKO	3270	TW	R270EKO
3262	TW	R262EKO	3265	TW	R265EKO	3268	NF	R268EKO	3271	TW	R271EKO
3263	NF	R263EKO	3266	TW	R266EKO	3269	TW	R269EKO	3272	NF	R272EKO

3273-3289   Dennis Dart SLF 10.1m   Plaxton Pointer 2   N39F*   1999   *3276-81 are N37F

3273	NF	T273JKM	3278	SE	T278JKM	3282	TW	T282JKM	3286	NF	T286JKM
3274	NF	T274JKM	3279	SE	T279JKM	3283	NF	T283JKM	3287	TW	T287JKM
3275	NF	T275JKM	3280	SE	T280JKM	3284	NF	T284JKM	3288	NF	T288JKM
3276	SE	T276JKM	3281	SE	T281JKM	3285	NF	T285JKM	3289	SE	T289JKM
3277	SE	T277JKM									

3291-3303   Dennis Dart SLF 10.1m   Plaxton Pointer 2   N34D   2001

3291	DA	Y291TKJ	3294	DA	Y294TKJ	3297	DA	Y297TKJ	3301	DA	Y301TKJ
3292	DA	Y292TKJ	3295	DA	Y295TKJ	3298	DA	Y298TKJ	3302	DA	Y302TKJ
3293	DA	Y293TKJ	3296	DA	Y296TKJ	3299	DA	Y299TKJ	3303	DA	Y303TKJ

3304-3308   Dennis Dart SLF 10.1m   Plaxton Pointer 2   N39F   1997

| 3304 | GU | R304CMV | 3306 | GU | R296CMV | 3307 | SE | R307CMV | 3308 | SE | R308CMV |
| 3305 | GU | R305CMV | | | | | | | | | |

3318-3326   Dennis Dart SLF   Plaxton Pointer 2   N33F*   1998   * 3224-6 are N39F

| 3318 | SE | T218NMJ | 3321 | SE | T821NMJ | 3323 | SE | T823NMJ | 3325 | SE | T825NMJ |
| 3320 | SE | T820NMJ | 3322 | SE | T822NMJ | 3324 | SE | T824NMJ | 3326 | SE | T826NMJ |

3387-3397   Dennis Dart SLF   Plaxton Pointer   N39F   1997

3387	SE	P257FPK	3390	SE	P259FPK	3393	SE	P263FPK	3396	SE	P266FPK
3388	SE	P258FPK	3391	SE	P261FPK	3394	SE	P264FPK	3397	SE	P267FPK
3389	SE	P259FPK	3392	SE	P262FPK	3395	SE	P265FPK			

3400	SE	R310NGM	Dennis Dart SLF			Plaxton Pointer 2		N33F	1997	Town & Country, Corringham, '00
3401	SE	R311NGM	Dennis Dart SLF			Plaxton Pointer 2		N33F	1997	Town & Country, Corringham, '00
3402	SE	R312NGM	Dennis Dart SLF			Plaxton Pointer 2		N33F	1997	Town & Country, Corringham, '00
3403	SE	R313NGM	Dennis Dart SLF			Plaxton Pointer 2		N33F	1997	Town & Country, Corringham, '00

3404-3413 · Dennis Dart · Plaxton Pointer · B34F · 1996

3404	NF	P324HVX	3409	TW	P329HVX	3411	u	P331HVX	3413	TW	P833HVX
3408	NF	P328HVX	3412	TW	P332HVX						

3421-3431 · Dennis Dart SLF · Plaxton Pointer · N39F · 1996

3421	SE	P421HVX	3425	SE	P425HVX	3427	SE	P427HVX	3429	SE	P429HVX
3423	SE	P423HVX	3426	SE	P426HVX	3428	SE	P428HVX	3431	SE	P431HVX

3500-3510 · DAF SB120 10.2m · Wrightbus Cadet · N31D · 2002

3500	GY	KE51PTY	3503	GY	KE51PUF	3506	GY	KE51PUK	3509	GY	KE51PUV
3501	GY	KE51PTZ	3504	GY	KE51PUH	3507	GY	KE51PUO	3510	GY	KC51NFO
3502	GY	KE51PUA	3505	GY	KE51PUJ	3508	GY	KE51PUU			

3511	GY	KE51PUY	DAF SB120 9.4m			Wrightbus Cadet		N27F	2002	
3512	GY	KC51PUX	DAF SB120 9.4m			Wrightbus Cadet		N27F	2002	
3513	TW	KE51PVD	DAF SB120 9.4m			Wrightbus Cadet		N27F	2002	
3591	GU	T591CGT	Dennis Dart SLF 10.1m			Plaxton Pointer 2		N39F	1999	*Operated for Surrey CC*
3592	GU	T592CGT	Dennis Dart SLF 10.1m			Plaxton Pointer 2		N39F	1999	*Operated for Surrey CC*
3619	TO	M619PKP	Volvo B6-9.9M			Plaxton Pointer		B40F	1995	

3701-3706 · Dennis Dart SLF 11.3m · Plaxton Pointer SPD · N44F · 1998

3701	ME	S701VKM	3703	ME	S703VKM	3705	ME	S705VKM	3706	ME	S706VKM
3702	ME	S702VKM	3704	ME	S704VKM						

3707	GU	LK55ACY	ADL Dart 11.3m			East Lancs Myllennium		NC40F	2005	*Operated for Surrey CC*

3731-3735 · Volvo B7RLE · Wrightbus Eclipse Urban · N44F · 2006

3731	GU	GN54MYO	3733	GU	GN54MYR	3734	GU	GN54MYT	3735	GU	GN54MYU
3732	GU	GN54MYP									

3751-3762 · VDL Bus SB200 · Wrightbus Pulsar · NC44F · 2008

3751	NF	YJ08DZA	3754	NF	YJ08DZD	3757	NF	YJ08DZG	3760	NF	YJ08DZL
3752	NF	YJ08DZB	3755	NF	YJ08DZE	3758	NF	YJ08DZH	3761	NF	YJ08DZM
3753	NF	YJ08DZC	3756	NF	YJ08DZF	3759	NF	YJ08DZK	3762	NF	YJ08DZN

3801-3814 · Volvo B7RLE · Wrightbus Eclipse Urban · NC43F · 2006

3801	NF	GN06EVG	3805	NF	GN06EVH	3809	NF	GN06EVL	3812	NF	GN06EVT
3802	NF	GN06EWC	3806	NF	GN06EVJ	3810	NF	GN06EVP	3813	NF	GN06EVU
3803	NF	GN06EWD	3807	NF	GN06EVK	3811	NF	GN06EVR	3814	NF	GN06EUU
3804	NF	GN06EWE	3808	NF	GN06EVM						

3815-3826 · Volvo B7RLE · Wrightbus Eclipse Urban · N43F · 2007

3815	NF	GN07AVB	3818	NF	GN07AVE	3821	NF	GN07AVJ	3824	NF	GN07AVN
3816	NF	GN07AVC	3819	NF	GN07AVF	3822	NF	GN07AVL	3825	NF	GN07AVO
3817	NF	GN07AVD	3820	NF	GN07AVG	3823	NF	GN07AVM	3826	NF	GN07AVP

3901	GU	BX56VTU	Mercedes-Benz Citaro O530			Mercedes-Benz		N42F	2006	
3902	GU	BX56VTV	Mercedes-Benz Citaro O530			Mercedes-Benz		N42F	2006	
3903	GU	BX56VTW	Mercedes-Benz Citaro O530			Mercedes-Benz		N42F	2006	

3911-3921 · DAF SB220 · Plaxton Prestige · N39F · 1999

3911	SE	T911KKM	3914	SE	T914KKM	3916	SE	T916KKM	3919	SE	T919KKM
3912	SE	T912KKM	3915	SE	T915KKM	3918	SE	T918KKM	3921	SE	T921KKM
3913	SE	T913KKM									

3923-3932 · DAF SB120 · Wrightbus Cadet · N39F · 2002

3923	GU	GK51SYY	3926	GU	GK51SZD	3929	GU	GK51SZG	3931	GU	GK51SZL
3924	GU	GK51SYZ	3927	GU	GK51SZE	3930	GU	GK51SZJ	3932	GU	GK51SZN
3925	GU	GK51SZC	3928	GU	GK51SZF						

3933-3944 · DAF SB120 · Wrightbus Cadet · N39F · 2002

3933	GU	GK52YUW	3937	GU	GK52YVB	3940	GU	GK52YVE	3943	GU	GK52YVJ
3934	GU	GK52YUX	3938	GU	GK52YVC	3941	GU	GK52YVF	3944	GU	GK52YVL
3935	GU	GK52YUY	3939	GU	GK52YVD	3942	GU	GK52YVG			

Seen in Dartford is one of several Southern Counties vehicles that are built to TfL specification for work on the London routes. The view of 3990, GN07DLY, illustrates the use of operator letters and fleet number on the roof for service performance monitoring. *Laurie Rufus*

3945-3960

			VDL Bus SB120			Wrightbus Cadet 2		N39F	2004
3945	DA	GK53AOH	3949	DA	GK53AOO	3953	DA	GK53AOU	3957	DA	GK53AOY
3946	DA	GK53AOJ	3950	DA	GK53AOP	3954	DA	GK53AOV	3958	ME	GK53AOZ
3947	DA	GK53AOL	3951	DA	GK53AOR	3955	DA	GK53AOW	3959	ME	GN04UFW
3948	DA	GK53AON	3952	DA	GK53AOT	3956	DA	GK53AOX	3960	ME	GN04UFX

3961-3969

			VDL Bus SB200			Wrightbus Commander 2		N44F	2004
3961	ME	GN04UFY	3964	ME	GN04UGB	3966	ME	GN04UGD	3968	ME	GN04UGF
3962	ME	GN04UFZ	3965	ME	GN04UGC	3967	ME	GN04UGE	3969	ME	GN04UGG
3963	ME	GN04UGA								

3970	GU	YJ06LFZ	DAF SB120 10.8m			Wrightbus Cadet 2	N39F	2006
3971	GY	YE06HPX	DAF SB120 10.8m			Wrightbus Cadet 2	N28D	2006
3972	GY	YE06HPY	DAF SB120 10.8m			Wrightbus Cadet 2	N28D	2006
3973	GY	YE06HPZ	DAF SB120 10.8m			Wrightbus Cadet 2	N28D	2006

3982-3999

			ADL Dart 4			ADL Enviro 200		N29D	2007
3982	DA	GN07DLE	3987	DA	GN07DLU	3992	DA	GN07DME	3996	DA	GN07DMV
3983	DA	GN07DLF	3988	DA	GN07DLV	3993	DA	GN07DMF	3997	GY	GN57BOU
3984	DA	GN07DLJ	3989	DA	GN07DLX	3994	DA	GN07DMO	3998	GY	GN57BOV
3985	DA	GN07DLK	3990	DA	GN07DLY	3995	DA	GN07DMU	3999	GY	GN57BPE
3986	DA	GN07DLO	3991	DA	GN07DLZ					

4000-4010

			ADL Dart 4			ADL Enviro 200		N29D	2008
4000	GY	GN08CGO	4003	GY	GN08CGX	4006	GY	GO58CHC	4009	GY	GO58CHG
4001	GY	GN08CGU	4004	GY	GN08CGY	4007	GY	GO58CHD	4010	GY	GO58CHH
4002	GY	GN08CGV	4005	GY	GN08CGZ	4008	GY	GO58CHF			

4011-4022

			ADL Dart 4			ADL Enviro 200		N38F	2008
4011	ME	GN58BTO	4014	ME	GN58BTX	4017	GU	GN58BUA	4020	GU	GN58BUH
4012	ME	GN58BTU	4015	ME	GN58BTY	4018	GU	GN58BUE	4021	GU	GN58BUJ
4013	ME	GN58BTV	4016	ME	GN58BTZ	4019	GU	GN58BUF	4022	GU	GN58BUO

Recently placed into service at Grays is Enviro 200 4073, GN10KWK, seen here on Route 66 to Romford rail station. *Dave Heath*

4023-4027

			ADL Dart 4	10.2m		ADL Enviro 200		N29D	2009		
4023	DA	GN58BUP	**4025**	DA	GN58BUV	**4026**	DA	GN58LVA	**4027**	DA	GN58LVB
4024	DA	GN58BUU									

4028-4035

			ADL Dart 4	10.8m		ADL Enviro 200		N32D	2009		
4028	DA	GN09AVV	**4030**	DA	GN09AVX	**4032**	DA	GN09AVZ	**4034**	DA	GN09AWB
4029	DA	GN09AVW	**4031**	DA	GN09AVY	**4033**	DA	GN09AWA	**4035**	DA	GN09AWC

4036-4059

			ADL Dart 4	10.8m		ADL Enviro 200		N38F	2009		
4036	NF	GN09AWG	**4042**	NF	GN09AWR	**4048**	GI	GN09AWZ	**4054**	GI	GN09AXG
4037	NF	GN09AWH	**4043**	NF	GN09AWU	**4049**	GI	GN09AXA	**4055**	GI	GN09AXH
4038	NF	GN09AWJ	**4044**	GI	GN09AWV	**4050**	GI	GN09AXB	**4056**	GI	GN09AXJ
4039	NF	GN09AWM	**4045**	GI	GN09AWW	**4051**	GI	GN09AXC	**4057**	GI	GN09AXK
4040	NF	GN09AWO	**4046**	GI	GN09AWX	**4052**	GI	GN09AXD	**4058**	GI	GN09AXM
4041	NF	GN09AWP	**4047**	GI	GN09AWY	**4053**	GI	GN09AXF	**4059**	GI	GN09AXO

4060-4067

			ADL Dart 4	10.8m		ADL Enviro 200		N38F	2009		
4060	ME	GN59FVB	**4062**	ME	GN59FVD	**4064**	ME	GN59FVF	**4066**	ME	GN59FVH
4061	ME	GN59FVC	**4063**	ME	GN59FVE	**4065**	ME	GN59FVG	**4067**	ME	GN59FVJ

4068-4079

			ADL Dart 4	10.8m		ADL Enviro 200		N38F	2010		
4068	GY	GN10KWE	**4071**	GY	GN10KWH	**4074**	GY	VX10EBN	**4077**	GY	VX10EBU
4069	GY	GN10KWF	**4072**	GY	GN10KWJ	**4075**	GY	VX10EBO	**4078**	GY	VX10EBV
4070	GY	GN10KWG	**4073**	GY	GN10KWK	**4076**	GY	VX10EBP	**4079**	GY	VX10EBX

5213	ME	N713TPK	Dennis Dominator DDA2006		East Lancs			B45/31F	1996		
5214	ME	N714TPK	Dennis Dominator DDA2006		East Lancs			B45/31F	1996		
5215	ME	N715TPK	Dennis Dominator DDA2006		East Lancs			B45/31F	1996		

The 2011 Arriva Bus Handbook

Carrying an interesting wrap-round advertisement, 5941, R637MNU, is seen in Tunbridge Wells having recently been transferred from the Midlands fleet. It is a Volvo Olympian with Northern Counties Palatine bodywork. *Mark Doggett*

5434-5441 — Dennis Trident — Alexander ALX400 — N47/31F — 2000

5434	ME	W434XKX	5436	ME	W436XKX	5438	ME	W438XKX	5441	ME	W441XKX
5435	ME	W435XKX	5437	ME	W437XKX	5439	ME	W439XKX			

| 5769 | SR | H769EKJ | Leyland Olympian ON2R50C13Z4 Northern Counties | B47/30F | 1991 | Boro'line, Maidstone, 1992 |

5906-5910 — Leyland Olympian ON2R50C13Z4 Northern Counties Palatine — B45/30F — 1993

5906	TO	K906SKR	5908	TW	K908SKR	5909	TW	K909SKR	5910	TO	K910SKR
5907	TO	K907SKR									

5911-5925 — Volvo Olympian — Northern Counties Palatine — B47/30F — 1994-95 — 5913 re-bodied 1995

5911	TW	M911MKM	5915	ME	M915MKM	5918	TW	M918MKM	5922	TW	M922PKN
5913	ME	M913MKM	5916	ME	M916MKM	5919	TW	M919MKM	5923	TW	M923PKN
5914	ME	M914MKM	5917	TW	M917MKM	5920	ME	M920MKM	5925	GU	M925PKN

5926-5937 — Volvo Olympian — Northern Counties Palatine — B47/30F — 1997

5926	TW	P926MKL	5929	TW	P929MKL	5932	TW	P932MKL	5935	SE	P935MKL
5927	TW	P927MKL	5930	ME	P930MKL	5933	ME	P933MKL	5936	SR	P936MKL
5928	TW	P928MKL	5931	ME	P931MKL	5934	SE	P934MKL	5937	GI	P937MKL

5938	GI	P609CAY	Volvo Olympian	Northern Counties Palatine	B47/29F	1996	Arriva Midlands, 2009
5939	NF	P610CAY	Volvo Olympian	Northern Counties Palatine	B47/29F	1996	Arriva Midlands, 2009
5940	NF	P613CAY	Volvo Olympian	Northern Counties Palatine	B47/29F	1996	Arriva Midlands, 2009
5941	TW	R637MNU	Volvo Olympian	Northern Counties Palatine	B47/29F	1998	Arriva Midlands, 2009
5942	TW	R639MNU	Volvo Olympian	Northern Counties Palatine	B47/29F	1998	Arriva Midlands, 2009
5943	TW	S653KJU	Volvo Olympian	Northern Counties Palatine	B47/29F	1998	Arriva Midlands, 2010
6210	TW	R210CKO	DAF DB250	Northern Counties Palatine 2	B43/24D	1998	
6211	TW	R211CKO	DAF DB250	Northern Counties Palatine 2	B43/24D	1998	
6212	TW	R212CKO	DAF DB250	Northern Counties Palatine 2	B43/24D	1998	

6213-6219 — DAF DB250 — Wrightbus Pulsar Gemini — N43/21D — 2004

6213	DA	GK53AOA	6215	DA	GK53AOC	6217	DA	GK53AOE	6219	DA	GK53AOG
6214	DA	GK53AOB	6216	DA	GK53AOD	6218	DA	GK53AOF			

6224-6236

			DAF DB250 10.2m			Alexander ALX400			N43/20D	2000-01	Arriva London, 2006
6224	DA	X457FGP	6228	DA	Y461UGC	6231	DA	Y464UGC	6234	DA	Y467UGC
6225	DA	X458FGP	6229	DA	Y462UGC	6232	DA	Y465UGC	6235	DA	Y468UGC
6226	DA	X459FGP	6230	DA	Y463UGC	6233	DA	Y466UGC	6236	DA	Y469UGC
6227	DA	Y451UGC									

6237-6240

			DAF DB250			East Lancs Olympus			N51/28F	2008	
6237	ME	YJ57BKD	6238	ME	YN57BKE	6239	ME	YN57BKF	6240	ME	YN57BKG

6401-6449

			Volvo B7TL			TransBus ALX400			N45/27F	2004	
6401	GI	GN04UDM	6413	SR	GN04UEC	6426	u	GN04UET	6438	TW	GN04UFG
6402	GU	GN04UDP	6414	SR	GN04UED	6427	GI	GN04UEU	6439	TW	GN04UFH
6403	GU	GN04UDS	6415	GI	GN04UEE	6428	GI	GN04UEV	6440	GI	GN04UFJ
6404	ME	GN04UDT	6417	GI	GN04UEG	6429	GI	GN04UEW	6441	GI	GN04UFK
6405	ME	GN04UDU	6418	GI	GN04UEH	6430	GI	GN04UEX	6442	GI	GN04UFL
6406	ME	GN04UDV	6419	GI	GN04UEJ	6431	GI	GN04UEY	6443	GI	GN04UFM
6407	ME	GN04UDW	6420	GI	GN04UEK	6432	GI	GN04UEZ	6444	TW	GN04UFP
6408	ME	GN04UDX	6421	GI	GN04UEL	6433	GI	GN04UFA	6445	TW	GN04UFR
6409	ME	GN04UDY	6422	GI	GN04UEM	6434	GI	GN04UFB	6446	ME	GN04UFS
6410	SR	GN04UDZ	6423	GI	GN04UEP	6435	GI	GN04UFC	6447	ME	GN04UFT
6411	SR	GN04UEA	6424	GI	GN04UER	6436	ME	GN04UFD	6448	ME	GN04UFU
6412	SR	GN04UEB	6425	GI	GN04UES	6437	GI	GN04UFE	6449	ME	GN04UFV

6450-6457

			ADL Trident 2			ADL Enviro 400			NC47/33F	2008	
6450	GI	GN58BSO	6452	GI	GN58BSV	6454	GI	GN58BSY	6456	GI	GN58BTE
6451	GI	GN58BSU	6453	GI	GN58BSX	6455	GI	GN58BSZ	6457	GI	GN58BTF

7624-7636

			Volvo Citybus B10M-50			Northern Counties			B45/31F	1989	Londonlinks, 1997
7624	GI	G624BPH	7630	GI	G630BPH	7633	GI	G633BPH	7635	GI	G635BPH
7629	GI	G629BPH	7631	GI	G631BPH	7634	GI	G634BPH	7636	GI	G636BPH

Ancillary vehicles:

T4	MEt	L506CPJ	Volvo B6-9.9M	Plaxton Pointer	TV	1994	
T5	MEt	L507CPJ	Volvo B6-9.9M	Plaxton Pointer	TV	1994	
T7	MEt	L509CPJ	Volvo B6-9.9M	Plaxton Pointer	TV	1994	
T14	MEt	M525MPM	Dennis Dart 9.8m	East Lancs EL2000	B40F	1995	
T19	NFt	N539TPF	Dennis Dart 9.8m	East Lancs EL2000	B40F	1995	
T175	NFt	M200CBB	Dennis Dart 9.8m	Plaxton Pointer	B40F	1995	Cardiff Bluebird, 1996

T207-211

			Volvo B6-9.9M			Northern Counties Paladin	TV	1994	Londonlinks, 1997
207	GY	L207YCU	208	GI	L208YCU	210	GI	L210YCU	211 DA L211YCU

T605	SEt	L605EKM	Volvo B6-9.9M	Plaxton Pointer	TV	1994	

Previous registrations:

SCZ9651	99D81499, T178AUA	SCZ9652	99D81498, T179AUA

Depots and allocations:

Dartford (Central Road) - DA

Dart SLF	1624	1625	1626	1627	1628	1629	1630	1631
	1632	3291	3292	3293	3294	3295	3296	3297
	3298	3299	3301	3302	3303			
Dart 4	1643	1644	1645	1646	1647	1648	1649	3982
	3983	3984	3985	3986	3987	3988	3989	3990
	3991	3992	3993	3994	3995	3996	4023	4024
	4025	4026	4027	4028	4029	4030	4031	4032
	4033	4034	4035					
DAF/VDL SB120	3945	3946	3947	3948	3949	3950	3951	3952
	3953	3954	3955	3956	3957			
DAF/VDL DB250	6213	6214	6215	6216	6217	6218	6219	6224
	6225	6226	6227	6228	6229	6230	6231	6232
	6233	6234	6235	6236				

Gillingham (Nelson Road) - GI

Dart SLF	1610	1611	1612	1613	1614	1615	1616	1617
	3037	3038	3050	3051	3053	3054	3070	3071
	3072	3073	3075	3076	3077	3178	3188	3189
	3190	3191	3198	3219	3220	3221	3223	3224
	3225	3226	3227	3228	3229	3230	3231	3232
	3233	3234	3235	3236	3237	3238	3239	3240
	3241	3242	3243	3244	3245	3246		
Dart 4	4044	4045	4046	4047	4048	4049	4050	4051
	4052	4053	4054	4055	4056	4057	4058	4059
Volvo Olympian	5937	5938						
Volvo Citybus	7624	7629	7630	7631	7633	7634	7635	7636
Volvo B7TL	6401	6415	6417	6418	6419	6420	6421	6422
	6423	6424	6425	6427	6428	6429	6430	6431
	6432	6433	6434	6435	6436	6437	6440	6441
	6442	6443						
Trident 2	6450	6451	6452	6453	6454	6455	6456	6457

Grays (Europa Park, London Road) - GY

SB120 Cadet	3500	3501	3502	3503	3504	3505	3506	3507
	3508	3509	3510	3511	3512	3513	3971	3972
	3973							
Dart 4	3997	3999	4000	4001	4002	4003	4004	4005
	4006	4007	4008	4009	4010	4068	4069	4070
	4071	4072	4073	4074	4075	4076	4077	4078
	4079							

Guildford (Leas Road) - GU

Mercedes-Benz	1110	1111	1119	1186				
Optare Solo	1507	1508						
Dart SLF	1606	1607	3024	3025	3026	3028	3030	3031
	3033	3035	3036	3086	3088	3090	3091	3092
	3093	3094	3095	3096	3097	3098	3099	3100
	3101	3102	3109	3110	3112	3113	3187	3213
	3304	3305	3306	3591	3592	3707		
DAF/VDL SB120	3923	3924	3925	3926	3927	3928	3929	3930
	3931	3932	3933	3934	3935	3937	3938	3939
	3940	3941	3942	3943	3944	3970		
Dart 4	4017	4018	4019	4020	4021	4022		
Lance	3024							
Mercedes-Benz O530	3901	3902	3903					
Volvo B7RLE	3731	3732	3733	3734	3735			
Volvo Olympian	5925							
Volvo B7TL	6402	6403						

Maidstone (Armstrong Road) - ME

Dart SLF	3177	3194	3195	3202	3203	3205	3207	3208
	3209	3215	3249	3703	3704	3705	3706	
Dart 4	4011	4012	4013	4014	4015	4016	4060	4061
	4062	4063	4064	4065	4066	4067		
DAF/VDL SB120	3958	3959	3960					
DAF/VDL SB200	3961	3962	3963	3964	3965	3966	3967	3968
	3969							
Dominator	5213	5214	5215					
Olympian	5913	5914	5915	5916	5919	5920	5930	5931
	5933							
Trident	5434	5435	5436	5437	5438	5439	5441	
DAF/VDL SB250	6237	6238	6239	6240				
Volvo B7TL	6404	6405	6406	6407	6408	6409	6446	6447
	6448	6449						

Northfleet (London Road) - NF

Mercedes-Benz	1122							
Optare Solo	1504	1505	1506					
Dart	3404	3408						
Dart SLF	1618	1619	1620	1621	1622	1623	3111	3114
	3115	3197	3247	3261	3263	3267	3268	3272
	3273	3274	3275	3283	3284	3285	3286	3288
Dart 4	4036	4037	4038	4039	4040	4041	4042	4043
VDL Bus SB200	3751	3752	3753	3754	3755	3756	3757	3758
	3759	3760	3761	3762				
Volvo B7RLE	3801	3802	3803	3804	3805	3806	3807	3808
	3809	3810	3811	3812	3813	3814	3815	3816
	3817	3818	3819	3820	3821	3822	3823	3824
	3825	3826						
Olympian	5939	5940						

Sheerness (Bridge Road) - SR

Mercedes-Benz	1120	1121	1172					
Dart SLF	1633	1634	1635	1636	3027	3029	3084	3176
	3184	3199	3201	3216				
Olympian	5769	5936						
Volvo B7TL	6410	6411	6412	6413	6414			

Southend (Short Street) - SE

Dart SLF	1608	1609	3172	3181	3276	3277	3278	3279
	3280	3281	3289	3307	3308	3318	3320	3321
	3322	3323	3324	3325	3326	3387	3388	3389
	3390	3391	3392	3393	3394	3395	3396	3397
	3400	3401	3402	3403	3421	3423	3425	3426
	3427	3428	3429	3431				
Lance	3021	3022						
Scania L113	3250	3251	3252	3253	3254	3255	3256	3257
	3258	3259						
DAF/VDL SB220	3911	3912	3913	3914	3915	3916	3918	3919
	3921							
Olympian	5934	5935						

The latest double-deck buses for Southern Counties form a batch of eight Alexander Dennis Trident 2s with Enviro 400 bodies that feature high-back seating. All are allocated to Gillingham with 6450, GN58BSO, working the express service to Maidstone. *Richard Godfrey*

Tonbridge (Cannon Lane) - New Enterprise - TO

Merced-Benz	1118	1190						
Setra coach	2000							
DAF/VDL SB3000	2889	2894	2895	2896	2898	2903	2904	2905
	2906	2907	2908					
Dart	3039	3055						
Volvo B6	3619							
Volvo B7 coach	2853	2854						
Javelin coach	2855							
Volvo B10M coach	2852							
Volvo B12B	2856							
Scania coach	2857							
Olympian	5906	5907	5910					

Tunbridge Wells (St John's Road) - TW

Optare Solo	1501	1502	1503					
Dart	3409	3412	3413					
Dart SLF	1601	1602	1603	1604	1605	3046	3047	3089
	3185	3192	3193	3196	3206	3218	3262	3264
	3265	3266	3269	3270	3271	3282	3287	3701
	3702							
Dart 4	1637	1638	1639	1640	1641	1642		
Olympian	5908	5909	5911	5917	5918	5922	5923	5926
	5927	5928	5929	5932	5941	5942	5943	
DAF/VDL DB250	6210	6211	6212					
Volvo B7TL	6438	6439	6444	6445				

Unallocated and stored - u/w

Remainder

TELLINGS - GOLDEN MILLER

Tellings Golden Miller Group plc; Tellings-Golden Miller Coaches Ltd,
Ensign Close, Exeter Way, London Heathrow Airport, TW6 2PQ
Burton's Coaches, Dudery Hill, Haverhill, CB9 8DR
Classic Coaches, Classic House, Morrison Road, Stanley, DA9 7RX
Excel Passenger Logistics, Monometer House, Rectory Road, Leigh-on-Sea, SS2 9HN
Flight Delay Services, Commonwealth House, Chicago Avenue, Wythenshawe, M90 3FL
Link Coaches, 1 Wrottesley Road, Harlesden, NW10 5XA
OFJ Connections, 16300 Electra Avenue, London Heathrow Airport, Hounslow, TW6 2DN
Network Colchester, 5 Whitehall Industrial Estate, Grange Way, Colchester, CO2 8GU

Tellings-Golden Miller

GJ02XZK	Citroën Relay	Citroën	M8	2002	
LN02HJO	Vauxhall Mover	Vauxhall	M8	2002	
EA52OJL	Vauxhall Vivaro	Vauxhall	M8	2002	
WR52OPJ	Ford Transit	Ford	M16	2002	
EO52OZT	LDV 400	LDV	M16	2003	
KN52NDF	Dennis Trident	Alexander ALX400	B43/20D	2003	Metroline, 2009
KN52NDK	Dennis Trident	Alexander ALX400	B43/20D	2003	Metroline, 2009
KN52NDL	Dennis Trident	Alexander ALX400	B43/20D	2003	Metroline, 2009
KN52NDU	Dennis Trident	Alexander ALX400	B43/20D	2003	Metroline, 2009
KN52NDV	Dennis Trident	Alexander ALX400	B43/20D	2003	Metroline, 2009
BV03RXN	Ford Transit	Ford	M8	2003	
RN03EOA	Ford Transit	Ford	M7	2003	
AE53KVO	LDV 400	LDV	M16	2003	
LJ53LDE	LDV 400	LDV	M16	2003	
RA53BLJ	Mercedes-Benz Sprinter 311cdi	Excel	M8	2003	
RA53BLK	Mercedes-Benz Sprinter 311cdi	Excel	M8	2003	
YN53CDE	Scania K114 IB4	Irizar Century	C49FT	2003	
CC04MAL	Scania K114 IB4	Irizar Century	C57FT	2004	
RL04EXL	Scania K114 IB4	Irizar Century	C57FT	2004	

Many changes to the composition of the Tellings-Golden Miller operations have taken place since the last edition of this Handbook, with more services now based around London's airports. Pictured in Surbiton is Alexander-bodied Trident KN52NDU. *Mark Lyons*

Hatton Cross is the location for this view of Alexander Dennis Dart with Enviro 200 bodywork KX57OWO. Of note is the amber light to allow airside workings. *Dave Heath*

GB04TGM	Volvo B12B	Caetano Enigma	C53F	2004	
UK04TGM	Volvo B12B	Caetano Enigma	C53F	2004	
UK04BCL	Volvo B12B	Caetano Enigma	C53F	2004	
YU04XFD	Volvo B12B	Caetano Enigma	C53F	2004	
AX04XJY	Ford Transit	Ford	M8	2004	
LT04CTV	Ford Transit	Ford	M8	2004	
LT04CWL	Ford Transit	Ford	M8	2004	
NL04PKZ	Ford Transit	Ford	M8	2004	
NL04RBF	Ford Transit	Ford	M8	2004	
LT04CTV	Ford Transit	Ford	M8	2004	
VX04JHY	LDV 400	LDV	M16	2004	
YN54ANU	Scania K114 IB4	VDL Berkhof Axial 70	C53FT	2005	
FJ05KWV	LDV 400	LDV	M16	2005	
HT05YCP	Vauxhall Vivaro	Vauxhall	M8	2005	
HT05YCR	Vauxhall Vivaro	Vauxhall	M8	2005	
HT05YCV	Vauxhall Vivaro	Vauxhall	M8	2005	
HT05YCZ	Vauxhall Vivaro	Vauxhall	M8	2005	
HT05YDA	Vauxhall Vivaro	Vauxhall	M8	2005	
HT05YDB	Vauxhall Vivaro	Vauxhall	M8	2005	
HT05YDC	Vauxhall Vivaro	Vauxhall	M8	2005	
RA05XEB	Volkswagen Touran	Volkswagen	M8	2005	
RA05XEC	Volkswagen Touran	Volkswagen	M8	2005	
RY05AEZ	Volkswagen Touran	Volkswagen	M8	2005	
YJ05PVW	Temsa Safari	Temsa	C55F	2005	
GS05TGM	Volvo B12B	Van Hool T9 Alizée	M36FT	2005	
EU06BCL	Volvo B12B	Plaxton Panther	C50FT	2006	
YN06PFF	Volvo B12M	Plaxton Panther	C50FT	2006	
YN06CJV	Scania K340 EB4	VDL Berkhof Axial 50	C55FT	2006	
YN06CJX	Scania K340 EB4	VDL Berkhof Axial 50	C55FT	2006	
YN06CJY	Scania K114 EB4	Irizar Century Style	C53F	2006	
YN06CJZ	Scania K114 EB4	Irizar Century Style	C53F	2006	
KC06EVN	Mercedes-Benz Vito 111cdi	Mercedes-Benz	M7	2006	
KC06EVP	Mercedes-Benz Vito 111cdi	Mercedes-Benz	M7	2006	
LT06XDU	Ford Transit	Ford	M8	2006	
EU56GVG	ADL Dart	ADL Pointer	N27F	2006	
KX56HCP	ADL Dart	ADL Pointer	N29F	2006	
KX56OVL	Volvo B12B	Plaxton Panther	C50FT	2006	Wiltax, New Haw, 2007

LT56JXU	Ford Transit	Ford	M8	2006	
LT56JXV	Ford Transit	Ford	M8	2006	
LT56JYN	Ford Transit	Ford	M8	2006	
LT56JZM	Ford Transit	Ford	M8	2006	
YJ07JHH	Temsa Safari	Temsa	C51FT	2007	Solus, Tamworth, 2009
YN07LGW	Scania K340 EB4	Irizar PB	C53F	2007	
YN07OOX	Volvo B12B	Plaxton Panther	C53F	2007	
YN07OOY	Volvo B12B	Plaxton Panther	C53F	2007	
KX57OWK	ADL Dart 4	ADL Enviro 200	N29F	2008	
KX57OWM	ADL Dart 4	ADL Enviro 200	N29F	2008	
KX57OWO	ADL Dart 4	ADL Enviro 200	N29F	2008	
KX57OWP	ADL Dart 4	ADL Enviro 200	N29F	2008	
KX57FML	Enterprise Plasma EB01	Plaxton Primo	N28F	2007	
LF08DZW	Enterprise Plasma EB01	Plaxton Primo	N28F	2008	
AE08DJV	MAN 14.240	MCV Evolution	N28D	2008	
AE08DJW	MAN 14.240	MCV Evolution	N28D	2008	
AE08DJX	MAN 14.240	MCV Evolution	N28D	2008	
KX08HLR	Volvo B12B	Plaxton Panther	C49FT	2008	
KX08ONC	Mercedes-Benz Vario O816	Plaxton Cheetah	C29F	2008	
KX08ONG	Mercedes-Benz Vario O816	Plaxton Cheetah	C29F	2008	
YJ08DKN	Temsa Safari	Temsa	C53F	2008	
YJ08DLV	Temsa Safari	Temsa	C53F	2008	
LJ58GCF	Volvo B9TL	East Lancs Olympus	NC61/39F	2009	
LJ58GCK	Volvo B9TL	East Lancs Olympus	NC61/39F	2009	
KX59CYE	Volvo B12M	Plaxton Panther	C50FT	2009	
KX59CYF	Volvo B12M	Plaxton Panther	C50FT	2009	
KX59CZD	Ford Transit	Ford	M16	2009	
KX59CZE	Ford Transit	Ford	M16	2009	

Web: www.tellingsgoldenmiller.co.uk

Network Colchester

101	CO	AY55DKA	Scania N94 UD	East Lancs OmniDekka	N47/33F	2005	
102	CO	YN06TFZ	Scania N94 UD	East Lancs OmniDekka	N47/33F	2006	
103	CO	YN08OBY	Scania N230 UD	East Lancs Olympus	N47/33F	2008	
104	CO	YN08OBY	Scania N230 UD	East Lancs Olympus	N47/33F	2008	
105	CO	YT59NZM	Scania N230 UD	Optare Olympus	N47/33F	2009	
106	CO	YT59NZN	Scania N230 UD	Optare Olympus	N47/33F	2009	
131	CO	T131AUA	DAF DB250	Plaxton President	B45/22F	1999	Wiltax, 2008
133	CO	T133AUA	DAF DB250	Plaxton President	B45/22F	1999	Wiltax, 2008
155	CO	T405SMV	Dennis Trident	East Lancs Lolyne	B45/31F	1999	Metrobus, Crawley, 2009
156	CO	T406SMV	Dennis Trident	East Lancs Lolyne	B45/31F	1999	Metrobus, Crawley, 2009
185	CO	KN52NCD	Dennis Trident	Alexander ALX400	B43/24F	2002	Metroline, 2010
190	CO	KN52NDX	Dennis Trident	Alexander ALX400	B43/24F	2002	Metroline, 2010
191	CO	KN52NEJ	Dennis Trident	Alexander ALX400	B43/24F	2002	Metroline, 2010
195	CO	W395RBB	Dennis Trident	Alexander ALX400	B51/31F	2000	Arriva North East, 2009
196	CO	W396RBB	Dennis Trident	Alexander ALX400	B51/31F	2000	Arriva North East, 2009
213	CO	G613BPH	Volvo Citybus B10M-50	East Lancs	B49/39F	1989	Arriva Southern Counties, 2004
214	CO	G614BPH	Volvo Citybus B10M-50	East Lancs	B49/39F	1989	Arriva Southern Counties, 2004
215	CO	G615BPH	Volvo Citybus B10M-50	East Lancs	B49/39F	1989	Arriva Southern Counties, 2004
243	CO	G643BPH	Volvo B10M-50 Citybus	Northern Counties Palatine	B45/35F	1989	Arriva Southern Counties, 2008
510	CO	Y40TGM	Dennis Dart SLF	Caetano Compass	N30D	2001	
511	CO	Y50TGM	Dennis Dart SLF	Caetano Compass	N30D	2001	
512	CO	HX51LRK	Dennis Dart SLF	Caetano Compass	N40F	2001	
513	CO	HX51LRL	Dennis Dart SLF	Caetano Compass	N40F	2001	
514	CO	HX51LRN	Dennis Dart SLF	Caetano Compass	N40F	2001	
515	CO	HX51LRO	Dennis Dart SLF	Caetano Compass	N40F	2001	
516	CO	HX51LRJ	Dennis Dart SLF	Caetano Compass	N40F	2001	

525-529			ADL Dart 10.7m	ADL Pointer	N37F	2004	
525	CO	SN54HXD	**527**	CO	SN54HXF	**528**	CO	AY54FPZ	**529**	CO	AY54FRC
526	CO	SN54HXE						

901-907			Volvo B10BLE	Alexander ALX300	N44F	2000	Tellings-Golden Miller, 2005
901	CO	W901UJM	**903**	CO	W903UJM	**905**	CO	W905UJM	**907**	CO	W907UJM
902	CO	W902UJM	**904**	CO	W904UJM	**906**	CO	W906UJM		

Previous registrations:

HX51LRK	HX51LRK, R60BCL	HX51LRO	HX51LRO, R90BCL
HX51LRL	HX51LRL, R80BCL	HX51LRN	HX51LRN, R70BCL

Representing the Colchester operation and livery is Dennis Trident 196, W396RBB, which was transferred from Arriva North East in 2009. *Dave Heath*

OFJ Connections

28	BV57VGG	Mercedes-Benz Citaro O530	Mercedes-Benz	N30D	2008	NSL, Croydon, 2009
29	BV57VGJ	Mercedes-Benz Citaro O530	Mercedes-Benz	N30D	2008	NSL, Croydon, 2009
30	BV57VGK	Mercedes-Benz Citaro O530	Mercedes-Benz	N30D	2008	NSL, Croydon, 2009
31	BV57VGL	Mercedes-Benz Citaro O530	Mercedes-Benz	N30D	2008	NSL, Croydon, 2009
32	BV57VGM	Mercedes-Benz Citaro O530	Mercedes-Benz	N30D	2008	NSL, Croydon, 2009
33	BD08DZN	Mercedes-Benz Citaro O530	Mercedes-Benz	N30D	2008	APCOA, Uxbridge, 2009
34	BD08DZO	Mercedes-Benz Citaro O530	Mercedes-Benz	N30D	2008	APCOA, Uxbridge, 2009
35	BD08DZP	Mercedes-Benz Citaro O530	Mercedes-Benz	N30D	2008	APCOA, Uxbridge, 2009
36	BD08DZR	Mercedes-Benz Citaro O530	Mercedes-Benz	N30D	2008	APCOA, Uxbridge, 2009
37	BD08DZS	Mercedes-Benz Citaro O530	Mercedes-Benz	N30D	2008	APCOA, Uxbridge, 2009
38	BD08DZT	Mercedes-Benz Citaro O530	Mercedes-Benz	N30D	2008	APCOA, Uxbridge, 2009
39	BD08DZU	Mercedes-Benz Citaro O530	Mercedes-Benz	N30D	2008	APCOA, Uxbridge, 2009
151	AE08DKJ	MAN 14.240	MCV Evolution	N24D	2008	Meteor Parking, 2009
152	AE08DKK	MAN 14.240	MCV Evolution	N24D	2008	Meteor Parking, 2009
153	AE08DKL	MAN 14.240	MCV Evolution	N24D	2008	Meteor Parking, 2009
154	AE08DKN	MAN 14.240	MCV Evolution	N24D	2008	Meteor Parking, 2009
155	V672LWT	DAF SB220	Ikarus CitiBus	N26D	1999	Glasgow Airport, 2003
156	V673LWT	DAF SB220	Ikarus CitiBus	N26D	1999	Glasgow Airport, 2003
156	AE08DKJ	MAN 14.240	MCV Evolution	N24D	2008	Meteor Parking, 2009
157	YN53CHG	Scania N94 UB	East Lancs	N36D	2003	
158	YN53CHH	Scania N94 UB	East Lancs	N36D	2003	
159	YN53CHJ	Scania N94 UB	East Lancs	N36D	2003	
160	YN53CHK	Scania N94 UB	East Lancs	N36D	2003	
161	YN53CHL	Scania N94 UB	East Lancs	N36D	2003	
168	YN04AHG	Scania OmniCity N94 UB	Scania	N36F	2004	
169	YN04AHJ	Scania OmniCity N94 UB	Scania	N36F	2004	
170	YN04AHK	Scania OmniCity N94 UB	Scania	N36F	2004	
171	YN04AHL	Scania OmniCity N94 UB	Scania	N36F	2004	
172	YN04AHP	Scania OmniCity N94 UB	Scania	N36F	2004	
175	AE04PJY	MAN 14.220	MCV Evolution	N22F	2004	
176	AE04PKA	MAN 14.220	MCV Evolution	N22F	2004	

177	AE05OVB	MAN 14.220	MCV Evolution	N22F	2005	
184	YN05GWZ	Scania K114 IB4	Irizar Century	C55F	2005	
185	YN55YSA	Volvo B7R	Plaxton Profile	C53F	2006	
186	YN05XZJ	Mercedes-Benz Vario 0814	Plaxton Cheetah	C25F	2005	
188	YN55WTK	Mercedes-Benz Vario 0814	Plaxton Cheetah	C25F	2005	
192	YN07OZP	Mercedes-Benz Vario 0816	Plaxton Cheetah	C25F	2007	
193	YN07OZR	Mercedes-Benz Vario 0816	Plaxton Cheetah	C25F	2007	
194	YN07OZS	Mercedes-Benz Vario 0816	Plaxton Cheetah	C25F	2007	
195	YN07OZT	Mercedes-Benz Vario 0816	Plaxton Cheetah	C25F	2007	
196	YN07OZU	Mercedes-Benz Vario 0816	Plaxton Cheetah	C25F	2007	
197	YN07OZV	Mercedes-Benz Vario 0816	Plaxton Cheetah	C25F	2007	
204	H804RWJ	Scania N113 DRB	Northern Counties	B47/33F	1989	Excel, 2009
225	G725RYJ	Scania N113 DRB	East Lancs	B47/33F	1988	
231	N161VVO	Scania N113 DRB	East Lancs	B45/33F	1996	Arriva Midlands, 2009
234	G34HKY	Scania N113 DRB	Northern Counties	B47/33F	1988	Network Colchester, 2009
237	G37HKY	Scania N113 DRB	Northern Counties	B47/33F	1988	Network Colchester, 2009
239	P639LMJ	Olympian ONCL10/1RZ	Alexander	B47/32F	1997	TGM Burtons 2009
240	P640LMJ	Olympian ONCL10/1RZ	Alexander	B47/32F	1997	TGM Burtons 2009
261	M161GRY	Scania N113 DRB	East Lancs	B47/33F	1995	Arriva Midlands, 2009
262	M162GRY	Scania N113 DRB	East Lancs	B47/33F	1995	Arriva Midlands, 2009
264	M834SDA	Scania N113 DRB	East Lancs	B47/33F	1995	Arriva Midlands, 2009
326	BU51REG	Dennis Dart SLF	Plaxton Pointer	N29F	2001	
327	EU56FTO	ADL Dart SLF	ADL Pointer	N31F	2006	
360	SN54HWY	TransBus Dart	TransBus Pointer	N37F	2004	Network Colchester, 2010
361	SN54HWZ	TransBus Dart	Transbus Pointer	N37F	2004	Network Colchester, 2010
362	SN54HXA	TransBus Dart	Transbus Pointer	N37F	2004	Network Colchester, 2010
363	SN54HXB	TransBus Dart	Transbus Pointer	N37F	2004	Network Colchester, 2010
364	SN54HXC	TransBus Dart	Transbus Pointer	N37F	2004	Network Colchester, 2010
401	S301JUA	Dennis Dart SLF	Plaxton Pointer	N26D	1998	Arriva London, 2010
402	S302JUA	Dennis Dart SLF	Plaxton Pointer	N26D	1998	Arriva London, 2010
403	S303JUA	Dennis Dart SLF	Plaxton Pointer	N26D	1998	Arriva London, 2010
410	S310JUA	Dennis Dart SLF	Plaxton Pointer	N26D	1998	Arriva London, 2010
412	S312JUA	Dennis Dart SLF	Plaxton Pointer	N26D	1998	Arriva London, 2010
414	S314JUA	Dennis Dart SLF	Plaxton Pointer	N26D	1998	Arriva London, 2010
	KM51BFX	Dennis Dart SLF	Caetano Compass	N31D	2001	
	RL51ZKR	Dennis Dart SLF	Caetano Compass	N29F	2001	
	RL51ZKS	Dennis Dart SLF	Caetano Compass	N29F	2001	
	KU52EYH	Dennis Dart SLF	Caetano Compass	N29F	2002	
	KU52EYJ	Dennis Dart SLF	Caetano Compass	N29F	2002	
	HX04HUH	Dennis Dart SLF	Caetano Compass	N29F	2004	
	HX04HUK	Dennis Dart SLF	Caetano Compass	N29F	2004	
	HX04HRD	Dennis Dart SLF	Caetano Compass	N32D	2004	
550	KP54BYY	Dennis Dart SLF	Plaxton Pointer 2	N39F	2004	
551	KU52RXT	Dennis Dart SLF	Plaxton Pointer 2	N37F	2002	
552	KP51UFL	Dennis Dart SLF	Plaxton Pointer 2	N37F	2001	
	KU52RXG	Dennis Dart SLF	Plaxton Pointer 2	N29F	2002	
	KU52RYO	Dennis Dart SLF	Plaxton Pointer 2	N37F	2002	
556	KP54BYZ	Dennis Dart SLF	Plaxton Pointer 2	N39F	2004	
561	AE56MDV	MAN 14.220	MCV Evolution	N31F	2006	
562	AE56MDX	MAN 14.220	MCV Evolution	N31F	2006	
563	AE56MDY	MAN 14.220	MCV Evolution	N31F	2006	
564	AE55VGK	MAN 14.220	MCV Evolution	N37F	2005	
565	AE55VGL	MAN 14.220	MCV Evolution	N40F	2005	
580	u/r	Cobus 2700S		B12D	2004	
581	-	Cobus 2700S		B12D	2004	
582	-	Cobus 2700S		B12D	2004	
583	-	Cobus 2700S		B12D	2004	
584	-	Cobus 2700S		B12D	2004	
585	-	Cobus 2700S		B12D	2004	
710	S550BNV	Mercedes-Benz Vario 0814	Plaxton Beaver 2	B31F	1998	Meteor Parking, 2010
713	S553BNV	Mercedes-Benz Vario 0814	Plaxton Beaver 2	B31F	1998	Meteor Parking, 2010
802	M722CGO	Dennis Dart SLF	Plaxton Pointer	B35F	1996	Metrobus, Crawley, 2009
867	N167PUT	Scania L113 CRL	East Lancs	B51F	1996	Arriva Midlands, 2009
869	N169PUT	Scania L113 CRL	East Lancs	B51F	1996	Arriva Midlands, 2009
870	N430XRC	Scania L113 CRL	East Lancs	B51F	1996	Arriva Midlands, 2009
872	N172PUT	Scania L113 CRL	East Lancs	B51F	1996	Arriva Midlands, 2009
873	N433XRC	Scania L113 CRL	East Lancs	B51F	1996	Arriva Midlands, 2009
876	N176PUT	Scania L113 CRL	East Lancs	B51F	1996	Arriva Midlands, 2009
898	LT04CTV	Ford Transit	Ford	M11	2004	
899	LT04CWC	Ford Transit	Ford	M11	2004	
	GSU348	DAF SB4000	Van-Hool T9 Alizée	C49FT	2002	TGM Classic, 2010
	R958RCH	Volvo B9M	Plaxton Première 320	C43F	1997	Airlinks, Feltham, 2005
	X715HCD	Mercedes-Benz Sprinter 311cdi	Frank Guy	M8	2001	Airlinks, Feltham, 2005

	Reg	Chassis	Body	Seating	Year	Notes
	X153ENJ	Mercedes-Benz Vario 0814	Plaxton Cheetah	C24F	2001	Airlinks, Feltham, 2005
	X157ENJ	Mercedes-Benz Vario 0814	Plaxton Cheetah	C24F	2001	Airlinks, Feltham, 2005
	X158ENJ	Mercedes-Benz Vario 0814	Plaxton Cheetah	C24F	2001	Airlinks, Feltham, 2005
	X216HCD	Mercedes-Benz Vario 0814	Plaxton Cheetah	C24F	2001	Airlinks, Feltham, 2005
	X217HCD	Mercedes-Benz Vario 0814	Plaxton Cheetah	C24F	2001	Airlinks, Feltham, 2005
	X221HCD	Mercedes-Benz Vario 0814	Plaxton Cheetah	C24F	2001	Airlinks, Feltham, 2005
	X734MFL	Mercedes-Benz Vario 0814		C29F	2001	
	Y30TGM	Volvo B10M-62	Plaxton Première 350	C49FT	2001	
	Y83HHE	Scania L94 IB	Irizar Century	C44FT	2001	
	EJ02OVU	Mercedes-Benz Sprinter 108cdi	Co-Trim	M6	2002	Meteor, 2009
	EJ02OVV	Mercedes-Benz Sprinter 108cdi	Co-Trim	M6	2002	Meteor, 2009
	EJ02OVW	Mercedes-Benz Sprinter 108cdi	Co-Trim	M6	2002	Meteor, 2009
	EJ02OVX	Mercedes-Benz Sprinter 108cdi	Co-Trim	M6	2002	Meteor, 2009
	EJ02OVY	Mercedes-Benz Sprinter 108cdi	Co-Trim	M6	2002	Meteor, 2009
	EJ02OVZ	Mercedes-Benz Sprinter 108cdi	Co-Trim	M6	2002	Meteor, 2009
	EJ02OWA	Mercedes-Benz Sprinter 108cdi	Co-Trim	M6	2002	Meteor, 2009
	EO52HZU	Mercedes-Benz Sprinter 108cdi	Co-Trim	M6	2002	Meteor, 2009
	EO52HZV	Mercedes-Benz Sprinter 108cdi	Co-Trim	M6	2002	Meteor, 2009
	GB53BCL	Volvo B12B	Caetano Enigma	C53F	2003	TGM Burtons, 2007
	RX53LBJ	Mercedes-Benz Vario 0814	Plaxton Beaver 2	BC33F	2003	
	FN04FSE	Volvo B12B	Caetano Enigma	C53F	2004	TGM Classic, 2008
	FN04FSF	Volvo B12B	Caetano Enigma	C53F	2004	TGM Classic, 2008
	GB04LLC	Volvo B7R	Plaxton Profile	C53F	2004	TGM Linkline, 2007
	XL04XEL	Scania K114 EB4	Irizar Century	C53F	2004	TGM Burtons, 2010
	YU04XFB	Volvo B12B	Plaxton Panther	C49FT	2004	TGM Flight Delay 2010
	YU04XFC	Volvo B12B	Plaxton Panther	C49FT	2004	TGM Flight Delay 2010
	YN54ANU	Scania K114 EB4	Burkhof	C53FT	2005	TGM Classic, 2010
	YN54DDJ	Volvo B12B	Plaxton Panther	C49FT	2005	TGM Burton 2009
	YN54DDK	Volvo B12B	Plaxton Panther	C49FT	2005	TGM Burton 2009
	YN54DDL	Volvo B12B	Plaxton Panther	C49FT	2005	TGM Burton 2009
	YN54DDO	Volvo B12B	Plaxton Panther	C49FT	2005	TGM Burton 2009
	HT05YCX	Vauxhall Vivaro	Vauxhall	M8	2005	
	HT05YDA	Vauxhall Vivaro	Vauxhall	M8	2005	
	HT05YDB	Vauxhall Vivaro	Vauxhall	M8	2005	
	HT05YDC	Vauxhall Vivaro	Vauxhall	M8	2005	
	YN05VRT	Volvo B12B	Plaxton Panther	C49FT	2005	
	YN55WSU	Volvo B12B	Plaxton Panther	C49FT	2005	
	YN55WSW	Volvo B12B	Plaxton Panther	C49FT	2005	
	KC06EVN	Mercedes-Benz Sprinter 111cdi	Mercedes	M7	2006	
	KC06EVP	Mercedes-Benz Sprinter 111cdi	Mercedes	M7	2006	
	LS06YCR	Ford Transit	Ford	M8	2006	
	LS06YCT	Ford Transit	Ford	M8	2006	
104	YN56DYU	Mercedes-Benz Vario 0814	Plaxton Cheetah	C25F	2006	
	YN56DYV	Mercedes-Benz Vario 0814	Plaxton Cheetah	C29F	2006	
	YN56DYW	Mercedes-Benz Vario 0814	Plaxton Cheetah	C29F	2006	
105	YN56DYX	Volvo B7R	Plaxton Profile	C53F	2006	
	YN56SGU	Volvo B12B	Plaxton Panther	C49FTL	2007	
	WX07WTX	Volvo B12B	Plaxton Panther	C53F	2007	Wiltax, New Haw, 2007
	YN07LJU	Scania K114 EB4	Irizar Century	C49Ft	2007	
	RX07KPG	ADL Dart SLF	Caetano Compass	N29F	2007	
	RX07KPJ	ADL Dart SLF	Caetano Compass	N29F	2007	
	RY07BJU	Volkswagen Crafter	Volkswagen	M8	2007	
	RF57KTT	Volkswagen Crafter	Volkswagen	M8	2007	
	RO57PJU	Volkswagen Crafter	Volkswagen	M8	2007	
	RO57WJM	Volkswagen Crafter	Volkswagen	M8	2007	
	RV57DXO	Volkswagen Crafter	Volkswagen	M8	2007	
	RV57DXY	Volkswagen Crafter	Volkswagen	M8	2007	
	YJ57BTU	VDL Bus SB4000	Van-Hool T9 Alizée	C52FL	2007	
	YN57OUH	Mercedes-Benz Vario 0816	Plaxton Cheetah	C25F	2007	
	YN57OUJ	Mercedes-Benz Vario 0816	Plaxton Cheetah	C25F	2007	
	YN57OUK	Mercedes-Benz Vario 0816	Plaxton Cheetah	C25F	2007	
	YN57OUL	Mercedes-Benz Vario 0816	Plaxton Cheetah	C25F	2007	
	YN57OUM	Mercedes-Benz Vario 0816	Plaxton Cheetah	C25F	2007	
	YN57OUO	Mercedes-Benz Vario 0816	Plaxton Cheetah	C25F	2007	
	YN57OUP	Mercedes-Benz Vario 0816	Plaxton Cheetah	C25F	2007	
	KX08ONG	Mercedes-Benz Vario 0816	Plaxton Cheetah	C25F	2008	
	LF08DZX	Enterprise Plasma	Plaxton	B22F	2008	
	YN08MPE	Scania K340 EB4	Irizar Century	C53FL	2008	
	YN08MPF	Scania K340 EB5	Irizar Century	C53FL	2009	
	KX59CZA	Volvo B12B	Plaxton Panther	C53F	2009	
	KX59CZB	Volvo B12B	Plaxton Panther	C53F	2009	
	KX59CZC	Ford Transit	Ford	M16	2009	
	KX59CZF	Mercedes-Benz 0.816D	Plaxton Cheetah 2	C29F	2009	

Ofj operates a large number of mini-coaches with a variety of seating capacities mostly for work in and around Heathrow. Aldwich is the location for this view of Mercedes-Benz Vario KX08ONG. *Colin Lloyd*

KX59CZG	ADL Dart SLF	ADL Pointer	N26F	2009
KX59CZH	ADL Dart SLF	ADL Pointer	N26F	2009
KX59CZJ	ADL Dart SLF	ADL Pointer	N26F	2009
KX59CZK	ADL Dart SLF	ADL Pointer	N26F	2009
KX59CZL	ADL Dart SLF	ADL Pointer	N26F	2009
KX59CZM	ADL Dart SLF	ADL Pointer	N26F	2009
KX59CZN	ADL Dart SLF	ADL Pointer	N26F	2009
SF59AWR	PT Express	Monarch	M8	2009
OV59WJX	Mercedes-Benz 311CDI	Mercedes	M8	2010
OV59WJY	Mercedes-Benz 311CDI	Mercedes	M8	2010
OV59WJZ	Mercedes-Benz 311CDI	Mercedes	M8	2010
OV59WKA	Mercedes-Benz 311CDI	Mercedes	M8	2010
OV59WKB	Mercedes-Benz 311CDI	Mercedes	M8	2010
OV59WKC	Mercedes-Benz 311CDI	Mercedes	M8	2010

Previous registration:

GSU348	NL52XZY

Classic's bright red livery is displayed on Berkhof-bodied Scania YN54ANU from the 2005 intake. *Colin Lloyd*

Excel

H9 Gatwick Business Park, Kennel Lane, Hookwood, Surrey RH6 OAY

P417HVX	Dennis Dart SLF	Wright	N41F	1997	
R169GNW	Dennis Dart SLF	Wright	N36F	1997	
R170GNW	Dennis Dart SLF	Wright	N36F	1997	
S311JUA	Dennis Dart SLF	Plaxton Pointer	N26D	1998	Arriva London, 2010
S313JUA	Dennis Dart SLF	Plaxton Pointer	N26D	1998	Arriva London, 2010
V250HBU	Volvo B6LE	Wright	N40D	1999	
V251HBU	Volvo B6LE	Wright	N40D	1999	
V255HBU	Volvo B6LE	Wright	N40D	1999	
GO03CLA	Scania K114 IB4	Irizar Century	C49Ft	2003	
YN06PFD	Volvo B12M	Plaxton Panther	C52Ft	2006	
YN06PFE	Volvo B12M	Plaxton Panther	C52Ft	2006	
YN06PFG	Volvo B12M	Plaxton Panther	C52Ft	2006	
YN06RVP	Mercedes-Benz O.814D	Plaxton Cheetah	C29F	2006	
KX08HLU	Volvo B12B	Plaxton Panther	C49Ft	2008	Stansted Transit, 2009
YJ58FFL	VDL SB200	Plaxton Centro	N45F	2009	
YJ58FFN	VDL SB200	Plaxton Centro	N45F	2009	

Classic Coaches

Classic House, Morrison Road, Annfield Plain, DH9 7RX

TJI1683	Volvo B10M-61	Plaxton Supreme IV	C53FT	1982	Wickson, Walsall Wood, 1997
B737GCN	Olympian ONCL10/1RV	Eastern Coach Works	B45/32F	1985	Go North East, 2005
D78JHY	Tiger TRCTL11/3LZ	Plaxton Derwent	BC70F	1986	Turner, Bristol, 2008
E691NOU	Tiger TRCTL11/3LZ	Plaxton Derwent	BC70F	1987	Turner, Bristol, 2008
PIL2160	Tiger TRCTL11/3RZM	Plaxton Bustler	BC69F	1989	TGM, Burtons, 2005
PIL2170	Tiger TRCTL11/3RZM	Plaxton Bustler	BC69F	1989	TGM, Burtons, 2005
S10BCL	Volvo Olympian	East Lancs	B47/29F	1998	TGM, Burtons, 2006

S20BCL	Volvo Olympian	East Lancs	B47/29F	1998	TGM, Burtons, 2006
S649KJU	Volvo Olympian	Northern Counties	B47/29F	1998	Arriva Midlands, 2010
V735FPT	Volvo B10M-62	Jonckheere	C40FT	1999	
V1SFC	Van-Hool Altano TD921	Van-Hool	C38/5FT	2009	
W427CWX	Optare Solo M850	Optare	N30F	2000	TGM, Burtons, 2009
W442CWX	Optare Solo M920	Optare	N30F	2000	TGM, Burtons, 2008
X129PTW	Mercedes-Benz 110cdi	Traveliner	M8	2001	
Y291PDN	Optare Solo M920	Optare	N27F	2001	Metrobus, Crawley 2006
Y292PDN	Optare Solo M920	Optare	N31F	2001	TGM, Burtons, 2010
Y293PDN	Optare Solo M920	Optare	N27F	2001	Metrobus, Crawley, 2006
Y295PDN	Optare Solo M850	Optare	N24F	2001	TGM, Burtons, 2009
YJ51JWW	Optare Solo M850	Optare	N29F	2001	TGM, Burtons, 2009
OSU895	DAFSB4000	Van-Hool Alizée	C49FT	2002	Arriva North East ,2006
BX02CLO	Mercedes-Benz Sprinter 411cdi	Koch	M14	2002	
YL02FKY	Optare Solo M850	Optare	N28F	2002	Stagecoach, 2006
G2PGL	Volvo B12B	Caetano Enigma	C49FT	2004	TGM, Burtons, 2007
YN53OZP	Scania K114 IB4	Irizar Century	C51FT	2004	
YN53OZR	Scania K114 IB4	Irizar Century	C49FT	2004	
NK04VMD	Mercedes-Benz Sprinter 411cdiI	Koch	M14	2004	
YD04MFJ	Mercedes-Benz Vito 109cdi	Mercedes-Benz	M8	2004	
YD04MFK	Mercedes-Benz Vito 109cdi	Mercedes-Benz	M8	2004	
YD04MFN	Mercedes-Benz Vito 109cdi	Mercedes-Benz	M8	2004	
AY54APK	Mercedes-Benz 111cdi	Mercedes-Benz	M8	2004	TGM, Burtons, 2007
BX54EBU	Mercedes-Benz Sprinter 416cdi	Koch	M16	2004	
BX54EBV	Mercedes-Benz Sprinter 416cdi	Koch	M16	2004	
YN54WWF	Volvo B12B	Plaxton Panther	C49FT	2004	TGM, 2005
YN54ZHK	Volvo B12B	Plaxton Panther	C49FT	2005	TGM, Burtons, 2008
YN54ZHL	Volvo B12B	Plaxton Panther	C49Ft	2005	TGM, Burtons, 2008
YN54ZHM	Volvo B12B	Plaxton Panther	C49Ft	2005	TGM, Burtons, 2008
YN54AGV	Scania K114 EB4	VDL Berkhof Axial	C55DTL	2005	
YN54AJO	Scania K114 EB4	VDL Berkhof Axial	C55FT	2005	
YN54AKO	Scania K114 EB4	VDL Berkhof Axial	C55FT	2005	
YN54AMO	Scania K114 EB4	VDL Berkhof Axial	C55FT	2005	
YN54ANU	Scania K114 EB4	VDL Berkhof Axial	C55FT	2005	
WSV570	Scania K114 EB6	Irizar Century PB	C32FT	2005	
AU05GCK	Mercedes-Benz Vito 111cdi	Mercedes-Benz	M8	2005	TGM, Burtons, 2007
YN05VRU	Volvo B12B	Plaxton Panther	C49FT	2005	TGM, Burtons, 2008
FJ06ZKK	Volvo B12B	VDL Berkhof Axial	C55FT	2006	
FJ06ZKL	Volvo B12B	VDL Berkhof Axial	C55FT	2006	
YN06CJU	Scania K114 EB4	VDL Berkhof Axial	C55FT	2006	
EU56GVG	ADL Dart SLF	ADL Pointer	N27F	2006	Tellings-Golden Miller, 2010
YN56SGO	Volvo B12B	Plaxton Panther	C49FT	2007	
FJ07DWF	Scania K114 EB4	Caetano Levante	C49FT	2007	
FJ07DWG	Scania K114 EB4	Caetano Levante	C49FT	2007	
MR07FDS	Ayats A3E-15/BR1	Ayats	C55/27CT	2007	TGM, Flight Delay, 2010
YJ07JFY	VDL Bus SB4000	Van-Hool Alizée T9	C49FT	2007	Edinburgh Coachlines, 2010
YN07LHF	Scania K340 EB6	Irizar Century PB	C59FT	2007	
YN07LHG	Scania K340 EB6	Irizar Century PB	C59FT	2007	
5579MW	Volvo B12BT	Van-Hool Astrobel	C61/14CT	2008	
5877MW	Volvo B12BT	Van-Hool Astrobel	C61/18CT	2008	
6963MW	Volvo B12BT	Van-Hool Astrobel	C61/18CT	2006	
FJ57KGK	Scania K340 EB6	Caetano Levante	C61FT	2008	
FJ08KMA	Scania K340 EB6	Caetano Levante	C61FT	2008	
FJ08KME	Scania K340 EB6	Caetano Levante	C61FT	2008	
FJ08KMF	Scania K340 EB6	Caetano Levante	C61FT	2008	
FJ08KMG	Scania K340 EB6	Caetano Levante	C61FT	2008	
FJ60HYH	Volvo B9R	Caetano Levante	C48FT	2010	
FJ60HYK	Volvo B9R	Caetano Levante	C48FT	2010	
FJ60HYL	Volvo B9R	Caetano Levante	C48FT	2010	
FJ60HYM	Volvo B9R	Caetano Levante	C48FT	2010	

Previous registrations:

6963MW	WA56ENN, V1SFC	PIL2170	G234BRT, 03KJ43
D78JHY	3138DP, 82KF21	S10BCL	S849DGX
E691NOU	XHY256, 87KF17	S20BCL	S852DGX
G2PGL	UK04BCL	TJI1683	UCX429X
OSU985	NL52XZX	WSV570	YN55PXX
PIL2160	G235BRT, 03KJ44	WSV571	V735FPT

ARRIVA SKANDINAVIEN

Arriva Danmark A/S; Arriva Scandinavia A/S
Herstedvang 7C, DK-2650 Albertslund, Danmark

1006-1011   Volvo B10LA   Åbenrå   AN44D   1998

1006	w	PC95843	1009	w	PC95872	1010	w	PC95863	1011	w	PC95873
1008	w	PC95862									

1014-1029   Volvo B10BLE   Åbenrå   N30D*   1998   1028/9 are N32D

1014	EJ	PJ88.334	1018	RK	PJ88.338	1023	RK	PJ88.343	1027	RK	PJ88.347
1015	EJ	PJ88.335	1019	RK	PJ88.339	1024	RK	PJ88.344	1028	RK	PJ97769
1016	EJ	PJ88.336	1020	RK	PJ88.340	1025	RK	PJ88.345	1029	RK	PJ97770
1017	EJ	PJ88.337	1022	RK	PJ88.342	1026	RK	PJ88.346			

1030-1057   Volvo B7RLE   Säffle   N35D   2009

1030	GX	XN90751	1037	GX	XN90760	1044	GX	XN90789	1051	RG	XN90817
1031	GX	XN90752	1038	GX	XN90761	1045	GX	XN90790	1052	RG	XN90818
1032	GX	XN90753	1039	GX	XN90762	1046	GX	XN90797	1053	RG	XN90819
1033	GX	XN90754	1040	GX	XN90763	1047	RG	XN90798	1054	RG	XN90820
1034	GX	XN90755	1041	GX	XN90764	1048	RG	XN90799	1055	RG	XN90821
1035	GX	XN90756	1042	GX	XN90787	1049	RG	XN90800	1056	RG	XN90822
1036	GX	XN90759	1043	GX	XN90788	1050	RG	XN90801	1057	RG	XN90823

1084-1147   DAB Citibus S15 (LPG)   DAB Silkeborg   N31D   1998

1084	w	PE97340	1096	GX	PE97352	1127	w	PL96059	1138	w	PM95490
1086	RG	PE97342	1097	w	PE97359	1128	w	PL96060	1139	w	PM95491
1087	w	PE97343	1098	w	PE97424	1129	w	PL96061	1140	RG	PM95507
1088	w	PE97344	1099	w	PE97444	1130	w	PM95387	1141	w	PM95508
1089	RG	PE97345	1100	w	PE97445	1131	RG	PM95388	1142	w	PM95509
1090	w	PE97346	1102	w	PJ96813	1132	w	PM95408	1143	RG	PP94068
1091	RG	PE97347	1103	w	PJ96814	1133	RG	PM95409	1144	w	PP94069
1092	RG	PE97348	1104	w	PJ96815	1134	w	PM95410	1145	w	PP94070
1093	RG	PE97349	1108	w	PJ96904	1135	w	PM95453	1146	w	PP94071
1094	w	PE97350	1109	w	PJ96905	1137	w	PM95455	1147	w	PP94072
1095	w	VZ89061	1110	w	PJ96906						

Taken into stock during 2009 for service in Copenhagen was a batch of Volvo B7RLEs with bodywork built in the former Säffle factory in Sweden which is now part of the Volvo group. 1043, XN90788, is shown.
Mark Doggett

Movia is the name of the Transport Authority for Copenhagen with Arriva being one of the main suppliers of vehicles. Carrying number 1224, TT94337, is dual-purpose VDL SB4000 with Jonckheere bodywork.
Mark Doggett

1157-1171

Scania L113 CLL · Berkhof · N31D · 1998-99

1157	w	PP94306	1160	RK	PP94326	1164	w	PR93210	1170	w	PR93374
1159	w	PP94325	1162	w	PP94356	1167	w	PR93314	1171	w	PR93328

1174-1181

DAB Citibus S15 (LPG) · DAB Silkeborg · N31D · 1999

1174	w	PZ90196	1177	w	PZ89838	1180	w	PZ89893	1181	w	PZ89894
1176	w	PZ89723									

1189-1219

DAB Citybus S15 (LPG) · DAB Silkeborg · N31D · 1997-99

1189	w	OY91770	1198	GX	OY91997	1205	RG	PE88121	1212	RG	PE88128
1190	w	OY91908	1200	w	OZ91743	1206	w	PE88122	1213	w	PE97294
1191	RG	OY91910	1201	w	OZ91744	1207	RG	PE88123	1214	w	PL96188
1193	w	OY91917	1202	w	PC97856	1208	RG	PE88124	1217	RG	PP94098
1194	w	OY91918	1203	w	PE88119	1209	RG	PE88125	1218	w	PZ89777
1197	w	OY91996	1204	w	PE88120	1211	w	PE88127	1219	w	PZ89909

1220	w	RH90875	VDL Bus 2000LF gas	Berkhof		N31F	2000

1221-1235

VDL Bus SB4000 · VDL Jonckheere · NC33D · 2005

1221	GX	TT94215	1225	GX	TT94338	1229	GX	TT94342	1233	GX	TT94346
1222	GX	TT94216	1226	GX	TT94339	1230	GX	TT94343	1234	GX	TT94347
1223	GX	TT94214	1227	GX	TT94340	1231	GX	TT94344	1235	GX	TT94348
1224	GX	TT94337	1228	GX	TT94341	1232	GX	TT94345			

1236	KO	UB95799	Volvo B12BLE	Volvo 8500		N33D	2006
1237	GX	UK96354	VDL Bus SB4000	VDL Jonckheere		N33D	2006

1238-1249

Volvo B7BLE · Volvo 8500 · N33D · 2006

1238	RG	UR90587	1241	RG	UR90657	1244	RG	UR90690	1247	RG	UR90693
1239	RG	UR90588	1242	RG	UR90669	1245	RG	UR90691	1248	RG	UR90713
1240	RG	UR90656	1243	RG	UR90670	1246	RG	UR90692	1249	RG	UR90714

1250-1271 — Volvo B12BLE — Åbenrå — N32D — 2004

1250	RK	TD91367	1256	RK	TJ97103	1262	RK	TJ97844	1267	RK	TJ97896
1251	RK	TD91368	1257	RK	TJ97105	1263	RK	TJ97843	1268	RK	TL89534
1252	RK	TD91375	1258	RK	TJ97811	1264	RK	TJ97870	1269	RK	TL89537
1253	RK	TJ97101	1259	RK	TJ97812	1265	RK	TJ97869	1270	RK	TL89536
1254	RK	TJ97102	1260	RK	TJ97813	1266	RK	TJ97889	1271	RK	TL89635
1255	RK	TJ97104	1261	RK	TJ97842						

1272-1275 — Volvo B7BLE — Volvo 8500 — N33D — 2006

1272	RG	UR90715	1273	RG	UR90716	1274	RG	UR90710	1275	RG	UR90711

1276	RK	TJ92702	Volvo B10BLE	Säffle	N43D	1997
1277	RK	TJ92703	Volvo B10BLE	Säffle	N43D	1997
1278	AM	TX89413	VDL Bus SB4000	VDL Jonckheere	N33D	2005

1300-1311 — Volvo B10BLE — Säffle — N43D — 1997

1300	RK	TD89898	1304	RK	TD89753	1308	RK	TD89748	1310	RK	TD89707
1302	RK	TD89710	1305	RK	TD89751	1309	RK	TD89749	1311	RK	TD89708
1303	RK	TJ92700	1307	RK	TD89750						

1314-1339 — Volvo B7RLE — Volvo — N43D — 2007

1314	RG	VN96086	1321	RG	VN92352	1328	RG	VN92397	1334	RG	VN92403
1315	RG	VN96087	1322	RG	VN92353	1329	RG	VN92398	1335	RG	VN92416
1316	RG	VN92347	1323	RG	VN92355	1330	RG	VN92399	1336	RG	VN92423
1317	RG	VN92348	1324	RG	VN92354	1331	RG	VN92400	1337	RG	VN92431
1318	RG	VN92349	1325	RG	VN92370	1332	RG	VN92401	1338	RG	VN92443
1319	RG	VN92350	1326	RG	VN92371	1333	RG	VN92402	1339	RG	VN92444
1320	RG	VN92351	1327	RG	VN92396						

1340-1381 — Volvo B10BLE 12m — Åbenrå — N32D — 2000

1340	GX	RM90995	1355	GX	RM91010	1361	RK	RM91016	1376	HI	RN90322
1341	w	RM90996	1356	w	RM91011	1362	RK	RM91017	1377	HI	RN90323
1342	GX	RM90997	1357	GX	RM91012	1363	RK	RM91018	1378	HI	RN90379
1343	w	RM90998	1358	GX	RM91013	1364	RK	RM91019	1379	HI	RN90380
1344	GX	RM90999	1359	GX	RM91014	1365	RK	RM91020	1380	HI	RN90381
1345	RG	RM91000	1360	RK	RM91015	1367	RK	RM91022	1381	HI	RN90382

1385-1403 — Volvo B10BLE 13.7m — Åbenrå — NC45D — 2000

1385	w	SN89817	1392	RG	RN95511	1396	RG	RN95515	1400	HI	RP88736
1387	w	RN95486	1393	RG	RN95512	1397	HI	RP88732	1401	HI	RP88737
1388	w	RN95487	1394	RG	RN95513	1398	HI	RP88733	1402	w	RP88738
1391	RG	RN95490	1395	RG	RN95514	1399	HI	RP88735	1403	w	RP88734

1406-1435 — Volvo B10BLE 13.7m — Åbenrå — NC45D — 2001

1406	w	RX93856	1414	RG	RV92762	1425	RG	RV92764	1430	RG	RV96461
1411	FN	RV92729	1415	EJ	RX93812	1426	RG	RV92765	1431	w	RV96462
1412	RG	RX93811	1418	w	RX93859	1428	w	RX93860	1434	RG	RV96464
1413	w	RX93857	1419	RG	RV92763	1429	w	RV96460	1435	RG	RX96754

1456-1472 — Volvo B10BLE 13.7m — Åbenrå — N45D — 2002

1456	EJ	SC90611	1459	w	SC90677	1466	AA	SB93616	1471	EJ	SD88253
1457	w	SC90651	1462	w	SD88165	1467	w	SB93617	1472	w	SD88254
1458	RG	SC90652	1464	w	SD88212						

1474-1498 — DAB Citybus S15 (LPG) — Silkeborg — N31D — 1997-99

1474	w	OY91990	1483	w	PL96254	1489	w	PP94132	1494	w	PZ89715
1475	w	OY91991	1484	w	PM95290	1490	RG	PP94133	1495	GX	PZ89724
1479	GX	PE88132	1486	GX	PM95345	1491	RG	PZ89701	1496	GX	PZ89735
1480	GX	PE88139	1487	w	PP94099	1492	RG	PZ89714	1497	w	PZ89736
1481	GX	PL96097	1488	w	PP94100	1493	RG	PZ89676	1498	GX	PZ89756
1482	GX	PL96253									

1500	w	RH90371	VDL Bus 2000LF (LPG)	Berkhof	N31D	1999
1501	w	UT97040	VDL Bus 2000LF (LPG)	Berkhof	N31D	1999
1502	w	RE88967	VDL Bus 2000LF (LPG)	Berkhof	N31D	1999
1503	w	RH90134	VDL Bus 2000LF (LPG)	Berkhof	N31D	1999

From the 2005 order for Scania OmniCity buses, 1547, TZ89234, is seen near the central bus station. The red quarter marking, which is also on the rear corner indicates low-floor access for push-chairs. *Harry Laming*

1518-1580

Scania OmniCity CL94 UB   Scania   AN43D   2005-06

1518	AA	TX92484	1534	EJ	TX92615	1550	GX	TZ89326	1566	GX	UB94158
1519	EJ	TX92485	1535	EJ	TX92616	1551	GX	TZ89327	1567	GX	UB94159
1520	RG	TX92486	1536	EJ	TX92619	1552	GX	TZ89328	1568	GX	UB94223
1521	EJ	TX92487	1537	EJ	TX92649	1553	GX	TZ89399	1569	GX	UB94224
1522	EJ	TX92488	1538	EJ	TZ89150	1554	GX	TZ89423	1570	GX	UB94225
1523	EJ	TX92489	1539	EJ	TZ89151	1555	GX	TZ89448	1571	GX	UB94243
1524	EJ	TX92523	1540	EJ	TZ89152	1556	GX	TZ89463	1572	GX	UB94244
1525	EJ	TX92524	1541	EJ	TZ89203	1557	GX	UB94098	1573	GX	UB94245
1526	EJ	TX92525	1542	EJ	TZ89204	1558	GX	UB94099	1574	GX	UB94246
1527	EJ	TX92526	1543	EJ	TZ89205	1559	GX	UB94100	1575	GX	UB94284
1528	EJ	TX92527	1544	EJ	TZ89206	1560	GX	UB94117	1576	GX	UB94285
1529	EJ	TX92528	1545	EJ	TZ89232	1561	W	UB94118	1577	GX	UB94286
1530	EJ	TX92569	1546	EJ	TZ89233	1562	GX	UB94283	1578	GX	UM94114
1531	EJ	TX92570	1547	EJ	TZ89234	1563	GX	UB94155	1579	GX	UM94113
1532	EJ	TX92571	1548	EJ	TZ89235	1564	GX	UB94156	1580	GX	UM94112
1533	EJ	TX92572	1549	EJ	TZ89236	1565	GX	UB94157			

1583-1590

DAB Citybus S15 Mk3 LPG   DAB Silkeborg   N31D   1997

1583	w	OZ91959	1586	w	OZ91681	1589	GX	OZ91685	1590	GX	OZ91686
1584	w	OY91998	1587	w	OZ91682						

1592-1611

Volvo B10BLE 13.7m   Åbenrå   N32D   1998

1592	GX	PJ88362	1597	GX	PJ88368	1602	GX	PJ88373	1607	GX	PJ88379
1593	GX	PJ88365	1598	w	PC92482	1603	w	PJ88374	1608	GX	PJ88360
1594	GX	PJ88364	1599	GX	PJ88369	1604	w	PJ88375	1609	w	PJ88361
1595	GX	PC92476	1600	GX	PJ88370	1605	GX	TT94683	1610	GX	PJ97773
1596	GX	PC92477	1601	GX	PJ88371	1606	GX	PJ88378	1611	GX	PJ97775

1612-1641 DAB Citybus S15 Mk3 (LPG) DAB Silkeborg N31D 1998-99

1612	GX	PE88117	**1620**	w	PM95243	**1629**	w	PZ89707	**1635**	w	PZ89713
1613	w	PC90580	**1621**	GX	PM95246	**1630**	GX	PZ89708	**1636**	GX	PZ89677
1614	GX	PE88129	**1623**	GX	PZ94130	**1631**	GX	PZ89709	**1637**	GX	PZ89796
1615	GX	PE97295	**1624**	w	PZ94131	**1632**	GX	PZ89710	**1638**	GX	PZ89797
1616	GX	PL96096	**1625**	GX	PZ89703	**1633**	GX	PZ89711	**1640**	GX	RC88817
1618	w	PL96186	**1627**	w	PZ89705	**1634**	GX	PZ89712	**1641**	GX	RC88888
1619	GX	PL96187									

1642-1673 Volvo B12BLE Volvo 8500 N33D 2003

1642	RG	SR93011	**1650**	RG	ST97814	**1658**	RG	ST97831	**1666**	RG	ST97844
1643	RG	SR93012	**1651**	RG	SR93093	**1659**	RG	SR93081	**1667**	RG	ST97847
1644	RG	ST97813	**1652**	RG	SR93053	**1660**	RG	ST97837	**1668**	RG	ST97848
1645	RG	SR93034	**1653**	RG	SR93065	**1661**	RG	ST97841	**1669**	RG	ST97854
1646	RG	SR93092	**1654**	RG	SR93083	**1662**	w	ST97846	**1670**	RG	ST97855
1647	RG	SR93080	**1655**	RG	SR93094	**1663**	RG	ST97832	**1671**	RG	ST97856
1648	RG	SR93064	**1656**	RG	ST97815	**1664**	RG	ST97842	**1672**	RG	ST97869
1649	RG	SR93082	**1657**	RG	ST97830	**1665**	RG	ST97843	**1673**	RG	ST97876

1674-1682 VDL Bus SB4000 VDL Jonckheere Citybus N33D 2005

1674	GX	TU92380	**1677**	GX	TU92377	**1679**	GX	TU92375	**1681**	GX	TU92373
1675	GX	TU92379	**1678**	GX	TU92376	**1680**	GX	TU92374	**1682**	GX	TU92372
1676	GX	TU92378									

1683-1686 Volvo B12BLE Volvo 8500 N33D 2005

1683	RG	TS94892	**1684**	RG	TS94893	**1685**	RG	TS94894	**1686**	RG	TS94895

1687	GX	TV88714	VDL Bus SB4000	VDL Jonckheere Citybus	N33D	2005

1688-1695 Scania OmniLink CL94 UB 12m Scania N31D 2002

1688	GX	SH93771	**1690**	GX	SH93775	**1692**	GX	SH93777	**1694**	GX	SH93739
1689	GX	SH93774	**1691**	GX	SH93776	**1693**	GX	SH93778	**1695**	GX	SH93773

1700-1733 Volvo B10BLE 12m Åbenrå AN32D 1999

1700	HI	PZ95450	**1707**	RK	PZ95457	**1714**	RK	PZ95496	**1723**	EJ	PZ95505
1701	HI	PZ95451	**1708**	HI	PZ95458	**1715**	HI	PZ95497	**1725**	RG	PZ95546
1702	RK	PZ95452	**1709**	GX	PZ95459	**1716**	HI	PZ95498	**1728**	RG	PZ95549
1703	RK	PZ95453	**1710**	GX	PZ95492	**1717**	HI	PZ95499	**1730**	HI	PZ95551
1704	RK	PZ95454	**1711**	GX	PZ95493	**1718**	HI	PZ95500	**1731**	RG	PZ95552
1705	RK	PZ95455	**1712**	HI	PZ95494	**1719**	HI	PZ95501	**1732**	RG	PZ95553
1706	RK	PZ95456	**1713**	HI	PZ95495	**1720**	RK	PZ95502	**1733**	RG	PZ95554

1740	GX	PZ95592	Volvo B10BLE	Åbenrå	N32D	1999
1741	GX	PZ95593	Volvo B10BLE	Åbenrå	N32D	1999
1742	EJ	PZ95594	Volvo B10BLE	Åbenrå	N32D	1999
1746	GX	PC95824	Volvo B10BLE	Åbenrå	N32D	1999
1750	w	RU97094	DAB Citybus S11	DAB	N15F	2001
1751	w	RU97095	DAB Citybus S11	DAB	N15F	2002
1753	ND	PP94330	DAB Citybus S11	DAB	N15F	1998

1754-1760 Optare Solo M920L Optare N23D 2005

1754	EJ	TP97969	**1756**	RK	TP97968	**1758**	RK	TR88011	**1760**	RK	TR88009
1755	RK	TP97967	**1757**	RK	TP97966	**1759**	RK	TR88010			

1761	KG	XE97902	VDL Bus ALE120	VDL Ambassadør	N27D	2009
1762	KG	XE97901	VDL Bus ALE120	VDL Ambassadør	N27D	2009
1763	w	PP94331	DAB Citybus S11	DAB	N15D	1998
1764	w	PP94332	DAB Citybus S11	DAB	N15D	1998
1769	w	RV89.288	Mercedes-Benz O520 Cito S	Mercedes-Benz	N29F	2002
1773	EJ	PP89440	Volvo B10BLE	Åbenrå	N32D	1997
1781	w	RC89417	Volvo B10BLE	Åbenrå	N32D	1998

1783-1794 Scania OmniLink CL94 UB 12m Scania N42D 2003

1783	EJ	SU96129	**1786**	EJ	SU96126	**1789**	EJ	SU96123	**1792**	EJ	SU96135
1784	EJ	SU96128	**1787**	EJ	SU96125	**1790**	EJ	SU96122	**1793**	EJ	SU96148
1785	EJ	SU96127	**1788**	EJ	SU96124	**1791**	EJ	SU96136	**1794**	EJ	SU96147

The Scania OmniCity and higher OmniLink have been selected by Arriva for several operations, including over a hundred for service in Copenhagen. From the 2008 intake is 1923, XD92774, shown here. *Mark Doggett*

1795-1813
Scania OmniLink CL94 UB 13.7m Scania   NC43D   2003

1795	RG	SV97011	1800	RG	SX90752	1805	RG	SY89362	1810	RG	SY89417
1796	RG	SV97012	1801	RG	SX90819	1806	RG	SY89361	1811	RG	SY89416
1797	RG	SV97013	1802	RG	SX90854	1807	RG	SY89360	1812	RG	SY89479
1798	RG	SV97044	1803	RG	SX90839	1808	RG	SY89393	1813	RG	SY89496
1799	RG	SX90788	1804	RG	SX90875	1809	RG	SY89392			

1827-1858
Scania OmniLink CL94 UB 13.7m Scania   NC43D   2003-04

1827	RG	SY93825	1835	RG	SY93783	1843	RG	TB88449	1851	RG	TB88489
1828	RG	SY93784	1836	RG	SZ91745	1844	RG	TB88417	1852	RG	TB88477
1829	RG	SY93824	1837	RG	SZ91744	1845	RG	TB88418	1853	RG	TB88490
1830	RG	SY93774	1838	RG	SZ91749	1846	RG	TB88450	1854	RG	TB88491
1831	RG	SY93775	1839	RG	SZ91755	1847	RG	TB88444	1855	RG	TB88493
1832	RG	SY93776	1840	RG	SZ91756	1848	RG	TB88445	1856	RG	TB88492
1833	RG	SY93777	1841	RG	SZ91765	1849	RG	TB88483	1857	RG	TB88469
1834	RG	SY93778	1842	RG	TB88448	1850	RG	TB88484	1858	RG	TB88470

1862-1885
Volvo B10BLE 12m   Åbenrå   AN38D   1997-98

1862	KG	TX94432	1868	KG	PJ88291	1874	KG	PJ88366	1880	KG	PC92479
1863	KG	OY97165	1869	KG	PJ88300	1875	KG	TP90383	1881	KG	PC92480
1864	KG	OY97164	1870	KG	PJ88306	1876	KG	TP90384	1882	KG	PC92481
1865	KG	OY97163	1871	KG	PJ88307	1877	KG	PC92474	1883	KG	PJ88372
1866	KG	OY97251	1872	KG	UV90371	1878	KG	PC92475	1884	w	PJ88376
1867	GX	OY97267	1873	KG	PJ88363	1879	KG	PC92478	1885	KG	PX96095

1886-1900
VDL Bus SB220 LPG   Berkhof 2000LF   N31D   1999-2000

1886	w	RE88852	1890	w	RE88954	1894	w	RH90133	1898	w	TC94631
1887	w	RE88813	1891	w	RE88888	1895	w	RH90763	1899	w	UT97175
1888	w	RE89023	1892	w	RE88966	1896	w	RH90847	1900	w	US96803
1889	w	RE88955	1893	w	RE89033	1897	w	RH90848			

1901-1915
Volvo B7BLE   Volvo 8500   N31D   2006

1901	KG	UU96912	1905	KG	UU96933	1909	KG	UU96986	1913	KG	UU97006
1902	KG	UU96913	1906	KG	UU96952	1910	KG	UU96987	1914	KG	UU97019
1903	KG	UU96914	1907	KG	UU96953	1911	KG	UU96997	1915	KG	UU97020
1904	KG	UU96932	1908	KG	UU96985	1912	KG	UU97005			

1916	RG	UJ96430	Volvo B12BLE			Åbenrå			N34D		2003

1917-1945 Scania OmniLink CK230 UB4 — Scania — N33D — 2008

1917	RG	XD92766	**1925**	AM	XD92776	**1932**	AM	XD92783	**1939**	AM	XD92789
1918	RG	XD92765	**1926**	AM	XD92777	**1933**	AM	XD92784	**1940**	AM	XJ90253
1919	RG	XD92770	**1927**	AM	XD92778	**1934**	AM	XD92785	**1941**	AM	XD88321
1920	RG	XD92771	**1928**	AM	XD92779	**1935**	AM	XD92786	**1942**	AM	XJ90254
1921	RG	XD92772	**1929**	AM	XD92780	**1936**	AM	XD92787	**1943**	AM	XJ90255
1922	RG	XD92773	**1930**	AM	XD92781	**1937**	AM	XJ90252	**1944**	AM	XJ90256
1923	RG	XD92774	**1931**	AM	XD92782	**1938**	AM	XD92788	**1945**	RG	XD88322
1924	RG	XD92775									

1946-1956 Renault Urban 40 Electrico — Carlnd — N9F — 2009

1946	RG	XJ96827	**1949**	RG	XJ96925	**1952**	RG	XJ96824	**1955**	RG	XJ96807
1947	RG	XJ96806	**1950**	RG	XJ97199	**1953**	RG	XJ96924	**1956**	RG	XJ9686
1948	RG	XJ96805	**1951**	RG	XJ96826	**1954**	RG	XJ96825			

1957-1967 Scania OmniLink CK230 UB 12m — NC33D — 2009

1957	RG	XJ90846	**1960**	RG	XJ90852	**1963**	RG	XJ90860	**1966**	RG	XJ90863
1958	RG	XJ90847	**1961**	RG	XJ90853	**1964**	RG	XJ90861	**1967**	RG	XJ90864
1959	RG	XJ90848	**1962**	RG	XJ90854	**1965**	RG	XJ90862			

1968-1984 Volvo B7BLE — Volvo 8500 — N34D — 2009

1968	RG	XN90826	**1973**	RG	XN90831	**1977**	RG	XN90839	**1981**	RG	XN90843
1969	RG	XN90827	**1974**	RG	XN90832	**1978**	RG	XN90840	**1982**	RG	XN90844
1970	RG	XN90828	**1975**	RG	XN90837	**1979**	RG	XN90841	**1983**	RG	XN90845
1971	RG	XN90829	**1976**	RG	XN90838	**1980**	RG	XN90842	**1984**	RG	XN90846
1972	RG	XN90830									

1993	AM	OX94339	Volvo B10BLE	Åbenrå	N32D	1997	
1994	AM	OX94346	Volvo B10BLE	Åbenrå	N32D	1997	
2066	w	RV89287	Mercedes-Benz Cito O520	Mercedes-Benz	N13D	2001	
2173	SJ	LX94925	Volvo B10M	Åbenrå	B--D	1989	
2249	SJ	MJ95476	Volvo B10M	Åbenrå	B38D	1991	
2268	FY	MR93469	Volvo B10M	Åbenrå	B38D	1991	
2287	FY	MS91113	Volvo B10M	Åbenrå	B38D	1991	
2291	SJ	MS97752	Volvo B10M	Åbenrå	B38D	1992	
2344	HG	NB97681	Volvo B10M	DAB Silkeborg	B38D	1992	
2351	w	NJ9327	Volvo B10M	Åbenrå	B38D	1993	
2369	AA	NN89575	Volvo B10M	DAB Silkeborg	B38D	1993	
2405	u	NX93001	Volvo B10M	DAB Silkeborg	B38D	1994	
2406	FS	NX93002	Volvo B10M	DAB Silkeborg	B38D	1994	
2482	FY	OJ92350	Volvo B10M	DAB/Silkeborg	B38D	1996	
2490	FY	OL96.926	Volvo B10M	Åbenrå	B38D	1996	
2509	FS	OM97854	Volvo B10M	Åbenrå	B38D	1996	
2521	FS	OX91625	Volvo B10M	DAB Silkeborg	B47D	1997	
2526	FS	OX91679	Volvo B10M	DAB Silkeborg	B47D	1997	
2534	AA	OX94494	Volvo B10M	Åbenrå	B38D	1997	

2536-2543 Scania N112 CL — Scania — B47D — 1997

2536	FY	PB91473	**2538**	FY	PB91475	**2541**	FS	PB91480	**2543**	FY	PB91482
2537	FS	PB91474	**2539**	FY	PB91476	**2542**	FS	PB91481			

2546	FS	PB91477	Scania N112 CL	DAB Silkeborg	B47D	1997	
2547	FS	PB91478	Scania N112 CL	DAB Silkeborg	B47D	1997	
2552	AA	PB89095	Volvo B10M	Åbenrå	B44D	1997	
2553	AA	PB89103	Volvo B10M	Åbenrå	B44D	1997	
2554	AA	PB89102	Volvo B10M	Åbenrå	B44D	1997	
2566	w	PC89064	Volvo B10M	Åbenrå	B44D	1997	
2568	AA	PC89080	Volvo B10M	Åbenrå	B44D	1997	
2574	FS	PC97949	Scania N112 CL	DAB Silkeborg	B47D	1998	
2575	FY	PE92039	Volvo B10M	Vest	B47D	1998	
2576	FS	PE92042	Volvo B10M	Vest	B47D	1998	
2578	HV	PP89431	Volvo B10M	Vest	B47D	1998	

2581-2589 Volvo B10M — Vest — B47D — 1998

2581	FS	PE92002	**2585**	FY	PP93852	**2587**	FY	PP93854	**2589**	FN	PR94089
2582	FS	PE92001	**2586**	FY	PP93855	**2588**	FY	PP93852			

2595-2634 Volvo B10M — Åbenrå — B43D — 1998-99

2595	FY	PP89414	**2619**	FN	PT95340	**2633**	FY	PT95382	**2634**	AA	PT95381
2596	FS	PP89417									

2647	HV	PX96158	Volvo B10M	Åbenrå	B47D	1999
2648	HV	PX96158	Volvo B10M	Åbenrå	B47D	1999

2658-2663 Volvo B10M — Åbenrå — B47D — 1999

2658	FS	PX96253	2660	FN	PX96265	2662	FS	RC89372	2663	FY	RC89383
2659	FN	PX96266	2661	FS	PX96271						

2667	FN	RC89395	Volvo B10M	Åbenrå	B47D	1999
2668	FS	RC89396	Volvo B10M	Åbenrå	B47D	1999
2669	FY	RC89397	Volvo B10M	Åbenrå	B47D	1999

2672-2676 Volvo B10M — Åbenrå — B47D — 1999

2672	HV	RD91994	2674	FY	PX96241	2675	FY	RE94201	2676	FY	RD91993
2673	HV	RD91999									

2707-2718 Scania L113 CLL — DAB Silkeborg — N47D — 2000

2707	AA	RM96994	2712	FS	RN96024	2715	FN	RN96188	2717	FS	RN95954
2710	AA	RM96996	2713	FS	RN96048	2716	FN	RN96189	2718	FS	RN95953

2745	FS	RN96076	Scania	DAB Silkeborg	N47D	2000
2749	FY	RP91084	Volvo B10M	Åbenrå	B47D	2000

2777-2819 Scania OmniLine CL94 UB 12m — Scania — N47D — 2001

2777	FN	RV95328	2790	FN	RV95341	2800	FS	RV95385	2810	FS	RV95395
2780	FS	RV95331	2791	FN	RV95342	2801	FY	RV95386	2811	FS	RV95396
2781	FS	RV95332	2792	FS	RV95343	2802	FN	RV95387	2812	FS	RV95397
2782	FS	RV95333	2793	FN	RV95344	2803	FS	RV95388	2813	FN	RV95398
2783	FS	RV95334	2794	FN	RV95345	2804	FN	RV95389	2814	FN	RV95399
2784	FS	RV95335	2795	FN	RV95382	2805	FS	RV95390	2815	FN	RV95400
2785	FS	RV95336	2796	FS	RV95383	2806	FS	RV95391	2816	FY	RV95401
2786	FS	RV95337	2797	FN	RV95346	2807	FN	RV95392	2817	FS	RV95402
2787	FN	RV95338	2798	FN	RV95384	2808	FS	RV95393	2818	FS	RV95403
2788	FN	RV95339	2799	FN	RV95347	2809	FS	RV95394	2819	FN	RV95404
2789	FN	RV95340									

2820-2825 Scania 13.6m — Lahti Flyer — N55D — 2001-02

2820	FN	RV95405	2822	FY	RV95407	2824	FS	SJ94192	2825	FN	RX97975
2821	FN	RV95406	2823	FS	RV95408						

2826	HV	RX96850	Volvo B10M 13.7m	Åbenrå	NC46D	2002
2827	FS	SM97944	Scania 13.6m	Lahti Flyer	N55D	2002
2831	FN	RY88058	Scania 13.6m	Lahti Flyer	N55D	2002
2837	AA	SH93791	Volvo B10M 13.7m	Åbenrå	NC46D	2002

2844-2850 Scania OmniLine CL94UB 12m — Scania — N47D — 2002

2844	BJ	SH93791	2848	FS	SL95855	2849	FS	SL95856	2850	FN	SL95857
2847	FS	SL95830									

2853-2865 Scania OmniLink CL94UB 12m* — Scania — N47D — 2003 — *2864/5 are 13.5m

2853	HG	SX97361	2857	HG	SX97364	2860	HG	SX97367	2863	HG	SX97369
2854	HG	SX97362	2858	HG	SX97365	2861	HG	SX97340	2864	HG	SX97303
2855	HG	SX97363	2859	HG	SX97366	2862	HG	SX97368	2865	HG	SX97338
2856	HG	SX97339									

2866-2871 MAN 18.310 — Jonckheere Modulo — C47D — 2003

2866	FS	SY89049	2868	FS	SY89051	2870	FS	SY89.081	2871	FS	SY89.082
2867	FS	SY89050	2869	FS	SY89052						

2883-2886 Scania L94 UB 13.6m — Lahti Flyer — NC55D — 2004

2883	FS	TK94765	2884	FS	TK94766	2885	FS	TK94767	2886	FN	TM88197

2888	FS	TM88244	Scania OmniLine IL94 UB 12m	Scania	NC47D	2004

2892-2899 Volvo B12M — Carrus — NC47D — 2005

2892	HV	TT90158	2894	HV	TT90160	2896	HV	TT90162	2898	HV	TT90164
2893	HV	TT90159	2895	HV	TT90161	2897	HV	TT90163	2899	HV	TT90165

2901	FN	UJ92826	Scania OmniCity L94 UB 12m	Scania	NC49D	2006

Arriva liveried buses are used only on commercial service. 2850, SL95857, is seen working the express service to Aarhus. *Bill Potter*

2902-2925

Irisbus Arway 12.8m | Irisbus | N47D | 2006

2902	FN	UR94484	2908	FS	UM93572	2914	FS	UM93583	2920	FN	UM93581
2903	FY	UR94481	2909	FN	UM93591	2915	FN	UM93584	2921	FS	UM93598
2904	FS	UR94482	2910	FN	UM93570	2916	FN	UM93599	2922	FS	UM93585
2905	FN	UR94483	2911	FS	UM93568	2917	FN	UM93586	2923	FN	UM93582
2906	FY	UM93571	2912	FS	UM93590	2918	FN	UM93588	2924	FN	US91250
2907	FN	UM93569	2913	FS	UM93580	2919	FN	UR94633	2925	FN	UM93587

2926-2931

MAN Lions Regio 13.9m | MAN | NC53D | 2007

2926	FS	VH89850	2928	FS	VH89854	2930	FS	VH89853	2931	FS	VH89851
2927	FS	VH89855	2929	FS	VH89852						

2938-2941

Scania OmniLine K370 IB 12m | Scania | N47D | 2007

2938	AR	VJ93921	2939	AR	VJ93922	2940	AR	VJ93950	2941	AR	VJ93951

2942-2944

Scania OmniLine CL94 UB 13.7 | Lahti Flyer | N55D | 2007

2942	AR	VN93038	2943	AR	VN93039	2944	AR	VN93040

2945	AA	VY89078	Volvo B12M 13.7m	Volvo 8500	N46D	2008
2946	AA	VY89079	Volvo B12M 13.7m	Volvo 8500	N46D	2008
2947	AA	VY95469	Scania K230 UB	Lahti Scala	N49D	2008
2948	AA	VY95594	Scania OmniLink CK230 UB	Scania	N45D	2008
2949	AA	VZ90459	Scania K230 UB	Lahti Scala	N49D	2008
2950	AA	XD90098	Scania K230 UB	Lahti Scala	N49D	2008
2951	AA	XE89989	Scania K230 UB	Lahti Scala	N49D	2008
2952	AA	XJ96062	Scania K230 UB	Lahti Scala	N49D	2008
2953	AA	XE96555	Scania OmniLink CK230 UB	Scania	N45D	2008
2954	DJ	XE90177	Scania Omniline	Scania	N47D	2008
2955	DJ	XE96364	Scania Omniline	Scania	N47D	2008

2956-2965

Volvo B12MA | Volvo/Säffle 8500 | AN64D | 2008

2956	AR	XJ89610	2959	AR	XJ89561	2962	AR	XJ94885	2964	AR	XJ94825
2957	AR	XJ89559	2960	AR	XJ89562	2963	AR	XJ89611	2965	AR	XJ94823
2958	AR	XJ89560	2961	AR	XJ89612						

2966-2973   Scania K230 IB6 13.6m   Lahti Flyer   N55D   2008

2966	AR	XE89965	2968	AR	XE89990	2970	AR	XE90026	2972	AR	XE90193
2967	AR	XE89964	2969	AR	XE89991	2971	AR	XE90027	2973	AR	XE90199

2974-2991   Scania OmniLine CL230   Scania   N47D   2008-09

2974	BO	XE96365	2979	AR	XE96428	2984	AR	XE96496	2988	AR	XE96586
2975	BO	XE96387	2980	AR	XE96494	2985	BO	XE96508	2989	AR	XE96587
2976	AR	XE96414	2981	AR	XE96495	2986	AR	XE96566	2990	AR	XJ96060
2977	AR	XE96415	2982	AR	XE96509	2987	AR	XE96567	2991	AR	XJ96061
2978	AR	XE96427	2983	AR	XE96544						

2992-2995   Volvo B7RLE   Volvo 8500   N40D   2007-08

2992	RA	XD90746	2993	RA	XD90747	2994	RA	XD90748	2995	RA	XD90749

2996	AR	XJ89717	Volvo B12MA	Volvo 8500	AN64D	2008
2997	AR	XJ89716	Volvo B12MA	Volvo 8500	AN64D	2008

2998-3009   Scania K230 UB   Lahti Flyer   N55D   2009

2998	AR	XJ96146	3001	AR	XJ96161	3004	AR	XJ96198	3007	AR	XJ96224
2999	AR	XJ96160	3002	AR	XJ96173	3005	AR	XJ96199	3008	AR	XJ96243
3000	AR	XJ96162	3003	AR	XJ96172	3006	AR	XJ96218	3009	AR	XJ96244

3010	HV	XJ95169	Volvo B7RLE	Volvo 8500	N35D	2009
3011	HV	XJ95170	Volvo B7RLE	Volvo 8500	N35D	2009

3017-3020   Scania OmniLine CK280 UB4   Scania   N45D   2009

3017	AA	XM91386	3018	AA	XM91387	3019	AA	XM91389	3020	AA	XM91388

3168	HN	SJ92752	DAF/DAB	DAB Citybus S15 Mk1	B--D	1993
3174	SJ	MB92888	Volvo B10M	Åbenrå	B--D	1995
3176	AA	OB93469	MAN/DAB	DAB Citybus S15 Mk2	B--D	1995
3185	AA	RL91182	Volvo B10M	Åbenrå	B--D	1997
3187	AA	PE94555	Volvo B10M	Åbenrå	B--D	1998
3188	OT	OZ92476	Volvo B10M	Vest	B--D	1998
3189	AA	PL97691	Volvo B10M	Åbenrå	B--D	1998
3190	AA	PE94573	Volvo B10M	Åbenrå	B--D	1998
3191	AA	PE94583	Volvo B10M	Åbenrå	B--D	1998
3192	AA	PE94587	Volvo B10M	Åbenrå	B--D	1998
3193	FN	OZ92475	Volvo B10M	Vest	B--D	1998
3194	FN	OZ92511	Volvo B10M	Vest	B--D	1998
3195	OT	OZ92510	Volvo B10M	Vest	B--D	1998
3196	AA	PL97595	Volvo B10BLE	Åbenrå	B--D	1998
3197	FN	PL97652	Volvo B10M	Vest	B--D	1998
3198	w	PP89464	Volvo B10M	Vest	B--D	1998
3199	AA	PX96127	Volvo B10BLE	Åbenrå	B--D	1999
3200	AA	PX96128	Volvo B10BLE	Åbenrå	N39D	1999
3202	RA	PZ89729	Scania/DAB	DAB	B--D	1999
3203	AR	PZ89726	Scania/DAB	DAB	B--D	1999
3204	AR	PZ89727	Scania/DAB	DAB	B--D	1999
3206	w	RC89418	Volvo B10M	Vest	B--D	1999
3207	AA	RX96461	Scania/DAB	DAB	B--D	1999

3213-3218   Volvo B10M   Åbenrå   B36D   2000

3213	w	RK97522	3215	AA	RL91165	3217	AA	RL91164	3218	AA	RL91162
3214	w	RK97521	3216	AA	RL91181						

3219-3225   Volvo B10M   Åbenrå   B36D   2000

3219	AA	RL91231	3221	AA	RL91230	3223	AA	RL91240	3225	AA	RL91242
3220	AA	RL91232	3222	AA	RL91197	3224	AA	RL91244			

3228-3232   Volvo B10M   Åbenrå   B36D   2000

3228	AA	RL91163	3230	AA	RL91229	3231	AA	RL91241	3232	AA	RL91161
3229	AA	RL91245									

3265-3284   Volvo B12BLE   Åbenrå   N39D   2002

3265	HN	SJ89558	3270	VJ	SJ89639	3275	VJ	SJ89651	3280	HN	SJ89664
3266	VJ	SJ89569	3271	VJ	SJ89640	3276	VJ	SJ89650	3281	HN	SJ89675
3267	VJ	SJ89581	3272	VJ	SJ89643	3277	VJ	SJ89649	3282	VJ	SJ89676
3268	VJ	SJ89633	3273	VJ	SJ89644	3278	VJ	SJ89663	3283	VJ	SJ89661
3269	VJ	SJ89634	3274	VJ	SJ89645	3279	HN	SJ89662	3284	VJ	SJ89668

The Optare Solo has gained several continental sales and now operates with Arriva in both the Netherlands and in Denmark. Pictured at the terminus on the outskirts of Roskilde is 1757, TP97966, which is used in dual-door operation. *Bill Potter*

3288-3307

Volvo B12BLE — Åbenrå — N39D — 2002

3288	VJ	SJ89718	**3293**	HN	SL91813	**3298**	HN	SL91788	**3303**	HN	SL91807
3289	VJ	SJ89724	**3294**	HN	SL91821	**3299**	HN	SL91791	**3304**	HN	SL91811
3290	VJ	SJ89725	**3295**	HN	SL91780	**3300**	HN	SL91794	**3305**	HN	SL91881
3291	KO	SJ89732	**3296**	HN	SL91786	**3301**	HN	SL91798	**3306**	HN	SL91883
3292	VJ	SJ89734	**3297**	HN	SL91787	**3302**	HN	SL91804	**3307**	HN	SL91993

3308-3311

MAN — MAN — N38D — 2002

3308	VJ	SM90243	**3309**	VJ	SM90244	**3310**	VJ	SM90244	**3311**	VJ	SM90245

3316	AA	SX93476	Volvo B12B	Åbenrå	N47D	2004
3317	AR	TM88210	Scania OmniLine CL94UB 12m	Scania	N42D	2004
3318	AR	TM88211	Scania OmniLine CL94UB 12m	Scania	N42D	2004
3319	AR	TM88212	Scania OmniLine CL94UB 12m	Scania	N42D	2004
3322	SO	SD92675	Volvo B12M	Åbenrå	NC39D	2002
3323	AA	SU94086	Scania OmniLine CL94UB 12m	Scania	N42D	2003
3831	SO	PZ94542	Mercedes-Benz Sprinter 416 cdi	Mercedes-Benz	M8	1999	Handicap service
3832	FY	RL96681	Iveco Ducato	Iveco	M8	2000	Handicap service
3833	FN	RP89432	Iveco Ducato	Iveco	M8	2000	Handicap service
3834	AR	RP89433	Iveco Ducato	Iveco	M8	2000	Handicap service
3837	VJ	RP89436	Iveco Ducato	Iveco	M8	2000	Handicap service
3838	FS	RP89437	Iveco Ducato	Iveco	M8	2000	Handicap service
3839	RA	RP89438	Iveco Ducato	Iveco	M8	2000	Handicap service
3841	FS	RP89440	Iveco Ducato	Iveco	M8	2000	Handicap service
3842	w	RP89441	Iveco Ducato	Iveco	M8	2000	Handicap service
3843	AR	RV91296	Mercedes-Benz Sprinter 413	Mercedes-Benz	M8	2001	Handicap service
3847	AA	SZ93361	Mercedes-Benz Vario	Mercedes-Benz	M18	2001	Handicap service
3849	AH	RX95266	Iveco Ducato	Iveco	M8	2001	Handicap service

3852-3871

Mercedes-Benz Sprinter 313 — Mercedes-Benz — M8 — 2003 — Handicap service

3852	FY	SP92838	**3857**	SO	SP92845	**3863**	SO	SP92842	**3868**	AR	SP93828
3853	SO	SP92848	**3858**	SO	SP92844	**3865**	SO	SP93819	**3869**	SO	SP93831
3854	FY	SP92846	**3860**	AR	SP92843	**3866**	SO	SP93818	**3870**	AR	SP93829
3855	SO	SP92839	**3861**	SO	SP92847	**3867**	AR	SP93816	**3871**	AR	SP93920
3856	SO	SP92840	**3862**	SO	SP92849						

Another small bus model to be found in Arriva fleets is the Mercedes-Benz Cito, a model no longer in production. Recent moves have seen the model transferred between fleets. Here, 4415, SD96.847, is allocated to Ålborg.
Bill Potter

3872	AR	SP93879	Mercedes-Benz Vario	Mercedes-Benz	M8	2003	Handicap service
3873	VJ	SR92735	Citroën Jumper	Citroën	M8	2003	Handicap service
3874	AA	SR92736	Citroën Jumper	Citroën	M8	2003	Handicap service
3875	FS	SY92902	Ford Transit	Ford	M8	2004	Handicap service
3876	SE	SZ92876	Mercedes-Benz Vario	Mercedes-Benz	M8	2004	Handicap service
3878	HN	UK89858	Citroën Jumper	Citroën	M8	2004	Handicap service
3879	HV	SX90495	Citroën Jumper	Citroën	M8	2004	Handicap service

3880-3910 — Mercedes-Benz Sprinter 315 — Mercedes-Benz — M8 — 2007-09

3880	AR	UZ90025	3888	SO	VU96612	3896	SO	VP88846	3904	AR	VU96925
3881	AR	UZ90026	3889	SO	VU96608	3897	SO	VS95356	3905	AR	VU96886
3882	FY	VB96655	3890	SO	VU96641	3898	SO	VS95357	3906	AR	VU96887
3883	FY	VB96656	3891	SO	VP88723	3899	SO	VS95358	3907	AR	VU96924
3884	FY	VH94941	3892	SO	VP88726	3900	SO	VS95359	3908	AR	VU96927
3885	SO	VU96609	3893	SO	VP88722	3901	SO	VS95360	3909	SE	XM88940
3886	SO	VU96610	3894	FY	VP88725	3902	SO	VS95361	3910	SE	XM88884
3887	SO	VU96611	3895	SO	VP88724	3903	AR	VU96926			

3911	SO	XJ88661	Volkswagen Passat	Volkswagen	4-seat	2009	Handicap service
3912	FY	XK91238	Volkswagen Passat	Volkswagen	4-seat	2009	Handicap service
4001	HG	OV92022	Volvo B10L	Åbenrå	N40D	1997	

4021-4030 — Volvo B10BLE — Vest — N36D — 2002

4021	SE	SN90043	4024	SE	SN90046	4027	SE	SM97699	4029	SE	SM97737
4022	SE	SN90044	4025	SE	SN90047	4028	SE	SM97714	4030	SE	SM97752
4023	SE	SN90045	4026	SE	SM97688						

4319	AA	OE92917	MAN/DAB Citybus S15	DAB Silkeborg	N35D	1995	
4320	AA	OE92917	MAN/DAB Citybus S15	DAB Silkeborg	N35D	1995	
4356	w	OS89287	MAN/DAB Citybus S15	DAB Silkeborg	N35D	1996	

4361-4367 — Volvo B10L — Åbenrå — N40D — 1997

4361	w	PB89204	4363	AA	PB89218	4365	AA	PB89226	4367	AA	PB89507
4362	AA	PB89215	4364	AA	PB89223						

4372	AA	PX96281	Volvo B7L	Åbenrå	N39D	1999

4375-4388 — Volvo B10BLE — Åbenrå — N32D — 2000

4375	AA	RE94369	**4377**	AA RE94371	**4386** AA RN88149	**4388** AA RN88151
4376	AA	RE94370	**4378**	AA RE94372	**4387** AA RN88150	

4389-4393 — Scania OmniLink 13.7m — Scania — N42D — 2002

4389	AA	RU97030	**4391** AA RU97078	**4392** AA RU97079	**4393** AA RU97080
4390	AA	RU97031			

4394	AA	SJ89557	Volvo B10BLE 13.7m	Åbenrå	NC42D	2002

4395-4409 — Volvo B10BLE — Vest — N32D — 2002

4395	AA	SJ88780	**4399** AA SJ88784	**4403** AA SJ88788	**4407** AA SJ88792
4396	AA	SJ88781	**4400** AA SJ88785	**4404** AA SJ88789	**4408** AA SJ88793
4397	AA	SJ88782	**4401** AA SJ88786	**4405** AA SJ88790	**4409** AA SJ88794
4398	AA	SJ88783	**4402** AA SJ88787	**4406** AA SJ88791	

4410-4419 — Mercedes-Benz Cito — Mercedes-Benz — N17F — 2002

4410	AA	SD96.842	**4413** AA SD96.845	**4416** AA SD96.848	**4418** AA SD96.850
4411	AA	SD96.843	**4414** AA SD96.846	**4417** AA SD96.849	**4419** RA SD96.851
4412	AA	SD96.844	**4415** AA SD96.847		

4420-4430 — Scania OmniLink CL94UB 12m — Scania — N42D — 2004

4420	AA	TB90824	**4423** AA TB90827	**4426** AA TB90830	**4429** AA TB90833
4421	AA	TB90825	**4424** AA TB90828	**4427** AA TB90831	**4430** AA TB90834
4422	AA	TB90826	**4425** AA TB90829	**4428** AA TB90832	

5047	SJ	KV94783	Volvo B10M	Åbenrå	BC43D	1986
5195	SJ	LY93265	Volvo B10M	Åbenrå	BC43D	1989

5402-5417 — Mercedes-Benz Sprinter 312 — Mercedes-Benz — M8 — 1997

5402	FY	OZ97632	**5404** FY OX91313	**5416** FY SM90263	**5417** FY SM90290
5403	FY	OY95589	**5414** SO SM90147		

5420	FY	PE94546	Mercedes-Benz Sprinter 412	Mercedes-Benz	M8	1998
5422	FY	PE94547	Mercedes-Benz Sprinter 412	Mercedes-Benz	M8	1998
5424	FY	PE94548	Mercedes-Benz Sprinter 412	Mercedes-Benz	M8	1998
5437	FY	PE94549	Mercedes-Benz Sprinter 312	Mercedes-Benz	M8	1997

5451-5463 — Mercedes-Benz Sprinter 412 — Mercedes-Benz — M8 — 1998-99

5451	OV	SB92849	**5455** OV PJ96270	**5458** OV TB94358	**5461** OV TB94448
5452	OV	SM90148	**5456** OV SM90201	**5459** OV TB94359	**5462** OV TC93364
5453	OV	SB92850	**5457** OV TB94338	**5460** OV TB94449	**5463** OV TC93363
5454	OV	SB92851			

5465	OV	SV88830	Mercedes-Benz Sprinter 412	Mercedes-Benz	M8	1997
5466	OV	TC93409	Mercedes-Benz Sprinter 412	Mercedes-Benz	M8	1997
5468	FY	TC93647	Mercedes-Benz Vario O814	Mercedes-Benz	M8	1998
5479	OV	OJ90646	Mercedes-Benz Sprinter 400	Mercedes-Benz	M8	1996

5480-5483 — Hyundai Trajet 2.0 — Hyundai — M8 — 2006

5480	OV	YJ21272	**5481** OV YJ21353	**5482** SO YJ21354	**5483** OV YJ21352

5484-5493 — Mercedes-Benz Sprinter 315 — Mercedes-Benz — M8 — 2007

5484	SO	VN94176	**5487** OV VN94179	**5490** OV VN94182	**5492** OV VN94184
5485	FY	VN94177	**5488** OV VN94180	**5491** OV VN94183	**5493** OV VN94185
5486	SO	VN94178	**5489** SO VN94181		

5501	HO	PE94575	Volvo B10M	Åbenrå	B44D	1998
5502	HO	PJ97593	Volvo B10M	Åbenrå	B44D	1998
5503	HO	PJ97694	Volvo B10M	Åbenrå	B44D	1998
5504	w	PB89259	Volvo B10M	Åbenrå	B44D	1998
5506	w	PE94568	Volvo B10M	Åbenrå	B44D	1998
5507	w	PE94544	Volvo B10M	Åbenrå	B44D	1998
5509	RI	SN97730	Volvo B12M	Åbenrå	B44D	2003
5510	RI	SN97741	Volvo B12M	Åbenrå	B44D	2003
5511	SL	SN97734	Volvo B12M	Åbenrå	B44D	2003
5512	ST	PE94532	Volvo B10M	Åbenrå	B44D	1998
5513	NF	VH94957	Volvo B12M	Carrus	B44D	2007
5514	NF	PJ97612	Volvo B10M	Åbenrå	B44D	1998
5515	NF	PL67653	Volvo B10M 10.2m	Åbenrå	B35D	1998

In 2009 a batch of Electric Renault Urban 40s was placed in service in Copenhagen. These vehicles feature Carlnd bodywork as shown by 1954, XJ96825. *Mark Doggett*

5516	NF	PL97644	Volvo B10M 10.2m	Åbenrå		B35D	1998
5517	w	OZ92514	Volvo B6BLE	-		N29D	1998
5518	NF	SZ89491	MAN 14.220	Goppel		NC27D	2004
5519	NF	SZ89493	MAN 14.220	Goppel		NC27D	2004
5520	w	OU89850	Volvo B6	Vest		B29D	1996
5521	NF	SZ89492	MAN 14.220	Goppel		NC27D	2004
5522	w	TS97877	Volvo B6	Vest		B29D	1996
5523	NF	UL95101	Volvo B12M	Volvo 8700		BC47D	2006
5524	NF	UR91648	Volvo B12M	Volvo 8700		BC47D	2006
5525	NF	UR91649	Volvo B12M	Volvo 8700		BC47D	2006
5526	NF	PT95352	Volvo B10M	Åbenrå		BC43D	1999
5527	NF	PX96180	Volvo B10M	Åbenrå		BC43D	1999
5528	AR	UY93624	Volvo B12M	Carrus		B47D	2006

5529-5536   Volvo B10M   Åbenrå   BC43D   1999

5529	NF	PX96190	**5531**	NF	PX96172	**5534**	NF	PX96176	**5536**	w	PX9178
5530	NF	PX96192	**5532**	NF	PX96174	**5535**	NF	PT95334			

5537	w	PL91046	Volvo B6	Vest V10	B29D	1999
5538	NY	TS94839	Volvo B12M 13.7m	Volvo 8700	BC47D	2005
5539	NY	TS94840	Volvo B12M 13.7m	Volvo 8700	BC47D	2005
5540	NY	OS89924	Volvo B10M	Åbenrå	B44D	1996
5541	SK	OS89936	Volvo B10M	Åbenrå	B44D	1996
5542	SK	OS89900	Volvo B10M	Åbenrå	B44D	1996
5543	NY	PJ97619	Volvo B10M	Åbenrå	B44D	1998
5544	SK	OS89908	Volvo B10M	Åbenrå	B44D	1996
5545	PR	NM90222	DAB S12	DAB	B44D	1993
5546	PR	TD96637	Mercedes-Benz Sprinter 315	Mercedes-Benz	M8	2004
5547	PR	TD96639	Mercedes-Benz Sprinter 315	Mercedes-Benz	M8	2004
5554	SK	PB89168	Volvo B10M	Åbenrå	B44D	1997
5557	EJ	PL97643	Volvo B10M 10.2m	Åbenrå	B39D	1998
5559	KO	UV90046	Volvo B12M 13.7m	Åbenrå	B47D	2002
5560	KO	UV90047	Volvo B12M 13.7m	Åbenrå	B47D	2002

5562-5575 — Volvo B10M — Åbenrå — B44D — 1998

5562	SL	RZ92525	5566	SL	PE94567	5570	ST	PJ97629	5573	w	PJ97692
5563	w	PE94533	5567	ST	PJ97620	5571	RK	PJ97636	5574	SL	PJ97709
5564	ST	PB89258	5568	ST	PJ97625	5572	SL	PJ97637	5575	w	PE94507
5565	SL	PE94565	5569	SL	PJ97624						

5576	w	XE92609	Volvo B10BLE	Åbenrå	N47D	1999

5577-5588 — Volvo B10M — Åbenrå — B44D — 1998

5577	w	PB89174	5580	SO	PB89267	5584	w	PB89293	5587	ST	PC92292
5578	SL	PB89265	5582	SO	PB89285	5585	SL	PC92290	5588	ST	PC92294
5579	SL	PB89266	5583	SL	PZ92815	5586	SL	PC92291			

5593	SL	SN97729	Volvo B12M 13.7m	Åbenrå	BC47D	2003	
5594	SO	PJ97702	Volvo B10M	Åbenrå	B44D	1998	
5595	SL	PJ97703	Volvo B10M	Åbenrå	B44D	1998	
5596	SL	PJ97716	Volvo B10M	Åbenrå	B44D	1998	
5597	RI	SN97728	Volvo B12M	Åbenrå	B44D	2003	
5598	SL	SN97748	Volvo B12M	Åbenrå	B44D	2003	
5599	SL	SN97740	Volvo B12M	Åbenrå	B44D	2003	
5600	w	PE94537	Volvo B10BLE	Säffle	N32D	1998	
5601	HV	PE94486	Volvo B10BLE	Säffle	N32D	1998	
5602	SE	PE94487	Volvo B10BLE	Säffle	N32D	1998	
5603	RK	PE94488	Volvo B10BLE	Säffle	N32D	1998	
5604	SE	PE94504	Volvo B10BLE	Säffle	N32D	1998	
5605	w	PE94505	Volvo B10BLE	Säffle	N32D	1998	
5606	w	XE92630	Volvo B10BLE	Säffle	N32D	1998	
5607	w	PE94520	Volvo B10BLE	Säffle	N32D	1998	
5608	SL	OS89899	Volvo B10M	Åbenrå	B45D	1996	
5609	ST	SN97878	Volvo B12M 13.7m	Åbenrå	B55D	2003	
5610	ST	SU97087	Volvo B12M	Åbenrå	B44D	2003	
5611	ST	SU97085	Volvo B12M	Åbenrå	B44D	2003	
5612	w	UE92316	Mercedes-Benz Vario 0614	Mercedes-Benz		1998	

5613-5626 — Volvo B10M — Åbenrå — B47D — 1999

5613	w	PL97649	5617	ST	PX96183	5620	ST	PX96179	5623	ST	PX96191
5614	w	PL97648	5619	ST	PX96185	5622	ST	PX96188	5626	ST	PT95332
5616	ST	PX96182									

5627-5630 — Volvo B10MA — Åbenrå — AB56D — 1999

5627	ST	PX96224	5628	ST	PX96225	5629	ST	PX96226	5630	ST	PX96227

5631	w	PR94857	Mercedes-Benz OB6140	-	-	1999
5632	ST	PL91038	Mercedes-Benz OB6140	-	-	1999
5633	w	OZ92464	Volvo B10M	Åbenrå	B47D	1997
5634	ST	TD96638	Mercedes-Benz Vario 0614	Mercedes-Benz		2004
5635	ST	TK89525	Mercedes-Benz Vario 0614	Mercedes-Benz		2004
5636	ST	PT95335	Volvo B10M	Åbenrå	B47D	1997
5637	ST	VH94955	Volvo B12M	Volvo	B47D	2007
5638	ST	XD91378	Volvo B7R	Volvo	N47D	2008
5639	ST	XD91379	Volvo B7R	Volvo	N47D	2008
5640	NF	XM93921	VDL Ambassador 10.6m	VDL	N28D	2009
5641	NF	XM93920	VDL Ambassador 10.6m	VDL	N28D	2009

5642-5665 — Volvo B7LE — Volvo 8500 — N40D — 2009

5642	NF	XM90554	5648	ND	XM90552	5654	SL	XM90590	5660	SL	XM90596
5643	NF	XM90555	5649	SL	XM90553	5655	SL	XM90591	5661	SL	XM90597
5644	NF	XM90547	5650	SL	XM90586	5656	SL	XM90592	5662	SL	XM90598
5645	NF	XM90549	5651	RI	XM90587	5657	SL	XM90593	5663	SL	XM90599
5646	ND	XM90550	5652	RI	XM90588	5658	SL	XM90594	5664	SL	XM90600
5647	ND	XM90551	5653	RI	XM90589	5659	SL	XM90595	5665	SL	XM90601

5701	ND	VJ92443	DAB Citybus S11	DAB	N15D	1995
5702	ND	RN88117	Volvo B10BLE	Åbenrå	N32D	2000
5703	SJ	TD95436	Volvo B10M	Åbenrå	B47D	1987
5704	SJ	LP94443	Volvo B10M	Åbenrå	B47D	1988
5705	RI	NB89308	Volvo B10M	Åbenrå	B47D	1992
5706	w	OU94973	Volvo B6LE	-		1997
5707	ND	OV91931	Volvo B10M	Åbenrå	B47D	1997

5708-5712 — Volvo B10M HLB · Åbenrå · BC42D · 1997-98

No.		Reg	No.		Reg	No.		Reg	No.		Reg
5708	ND	PB89085	5710	ND	OZ94283	5711	ND	PC89056	5712	ND	PC89105
5709	ND	OZ94278									

5713-5717 — Volvo B10M · Åbenrå · B47D · 1999

No.		Reg	No.		Reg	No.		Reg	No.		Reg
5713	ND	RC91287	5715	ND	RC91289	5716	ND	RC91290	5717	ND	RC91291
5714	ND	RC91288									

No.		Reg	Type	Body	Code	Year
5718	ND	RD94746	DAB Citybus S11	DAB	N15D	1999
5719	w	RD94747	DAB Citybus S11	DAB	N15D	1999
5720	ND	RD90971	Volvo B10M	Åbenrå	B47D	1999
5721	ND	RE94201	Volvo B10M	Åbenrå	B47D	1999
5722	ND	RP91142	Volvo B10BLE	Åbenrå	N32D	2000
5723	ND	RT95351	MAN 12.220	-	N26D	2001

5724- 5730 — Volvo B10M HLB · Åbenrå · BC44D · 2001

No.		Reg	No.		Reg	No.		Reg	No.		Reg
5724	ND	RT95270	5726	ND	RT95272	5728	ND	RT95274	5730	ND	RT95276
5725	ND	RT95271	5727	ND	RT95273	5729	ND	RT95275			

5731-5743 — Scania OmniLink · Scania · N45D · 2002-05

No.		Reg	No.		Reg	No.		Reg	No.		Reg
5731	ND	SM97681	5735	ND	TJ88588	5738	ND	TJ88591	5741	ND	TJ88593
5732	ND	TJ88585	5736	ND	TJ88589	5739	ND	TJ88555	5742	ND	TJ88594
5733	ND	TJ88586	5737	ND	TJ88590	5740	ND	TJ88592	5743	ND	TZ97302
5734	ND	TJ88587									

No.		Reg	Type	Body	Code	Year
5744	ND	UU97057	Volvo B12M	Volvo	B47D	2006
5745	ND	PP94329	DAB Citybus S11	DAB	N15D	1998
5746	SJ	ME94417	DAF/DAB S12	DAB	B47D	1990
5747	NF	PP89432	Volvo B10M	Åbenrå	BC44D	1998
5748	NF	RN88014	Volvo B10M	Åbenrå	BC44D	2000
5752	NF	OX94453	Volvo B10M	Åbenrå	B47D	1997
5753	NF	RT95350	MAN 12.220 9m	-	N26D	2001

5754-5759 — MAN 18.310 · MAN · N47D · 2003

No.		Reg	No.		Reg	No.		Reg	No.		Reg
5754	NF	SX88391	5756	NF	SX88393	5758	NF	SX88395	5759	NF	SX88396
5755	NF	SX88392	5757	NF	SX88394						

No.		Reg	Type	Body	Code	Year
5760	NF	PX96500	MAN 12.220 9m	-	B16D	1999
5761	NF	RT95499	MAN 12.220 9m	-	B16D	1999

5762-5766 — Volvo B10BLE · - · N32D · 1997

No.		Reg	No.		Reg	No.		Reg
5762	RI	PP89362	5763	HG	OV91884	5766	w	XD93063

5769-5776 — Volvo B10M HLB · Åbenrå · BC44D · 1998-2001

No.		Reg	No.		Reg	No.		Reg	No.		Reg
5769	HO	PP89434	5771	HO	RT95266	5774	RI	PE91021	5776	RI	RD91919
5770	RI	RT95267	5772	HO	RT95265	5775	RI	RD91904			

5778-5784 — Volvo B10M HLB · Åbenrå · BC44D · 2001

No.		Reg	No.		Reg	No.		Reg	No.		Reg
5778	RI	RT95277	5780	SL	RT95262	5782	RI	RT95264	5784	RI	RT95269
5779	RI	RT95261	5781	RI	RT95263	5783	RI	RT95268			

5785-5789 — Volvo B12M HLB · Volvo · NC44D · 2006

No.		Reg	No.		Reg	No.		Reg	No.		Reg
5785	RI	UU97026	5787	RI	UU97104	5788	SL	UU97034	5789	RI	UU97040
5786	RI	UU97025									

5792-5795 — Volvo B10M HLB · Åbenrå · BC44D · 1996

No.		Reg	No.		Reg	No.		Reg	No.		Reg
5792	SO	OL96921	5793	SO	OM97903	5794	SO	OM97918	5795	w	OM97927

No.		Reg	Type	Body	Code	Year
5796	ND	XD91377	Volvo B7R	Volvo	N47D	2008

5797-5805 — Scania OmniLink CL94 UB 12m · Scania · N31D · 2002

No.		Reg	No.		Reg	No.		Reg	No.		Reg
5797	RI	SH93716	5800	RI	SH93742	5802	u	SH93744	5804	u	SH93749
5798	RI	SH93740	5801	RI	SH93743	5803	u	SH93717	5805	u	SH93750
5799	RI	SH93741									

No.		Reg	Type	Body	Code	Year
6030	JL	WCE566	Peugeot Partner	Peugeot	M8	2006

6051-6059 — MAN Lion's City A26 · MAN · N50D · 2009

No.		Reg	No.		Reg	No.		Reg	No.		Reg
6051	TG	WLD052	6054	TG	DEH973	6056	TG	CDS152	6058	TG	EFA656
6052	TG	UNO157	6055	TG	XYP839	6057	TG	XYP849	6059	TG	EBH493
6053	TG	XJM067									

Pictured passing Malmo rail station is Volvo B10LA 6539, SHH016. Powered by natural gas, it has bodywork supplied by Volvo's Säffle plant. *Tom Johnson*

6101	RI	HSO203	Scania L113CLB	Scania	B55D	1995
6102	JD	HSL103	Scania L113CLB	Scania	B55D	1995
6105	SD	RL92.435	Volvo B10LA	Säffle S	AN65D	2000
6112	JD	HLR063	Scania L113CLB	DAB	B55D	1995
6113	JD	HTS063	Scania L113CLB	DAB	B55D	1995
6114	JG	TFY796	Volvo B10B	Carrus Delta Star	B42D	1993
6115	SD	SD88164	Volvo B10BLE	Åbenrå	N45D	1999
6116	SD	SD88255	Volvo B10BLE	Åbenrå	N45D	1999
6117	w	GNX410	Scania CN113ALB	Scania	AB70D	1996
6118	w	GOE130	Scania CN113ALB	Scania	AB70D	1996

6126-6132
		Scania L113TLL	Carrus		AB56D	1996

6126	JD	AEO541	6128	w	AEO661	6130	w	AES611	6132	JG	ASX602
6127	JD	AER941	6129	JG	AES661	6131	w	ASX692		

6133	JD	RZ88061	Scania OmniLine L94UB	DAB	N47D	2002
6134	SD	SD91475	Scania OmniLine CL94UB 12m	Scania	N47D	2002
6135	SD	SL96650	Scania OmniLine CL94UB 12m	Scania	N47D	2002

6136-6142
		Scania L94UB	Vest	N55D	2001

6136	AN	SCH145	6138	AN	SCH094	6140	AN	SCH106	6142	AN	SKL304
6137	AN	SCH103	6139	AN	SCH175	6141	AN	SKL439		

6143	JG	DLE670	Volvo B10M-70	Vest	B55D	1997
6144	JG	DLE630	Volvo B10M-70	Vest	B55D	1997

6146-6159
		Scania L94UB 14.8m	Lahti	N49D	2003

6146	JD	STU583	6150	JG	TPM226	6154	JG	TPL931	6157	JG	TPL703
6147	JD	TPM241	6151	JG	TPM082	6155	JG	TPL922	6158	JG	TPL691
6148	JD	TPM238	6152	JG	TPM079	6156	JG	TPL916	6159	JG	TPL673
6149	JD	TPM232	6153	JG	TPM073					

Malmo is the location for this view of Scania OmniCity 6222, XDB832, as it sets out for Falsterbo. *Tom Johnson*

6160-6166

Scania L94UB 13.5m   Vest   N47D   2003

6160	JD	TPL913	6162	JD	TPL955	6164	JD	TPL712	6166	JD	TPM811
6161	JD	TPL940	6163	JD	TPL685	6165	JD	TPM802			

6167-6171

Scania L94UB 13.5m   Vest   N47D   2003

6167	SV	TSX610	6169	SV	TSX601	6170	SV	TSX559	6171	SV	TSX583
6168	SV	TSX562									

6172-6176

Scania L94 UB 14.8m   Vest   N38D   2003

6172	SV	TSX574	6174	SV	TSX532	6175	SV	TSX538	6176	SV	TSX547
6173	SV	TSX580									

6178	JG	RS97157	Scania OmniLine IL94 IB	Scania	N47D	2000
6198	SV	RGP523	Scania L94 UB	Vest	N47D	2000
6199	AN	RGP529	Scania L94 UB	Vest	N47D	2000

6221-6263

Scania OmniCity CL94 UB6   Scania   N49D   2005

6221	SD	XDC498	6232	SD	XDB747	6243	SD	XDB772	6254	SD	XDB682
6222	SD	XDB832	6233	SD	XDB667	6244	SD	XDB761	6255	SD	XDB762
6223	SD	XDB822	6234	SD	XDB652	6245	SD	XDB702	6256	SD	XDB647
6224	SD	XDB707	6235	SD	XDB641	6246	SD	XDB771	6257	SD	XDC037
6225	SD	XDB692	6236	SD	XDB632	6247	SD	XDB762	6258	SD	XDB841
6226	SD	XDB827	6237	SD	XDB631	6248	SD	XDB757	6259	SV	XDC053
6227	SD	XDB701	6238	SD	XDC453	6249	SD	XDB737	6260	SV	XDB681
6228	SD	XDB671	6239	SD	XDB637	6250	SD	XDB642	6261	SV	XDB651
6229	SD	XDB691	6240	SD	XDB831	6251	SD	XDB697	6262	SV	XDB847
6230	SD	XDB661	6241	SD	XDB622	6252	SD	XDB651	6263	SV	XDB862
6231	SD	XDB687	6242	SD	XDB617	6253	SD	XDB857			

6264-6272

Scania CL94 UB6   Scania   N49D   2007

6264	SD	XYD388	6267	SD	XYD497	6269	SD	XYD508	6271	SD	XYD397
6265	SD	XYD478	6268	SD	XYD387	6270	SD	XYD417	6272	SD	XYD367
6266	SD	XYD378									

Seen in the colours of the Malmo transport authority, 6302, ALR790, is a MAN Lion's City articulated bus, one of ten added to the fleet in 2007. *Tom Johnson*

6300-6309

MAN Lion's City G   MAN   AN46D   2007

6300	MO	ALR532	6303	MO	ALR792	6306	MO	FFW958	6308	MO	FEC737
6301	MO	ALR661	6304	MO	ALR642	6307	MO	CBJ997	6309	MO	ALS333
6302	MO	ALR790	6305	MO	ALR652						

6310-6317

MAN Lion's City G   MAN   AN45D   2008-09

6310	MO	BNA670	6312	MO	BNH454	6314	MO	SWN298	6316	MO	DEO242
6311	MO	BNA886	6313	MO	BNH426	6315	MO	SWK829	6317	MO	DEO255

6391-6398

Scania OmniLink CL94UB   Scania   N32D   2001

6391	w	SFW553	6393	JK	SHA709	6395	JK	SHB571	6397	JK	SOB811
6392	SD	SFW559	6394	JK	SHA715	6396	JK	SOB844	6398	JK	SOB832

6399	AN	TUS256	DAB GS200 8.6m	DAB	N18D	1996
6400	AN	TWG436	DAB GS200 8.6m	DAB	N18D	1996
6424	AN	DHE670	Volvo B10BLE	Carrus City L	N36D	1997
6425	AN	DHE680	Volvo B10BLE	Carrus City L	N36D	1997

6451-6458

Scania OmniCity CN94UB (cng)   Scania   N32D   1998-99

6451	JK	JKF208	6453	TG	JJZ208	6456	TG	JJZ138	6458	TG	DSO632
6452	AN	JKA408	6455	TG	JKA158	6457	TG	DSO512			

6461-6479

Scania OmniCity CL94UB   Scania   N32D   2001

6461	JK	SEA778	6466	JK	SFA697	6471	JK	SFA682	6476	JK	SFW565
6462	JK	SEA769	6467	JK	SFC013	6472	JK	SFA679	6477	JK	SFW595
6463	JK	SEA841	6468	JK	SFA691	6473	JK	SFW571	6478	JK	SFW538
6464	JK	SEA847	6469	JK	SFA796	6474	JK	SFW580	6479	JK	SHA700
6465	JK	SFA700	6470	JK	SFA685	6475	JK	SFX187			

6488-6493

DAB Citybus S11   DAB   B36D   2000

6488	TG	RGP517	6490	TG	RGP574	6492	TG	RGP568	6493	AN	RGP610
6489	TG	RGP442	6491	TG	RGP577						

6516-6538 Volvo B10BLE (cng) Säffle N32D 2001

6516	MO	SHC256	6522	MO	SHC274	6528	MO	SHC727	6534	MO	SHB772
6517	MO	SHC259	6523	MO	SHC277	6529	MO	SHC736	6535	MO	SHB781
6518	MO	SHC252	6524	MO	SHC280	6530	MO	SHC739	6536	MO	SHD922
6519	MO	SHC265	6525	MO	SHC283	6531	MO	SHC748	6537	MO	SHD925
6520	MO	SHC288	6526	MO	SHC708	6532	MO	SHB760	6538	MO	SHD931
6521	MO	SHC271	6527	MO	SHC718	6533	MO	SHB763			

6539-6544 Volvo B10LA (cng) Säffle AN50D 2001

6539	MO	SHH016	6541	MO	SHH025	6543	MO	SHH031	6544	MO	SHH034
6540	MO	SHH019	6542	MO	SHH028						

6545-6550 MAN Lion's City NL313 (cng) MAN N42D 2005

6545	HB	XBD788	6547	HB	XBC066	6549	HB	XBC047	6550	HB	XBC057
6546	HB	XBC056	6548	HB	XBC202						

6551-6558 MAN Lion's City NL313 (cng) MAN N42D 2006-08

6551	HB	RZS673	6553	HB	ARC613	6555	HB	ARC374	6557	HB	BNA655
6552	HB	SAM553	6554	HB	DDB634	6556	HB	ARC405	6558	HB	BNA650

6559	HB	DCA850	Volvo B10L (cng)	Carrus	N32D	1999
6560	HB	TDR235	MAN Lion's City NL313 (cng)	MAN	N42D	2009
6561	HB	EEU628	MAN Lion's City NL313 (cng)	MAN	N42D	2009
6568	HB	DCE600	Volvo B10L (cng)	Carrus	N32D	1999
6570	HB	OOP953	Volvo B10L (cng)	Carrus	N32D	1999

6576-6626 MAN NL313 (cng) MAN N30D 2005

6576	HB	XBC076	6589	HB	XBC107	6602	HB	XBC211	6615	HB	XBC241
6577	HB	XBC091	6590	HB	XBC152	6603	HB	XBC212	6616	HB	XBC261
6578	HB	XBC071	6591	HB	XBC171	6604	HB	XBC176	6617	HB	XBC257
6579	HB	XBC077	6592	HB	XBC067	6605	HB	XBC206	6618	HB	XBC231
6580	HB	XBC092	6593	HB	XBC157	6606	HB	XBC217	6619	HB	XBC247
6581	HB	XBC117	6594	HB	XBC177	6607	HB	XBC221	6620	HB	XBC256
6582	HB	XBC136	6595	HB	XBC192	6608	HB	XBC232	6621	HB	XBC291
6583	HB	XBC132	6596	HB	XBC141	6609	HB	XBC216	6622	HB	XBC262
6584	HB	XBC082	6597	HB	XBC187	6610	HB	XBC227	6623	HB	XBC236
6585	HB	XBC131	6598	HB	XBC196	6611	HB	XBC242	6624	HB	XBC252
6586	HB	XBC142	6599	HB	XBC222	6612	HB	XBC237	6625	HB	XBC266
6587	HB	XBC156	6600	HB	XBC207	6613	HB	XBC197	6626	HB	XBC267
6588	HB	XBC166	6601	HB	XBC201	6614	HB	XBC246			

6627-6632 MAN Lion's City NL313 (cng) MAN N30D 2006

6627	HB	XMW744	6629	HB	XMW749	6631	HB	XSY560	6632	HB	RZT325
6628	HB	XMW714	6630	HB	XMW748						

6633	HB	REO601	MAN Lion's City A21 12m	MAN	N29D	2009
6634	HB	REO601	MAN Lion's City A21 12m	MAN	N29D	2009

6641-6649 MAN Lion's City A21 (cng) MAN N30D 2008

6641	JK	BLS716	6644	JK	BLS550	6646	JK	BLS634	6648	JK	BLS685
6642	JK	BLS726	6645	JK	EEE013	6647	JK	BLS645	6649	JK	BLS681
6643	JK	CDL251									

6650-6667 MAN Lion's City NL313 (cng) MAN N30D 2006

6650	MO	RZT460	6655	MO	TRP760	6660	MO	XWE499	6664	MO	ALG553
6651	MO	SRO031	6656	MO	TRO121	6661	MO	RZT295	6665	MO	ALG597
6652	MO	RZT445	6657	MO	RZS745	6662	MO	RZS703	6666	MO	ALG643
6653	MO	RZT373	6658	MO	RZT262	6663	MO	ALG489	6667	MO	DDS656
6654	MO	RZT394	6659	MO	RZT388						

6703-6729 Scania OmniCity CN94UA 18m Scania AN44D 2001

6703	JL	SCH199	6710	JL	SDD955	6717	JL	SEA832	6724	JL	SFA721
6704	JL	SCH181	6711	JL	SDD952	6718	JL	SEA820	6725	JL	SFA706
6705	JL	SCH184	6712	JL	SDE007	6719	JL	SEA817	6726	JL	SFW556
6706	JL	SCH226	6713	JL	SDD958	6720	JL	SEA784	6727	JL	SFW568
6707	JL	SCH220	6714	JL	SDD949	6721	JL	SEA775	6728	JL	SFW547
6708	JL	SDD964	6715	JL	SDM460	6722	JL	SEA766	6729	JL	SFZ649
6709	JL	SDD967	6716	JL	SDM457	6723	JL	SFA859			

6730-6744 — Volvo B10BLE — Åbenrå — N45D — 2001-02

6730	JK	DEM368	6734	JK	BUL618	6738	JK	BRS808	6742	JK	CDT528
6731	JK	BOO598	6735	JK	BUL128	6739	JK	BUK508	6743	JK	SD88214
6732	JK	CDT568	6736	JK	BUL298	6740	JK	BUL028	6744	JK	SD88166
6733	JK	BRS048	6737	JK	BRS748	6741	JK	BUK818			

6745-6750 — MAN Lion's City A26 14.7m — MAN — N40D — 2008

6745	JK	TXL604	6747	JK	TXF553	6749	JK	TWE682	6750	JK	XYF875
6746	JK	BMD390	6748	JK	TXG121						

6751-6759 — MAN Lion's City A78 12m — MAN — N30D — 2008

6751	JK	BHZ262	6754	JK	BHZ323	6756	JK	BHZ903	6758	JK	BHZ952
6752	JK	EEB599	6755	JK	CXF158	6757	JK	BHZ983	6759	JK	EBC319
6753	JK	BHZ283									

6760-6770 — MAN Lion's City A78 12m — MAN — N30D — 2008

6760	JK	ECB032	6763	JK	CZG247	6766	JK	BJB079	6769	JK	BHZ328
6761	JK	CWF079	6764	JK	BHZ210	6767	JK	BHZ353	6770	JK	BHZ312
6762	JK	BHZ184	6765	JK	BHZ964	6768	JK	BHZ463			

6830-6843 — Volvo B10BLE — Åbenrå — N32D — 2000

6830	MO	RWG871	6834	MO	RMK088	6838	MO	RMK106	6841	MO	RMK607
6831	MO	RMJ985	6835	MO	RMK091	6839	MO	RMK109	6842	MO	RMK613
6832	MO	RMK004	6836	MO	RMK094	6840	MO	RMK601	6843	MO	RMK619
6833	MO	RMK082	6837	MO	RMK103						

6844	AN	FGC857	Volvo B12BLE 13.8m	Åbenrå		N25D	2004
6845	AN	ANM627	Volvo B12BLE 13.8m	Åbenrå		N52D	2004
6846	AN	ANM307	Volvo B12BLE 13.8m	Åbenrå		N52D	2004

6849-6867 — Volvo B10BLE — Åbenrå — N32D — 2000

6849	MO	RJS325	6854	MO	RJS337	6859	MO	RJS145	6864	MO	RJS265
6850	MO	RJS328	6855	MO	RJS340	6860	MO	RJS169	6865	MO	RJS268
6851	MO	RRD190	6856	MO	RJS343	6861	MO	RJS172	6866	MO	RJS271
6852	MO	RJS331	6857	MO	RJS346	6862	MO	RJS178	6867	MO	RJS277
6853	MO	RJS334	6858	MO	RJS349	6863	MO	RJS256			

6868-6871 — Scania OmniLink CL94 UB 12m — Scania — N31D — 2001-02

6868	AN	RZ88231	6869	MO	RV95455	6870	MO	SH93772	6871	MO	RZ88245

6929	SD	TDD520	Scania L94 UB 13.8m	Scania		N55D	2002

7001-7025 — Scania OmniLink 18m — Scania — AN56D — 2009

7001	SX	ECD210	7008	SX	ECD207	7014	SX	CDP083	7020	SX	BOK472
7002	SX	BOK685	7009	SX	BOK364	7015	SX	BOK391	7021	SX	BOK521
7003	SX	BOK691	7010	SX	BOK443	7016	SX	DEF951	7022	SX	BOK562
7004	SX	BOK841	7011	SX	BOK426	7017	SX	BOK423	7023	SX	BOK540
7005	SX	BOK855	7012	SX	DEF943	7018	SX	BOK400	7024	SX	CDP093
7006	SX	BOK857	7013	SX	BOK382	7019	SX	BOK376	7025	SX	BOK541
7007	SX	BOK363									

7026-7043 — Scania OmniLink (Ethanol) — Scania — AN56D — 2009

7026	SM	BON617	7031	SM	DEG171	7036	SM	BON674	7040	SM	BON691
7027	SM	BON626	7032	SM	BON645	7037	SM	BON654	7041	SM	DEG180
7028	SM	BON627	7033	SM	DEG173	7038	SM	EET012	7042	SM	BON696
7029	SM	CDP325	7034	SM	CDP326	7039	SM	BON646	7043	SM	BON685
7030	SM	BON631	7035	SM	BON660						

7044-7056 — Scania CL94UA (Ethanol) — Scania — AN59D — 2006

7044	SM	XOS891	7048	SM	XOS837	7051	SM	XOS992	7054	SM	XOS842
7045	SM	XOS847	7049	SM	XOT037	7052	SM	XOS896	7055	SM	XOS907
7046	SM	XOS871	7050	SM	XOS877	7053	SM	XOS952	7056	SM	XOS946
7047	SM	XOS846									

7057-7068 — Scania CL94UB — Scania — N34D — 2006

7057	SM	XLG672	7060	SM	XLK365	7063	SM	XLK386	7066	SM	XLK326
7058	SM	XLK396	7061	SM	XLK356	7064	SM	XLK376	7067	SM	XLK316
7059	SM	XLK335	7062	SM	XLK336	7065	SM	XLK375	7068	SM	XLK505

										Type	Year
7069	SM	KLM154	Scania CN113 ALB			Lahti				AB61D	1995
7070	SM	KKC274	Scania CN113 ALB			Lahti				AB61D	1995

7071-7075 Volvo B10M-A Vest AB67D 2000-02

7071	SX	SOR313	7073	SX	RJZ184	7074	SX	RJZ229	7075	SX	RJZ232
7072	SX	SOR322									

7076	SM	DKK950	Scania CN113 ALB			Lahti				AB61D	1997

7077-7088 Volvo B10M-A Vest AB67D 1999-2002

7077	SX	OWR528	7080	SX	SOR181	7083	SX	SOR256	7086	SX	SOR295
7078	SX	SJJ643	7081	SX	SOR226	7084	SX	SOR262	7087	SX	SOR304
7079	SX	SJJ646	7082	SX	SOR235	7085	SX	SOR268	7088	SX	SOR307

7089-7092 Scania CN113 CLB Lahti B41D 1997

7089	SM	DAG659	7090	SM	DAH559	7091	SM	DBZ899	7092	SM	DBZ919

7093	SX	SSJ640	Volvo B10M-A			Vest				AB67D	2001

7094-7107 Scania CN113 CLB Lahti B41D 1995-96

7094	SM	KGF424	7098	SM	JKC435	7102	SM	BRA914	7105	SM	BRB854
7095	SM	KHM134	7099	SM	JKF085	7103	SM	BRB614	7106	SM	DEK769
7096	SM	JLZ175	7100	SM	JMG345	7104	SM	BRB774	7107	SM	DEK699
7097	SM	JMZ145	7101	SM	BRA814						

7108	SX	DEL389	Volvo B10BLE			-				N43D	2001
7109	SX	DEL629	Volvo B10BLE			-				N43D	2001
7110	SX	EFB999	Volvo B10BLE			-				N43D	2001
7111	SM	UNS440	Scania			Berkhof				BC32D	1998
7112	SM	BPB720	Scania			Berkhof				BC32D	1998
7113	SX	BOX410	Volvo B10BLE			-				N43D	2001
7114	SM	XYL909	Scania			Berkhof				BC32D	1998
7115	SM	EUZ379	Scania			Berkhof				BC32D	1998
7116	SX	UOD900	Volvo B10BLE			-				N43D	2001
7117	SM	XTH909	Scania			Berkhof				BC32D	1998
7118	SM	BSL039	Scania			Berkhof				BC32D	1998

7119-7143 Volvo B10BLE Vest N31D 1999-2002

7119	SX	BOX440	7126	SM	SXT649	7132	SM	BSK619	7138	SM	XYF360
7120	SX	DEH221	7127	SM	BRP909	7133	SM	SXN079	7139	SX	WHL260
7121	SM	XZZ919	7128	SM	BOO004	7134	SX	XZC159	7140	SX	BSK689
7122	SM	UNG090	7129	SM	BRP919	7135	SM	XLN959	7141	SX	SYS349
7123	SM	CDU469	7130	SM	XZN069	7136	SM	BRP999	7142	SM	BOX370
7124	SM	BOX130	7131	SM	CDR840	7137	SM	CDW609	7143	SM	XXA809
7125	SM	XTB179									

7144	SM	GPR410	Scania CN113 ALB			Lahti				AN70D	1996
7145	SM	DHD620	Volvo B10BLE			-				N36D	1997
7146	SM	DHD690	Volvo B10BLE			-				N36D	1997
7147	SM	DHE580	Volvo B10BLE			-				N36D	1997
7148	SM	DFS589	Scania CN94 UB							N34D	1997

7149-7157 Volvo B10BLE Vest N31D 1998-99

7149	SM	BRP749	7152	SX	DEK119	7154	SX	BRR809	7156	SM	BPR750
7150	SX	ATJ249	7153	SX	BRR759	7155	SM	UNG700	7157	SX	XJU534
7151	SX	ASB539									

7158-7162 Scania CN94 UB - N32D 2001

7158	SX	SFA796	7160	SX	SFA697	7161	SM	SFC013	7162	SM	SFA691
7159	w	SHA736									

7163	SM	SCH208	Scania CN94 UA			Lahti				AN44D	2001
7164	SM	SCH208	Scania CN94 UA			Lahti				AN44D	2001

7165-7170 Volvo B10M Vest B40D 1998-99

7165	SM	JGC055	7167	SM	JGD015	7169	SM	GMW990	7170	SM	GMX740
7166	SM	JGC355	7168	SM	GMU630						

7171	SX	SC90691	Volvo B10BLE			-				N45D	2002
7209	HG	NN91908	Volvo B10			Åbenrå				B39D	1994
7211	HG	OB94391	Volvo B10			Åbenrå				B39D	1995
8303	HV	OV89881	DAF/DAB Citybus S12			Silkeborg				B47D	1997
8305	HV	OV89883	DAF/DAB Citybus S12			Silkeborg				B47D	1997

8308	FY	OZ91788	Scania/DAB	Silkeborg	N38D	1997
8419	FY	RH95.798	Volvo B10M	Vest	BC47D	2000
8421	FY	PX90675	Volvo B10M	Vest	BC47D	1999
8422	FY	PX90674	Volvo B10M	Vest	BC47D	1999
8423	FY	PX90671	Volvo B10M	Vest	BC47D	1999
8424	HV	PX90718	Volvo B10M	Vest	BC47D	1999
8425	AR	PZ96612	Volvo B10M	Vest	BC47D	1999
8426	AR	RK95274	Scania L94	DAB	BC47D	2000
8427	AR	RX97899	Scania OmniLink CL94 UB 12m	Scania	N47D	2001
8428	AR	SN97877	Volvo B12M	Åbenrå	B47D	2003
8430	HV	TN94780	Volvo B10M	Vest	B50D	2000
8431	HV	TN94781	Volvo B10M	Vest	B50D	2000
8432	HV	TN94757	Volvo B10M	Vest	B50D	2000
8433	HV	SL91898	Volvo B10M	Vest	B50D	2002
8434	AR	TU91783	Scania OmniLink CL94 UB 12m	DAB facelift	N47D	1998
8435	w	RN88130	Volvo B10M	Åbenrå	B47D	2000
8436	AA	TB94707	Volvo B10M 12.7m	Vest	B50D	2004
8437	AA	TB94708	Volvo B10M	Vest	B50D	2004
8438	AA	PX96113	Volvo B10M	Vest	B50D	1999
8439	AA	PX96109	Volvo B10M	Vest	B50D	1999
8440	AA	RN88779	Volvo B10M	Vest	B50D	2000
8441	AA	RN88780	Volvo B10M	Vest	B50D	2000
8442	AA	RN88804	Volvo B10M	Vest	B50D	2000
8443	AA	RN88188	Volvo B10M	Vest	B50D	2000
8444	AA	RS92754	Volvo B10M	Vest	B50D	2000
8445	AA	PX96122	Volvo B10M	Vest	B50D	1999
8446	AA	PX96123	Volvo B10M	Vest	B50D	1999
8447	AA	RN88196	Volvo B10M	Vest	B50D	2000
8449	AA	RZ92524	Volvo B10M	Vest	B50D	2001
8450	AA	SD92720	Volvo B10M	Vest	B50D	2002
8451	AA	RS92753	Volvo B10M	Vest	B50D	2000
8452	AA	RL92253	Volvo B10M	Vest	B50D	2000
8453	AA	PX96129	Volvo B10M	Vest	B50D	1999
8454	AA	PX96130	Volvo B10M	Vest	B50D	1999
8456	AA	RD91795	Volvo B10M	Vest	B50D	1999
8458	AA	RL92426	Volvo B10M	Vest	B50D	2000
8459	AA	RN88178	Volvo B10M	Vest	B50D	2000
8460	AA	RN88179	Volvo B10M	Vest	B50D	2000
8461	AA	RN88180	Volvo B10M	Vest	B50D	2000
8462	AA	RL96887	Volvo B10M	Vest	B50D	2000
8463	AA	RP90928	Volvo B10M	Vest	B50D	2000
8464	AA	RL92413	Volvo B10M	Vest	B50D	2000
8465	AA	RN88131	Volvo B10M	Vest	B50D	2000
8466	AA	RN88187	Volvo B10M	Vest	B50D	2000
8467	AA	PX96112	Volvo B10M	Vest	B50D	1999
8468	AA	RN88129	Volvo B10M	Vest	B50D	2000

8472-8486

			Volvo B12BLE	Carrus	N47D	2004

8472	AA	TB96602	**8476**	AA	TB96655	**8480**	AA	TB96608	**8484**	AA	TB95429
8473	AA	TB96603	**8477**	AA	TB96605	**8481**	AA	TB96654	**8485**	AA	TB96660
8474	AA	TB96657	**8478**	AA	TB96606	**8482**	AA	TB96659	**8486**	AA	TB96656
8475	AA	TB96604	**8479**	AA	TB96607	**8483**	AA	TB96658			

8487	AA	RL97023	Scania	Scania/DAB	N47D	2000
8488	AA	TC90472	Scania OmniLine L94UB	DAB	N--D	2004
8489	AA	UT95386	Scania 13.8m	Lahti Laventre	N49D	2006
8490	AA	UT95387	Scania 13.8m	Lahti Laventre	N49D	2006
8491	AA	UT95388	Scania 13.8m	Lahti Laventre	N49D	2006
8492	AA	UT95389	Scania 13.8m	Lahti Laventre	N49D	2006
8493	AA	UT95399	Scania 13.8m	Lahti Laventre	N49D	2006
8494	AA	UX91358	Scania OmniLink CL94UB 12m	Scania	N--D	2007
8495	AA	UX91359	Scania OmniLink CL94UB 12m	Scania	N--D	2007
8496	AA	UX91360	Scania OmniLink CL94UB 12m	Scania	N--D	2007
8497	AA	UX91532	Scania 13.8m	Lahti Laventre	N49D	2007
8498	AA	UY93706	Scania 13.8m	Lahti Laventre	N49D	2007
8499	AA	VB94299	Scania 13.8m	Lahti Laventre	N49D	2007
8500	AA	VH93298	Scania 13.8m	Lahti Laventre	N49D	2007
8501	AA	UU96996	Volvo B12BLE 12m	Carrus	N44D	2006
8502	AA	UX95679	Volvo B12BLE 12m	Carrus	N44D	2007
8503	AA	UU96930	Volvo B12BLE 13.7m	Carrus	N46D	2006
8504	AA	UU96931	Volvo B12BLE 13.7m	Carrus	N46D	2006

From the 2003 intake of Volvo B12BLEs, 1668, ST97848, with Volvo's 8500 body style. Pictured in Copenhagen it carries lettering for route 6. *Mark Doggett*

8510-8533

Scania OmniLink CL94 UB 12m · Scania · N31D · 2002

8510	KO	SH93770	8518	KO	SH93746	8520	KO	SH93748	8533	KO	SH93779
8516	KO	SH93744	8519	KO	SH93747	8522	KO	SH93718		

8536	u	RL96987	Scania L94 IB 12m	DAB facelift	N47D	2000
8537	RO	RN96159	Scania L94 IB 12m	DAB facelift	N47D	2000

8543-8549

Volvo B12BLE · Carrus · N47D · 1998

8543	w	OL99340	8545	KO	PP97785	8548	KO	PE94519	8549	KO	PE94538
8544	KO	PO97786								

8551	KO	TJ94029	Scania OmniLink CL94 UB 12m	Scania	N31D	2004
8552	KO	TJ94030	Scania OmniLink CL94 UB 12m	Scania	N31D	2004
8553	KO	RN88118	Volvo B12BLE 12m	Carrus	N44D	2000
8554	KO	RZ88244	Scania OmniLink CL94 UB 12m	Scania	N31D	2001
8556	KO	SC91809	Scania OmniLink CL94 UB 12m	Scania	N31D	2002
8557	KO	SD91568	Scania OmniLink CL94 UB 12m	Scania	N31D	2002

8558-8568

Volvo B12BLE · Volvo · N47D · 2002-03

8558	KO	SM96039	8561	KO	SM96050	8564	KO	SM96067	8566	KO	ST97883
8559	KO	SM96040	8562	KO	SM96051	8565	KO	SM96068	8568	KO	UR94549
8560	KO	SM96045	8563	KO	SM96052					

8571	AR	RN96160	Scania L94 IB 12m	DAB facelift	N47D	2000
8581	AR	RC89301	Mercedes-Benz Sprinter	Mercedes-Benz	M	1999
8587	AR	RL92345	Volvo B10M	Vest	B50D	2000
8594	w	TB92523	Mercedes-Benz Sprinter	Mercedes-Benz	M	1999
8601	RA	UR90590	Volvo B7RLE	Volvo 8700	N40D	2006
8602	RA	UR90591	Volvo B7RLE	Volvo 8700	N40D	2006

8603-8607

Volvo B12BLE · Volvo · N39D · 2003

8603	RA	ST97904	8605	RA	ST97910	8606	RA	ST97912	8607	RA	ST97919
8604	RA	ST97909								

8609-8617

Volvo B10L · Volvo 8600 · N39D · 1996-98

8609	RA	OM97836	8612	RA	OX94374	8615	RA	PL97614	8617	RA	PL97630
8611	RA	OX94373	8614	w	PL97604	8616	RA	PL97617		

8618-8623 — Volvo B10BLE / Volvo / N40D / 2000

8618	RA	RP91114	8620	RA	RP91122	8622	RA	RP91115	8623	RA	RP91121
8619	RA	RP91123	8621	RA	RP91112						

8624	RA	VH95011	Volvo B7BLE	Volvo 8700	N40D	2007
8625	RA	VH95012	Volvo B7BLE	Volvo 8700	N40D	2007
8626	RA	VH95013	Volvo B7BLE	Volvo 8700	N40D	2007
8630	AR	NX93039	Volvo B10M	Vest	B50D	1994
8633	AR	RZ97959	Scania IL94 IB	Scania	N47D	2001
8634	AR	RE94208	Volvo B10M	Vest	B50D	1999
8635	AR	PX96187	Volvo B10M	Vest	B50D	1999
8636	AR	PJ97721	Volvo B10M	Vest	B50D	1998
8639	SJ	MC92536	Volvo B10M	Vest	B50D	1990
8644	w	RD91986	Volvo B10MA	Vest	AB66D	1999

8645-8649 — Scania L94 / DAB facelift / N47D / 2000

8645	RA	RL96988	8647	AR	RL96990	8648	AR	RL96991	8649	RA	RL96992
8646	RA	RL96989									

8650	AR	RP90963	Volvo B10M 13.7m	Vest	B50D	2000
8651	AR	RL92470	Volvo B10BLE	Volvo	N40D	2000
8652	AR	RY88107	Scania L94	Scania	N47D	2001
8653	w	PL97732	Volvo B10MA	Vest	AB66D	1998
8659	AR	PJ97739	Volvo B10M	Vest	B50D	1998
8663	AR	OS89253	Volvo B10M	Vest	B50D	1996
8664	AR	OS89255	Volvo B10M	Vest	B50D	1996
8665	AR	OS89256	Volvo B10M	Vest	B50D	1996
8667	AR	TP93418	Scania OmniLink CL94 UB 12m	Scania	N31D	2005
8668	AR	TP93419	Scania OmniLink CL94 UB 12m	Scania	N31D	2005
8669	AR	RP90962	Volvo B10M 13.7m	Vest	B50D	2000
8671	AR	OL97126	Volvo B10M	Vest	B40D	1996
8672	AR	RM96995	Scania CL94 UB 12m	DAB facelift	N47D	2000
8673	AR	RY88119	Scania OmniLink CL94 UB 12m	Scania	N31D	2001
8674	AR	RZ99057	Scania OmniLink CL94 UB 12m	Scania	N31D	2001
8675	AR	TR95130	Scania OmniLink CL94 UB 12m	Scania	N31D	2005
8676	RA	RD94836	Scania CL94 UB 12m	DAB facelift	N47D	1999
8677	RA	UR90589	Volvo B7RLE	Volvo 8700	N40D	2006
8679	w	UZ94742	Volvo B10M	Vest	B50D	1998
8680	AR	UX89357	Volvo B10M	Vest	B50D	1998
8681	AR	PJ97757	Volvo B10M	Vest	B50D	1998
8682	AR	UZ94743	Volvo B10M	Vest	B50D	1998
8683	AR	UZ94774	Volvo B10M	Vest	B50D	1998
8684	AR	PX96097	Volvo B10M	Vest	B50D	1999
8685	AR	RD94888	Scania CL94 UB 12m	DAB facelift	N47D	1999
8686	AR	RD94889	Scania CL94 UB 12m	DAB facelift	N47D	1999
8688	AR	PE92003	Volvo B10M	Vest	B50D	1998
8691	RA	UZ94845	Scania CL94 UB 12m	DAB facelift	N47D	2000
8692	AR	UZ95841	Scania CL94 UB 12m	DAB facelift	N47D	2000
8693	AR	UZ94897	Volvo B10M 13.7m	Vest	B50D	2000
8694	AR	RL92347	Volvo B10M 13.7m	Vest	B50D	2000
8695	AR	UZ94896	Volvo B10M 13.7m	Vest	B50D	2000
8696	AR	RS97266	Scania OmniLine	Scania	NC47D	2000
8697	AR	RS97154	Scania OmniLine	Scania	NC47D	2000
8698	AR	RM91513	Volvo B10MA	Vest	AB66D	2000
8699	AR	RL97017	Scania CL94 UB 12m	DAB facelift	N47D	2000
8700	AR	RL97018	Scania CL94 UB 12m	DAB facelift	N47D	2000
8701	AR	RL92430	Volvo B10M 13.7m	Vest	B50D	2000
8702	AR	RP97563	Scania OmniLine	Scania	NC47D	2000

8703-8707 — Volvo B10M / Vest / B50D / 2000

8703	RA	RL92431	8705	AR	RS90131	8706	AR	RE92095	8707	AR	RP97560
8704	RA	RE92067									

8708	w	RM91512	Volvo B10MA	Vest	AB66D	2000
8709	AR	RP97561	Volvo B12M	Volvo Carrus	BC44D	2000

8710-8717 — Scania OmniLine / Scania / NC47D / 2000

8710	AR	RP97564	8713	AR	RS97158	8715	FS	RS97268	8717	AR	RS97270
8711	RA	RS97156	8714	AR	RS97267	8716	AR	RS97269			

8718	AR	RL97014	Scania CL94 UB 12m			DAB facelift			N47D	2000		
8719	AR	RP97562	Scania OmniLine			Scania			NC47D	2000		
8720	AR	UZ94846	Scania OmniLine 13.6m			Lahti Flyer			NC55D	2001		

8721-8733
Scania OmniLine — Scania — NC47D — 2000-01

8721	AR	RS97155	8725	AR	RT96586	8728	AR	RT96893	8731	AR	RT96896
8722	FS	RT96582	8726	AR	RT96587	8729	AR	RT96894	8732	AR	RT96897
8723	AR	RT96583	8727	AR	RT96892	8730	AR	RT96895	8733	AR	RT96584
8724	AR	RT96898									

8734	AR	RS90289	Volvo B10M	Vest	B50D	2001
8735	AR	RT94703	Volvo B10M	Vest	B50D	2001

8736-8739
Volvo B10MA — Vest — AB66D — 2001

8736	AR	SB94592	8737	AR	SB94567	8738	AR	SB94594	8739	AR	SB94593

8740-8744
Scania OmniLine — Scania — NC47D — 2001

8740	AR	RV95329	8742	FS	RT96899	8743	AR	RT96585	8744	AR	RS96891
8741	AR	RV95330									

8745-8751
Volvo B12M — Volvo — BC55D — 2002

8745	AR	SM95991	8747	AR	SM95992	8749	AR	SH90380	8751	AR	SM95889
8746	AR	SM96003	8748	AR	SH90381	8750	AR	SH90382			

8752	AR	SH93632	Scania OmniLine	Scania	NC47D	2002
8753	AR	SM96002	Volvo B12M	Volvo Carrus	BC44D	2002
8754	AR	SU97086	Volvo B12M	Volvo Carrus	BC44D	2003
8755	AR	TT88410	Scania OmniLine	Scania	NC47D	2005
8756	AR	TT88270	Scania OmniLine	Scania	NC47D	2005
8757	AR	VH95033	Volvo B12M 13.7m	Volvo 8700	BC55D	2007
8758	RA	VH94956	Volvo B12M 12m	Volvo 8700	BC47D	2007

8759-8768
Volvo B12M 13.7m — Volvo 8700 — BC55D — 2007

8759	AR	VH95055	8762	AR	VH95083	8765	AR	VJ96917	8767	AR	VJ96988
8760	AR	VH95056	8763	AR	VH95097	8766	AR	VJ96980	8768	AR	VJ96987
8761	AR	VH95072	8764	AR	VJ96904						

8769	AR	VJ96981	Volvo B12M-A	Volvo 8700	AC65D	2007
8770	AR	VJ97023	Volvo B12M 13.7m	Volvo 8700	BC55D	2007
8771	AR	VN92492	Volvo B12M 13.7m	Volvo 8700	BC55D	2007
8772	AR	VS88406	Volvo B12M-A	Volvo 8700	AC65D	2007
8773	AR	VT91976	Volvo B7R	Volvo	N47D	2008
8774	AR	VS95959	Volvo B10M	Vest	B50D	1999
8775	AR	VS96062	Volvo B10M	Vest	B50D	1999
8776	AA	SL91903	Volvo B12M	Åbenrå	BC47D	2002
8777	AA	SL91904	Volvo B12M	Åbenrå	BC47D	2002

9035-9048
Volvo B10BLE — Volvo — N32D — 1997-98

9035	AA	PE94591	9040	KO	TV96477	9042	VJ	TV96500	9048	AA	RM91003
9038	AA	PE94616									

9060	SJ	KV94741	Volvo B10M	DAB Silkeborg	B39D	1986
9061	SJ	KV94742	Volvo B10M	DAB Silkeborg	B39D	1986

9070-9101
Volvo B10BLE — Volvo — N45D — 1997-2000

9082	AA	RN90413	9085	VJ	OV92039	9090	w	RN95489	9101	w	BDM460
9083	AA	RN90414									

9102	w	KNH164	Scania CN113 ALB	Lahti	AN70D	1995
9103	w	KMU024	Scania CN113 ALB	Lahti	AN70D	1995

Depots and codes: Copenhagen area - Amager (AM); Ejby (EJ); Falster (FA); Gladsaxe (GX); Glostrup (GL); Hillerød (HI); Holbæk (HO); Køge (KG) Kokkedal (KK); Maribo (MA); Næstved (ND); Ringsted (RI); Roskilde (RK); Ryvange (RG); Sorø (SO).

Other depots in Denmark and Sweden: Aalborg (AA); Ängelholm-Helsingborg (AN); Århus (AR)[Ebeltoft, Grenå, Hornslet; Jeksen, Odder, Rønde, Rostved, Ryomgård and Skanderborg]; Årslev (AS); Djursland (DJ); Ebeltoft (EB); Esbjerg (ES); Fyn North [Assens, Kerteminde, Bogense and Kildemosevej] (FN); Fyn South [Ærø, Nyborg, Ringe, Faaborg, Lohals and Svendborg] (FS); Fyn [Odense] (FY); Gislaved (GD); Gränna (JG); Haderslev (HV); Helsingborg (HB); Herning (HG); Hornslet (HT); Horsens (HN); Jönköping (JK); Jönköping Väst (JL); Kolding (KO); Løkken (LO); Malmö (MO); Nordjyllands [Hjørring, Hobro, Løkken, Sæby and Tversted] (ND); Odense (OV); Odder (OD); Ø.Kippinge (KI); Randers (RA); Rønde/Rostved (RO); Rudkøbing (RU); Ryomgård (RY); Skælskør (SK); Skanderborg (SG); Söderslätt regional (SD); Stockholm Ekerö (SX); Stockholm Märsta (SM); Svalöv (SV); Svendborg (SE); Trelleborg (TG); Vejile (VJ); Vinderup (VI); FDM Sjællandsringen (SJ)

ARRIVA NEDERLANDS

Arriva Nederlands BV, Trambaan 3, postbus 626, 8440 AP Heerenveen

152	LS	VR-10-LR	Mercedes-Benz O405G		Mercedes-Benz		AB49F	1992			
164	GR	BN-HN-60	Mercedes-Benz Citaro O530G		Mercedes-Benz		AB50F	2002			
165	GR	BN-HN-61	Mercedes-Benz Citaro O530G		Mercedes-Benz		AB50F	2002			
192-195			Mercedes-Benz Tourismo O350		Mercedes-Benz		C51F	1998-2002			
192	GR	BG-NP-90	**193**	GR	BL-VH-95	**194**	GR	BL-VH-96	**195**	HV	BL-VH-80
196-199			Setra S315 GT-HD		Setra		C51F	1999-2001			
196	WT	BH-FH-71	**197**	WT	BH-HG-65	**198**	SN	BJ-BG-36	**199**	GR	BL-BG-74
221-234			Mercedes-Benz Citaro O530 G		Mercedes-Benz		AN50D	2004			
221	GR	BP-NH-41	**224**	GR	BP-NH-54	**227**	DM	BP-NH-56	**232**	GR	BP-NL-71
223	GL	BP-NH-51	**225**	GR	BP-NH-53	**231**	GR	BP-NL-69	**234**	TG	BP-NL-75
241	TG	BR-NN-60	Mercedes-Benz Citaro O530 G		Mercedes-Benz		AN49D	2005			
251-260			MAN Lion's City CNG		MAN		AN46D	2008			
251	AM	BV-HH-09	**254**	AM	BV-HH-12	**257**	GR	BV-HP-22	**259**	GR	BV-HP-24
252	AM	BV-HH-10	**255**	GR	BV-HH-13	**258**	GR	BV-HP-23	**260**	GR	BV-HP-27
253	AM	BV-HH-11	**256**	GR	BV-HP-21						
459	GR	BP-LT-05	Setra S315 GT-HD		Setra		C51F	2000			
460	WT	BP-LV-72	Setra S315 GT-HD		Setra		C51F	2000			
461	SN	BL-TT-46	Mercedes-Benz Travego O580		Mercedes-Benz		C51F	2002			
462	SN	BL-TT-50	Mercedes-Benz Travego O580		Mercedes-Benz		C51F	2002			
463	LS	BN-RR-71	Mercedes-Benz Tourismo O350		Mercedes-Benz		C51F	2003			
464	LS	BN-PT-94	Mercedes-Benz Tourismo O350		Mercedes-Benz		C51F	2003			
465	GR	BP-JR-38	VDL SBR4000				C51F	2000			
466	GR	BV-VX-22	Setra S317 GT-HD		Setra		C51F	2000			
467	HV	BV-XR-77	Volvo B12B				C51F	2009			
468	GR	BX-NF-36	MAN Lion's Coach L		MAN		C51F	2010			
469	GR	BX-LZ-95	MAN Lion's Coach L		MAN		C51F	2010			
525	GR	BN-JD-03	Mercedes-Benz Citaro O530		Mercedes-Benz		N34D	2002			
536	DO	BN-TS-65	Mercedes-Benz Citaro O530		Mercedes-Benz		N34D	2003			
537	DO	BN-TS-66	Mercedes-Benz Citaro O530		Mercedes-Benz		N34D	2003			

Arriva currently has VDL's latest EEV specification Ambassador on demonstration at Purmerend depot. It was pictured while waiting time in Amsterdam with fleet number 3159, BT-BJ-79.. *Harry Laming*

Situated in the North Brabant region of the Netherlands, s-Hertogenbosch depot is home to the batch of 2007 Citaro buses, while the 2001 batch are all at Dordrecht. Seen in the latter town's bus station is 727, BL-RF-59.
Harry Laming

551-557

			Mercedes-Benz Citaro 0530		Mercedes-Benz		N35D	2004			
551	AM	BP-NH-40	553	TG	BP-NH-44	555	TG	BP-NH-47	557	TG	BP-NH-49
552	AM	BP-NH-43	554	TG	BP-NH-46	556	TG	BP-NH-48			

721-730

			Mercedes-Benz Citaro 0530		Mercedes-Benz		N28D	2001			
721	DO	BL-RF-48	724	DO	BL-RF-60	727	DO	BL-RF-59	729	DO	BL-RF-56
722	DO	BL-RF-50	725	DO	BL-RF-62	728	DO	BL-RF-64	730	DO	BL-RF-51
723	DO	BL-RF-52	726	DO	BL-RF-63						

751-784

			Mercedes-Benz Citaro 0530		Mercedes-Benz		N26D	2007			
751	SH	BT-GT-95	760	SH	BT-GX-08	769	SH	BT-GX-24	777	SH	BT-HF-89
752	SH	BT-GV-99	761	SH	BT-GX-09	770	SH	BT-GX-26	778	SH	BT-HF-88
753	SH	BT-GX-01	762	SH	BT-GX-11	771	SH	BT-HG-02	779	SH	BT-HF-87
754	SH	BT-GX-02	763	SH	BT-GX-13	772	SH	BT-HG-01	780	SH	BT-HF-86
755	SH	BT-GX-03	764	SH	BT-GX-14	773	SH	BT-HF-97	781	SH	BT-HF-85
756	SH	BT-GX-04	765	SH	BT-GX-17	774	SH	BT-HF-94	782	SH	BT-HF-83
757	SH	BT-GX-05	766	SH	BT-GX-18	775	SH	BT-HF-93	783	SH	BT-HF-82
758	SH	BT-GX-06	767	SH	BT-GX-19	776	SH	BT-HF-92	784	SH	BT-HF-81
759	SH	BT-GX-07	768	SH	BT-GX-20						

1280	ZK	BF-GJ-38	Iveco EuroRider	Berkhof 2000NL	N44D	1997
4751	HV	VX-18-DL	Volvo B10M-61	Berkhof 2000NL	B45D	1993
5810	GR	BH-TD-29	Mercedes-Benz Integro 0550ÜL 15m		NC50D	1999
5817	GR	BH-TR-97	Mercedes-Benz Integro 0550ÜL 15m		NC50D	1999
5847	MK	97-JS-XX	Mercedes-Benz Sprinter		M15	2002
5849	GR	99-JS-XX	Mercedes-Benz Sprinter		M15	2002

5852-5899

			Dennis Dart SLF		Alexander ALX200		N39D	2001			
5852	GR	BJ-XN-84	5874	GR	BJ-ZJ-45	5885	GR	BJ-ZT-76	5892	GR	BL-BS-20
5853	GR	BJ-XN-81	5878	LS	BJ-ZT-91	5887	GR	BL-BJ-82	5893	GR	BL-BS-21
5855	GR	BJ-XN-82	5881	GR	BJ-ZT-93	5888	GR	BL-BJ-83	5896	GR	BL-BV-37
5858	GR	BJ-XN-83	5882	GR	BJ-ZT-92	5889	GR	BL-BJ-78	5898	GR	BL-GN-77
5859	GR	BL-BS-18	5884	GR	BL-BJ-77	5891	GR	BL-BS-19	5899	GR	BJ-TB-91
5867	GR	BJ-ZJ-38									

While many of the Alexander-bodied Darts have migrated to other Arriva fleets the Wrigthbus-bodied Commanders all remain. Arriva Rivierenland's 5991, BN-HS-83, is one on the oldest, seen here in service at Tiel rail station. *Harry Laming*

5957-5999

DAF SB200 — Wrightbus Commander — N42D — 2002

5957	HE	BL-DS-82	5988	DM	BN-HS-67	5991	AL	BN-HS-83	5995	AL	BN-HS-80
5985	DO	BN-HS-79	5989	AL	BN-HS-68	5993	AL	BN-HS-77	5999	DM	BN-HS-75

6030-6045

Irisbus Crossway GX127 — Irisbus — N44F — 2007

6032	HE	BS-ZB-46	6036	GO	BS-ZB-50	6040	GO	BS-ZB-54	6043	DO	BS-ZB-58
6033	GO	BS-ZB-47	6037	GO	BS-ZB-51	6041	DO	BS-ZB-56	6044	DO	BS-ZB-59
6034	GO	BS-ZB-48	6038	GO	BS-ZB-52	6042	DO	BS-ZB-57	6045	DO	BS-ZB-60
6035	GO	BS-ZB-49	6039	GO	BS-ZB-53						

6050	SH	BX-HR-82	Iveco Electric	2009	
6051	SH	BX-LG-46	Iveco Electric	2009	
6052	SH	BX-LG-45	Iveco Electric	2009	

6061-6067

Optare Solo 8.1m — Optare — N16F — 2011

6061	-	BX-XB-08	6063	ZU	BX-XB-10	6065	-	BX-XB-12	6067	-	BX-XB-14
6062	-	BX-XB-09	6064	-	BX-XB-11	6066	-	BX-XB-13			

6071	PU	96-TB-JZ	Volkswagen LT 2.8tdi	Volkswagen	N8	2006

6073-6078

Mercedes-Benz Sprinter 207 CDi — Mercedes-Benz — M8 — 2007

6073	AL	94-TV-XF	6075	MK	41-XB-RG	6077	MK	81-TX-FK	6078	TL	11-FG-KP
6074	MK	89-TV-XF	6076	AL	55-XB-RG						

6079	TL	48-FS-DX	Volkswagen City Bus	Volkswagen	M8	2000

6080-6086

Mercedes-Benz Sprinter 207 CDi — Mercedes-Benz — M8 — 2004

6080	TL	08-LS-LD	6082	TL	37-PT-XL	6084	TL	25-NV-HK	6086	TL	89-PG-XZ
6081	TL	84-PG-XZ	6083	TL	38-PT-XL	6085	TL	35-PT-XL			

6103-6109

DAF SB200 — Berkhof Ambassador — N43D — 2002

6103	SG	BN-JB-07	6106	SG	BN-HH-82	6108	SG	BN-JT-79	6109	SG	BN-JT-80
6105	SG	BN-JB-09	6107	SG	BN-HH-85						

6112	SH	36-LD-NK	Mercedes-Benz Vito 208	Mercedes-Benz	M8	2002
6115	TL	05-LF-XH	Mercedes-Benz Vito 208	Mercedes-Benz	M8	2002
6120	TL	27-LK-BF	Mercedes-Benz Vito 208	Mercedes-Benz	M8	2003
6121	PU	28-LK-BF	Mercedes-Benz Vito 208	Mercedes-Benz	M8	2003
6123	TL	82-PJ-KL	Volkswagen City Bus	Volkswagen	M8	2004
6124	TL	31-PR-JP	Volkswagen City Bus	Volkswagen	M8	2004
6125	TL	32-PR-JP	Volkswagen City Bus	Volkswagen	M8	2004
6126	TL	63-RG-DN	Mercedes-Benz Vito 208	Mercedes-Benz	M8	2005
6127	TL	54-RK-BR	Mercedes-Benz Vito 208	Mercedes-Benz	M8	2005
6128	SH	25-RS-JL	Volkswagen City Bus	Volkswagen	M8	2005
6129	PU	52-SF-FR	Volkswagen City Bus	Volkswagen	M8	2005

6138-6156

Mercedes-Benz O550 — Mercedes-Benz Integro — NC43D — 2003

6138	AL	BN-NF-24	6144	GO	BN-NG-19	6149	AL	BN-NG-02	6153	GO	BN-NG-40
6141	GO	BN-NG-39	6145	GO	BN-NG-16	6150	AL	BN-NG-01	6154	AL	BN-NX-74
6142	GO	BN-NG-38	6146	AL	BN-NG-13	6151	GO	BN-NF-99	6155	AL	BN-NX-78
6143	GO	BN-NG-34	6148	AL	BN-NG-04	6152	GO	BN-NF-98	6156	AL	BN-NX-76

6200-6301

DAF SB200 — Wrightbus Commander — N42D — 2003

6200	MK	BN-PN-23	6226	AL	BN-RP-10	6252	AL	BN-SG-15	6277	AL	BN-TB-25
6201	MK	BN-PN-27	6227	AL	BN-RP-11	6253	AL	BN-SG-17	6278	AL	BN-TB-26
6202	MK	BN-PN-30	6228	DO	BN-RP-12	6254	AL	BN-TB-43	6279	AL	BN-TB-27
6203	MK	BN-PN-32	6229	AL	BN-RP-13	6255	AL	BN-TB-45	6280	AL	BN-TB-28
6204	MK	BN-PN-33	6230	AL	BN-RP-15	6256	AL	BN-TB-47	6281	AL	BN-TB-29
6205	MK	BN-PN-38	6231	AL	BN-RP-17	6257	AL	BN-TB-49	6282	AL	BN-TB-30
6206	MK	BN-PN-39	6232	AL	BN-RP-18	6258	AL	BN-TB-51	6283	AL	BN-TB-31
6207	GO	BN-PN-35	6233	AL	BN-RP-20	6259	AL	BN-TB-53	6284	DO	BN-TB-32
6208	GO	BN-PN-41	6234	AL	BN-RP-21	6260	AL	BN-TR-56	6285	DO	BN-TB-33
6209	GO	BN-PN-42	6235	AL	BN-RP-23	6261	DO	BN-TR-58	6286	AL	BN-TB-35
6210	AL	BN-RD-38	6236	AL	BN-RP-26	6262	AL	BN-TR-59	6287	DO	BN-TB-37
6211	AL	BN-RD-39	6237	AL	BN-RP-28	6263	AL	BN-TR-61	6288	AL	BN-TB-38
6212	DO	BN-RD-40	6238	AL	BN-RP-30	6264	AL	BN-TR-62	6289	AL	BN-TB-41
6213	AL	BN-RD-41	6239	AL	BN-RP-32	6265	AL	BN-TR-63	6290	AL	BN-TR-69
6214	AL	BN-RD-47	6240	AL	BN-SF-92	6266	AL	BN-TR-64	6291	DO	BN-TR-70
6215	AL	BN-RD-48	6241	AL	BN-SF-94	6267	AL	BN-TR-66	6292	DO	BN-TR-71
6216	AL	BN-RD-49	6242	AL	BN-SF-96	6268	AL	BN-TR-67	6293	DO	BN-TR-76
6217	AL	BN-RD-50	6243	AL	BN-SF-98	6269	AL	BN-TR-68	6294	DO	BN-TR-77
6218	AL	BN-RD-51	6244	AL	BN-SF-99	6270	AL	BN-SG-19	6295	DO	BN-TR-78
6219	AL	BN-RD-52	6245	AL	BN-SG-01	6271	GO	BN-SG-24	6296	DO	BN-TR-79
6220	GO	BN-RN-83	6246	AL	BN-SG-03	6272	AL	BN-SG-25	6297	DO	BN-TR-81
6221	GO	BN-RN-87	6247	AL	BN-SG-04	6273	AL	BN-SG-26	6298	DO	BN-TR-83
6222	GO	BN-RN-84	6248	AL	BN-SG-06	6274	MK	BN-SG-27	6299	DO	BN-TR-84
6223	GO	BN-RN-85	6249	AL	BN-SG-08	6275	AL	BN-SG-28	6300	DO	BN-TR-85
6224	GO	BN-RN-86	6250	AL	BN-SG-11	6276	AL	BN-TB-24	6301	DO	BN-TR-86
6225	AL	BN-RP-08	6251	AL	BN-SG-13						

| 6387 | LS | BF-XL-12 | MAN 11.220 | Berkhof 2000NLE | B25D | 1997 |

6401-6426

Mercedes-Benz Sprinter Buurtbus — M16 — 2010

6401	TL	07-NVP-8	6408	TL	80-NVP-7	6415	TL	04-NVP-8	6421	DM	95-NVP-7
6402	TL	78-NVP-7	6409	TL	77-NVP-7	6416	TL	81-NVP-7	6422	DM	10-NVP-8
6403	TL	11-NVP-8	6410	TL	06-NVP-8	6417	DM	93-NVP-7	6423	DM	09-NVP-8
6404	TL	76-NVP-7	6411	TL	00-NVP-8	6418	DM	96-NVP-7	6424	DM	05-NVP-8
6405	TL	94-NVP-7	6412	TL	01-NVP-8	6419	DM	97-NVP-7	6425	DM	02-NVP-8
6406	TL	03-NVP-8	6413	TL	92-NVP-7	6420	DM	08-NVP-8	6426	DM	99-NVP-7
6407	TL	17-NVP-7	6414	TL	83-NVP-7						

| 6431 | DM | 03-NBX-1 | Iveci Ducato Maxi 35 | | M16 | 2010 |
| 6432 | DM | 53-NVZ-9 | Iveci Ducato Maxi 35 | | M16 | 2010 |

7152-7174

Mercedes-Benz Integro O550ÜL — Mercedes-Benz — NC50D — 2004

7152	GD	BP-NN-73	7157	GD	BP-NN-86	7168	GR	BP-NT-57	7172	GR	BP-NT-51
7153	GD	BP-NN-74	7158	AL	BP-NN-76	7169	GR	BP-NT-55	7173	GR	BP-NT-47
7155	GD	BP-NN-80	7164	TG	BP-NT-63	7170	GR	BP-NT-54	7174	GR	BP-NT-46
7156	GD	BP-NN-84	7167	GR	BP-NT-56	7171	GR	BP-NT-53			

7181-7184

Mercedes-Benz Integro O550ÜL — Mercedes-Benz — NC50D — 2005

| 7181 | PU | BR-NL-85 | 7182 | PU | BR-NL-84 | 7183 | PU | BR-NL-83 | 7184 | GD | BR-XV-91 |

While Arriva's presence in the northern parts of the Netherlands has reduced, new contracts have been won in other areas. Amsterdam is the location for this view of 7860, BR-NP-84, a Scania OmniCity. *Mark Doggett*

7191-7195

		Mercedes-Benz Integro O550ÜL		Mercedes-Benz		NC50D	2009				
7191	GD	BX-GN-36	7193	GD	BX-GN-34	7194	GD	BX-GN-33	7195	GD	BX-GN-32
7192	GD	BX-GN-35									

7321	TL	37-JV-VN	Volkswagen City Bus	Volkswagen	M8	2002
7322	TL	89-JV-XP	Volkswagen City Bus	Volkswagen	M8	2002
7323	TL	TJ-DX-10	Mercedes-Benz Sprinter	Mercedes-Benz	M8	1998

7331-7354

		Mercedes-Benz Sprinter		Mercedes-Benz		M8	2007				
7331	VG	37-XZ-RH	7337	VG	34-XZ-RH	7343	VG	33-XZ-RH	7349	VG	40-XZ-RH
7332	VG	42-XZ-RH	7338	VG	46-XZ-RH	7344	VG	47-XZ-RH	7350	VG	41-XZ-RH
7333	VG	32-XZ-RH	7339	VG	35-XZ-RH	7345	VG	54-XZ-RH	7351	VG	45-XZ-RH
7334	VG	53-XZ-RH	7340	VG	44-XZ-RH	7346	VG	36-XZ-RH	7352	VG	51-XZ-RH
7335	VG	43-XZ-RH	7341	VG	49-XZ-RH	7347	VG	33-XZ-RH	7353	VG	52-XZ-RH
7336	VG	38-XZ-RH	7342	VG	48-XZ-RH	7348	VG	39-XZ-RH	7354	OT	50-XZ-RH

7801-7816

		Mercedes-Benz Citaro O530G		Mercedes-Benz		AN58D	2004-05				
7801	PU	BP-NZ-66	7805	PU	BP-NZ-73	7809	DM	BP-NZ-77	7813	MK	BP-NZ-85
7802	PU	BP-NZ-68	7806	PU	BP-NZ-74	7810	MK	BP-NZ-81	7814	MK	BP-NZ-86
7803	PU	BP-NZ-69	7807	PU	BP-NZ-75	7811	MK	BP-NZ-83	7815	MK	BP-NZ-87
7804	PU	BP-NZ-71	7808	PU	BP-NZ-76	7812	MK	BP-NZ-84	7816	MK	BP-NZ-88

7851-7898

		Scania OmniCity CN94UA		Scania		AN57D	2005				
7851	PU	BR-NP-73	7863	PU	BR-NP-87	7875	PU	BR-NR-19	7887	PU	BR-NR-01
7852	PU	BR-NP-74	7864	PU	BR-NP-88	7876	PU	BR-NR-22	7888	PU	BR-NP-03
7853	PU	BR-NP-75	7865	PU	BR-NP-96	7877	PU	BR-NR-24	7889	PU	BR-NP-10
7854	PU	BR-NP-77	7866	PU	BR-NP-97	7878	PU	BR-NR-26	7890	PU	BR-NP-12
7855	PU	BR-NP-78	7867	PU	BR-NP-99	7879	PU	BR-NR-28	7891	PU	BR-NP-13
7856	PU	BR-NP-80	7868	PU	BR-NR-02	7880	PU	BR-NP-90	7892	PU	BR-NP-15
7857	PU	BR-NP-81	7869	PU	BR-NR-08	7881	PU	BR-NP-91	7893	PU	BR-NP-18
7858	PU	BR-NP-82	7870	PU	BR-NR-09	7882	PU	BR-NP-92	7894	PU	BR-NP-20
7859	PU	BR-NP-83	7871	PU	BR-NR-11	7883	PU	BR-NP-93	7895	PU	BR-NP-21
7860	PU	BR-NP-84	7872	PU	BR-NR-14	7884	PU	BR-NP-94	7896	PU	BR-NP-23
7861	PU	BR-NP-85	7873	PU	BR-NR-16	7885	PU	BR-NP-95	7897	PU	BR-NP-25
7862	PU	BR-NP-86	7874	PU	BR-NR-17	7886	PU	BR-NP-98	7898	PU	BR-NP-27

The VDL Berkhof Ambassador is now the principal model in service with the Netherlands operation. Based on the VDL SB200 chassis also supplied to British fleets, it is produced at the Berkhof facility in Valkenswaard. Purmerend's 8039, BP-LT-79, is shown. *Mark Doggett*

7901-7948

		Mercedes-Benz Citaro O530G			Mercedes-Benz			AN57D	2005		
7901	PU	BR-NF-15	7913	PU	BR-LZ-70	7925	PU	BR-NJ-72	7937	PU	BR-NJ-95
7902	PU	BR-LV-67	7914	PU	BR-LZ-73	7926	PU	BR-NJ-73	7938	PU	BR-NJ-96
7903	PU	BR-LV-65	7915	PU	BR-LZ-74	7927	PU	BR-NJ-74	7939	PU	BR-NJ-94
7904	PU	BR-LV-60	7916	PU	BR-LZ-68	7928	PU	BR-NJ-76	7940	PU	BR-NJ-98
7905	PU	BR-LV-57	7917	PU	BR-LZ-66	7929	PU	BR-NJ-77	7941	PU	BR-NJ-99
7906	PU	BR-LV-54	7918	PU	BR-LZ-67	7930	PU	BR-NJ-78	7942	PU	BR-NL-02
7907	PU	BR-LV-70	7919	PU	BR-NJ-65	7931	PU	BR-NJ-79	7943	PU	BR-NL-03
7908	PU	BR-LV-72	7920	PU	BR-NJ-67	7932	PU	BR-NJ-84	7944	PU	BR-NL-04
7909	PU	BR-LV-53	7921	PU	BR-NJ-68	7933	PU	BR-NJ-85	7945	PU	BR-NL-05
7910	PU	BR-LZ-75	7922	PU	BR-NJ-69	7934	PU	BR-NJ-87	7946	PU	BR-NL-06
7911	PU	BR-LV-56	7923	PU	BR-NJ-70	7935	PU	BR-NJ-92	7947	PU	BR-NN-68
7912	PU	BR-LZ-71	7924	PU	BR-NJ-71	7936	PU	BR-NJ-93	7948	PU	BR-NN-70

8001-8069

		VDL Bus SB200			VDL Berkhof Ambassador			N40D	2005		
8001	ZE	BP-LT-50	8031	PU	BP-LT-70	8044	PU	BP-LT-85	8057	ZE	BP-NS-22
8014	VG	BP-LT-53	8032	PU	BP-LT-71	8045	PU	BP-LT-87	8058	ZE	BP-NS-23
8019	DM	BP-LT-58	8033	PU	BP-LT-73	8046	PU	BP-LT-88	8059	VG	BP-NS-26
8020	TL	BP-LT-59	8034	PU	BP-LT-74	8047	PU	BP-LT-89	8060	VG	BP-NS-27
8021	DM	BP-LT-60	8035	PU	BP-LT-75	8048	PU	BP-LT-90	8061	ZE	BP-NS-28
8022	DM	BP-LT-61	8036	PU	BP-LT-76	8049	PU	BP-LT-91	8062	ZE	BP-NS-29
8023	DM	BP-LT-62	8037	PU	BP-LT-77	8050	PU	BP-LT-92	8063	VG	BP-NS-30
8024	DM	BP-LT-63	8038	PU	BP-LT-78	8051	PU	BP-LT-93	8064	VG	BP-NS-14
8025	DM	BP-LT-64	8039	PU	BP-LT-79	8052	PU	BP-LT-94	8065	VG	BP-NS-16
8026	PU	BP-LT-65	8040	PU	BP-LT-80	8053	PU	BP-LT-95	8066	VG	BP-NS-18
8027	PU	BP-LT-66	8041	PU	BP-LT-81	8054	PU	BP-NS-96	8067	SH	BP-NS-19
8028	ZE	BP-LT-67	8042	PU	BP-LT-82	8055	ZE	BP-NS-97	8068	SH	BP-NS-20
8029	ZE	BP-LT-68	8043	PU	BP-LT-84	8056	ZE	BP-LT-98	8069	SH	BP-NS-21
8030	PU	BP-LT-69									

8071-8080

		Scania OmniCity C94UA 12m			Scania			N39D	2006		
8071	PU	BS-DZ-41	8074	PU	BS-DZ-43	8077	PU	BS-DZ-47	8079	PU	BS-DZ-51
8072	PU	BS-DZ-42	8075	PU	BS-DZ-44	8078	PU	BS-DZ-50	8080	PU	BS-DZ-79
8073	PU	BS-DZ-39	8076	PU	BS-DZ-45						

When Arriva was awarded the contracts for routes into Amsterdam in 2005, a new fleet of buses comprising both Mercedes-Benz Citaro and Scania OmniCity was sourced. Citaro 7934, BR-NJ-87, is seen heading out of Amsterdam. *Mark Doggett*

8201-8244   VDL Bus SB200   VDL Ambassador   N40D   2007

8201	SH	BT-BH-94	8212	ZE	BT-BJ-12	8223	VG	BT-BX-23	8234	VG	BT-BX-43
8202	SH	BT-BH-96	8213	ZE	BT-BJ-14	8224	VG	BT-BX-24	8235	VG	BT-BX-44
8203	SH	BT-BH-97	8214	ZE	BT-BJ-15	8225	VG	BT-BX-28	8236	SH	BT-BX-47
8204	SH	BT-BH-99	8215	ZE	BT-BJ-16	8226	VG	BT-BX-29	8237	SH	BT-DF-81
8205	SH	BT-BJ-03	8216	ZE	BT-BJ-19	8227	VG	BT-BX-30	8238	SH	BT-DF-84
8206	SH	BT-BJ-05	8217	ZE	BT-BJ-20	8228	VG	BT-BX-31	8239	SH	BT-DF-86
8207	SH	BT-BJ-07	8218	VG	BT-BJ-21	8229	VG	BT-BX-33	8240	SH	BT-DF-88
8208	ZE	BT-BJ-08	8219	VG	BT-BX-15	8230	VG	BT-BX-34	8241	VG	BT-DF-91
8209	ZE	BT-BJ-09	8220	VG	BT-BX-19	8231	VG	BT-BX-36	8242	VG	BT-DF-94
8210	ZE	BT-BJ-10	8221	VG	BT-BX-20	8232	VG	BT-BX-38	8243	ZE	BT-DF-95
8211	ZE	BT-BJ-11	8222	VG	BT-BX-22	8233	VG	BT-BX-40	8244	ZE	BT-DF-96

8301-8363   VDL Bus SB200   VDL Ambassador   N40D   2007

8301	HE	BT-JB-55	8317	HE	BT-LN-48	8333	HE	BT-LN-84	8349	HE	BT-LP-31
8302	HE	BT-JB-56	8318	HE	BT-LN-51	8334	HE	BT-LN-87	8350	HE	BT-LP-33
8303	HE	BT-JB-57	8319	HE	BT-LN-53	8335	HE	BT-LN-88	8351	HE	BT-LP-35
8304	HE	BT-JB-58	8320	HE	BT-LN-54	8336	HE	BT-LN-89	8352	HE	BT-LP-36
8305	HE	BT-JB-60	8321	HE	BT-LN-55	8337	HE	BT-LN-91	8353	HE	BT-LP-37
8306	HE	BT-JB-61	8322	HE	BT-LN-57	8338	HE	BT-LN-92	8354	HE	BT-LP-38
8307	HE	BT-JB-62	8323	HE	BT-LN-58	8339	HE	BT-LN-93	8355	HE	BT-LP-39
8308	HE	BT-JB-65	8324	HE	BT-LN-65	8340	HE	BT-LN-95	8356	HE	BT-LP-41
8309	HE	BT-JB-66	8325	HE	BT-LN-66	8341	HE	BT-LN-97	8357	HE	BT-LP-42
8310	HE	BT-JB-68	8326	HE	BT-LN-67	8342	HE	BT-LN-98	8358	HE	BT-LP-43
8311	HE	BT-JP-92	8327	HE	BT-LN-68	8343	HE	BT-LP-07	8359	HE	BT-LP-44
8312	HE	BT-JP-93	8328	HE	BT-LN-69	8344	HE	BT-LP-08	8360	HE	BT-LP-47
8313	HE	BT-JP-94	8329	HE	BT-LN-73	8345	HE	BT-LP-09	8361	HE	BT-ND-31
8314	HE	BT-JP-98	8330	HE	BT-LN-74	8346	HE	BT-LP-26	8362	HE	BT-ND-30
8315	HE	BT-JR-01	8331	HE	BT-LN-76	8347	HE	BT-LP-27	8363	HE	BT-ND-29
8316	HE	BT-LN-46	8332	HE	BT-LN-77	8348	HE	BT-LP-28			

8364-8382   VDL Bus SB200   VDL Ambassador   N40D   2007

8364	OT	BT-ND-28	8369	OT	BT-ND-23	8374	OT	BT-ND-06	8379	OT	BT-NB-93
8365	OT	BT-ND-27	8370	OT	BT-ND-21	8375	OT	BT-ND-02	8380	OT	BT-NB-95
8366	OT	BT-ND-26	8371	OT	BT-ND-11	8376	OT	BT-NB-99	8381	OT	BT-NP-15
8367	OT	BT-ND-25	8372	OT	BT-ND-10	8377	OT	BT-NB-98	8382	OT	BT-NP-14
8368	OT	BT-ND-24	8373	OT	BT-ND-08	8378	OT	BT-NB-96			

Recent arrivals for Dutch services are a further batch of VDL Ambassador buses fitted with the latest emission technology. Pictured early in 2011 is 8411, BX-TL-57. *Harry Laming*

8401-8451   VDL Bus SB200   VDL Ambassador   N40D   2010 and on order

8401	TL	BX-TL-42	8414	TL	BX-TR-60	8427	TL	BX-TV-69	8440	TL	BX-TX-19
8402	TL	BX-TL-44	8415	TL	BX-TR-63	8428	TL	BX-TV-71	8441	TL	BX-TX-20
8403	TL	BX-TL-45	8416	TL	BX-TR-64	8429	TL	BX-TV-72	8442	TL	BX-TX-23
8404	TL	BX-TL-46	8417	TL	BX-TR-65	8430	TL	BX-TV-73	8443	TL	BX-TX-24
8405	TL	BX-TL-47	8418	TL	BX-TR-66	8431	TL	BX-TV-74	8444	TL	BX-TX-25
8406	TL	BX-TL-49	8419	TL	BX-TR-67	8432	TL	BX-TV-75	8445	TL	BX-TX-26
8407	TL	BX-TL-51	8420	TL	BX-TR-68	8433	TL	BX-TV-76	8446	TL	BX-TX-28
8408	TL	BX-TL-53	8421	TL	BX-TR-69	8434	TL	BX-TV-78	8447	TL	BX-TX-29
8409	TL	BX-TL-54	8422	TL	BX-TR-70	8435	TL	BX-TV-79	8448	TL	BX-TX-30
8410	TL	BX-TL-56	8423	TL	BX-TR-71	8436	TL	BX-TV-81	8449	TL	BX-TX-31
8411	TL	BX-TL-57	8424	TL	BX-TR-72	8437	TL	BX-TV-82	8450	TL	BX-TX-32
8412	TL	BX-TL-58	8425	TL	BX-TV-67	8438	TL	BX-TX-17	8451	TL	BX-TX-33
8413	TL	BX-TR-57	8426	TL	BX-TV-68	8439	TL	BX-TX-18			

90	GS	BB-HB-77	Mercedes-Benz Tourismo O350	Mercedes-Benz	C51F	1994

Depots and Codes:

AL	Alblasserdam	GR	Groningen Stadt	SN	Sneek
AG	Algemeen	HE	Heinenoord	SV	Surhuisterveen
AM	Ameland	HV	Heerenveen	TG	Terschelling
DM	Doetinchem	LS	Leeuwarden Stad	TL	Tiel
DO	Dordrecht	OT	Oude Tonge	VG	Veghel
GD	HOV Groningen-Drenthe	PU	Purmerend	WT	Winschoten
GL	Groenlo	SG	Schiermonnikoo	ZE	Zeeland
GO	Gorinchem	SH	's Hertogenbosch	ZU	Zutphen

ARRIVA PORTUGAL

Arriva Portugal, Edificio Guimarães, Rua Eduardo de Almeida, No 162, 2°Sala-C,
4810-440 Guimarães, Portugal

75	GU	CJ-48-40	Scania K112S	Alfredo Caetano	C51D	1984	Belos Transportes, Setúbal, 1999
85	GU	JS-97-53	Scania K112S	Irmãos Mota	C49D	1986	
130	GU	99-70-EH	Mercedes-Benz O303	Mercedes-Benz	BC55D	1986	
148	GU	13-06-HJ	Mercedes-Benz O303	Mercedes-Benz	C51D	1988	
159	FA	46-36-ML	Mercedes-Benz O405	Mercedes-Benz	B44D	1986	
160	GU	46-37-ML	Mercedes-Benz O303	Mercedes-Benz	BC53D	1991	

163-179 Mercedes-Benz O405 Mercedes-Benz B44D 1987-91

163	FA	98-34-VU	168	FA	25-06-VU	172	FA	45-10-VX	176	FA	98-35-VU
164	FA	25-10-VU	169	FA	45-08-VX	173	FA	98-36-VU	177	FA	98-37-VU
165	FA	25-08-VU	170	FA	25-11-VU	174	FA	45-09-VX	178	FA	98-33-VU
166	FA	25-09-VU	171	FA	98-32-VU	175	FA	25-12-VU	179	FA	25-13-VU
167	FA	25-07-VU									

180-197 Mercedes-Benz O405 Mercedes-Benz B44D 1987-91

180	FA	76-70-NM	185	FA	75-95-ZN	190	FA	89-90-ZQ	194	FA	70-12-MM
181	FA	76-20-ZQ	186	FA	76-21-ZQ	191	FA	26-72-ZU	195	FA	62-53-OE
182	FA	76-18-ZQ	187	FA	76-00-ZN	192	FA	90-55-ZZ	196	FA	28-48-PQ
183	FA	75-93-ZN	188	FA	75-97-ZN	193	FA	90-59-ZZ	197	FPA	43-59-ZZ
184	FA	76-22-ZQ	189	FA	76-19-ZQ						

261	GU	72-54-HT	Mercedes-Benz O303/15R	Mercedes-Benz	C49D	1987	
269	GU	76-65-NM	Mercedes-Benz O303/15R	Mercedes-Benz	C49D	1987	
270	GU	76-66-NM	Mercedes-Benz O303/15R	Mercedes-Benz	C49DT	1984	
271	GU	SR-74-98	Volvo B58-60P	Irmãos Mota (1998)	C53D	1978	
272	GU	85-FQ-46	Mercedes-Benz O405	Mercedes-Benz	B53D	1997	
273	GU	22-FR-91	Mercedes-Benz O405	Mercedes-Benz	B53D	1997	
300	FA	RS-59-62	Pegaso 5036	Salvador Caetano	C47D	1983	
302	GU	QN-06-19	Volvo B10M-55G	CAMO	AB49D	1987	
309	GU	81-DH-99	Volvo B10M-55G	Sunsundegui	AB50D	1997	
310	GU	81-DH-98	Volvo B10M-55G	Sunsundegui	AB50D	1997	
311	GU	86-FV-97	Mercedes-Benz O405 GN	Mercedes-Benz	AB53D	1995	
312	GU	40-GC-89	Mercedes-Benz O405 GN	Mercedes-Benz	AB53D	1995	
313	GU	57-HE-00	Volvo B10M-55G	Castrosua	AB67D	1997	
314	GU	78-IH-78	Mercedes-Benz O405	Mercedes-Benz	B48D	1998	
315	FA	78-IH-79	Mercedes-Benz O405	Mercedes-Benz	B48D	1998	
331	GU	24-40-BT	Volvo B10B	CAMO	B37D	1993	
376	GA	70-16-TI	Volvo B10M-60	DAB	BC51D	1988	Arriva Danmark, 2002

380-389 Volvo B10M-60 DAB BC51D 1989-90 Arriva Danmark, 2001-03

380	GU	70-17-TI	382	FA	07-28-XC	385	FA	07-29-XC	388	FA	81-17-TH
381	FA	89-21-SR	384	FA	97-08-TD	387	FA	81-16-TH	389	GU	85-58-TL

392	FA	59-25-UP	Volvo B10M-60	Åbenrå	BC49D*	1987
400	FA	97-43-UZ	Volvo B10M-60	Åbenrå	BC43D*	1991

401-420 Mercedes-Benz OH1634L Irmãos Mota C51D 1994

401	FA	23-30-EH	406	GU	90-45-EI	411	FA	79-16-EJ	416	GU	42-79-EL
402	FA	49-07-EH	407	GU	90-46-EI	412	FA	79-37-EJ	417	GU	42-80-EL
403	FA	49-08-EH	408	GU	90-47-EI	413	FA	79-38-EJ	418	GU	42-81-EL
404	GU	49-09-EH	409	FA	90-48-EI	414	GU	79-39-EJ	419	GU	42-82-EL
405	GU	90-35-EI	410	FA	79-15-EJ	415	GU	42-78-EL	420	FA	42-88-EL

421	GU	VI-16-66	Mercedes-Benz O303	Irmãos Mota	C51D	1990
422	GU	17-59-ZL	Mercedes-Benz O303	Irizar	C52D	1984
423	GU	17-58-ZL	Mercedes-Benz O303	Irizar	C52D	1984

424-434 Mercedes-Benz Irmãos Mota NC55D 2006-07

424	FA	48-CD-67	427	GU	95-DQ-63	430	GU	95-DQ-66	433	GU	95-DQ-69
425	GU	72-DO-73	428	GU	95-DQ-64	431	FA	95-DQ-67	434	FA	95-DQ-70
426	GU	72-DO-74	429	GU	95-DQ-65	432	FA	95-DQ-68			

435-438 — Mercedes-Benz OC500 RF — Marcopolo — NC55D — 2008

435	GU	97-FZ-28	436	GU	97-FZ-29	437	GU	97-FZ-30	438	GA	97-FZ-31

441-487 — Mercedes-Benz O408 — Mercedes-Benz — BC49D — 1991

441	GU	90-63-ZZ	453	GU	56-71-ZU	465	GU	56-79-ZU	477	GU	23-AI-87
442	GU	56-72-ZU	454	FA	26-73-ZU	466	GU	75-91-ZN	478	GU	13-AS-28
443	GU	23-AT-62	455	GU	84-AC-56	467	GU	56-70-ZU	479	GU	23-AI-88
444	GU	81-AL-31	456	FA	90-58-ZZ	468	GU	75-96-ZN	480	GU	12-AS-29
445	GU	84-AC-58	457	FA	90-60-ZZ	469	GU	90-61-ZZ	481	GU	81-AL-29
446	FA	75-94-ZN	458	GU	26-71-ZU	470	GU	13-AS-30	482	GU	86-AH-12
447	FA	56-68-ZU	459	FA	75-98-ZN	471	GU	81-AL-28	483	GU	86-AH-13
448	GU	56-69-ZU	460	FA	23-AI-84	472	GU	86-AH-10	484	GU	23-AT-63
449	GU	56-67-ZU	461	GU	90-57-ZZ	473	GU	23-AI-86	485	GU	84-AC-57
450	GU	90-62-ZZ	462	GU	56-81-ZU	474	GU	81-AL-27	486	GU	86-AH-11
451	GU	56-80-ZU	463	GU	84-AC-55	475	GU	23-AT-64	487	GU	81-AL-30
452	FA	75-99-ZN	464	GU	75-92-ZN	476	GU	23-AI-85			

488-496 — Mercedes-Benz O408 — Mercedes-Benz — BC49D — 1991-96

488	GU	90-ID-66	491	GU	90-ID-70	493	GU	90-ID-72	495	GU	90-ID-74
489	GU	90-ID-67	492	GU	90-ID-71	494	GU	90-ID-73	496	GU	90-ID-75
490	GU	90-ID-68									

501	GU	75-37-DJ	Scania K113CLB	Irmãos Mota	C51D	1994
502	GU	66-89-FI	Scania K113CLB	Irmãos Mota	C51D	1995
503	GU	61-34-ND	Scania K124IB4	Irmãos Mota	C51D	1999
504	GU	70-12-NT	Scania K124IB4	Irmãos Mota	C55D	1999

521-527 — Scania K114IB4 — Caetano Bus — C59D — 2002

521	GU	10-70-TT	523	FA	10-68-TT	525	GU	10-66-TT	527	GU	10-64-TT
522	FA	10-69-TT	524	FA	10-67-TT	526	GU	10-65-TT			

589	FA	RD-57-84	Scania K113CLB	UTIC (Lisboa)	C49D	1988	
592	GU	UA-48-68	Scania K113CLB	UTIC (Lisboa)	C49D	1989	Cruz e Neves, Ilhavo, 2002
601	GU	68-35-SD	Scania L94IB4	CAMO	B47D	2001	
602	GU	68-34-SD	Scania L94IB4	CAMO	B47D	2001	
603	GU	62-12-SG	Scania L94IB4	CAMO	B47D	2001	
604	GU	62-06-SG	Scania L94IB4	CAMO	B47D	2001	
651	GU	32-05-GU	Scania K113CLL	Irmãos Mota	B47D	1996	
652	GU	32-06-GU	Scania K113CLL	Irmãos Mota	B47D	1996	
703	FA	29-69-FB	Scania K113CLB	Irmãos Mota	C(61)DT	1995	
704	FA	29-70-FB	Scania K113CLB	Irmãos Mota	C(61)DT	1995	
705	FA	06-01-IG	Scania K113CLB	Irmãos Mota	C(59)DT	1997	
801	GU	05-56-ZM	Mercedes-Benz Sprinter 616	Mercedes-Benz	M8	2005	
802	GU	69-72-ZP	Mercedes-Benz Sprinter 616	Mercedes-Benz	M8	2005	

Representing the TUG fleet is 4076, 97-FZ-27, Mercedes-Benz OC500 with Marcopolo bodywork.
Arriva

As we go to press, seven new Optare Solo buses are entering service at Zutphen in the Netherlands. Pictured in the town is 6063, BX-XB-10, the first to arrive. *Harry Laming*

4044	GU	97-41-ER	Volvo B10B	CAMO	N35D	1995	
4045	GU	97-42-ER	Volvo B10B	CAMO	N35D	1995	
4046	GU	43-71-GR	Volvo B10B	Irmãos Mota	N35D	1996	
4047	GU	43-72-GR	Volvo B10B	Irmãos Mota	N35D	1996	
4048	GU	58-51-HU	Volvo B10B	CAMO	N35D	1997	
4049	GU	58-52-HU	Volvo B10B	CAMO	N35D	1997	
4050	GU	99-34-LA	Volvo B10B	CAMO	N34D	1998	
4051	GU	99-35-LA	Volvo B10B	CAMO	N34D	1998	
4052	GU	99-24-QR	Volvo B10BLE	CAMO	N34D	2000	
4053	GU	96-89-SS	Volvo B7L	CAMO	N34D	2002	
4054	GU	96-90-SS	Volvo B7L	CAMO	N34D	2002	
4055	GU	19-22-ST	Volvo B7L	CAMO	N34D	2002	
4056	GU	27-57-SX	Volvo B7L	CAMO	N34D	2002	
4057	GU	24-40-BT	Volvo B7L	CAMO	N34D	2002	
4058	GU	35-33-UX	Mercedes-Benz Citaro O530	Mercedes-Benz	N33D	2003	
4059	GU	35-34-UX	Mercedes-Benz Citaro O530	Mercedes-Benz	N33D	2003	
4060	GU	70-09-XH	Mercedes-Benz Citaro O530	Mercedes-Benz	N33D	2004	

4061-4075 — Scania L113 CLB — Marcopolo — N37D — 1996

4061	GU	20-09-HF	4065	GU	20-13-HF	4069	GU	20-17-HF	4073	GU	49-68-HG
4062	GU	20-10-HF	4066	GU	20-14-HF	4070	GU	49-66-HG	4074	GU	49-70-HG
4063	GU	20-11-HF	4067	GU	20-15-HF	4071	GU	49-67-HG	4075	GU	49-71-HG
4064	GU	20-12-HF	4068	GU	20-16-HF	4072	GU	49-69-HG			

4076	GU	97-FZ-27	Mercedes-Benz OC500	Marcopolo	C42D	2008	
5017	FA	52-76-ZR	Mercedes-Benz OC500	Irmãos Mota	C39D	2005	

5018-5028 — Mercedes-Benz O405 — Mercedes-Benz — B44D* — 1989-90 — *Seating varies

5018	FA	46-40-ML	5021	FA	62-52-OE	5024	FA	83-81-QC	5027	FA	67-03-QT
5019	FA	46-41-ML	5022	FA	99-69-OI	5025	FA	83-82-QC	5028	FA	71-99-QV
5020	FA	70-11-MM	5023	FA	28-47-PQ	5026	FA	67-02-QT			

5030	FA	58-EQ-34	Iveco TurbuDaily 65C18	Marcopolo	N17D	2007	
5031	FA	68-BP-89	Mercedes-Benz OC500 EL	Marcopolo	C43D	2006	

Depots: Famalicão (FA) and Guimarães (GU)

TST

Transportes Sul do Tejo S.A, Rua Marcos de Portugal, nº 10 – 2810 Laranjeiro, Portugal

32	AL	87-35-EI	DAF FA45	URB	B19	1994	
34	SX	08-GN-34	Mercedes-Benz Sprinter 518cdi	Mercedes-Benz	N15C	2008	
35	SX	16-GQ-67	Mercedes-Benz Sprinter 518cdi	Mercedes-Benz	N15C	2008	
36	SX	58-GT-88	Mercedes-Benz Sprinter 518cdi	Mercedes-Benz	N15C	2008	
41	AL	61-20-XR	Mercedes-Benz O404	Mercedes-Benz	C49	1997	
42	AL	61-23-XR	Mercedes-Benz O404	Mercedes-Benz	C49	1997	
43	AL	51-29-XR	Mercedes-Benz O404	Mercedes-Benz	C49	1997	
44	AL	51-31-XR	Mercedes-Benz O404	Mercedes-Benz	C49	1997	
45	AL	51-31-XR	Mercedes-Benz O404	Mercedes-Benz	C55	1999	
46	VA	QO-44-22	MAN 16-290	TUR	C49	1988	
61	SE	OQ-55-82	MAN 16-290	TUR	C49	1991	
62	SE	OQ-55-84	MAN 16-290	TUR	C49	1991	
68	AZ	QR-31-58	MAN 24-360	TUR	C73	1989	
69	AZ	QR-31-57	MAN 24-360	TUR	C73	1989	
71	SE	QS-00-30	MAN 16-290	TUR	C51	1989	
72	SE	QN-95-82	MAN 16-290	-	C49	1988	

90-96

MAN 18-320 — C49 1995

90	AL	46-93-FV	92	AL	80-79-GA	94	AZ	80-83-GA	96	AZ	80-85-GA
91	AZ	46-94-FV	93	AL	80-80-GA						

100-104

MAN 18-360 — C59 2003-04

100	MO	49-40-VA	102	MO	49-42-VA	103	MO	49-43-VA	104	MO	17-18-XM
101	MO	49-41-VA									

111	MO	35-49-SO	Neoplan N4011	Neoplan	28	1994	
112	MO	35-52-SO	Neoplan N4011	Neoplan	28	1994	
150	MO	51-GN-76	Mercedes-Benz Integro O550	Mercedes-Benz	C69F	2002	
151	MO	09-GJ-67	Mercedes-Benz Integro O550	Mercedes-Benz	C69F	2002	
152	MO	50-GJ-40	Mercedes-Benz Integro O550	Mercedes-Benz	C69F	2002	
154	AZ	64-JA-56	Mercedes-Benz Integro O550	Mercedes-Benz	C69F	1999	
155	AZ	06-JB-51	Mercedes-Benz Integro O550	Mercedes-Benz	C69F	1999	
157	AL	64-JA-54	Mercedes-Benz Integro O550	Mercedes-Benz	C69F	2002	
197	AL	93-GH-61	Mercedes-Benz Integro O550	Mercedes-Benz	C49F	2000	
198	AL	93-GH-62	Mercedes-Benz Integro O550	Mercedes-Benz	C49F	1999	
199	SE	80-FN-68	Mercedes-Benz Integro O550	Mercedes-Benz	C53F	1997	

200-217

Mercedes-Benz Integro O550 Mercedes-Benz NC55D 2001

200	MO	05-03-SU	205	SE	05-08-SU	210	AL	05-56-SU	214	AL	05-60-SU
201	MO	05-04-SU	206	MO	05-09-SU	211	AL	05-57-SU	215	AL	05-61-SU
202	MO	05-05-SU	207	AZ	05-10-SU	212	AL	05-62-SU	216	AL	05-62-SU
203	MO	05-06-SU	208	AL	05-11-SU	213	AL	05-59-SU	217	AL	05-63-SU
204	SE	05-07-SU	209	AL	05-55-SU						

218	AL	85-FB-63	Mercedes-Benz Integro O550	Mercedes-Benz	C55F	1998	
219	SE	62-FN-55	Mercedes-Benz Integro O550	Mercedes-Benz	C49F	1999	
220	SE	51-BC-25	Mercedes-Benz O814	-	15	1998	
221	SE	92-BC-86	Mercedes-Benz O814	-	15	1998	
222	SE	35-BF-90	Mercedes-Benz O814	-	15	1998	

228-240

Mercedes-Benz O407 Mercedes-Benz NC49D 1992-96

228	MO	36-94-ZG	232	MO	51-32-XR	235	MO	91-72-XH	238	MO	67-42-XH
229	MO	60-39-XP	233	MO	40-71-XL	236	MO	91-71-XH	239	MO	30-63-XH
230	MO	02-17-XN	234	MO	34-50-XJ	237	MO	67-43-XH	240	MO	90-40-XG
231	MO	02-16-XN									

289	SX	05-89-FA	Mercedes-Benz O405	Mercedes-Benz	NC41D	1995	
290	SX	05-91-FA	Mercedes-Benz O405	Mercedes-Benz	NC41D	1995	
291	SX	05-92-FA	Mercedes-Benz O405	Mercedes-Benz	NC41D	1995	
292	SX	05-98-FA	Mercedes-Benz O405	Mercedes-Benz	NC41D	1995	
293	SX	18-10-FA	Mercedes-Benz O405	Mercedes-Benz	NC41D	1995	
304	VA	67-55-NE	Mercedes-Benz O303	Mercedes-Benz	O44D	1985	
306	VA	67-58-NE	Mercedes-Benz O303	Mercedes-Benz	O44D	1985	
313	VA	22-70-NL	Mercedes-Benz O303	Mercedes-Benz	O45D	1984	
319	VA	50-IE-42	Mercedes-Benz O408	Mercedes-Benz	BC49	1995	

320	VA	74-94-NL	Mercedes-Benz O303	Mercedes-Benz	O44D	1984
321	MO	05-BL-39	Mercedes-Benz O405N	Mercedes-Benz	B37D	1994
322	MO	05-BL-40	Mercedes-Benz O405N	Mercedes-Benz	B37D	1994
323	VA	95-GJ-24	Mercedes-Benz O405NU	Mercedes-Benz	N42D	1995
324	VA	35-BL-22	Mercedes-Benz O405N	Mercedes-Benz	B37D	1994
325	VA	18-GI-94	Mercedes-Benz O405NU	Mercedes-Benz	N42D	1995
326	VA	18-GI-95	Mercedes-Benz O405NU	Mercedes-Benz	N42D	1996
327	VA	90-GI-33	Mercedes-Benz O405NU	Mercedes-Benz	N42D	1995
328	MO	92-BO-10	Mercedes-Benz O408	Mercedes-Benz	BC49D	1992
329	VA	12-EJ-04	Mercedes-Benz O407	Mercedes-Benz	B49D	1995
330	VA	12-EJ-06	Mercedes-Benz O407	Mercedes-Benz	B49D	1995
331	SE	77-EJ-88	Mercedes-Benz O407	Mercedes-Benz	B49D	1995
332	MO	57-BP-60	Mercedes-Benz O408	Mercedes-Benz	BC49D	1992
333	AL	50-IE-44	Mercedes-Benz O408	Mercedes-Benz	BC49D	1995
334	AL	25-ID-42	Mercedes-Benz O408	Mercedes-Benz	BC49D	1996
335	AL	25-ID-43	Mercedes-Benz O408	Mercedes-Benz	BC49D	1996
336	SE	09-EM-64	Mercedes-Benz O407	Mercedes-Benz	B49D	1995
337	SE	10-FI-90	Mercedes-Benz O408	Mercedes-Benz	BC49D	1996
338	SE	50-GJ-38	Mercedes-Benz O407	Mercedes-Benz	B53D	1996
339	MO	25-BS-81	Mercedes-Benz O407	Mercedes-Benz	B44D	1997
340	VA	75-GI-06	Mercedes-Benz O407	Mercedes-Benz	B49D	1995
341	MO	36-BT-13	Mercedes-Benz O407	Mercedes-Benz	B49D	1993
342	VA	50-IE-43	Mercedes-Benz O408	Mercedes-Benz	BC49D	1995
343	MO	36-BT-14	Mercedes-Benz O405N	Mercedes-Benz	B37D	1993
344	MO	17-DU-91	Mercedes-Benz O408	Mercedes-Benz	BC49D	1996
345	MO	34-DX-05	Mercedes-Benz O408	Mercedes-Benz	BC49D	1996
346	MO	35-EH-19	Mercedes-Benz O408	Mercedes-Benz	BC49D	1996
347	VA	45-ID-45	Mercedes-Benz O408	Mercedes-Benz	BC49D	1996
348	AL	31-BI-30	Mercedes-Benz O405	Mercedes-Benz	B44D	1995
349	AL	31-BI-29	Mercedes-Benz O405N	Mercedes-Benz	B37D	1993
350	AL	35-BL-23	Mercedes-Benz O405N	Mercedes-Benz	B37D	1993
351	AL	26-BM-52	Mercedes-Benz O405N	Mercedes-Benz	B37D	1993
352	AL	35-BL-20	Mercedes-Benz O405N	Mercedes-Benz	B37D	1993
353	AL	87-BJ-03	Mercedes-Benz O405N	Mercedes-Benz	B37D	1993
354	AL	00-BM-36	Mercedes-Benz O405N	Mercedes-Benz	B37D	1993
355	AL	26-BM-51	Mercedes-Benz O405N	Mercedes-Benz	B37D	1993
356	VA	26-BM-50	Mercedes-Benz O405	Mercedes-Benz	B44D	1994
357	MO	63-BM-15	Mercedes-Benz O405N	Mercedes-Benz	B37D	1993
358	AL	17-BQ-71	Mercedes-Benz O405N	Mercedes-Benz	B44D	1995
359	VA	24-DI-16	Mercedes-Benz O405	Mercedes-Benz	B44D	1995
360	AL	68-BQ-34	Mercedes-Benz O405N	Mercedes-Benz	B44D	1995
361	AL	68-BQ-31	Mercedes-Benz O405N	Mercedes-Benz	B44D	1994
362	VA	60-BI-86	Mercedes-Benz O405	Mercedes-Benz	B44D	1994
363	VA	44-BI-75	Mercedes-Benz O405	Mercedes-Benz	B44D	1994
364	VA	44-BI-76	Mercedes-Benz O405	Mercedes-Benz	B44D	1994
365	VA	35-BL-42	Mercedes-Benz O405	Mercedes-Benz	B44D	1994
366	VA	24-DI-15	Mercedes-Benz O405	Mercedes-Benz	B44D	1995
367	MO	24-BV-70	Mercedes-Benz O407	Mercedes-Benz	B53D	1994
368	VA	57-BF-85	Mercedes-Benz O408	Mercedes-Benz	BC49	1993
369	VA	83-BF-43	Mercedes-Benz O408	Mercedes-Benz	BC49	1993

Open-top single-deck buses are less common than their double-deck tourist counterparts. TST's 304, 67-55-NE, is a Mercedes-Benz O303 with 44-seats and is one of several currently operated.
Ken MacKenzie

370	VA	83-BF-49	Mercedes-Benz O405	Mercedes-Benz	B44D	1994
371	VA	83-BF-48	Mercedes-Benz O405	Mercedes-Benz	B44D	1994
372	VA	44-BI-73	Mercedes-Benz O405	Mercedes-Benz	B44D	1994
373	MO	30-BX-07	Mercedes-Benz O407	Mercedes-Benz	B49D	1995
374	SE	07-CE-89	Mercedes-Benz O408	Mercedes-Benz	BC53D	1996
375	SE	30-BX-08	Mercedes-Benz O407	Mercedes-Benz	B49D	1995
376	SE	72-BH-26	Mercedes-Benz O408	Mercedes-Benz	BC53D	1993
377	SX	51-FV-92	Mercedes-Benz O408	Mercedes-Benz	BC53D	1995
378	MO	07-CE-87	Mercedes-Benz O408	Mercedes-Benz	BC53D	1994
379	SX	68-FV-78	Mercedes-Benz O408	Mercedes-Benz	BC53D	1995
380	SX	54-49-KB	Mercedes-Benz O307	Mercedes-Benz	B49D	1986
381	SX	05-FZ-99	Mercedes-Benz O408	Mercedes-Benz	BC49D	1996
382	VA	45-ID-46	Mercedes-Benz O408	Mercedes-Benz	BC49D	1996
383	VA	85-FS-95	Mercedes-Benz O407	Mercedes-Benz	B53D	1997
384	VA	07-DA-85	Mercedes-Benz O407	Mercedes-Benz	B49D	1995
385	VA	07-DA-84	Mercedes-Benz O407	Mercedes-Benz	B49D	1995
386	VA	84-DC-23	Mercedes-Benz O407	Mercedes-Benz	B49D	1995
387	SX	05-FZ-98	Mercedes-Benz O408	Mercedes-Benz	BC49D	1996
388	VA	10-DH-58	Mercedes-Benz O405	Mercedes-Benz	B44D	1995
389	VA	10-DH-52	Mercedes-Benz O405	Mercedes-Benz	B44D	1995
390	SX	23-94-JM	Mercedes-Benz O305	Mercedes-Benz	B36D	1987
391	MO	07-DA-86	Mercedes-Benz O408	Mercedes-Benz	BC49D	1993
394	MO	65-DH-08	Mercedes-Benz O405	Mercedes-Benz	B44D	1995
395	VA	65-DH-07	Mercedes-Benz O405	Mercedes-Benz	B44D	1995
396	SX	49-BH-35	Mercedes-Benz O405	Mercedes-Benz	B44D	1994
397	SX	49-BH-37	Mercedes-Benz O405	Mercedes-Benz	B44D	1995
398	SX	49-BH-34	Mercedes-Benz O405	Mercedes-Benz	B44D	1994
399	SX	49-BH-36	Mercedes-Benz O405	Mercedes-Benz	B44D	1996
400	AL	16-IG-26	Mercedes-Benz O408	Mercedes-Benz	BC49D	1995
401	SX	02-BQ-00	Mercedes-Benz O405N	Mercedes-Benz	B44D	1996
402	SX	21-BG-92	Mercedes-Benz O405N	Mercedes-Benz	B39D	1996
408	SX	02-BQ-01	Mercedes-Benz O405N	Mercedes-Benz	B44D	1996
409	SX	17-DU-90	Mercedes-Benz O405	Mercedes-Benz	B44D	1995
410	SX	01-BQ-97	Mercedes-Benz O405N	Mercedes-Benz	B44D	1996
411	SX	68-BQ-32	Mercedes-Benz O405N	Mercedes-Benz	B44D	1996
412	MO	47-79-HG	Setra S215 SL	Kässbohrer Setra	B46D	1985
413	VA	22-38-QG	Setra S215 UL	Kässbohrer Setra	BC49D	1990
414	VA	22-39-QG	Setra S215 UL	Kässbohrer Setra	BC49D	1990
415	SX	43-BF-89	Mercedes-Benz O 405	Mercedes-Benz	B44D	1995
416	SX	43-BF-90	Mercedes-Benz O 405	Mercedes-Benz	B44D	1995
417	VA	22-41-QG	Kässbohrer S215 UL	Kässbohrer Setra	BC49D	1990
418	VA	33-61-QL	Kässbohrer S215 UL	Kässbohrer Setra	BC53D	1985
419	VA	33-62-QL	Kässbohrer S215 UL	Kässbohrer Setra	BC49D	1985
420	VA	33-63-QL	Kässbohrer S215 UL	Kässbohrer Setra	BC49D	1989
421	VA	33-64-QL	Kässbohrer S215 UL	Kässbohrer Setra	BC49D	1989
422	VA	16-54-MX	Kässbohrer S215 SL	Kässbohrer Setra	B53D	1987
423	SX	25-BS-78	Mercedes-Benz O405	Mercedes-Benz	B44D	1995
424	MO	93-51-MV	Kässbohrer S215 SL	Kässbohrer Setra	B46D	1987
425	SX	25-BS-77	Mercedes-Benz O405	Mercedes-Benz	B44D	1995
426	MO	93-53-MV	Kässbohrer S215 SL	Kässbohrer Setra	B46D	1987
427	SX	68-BQ-36	Mercedes-Benz O405N	Mercedes-Benz	B44D	1995
428	VA	93-55-MV	Kässbohrer S215 SL	Kässbohrer Setra	B46D	1987
429	VA	24-92-PN	Kässbohrer S215 UL	Kässbohrer Setra	BC53D	1987
433	VA	73-12-OU	Kässbohrer S215 UL	Kässbohrer Setra	BC53D	1986
435	MO	05-FZ-91	Setra S319 ÜL	Setra	NC71D	1999
437	VA	06-16-PP	Kässbohrer S215 UL	Kässbohrer Setra	BC53D	1987
438	MO	01-FN-50	Setra S319 ÜL	Setra	NC71D	1999
440	AZ	79-EF-91	Setra S319 ÜL	Setra	NC71D	2000
441	AZ	39-EN-10	Setra S319 ÜL	Setra	NC71D	2000
442	MO	26-EM-10	Setra S319 ÜL	Setra	NC71D	1999
443	MO	26-EM-09	Setra S319 ÜL	Setra	NC71D	2000
444	MO	07-FR-03	Setra S319 ÜL	Setra	NC71D	1999
445	MO	26-EM-11	Setra S319 ÜL	Setra	NC71D	1999
446	AL	14-DT-71	Setra S315 ÜL	Setra	NC53D	1995
447	MO	79-EF-89	Setra S315 ÜL	Setra	NC47D	1999
448	AL	50-DT-63	Setra S315 ÜL	Setra	NC53D	1998
459	SE	62-FN-58	Setra S315 ÜL	Setra	NC53D	1995
460	AL	14-DT-70	Setra S315 ÜL	Setra	NC53D	1995
461	AL	14-DT-72	Setra S315 NF	Setra	NC45D	1996
463	AL	62-FN-59	Setra S315 NF	Setra	NC47D	1997
464	AL	58-GL-16	Setra S315 ÜL	Setra	NC53D	1997
473	SE	45-AZ-05	Mercedes-Benz O408	Mercedes-Benz	49	1992
475	MO	62-FN-56	Mercedes-Benz O405N	Mercedes-Benz	36	1995

477	SX	89-FJ-17	Mercedes-Benz O405N	Mercedes-Benz	34	1995					
478	SX	98-FJ-20	Mercedes-Benz O405N	Mercedes-Benz	34	1995					
479	SX	78-FL-14	Mercedes-Benz O405N	Mercedes-Benz	34	1995					
480	SX	78-FL-15	Mercedes-Benz O405N	Mercedes-Benz	34	1995					
481	SX	17-FQ-37	Mercedes-Benz O405N	Mercedes-Benz	34	1995					
482	SX	17-FQ-38	Mercedes-Benz O405N	Mercedes-Benz	34	1995					
483	MO	24-AS-35	Mercedes-Benz O405	Mercedes-Benz	37	1994					
484	SX	95-FB-61	Mercedes-Benz O405	Mercedes-Benz	44	1995					
485	VA	00-AV-75	Mercedes-Benz O405N	Mercedes-Benz	44	1994					
486	SX	95-FB-64	Mercedes-Benz O405	Mercedes-Benz	44	1995					
487	VA	00-AV-77	Mercedes-Benz O405N	Mercedes-Benz	44	1993					
489	MO	59-AU-45	Mercedes-Benz O405N	Mercedes-Benz	41	1993					
490	SX	01-ER-39	Mercedes-Benz O405N	Mercedes-Benz	44	1996					
491	SX	04-ER-66	Mercedes-Benz O405N	Mercedes-Benz	34	1997					
492	SX	04-ER-67	Mercedes-Benz O405N	Mercedes-Benz	36	1997					
493	SX	22-ET-50	Mercedes-Benz O405N	Mercedes-Benz	35	1997					
494	AL	21-AO-37	Mercedes-Benz O405N	Mercedes-Benz	45	1995					

495-499

			Mercedes-Benz O 405	Mercedes-Benz	44	1993-94

495	AL	21-AO-39	497	AL	80-AQ-85	498	AL	90-AQ-03	499	MO	90-AQ-04
496	AL	80-AQ-84									

500-504

		MAN 12-220	-	31	2003

500	AL	65-00-VC	502	AL	65-02-VC	503	AL	52-25-VC	504	AL	65-04-VC
501	AL	65-01-VC									

506-516

		MAN 18-310	-	41	2005-06

506	AL	32-BO-23	509	AL	32-BO-26	512	AL	04-AB-43	515	AL	04-AB-46
507	AL	32-BO-24	510	AL	04-AB-41	513	AL	04-AB-44	516	AL	04-AB-47
508	AL	32-BO-25	511	AL	04-AB-42	514	AL	04-AB-45			

518	VA	51-AJ-65	Mercedes-Benz O405N	Mercedes-Benz	36	1993
519	VA	51-AJ-64	Mercedes-Benz O405N	Mercedes-Benz	36	1993
520	VA	83-AH-87	Mercedes-Benz O405N	Mercedes-Benz	41	1993
521	MO	47-AI-19	Mercedes-Benz O405	Mercedes-Benz	44	1994
522	VA	47-AI-20	Mercedes-Benz O405N	Mercedes-Benz	41	1994
523	MO	47-AI-21	Mercedes-Benz O405N	Mercedes-Benz	37	1994
524	MO	60-AI-86	Mercedes-Benz O405N	Mercedes-Benz	36	1995
525	MO	60-AI-85	Mercedes-Benz O405N	Mercedes-Benz	41	1993
526	VA	60-AI-69	Mercedes-Benz O405N	Mercedes-Benz	42	1994
527	MO	60-AI-83	Mercedes-Benz O405N	Mercedes-Benz	37	1994
528	VA	77-AI-20	Mercedes-Benz O405	Mercedes-Benz	36	1995
529	VA	44-AL-72	Mercedes-Benz O407	Mercedes-Benz	49	1995
530	VA	47-AI-18	Mercedes-Benz O405	Mercedes-Benz	36	1995
531	AL	69-AI-52	Mercedes-Benz O405N	Mercedes-Benz	37	1994
532	AL	69-AI-48	Mercedes-Benz O405N	Mercedes-Benz	37	1994
533	VA	77-AI-19	Mercedes-Benz O405	Mercedes-Benz	44	1994
536	VA	86-95-PL	Kässbohrer S215 HR	Kässbohrer Setra	51	1987

537-543

		Kässbohrer S215 H	Kässbohrer Setra	55	1990	

537	VA	65-07-OC	539	VA	34-38-OH	542	VA	81-17-OH	543	VA	34-39-OH
538	VA	34-37-OH	540	VA	81-16-OH						

544	VA	29-06-PT	Kässbohrer S215 HR	Kässbohrer Setra	51	1987
545	VA	44-AL-71	Mercedes-Benz O407	Mercedes-Benz	49	1995
546	VA	44-AL-73	Mercedes-Benz O407	Mercedes-Benz	49	1996
547	VA	33-66-QL	Kässbohrer S215 H	Kässbohrer Setra	51	1987
548	VA	55-44-NU	Kässbohrer S215 H	Kässbohrer Setra	53	1987
549	VA	75-AL-61	Mercedes-Benz O407	Mercedes-Benz	49	1995
552	AL	09-42-DZ	Scania L113 CLB	-	45	1994
554	VA	66-AO-92	Mercedes-Benz O407	Mercedes-Benz	49	1995

556-560

		Scania L113 CLB	-	45	1994

556	AL	71-71-ED	558	AL	74-82-EE	560	AL	56-42-EE

565-582

		Mercedes-Benz O 408	Mercedes-Benz	BC49D*	1991-94	*Seating varies

565	SE	23-77-RP	570	SE	90-66-SF	575	SE	88-21-UV	579	SE	21-71-XR
566	VA	23-75-RP	571	SE	90-67-SF	576	SE	88-23-UV	580	VA	36-82-ZE
567	SE	23-76-RP	572	SE	84-27-UR	577	SE	90-39-XG	581	SE	13-24-ZF
568	SE	90-69-SF	573	SE	88-24-UV	578	SE	91-70-XH	582	SE	49-AB-90
569	SE	90-68-SF	574	SE	88-20-UV						

Operating from Varsina is MAN SG242 number 782, 59-51-QB. The majority of the fleet has been sourced from German suppliers. *Ken MacKenzie*

583-588

			Mercedes-Benz O 407			Mercedes-Benz		49	1992-94	Seating varies

583	SE	00-02-ZE	585	SE	33-04-XE	587	SE	00-03-ZE	588	SE	76-30-ZE
584	SE	27-02-ZF	586	SE	67-44-XH					

589	SX	60-47-VU	Mercedes-Benz 0405N	Mercedes-Benz	37	1991
590	SX	66-50-VT	Mercedes-Benz 0405N	Mercedes-Benz	37	1991

591-599

			Mercedes-Benz 0405N	Mercedes-Benz	41	1992

591	SX	65-20-VR	594	SX	18-96-VQ	596	SX	18-98-VQ	598	SX	22-45-VP
592	SX	55-38-VQ	595	SX	66-73-VP	597	SX	22-46-VP	599	SX	04-64-VP
593	SX	18-97-VQ								

600-650

			Mercedes-Benz O 405	Mercedes-Benz	B44D*	1985-89	*Seating varies

600	AL	77-47-LM	612	AL	45-84-NN	626	SX	24-46-PZ	639	AL	86-13-QP
601	AL	77-49-LM	613	AL	49-68-OP	628	SX	59-50-QB	640	AL	86-14-QP
602	AL	77-45-LM	614	AL	49-69-OP	629	SX	22-42-QG	641	AL	01-93-RD
603	AL	77-46-LM	615	SX	49-72-OP	630	SX	22-43-QG	642	AL	14-85-RG
604	AL	77-51-LM	617	SX	49-75-OP	631	SX	22-45-QG	644	AL	18-23-RI
605	AL	77-48-LM	618	SX	49-76-OP	632	SX	22-46-QG	645	AL	18-26-RI
606	SX	85-95-NB	619	SX	49-77-OP	633	SX	22-47-QG	646	SX	18-24-RI
607	SX	86-01-NB	620	SX	49-78-OP	634	SX	69-64-QG	647	SX	18-25-RI
608	SX	86-02-NB	622	SX	81-66-PP	636	AL	69-50-QP	648	SX	31-48-RL
609	SX	86-04-NB	623	SX	24-43-PZ	637	AL	69-51-QP	649	SX	31-46-RL
610	SX	86-05-NB	624	SX	24-44-PZ	638	AL	86-12-QP	650	VA	77-50-LM
611	SX	81-69-PP	625	SX	24-45-PZ					

616	SX	23-GM-87	Mercedes-Benz 0405N	Mercedes-Benz	B37D	1997
621	SX	23-GM-73	Mercedes-Benz 0405N	Mercedes-Benz	B37D	1997

651-699

			Mercedes-Benz 0405N	Mercedes-Benz	B44D*	1985-93	*Seating varies

651	MO	78-33-MS	659	SX	60-49-SJ	675	SX	63-84-NI	693	SX	01-92-RD
652	MO	86-03-NB	661	SX	57-69-MS	678	VA	63-87-NI	694	SX	84-49-SM
653	MO	67-57-NE	663	SX	63-81-NI	683	SX	45-80-NN	695	SX	84-48-SM
654	AL	31-49-RL	666	SX	78-36-MS	685	SX	45-82-NN	696	SX	41-98-SS
655	AL	31-47-RL	667	SX	78-37-MS	689	SX	45-87-NN	697	SX	41-99-SS
656	SX	31-77-RL	671	SX	42-97-MZ	690	SX	78-31-MS	698	SX	87-AF-45
657	SX	46-61-SJ	672	SX	85-94-NB	692	SX	81-67-PP	699	SX	42-00-SS
658	SX	99-58-SJ	673	SX	63-82-NI					

704	SE	30-01-BO	Renault B110-50	-	M12	1993

705-730 — Mercedes-Benz O405 — Mercedes-Benz — B44D* — 1986-91 — *Seating varies

705	SX	23-80-RP	712	SX	23-84-RP	718	SX	25-46-RZ	725	SX	84-25-UR
706	SX	23-78-RP	713	SX	25-44-RZ	720	SX	25-48-RZ	726	SX	84-28-UR
707	SX	23-79-RP	714	SX	21-30-RQ	721	SX	73-32-SZ	727	SX	84-29-UR
708	SX	23-81-RP	715	SX	21-31-RQ	722	SX	73-33-SZ	728	SX	88-22-UV
709	SX	21-29-RQ	716	SX	21-27-RQ	723	SX	73-34-SZ	729	SX	97-16-UX
710	SX	21-28-RQ	717	SX	25-45-RZ	724	SX	84-23-UR	730	SX	19-69-VA
711	SX	23-83-RP									

731	SX	26-57-XL	Mercedes-Benz O405N	Mercedes-Benz	B37D	1991
732	SX	55-66-XN	Mercedes-Benz O405	Mercedes-Benz	B36D	1991
733	SX	55-65-XN	Mercedes-Benz O405	Mercedes-Benz	B44D	1991
734	SX	88-70-XO	Mercedes-Benz O405	Mercedes-Benz	B44D	1994

735-744 — Mercedes-Benz O405N — Mercedes-Benz — B37D* — 1991-94 — *Seating varies

735	SX	87-AF-47	738	AL	01-67-ZC	741	AL	60-38-XP	743	AL	66-49-VT
736	SX	87-AF-48	739	AL	01-68-ZC	742	AL	05-69-XE	744	AL	44-18-VR
737	SX	87-AF-46									

745	AL	03-65-VM	Mercedes-Benz O405	Mercedes-Benz	B36D	1987
746	AL	14-20-VL	Mercedes-Benz O405N	Mercedes-Benz	B34D	1990
747	AL	14-21-VL	Mercedes-Benz O405N	Mercedes-Benz	B34D	1990

748-762 — Mercedes-Benz O405 — Mercedes-Benz — B44D* — 1986-93 — *Seating varies

748	AL	29-06-VD	752	AL	46-59-SJ	756	AL	68-56-SM	760	AL	84-47-SM
749	AL	36-03-VC	753	SX	23-85-RP	757	AL	06-37-SO	761	AL	41-97-SS
750	AL	23-82-RP	754	AL	46-60-SJ	758	AL	68-57-SM	762	AL	42-01-SS
751	AL	60-41-SJ	755	AL	46-62-SJ	759	AL	68-55-SM			

763	SX	66-AG-48	Mercedes-Benz O405N	Mercedes-Benz	B37D	1994
764	SX	66-AG-47	Mercedes-Benz O405N	Mercedes-Benz	B37D	1994

765-775 — Mercedes-Benz O405 — Mercedes-Benz — B43D — 1988-89

765	VA	07-14-QL	768	SX	07-17-QL	771	VA	07-26-QL	774	MO	84-26-UR
766	VA	07-15-QL	769	VA	07-18-QL	772	MO	84-22-UR	775	VA	48-26-ZR
767	SX	07-16-QL	770	VA	07-19-QL	773	MO	84-24-UR			

776	SX	60-AH-60	Mercedes-Benz O407	Mercedes-Benz	N49D	1994
777	SX	13-BC-32	Mercedes-Benz O405	Mercedes-Benz	B44D	1993
778	SX	04-BE-86	Mercedes-Benz O405	Mercedes-Benz	B44D	1993
779	SX	57-BF-86	Mercedes-Benz O407	Mercedes-Benz	N49D	1996
781	VA	59-49-QB	MAN SG242	-	AB54D	1988
782	VA	59-51-QB	MAN SG242	-	AB54D	1988
797	MO	51-30-XR	Volvo B10M-55	-	AB77D	1995

805-822 — Volvo B10M-55 — - — AB52D — 1987-91

805	SX	RP-51-85	815	SX	QT-33-70	816	SX	QT-71-27	822	AL	PQ-38-80
812	MO	QT-18-27								

834	MO	66-CE-43	Mercedes-Benz O405G	Mercedes-Benz	AB52D	1996
835	MO	07-CE-88	Mercedes-Benz O405G	Mercedes-Benz	AB52D	1996

841-849 — Volvo B6-50 — - — B33D — 1994

841	MO	43-42-DT	843	MO	43-44-DT	846	MO	21-12-EA	848	MO	21-14-EA
842	MO	43-43-DT	845	MO	21-11-EA	847	MO	21-13-EA	849	MO	21-15-EA

851	SX	47-FC-63	Van Hool A318	Van Hool	B36D	1996
853	VA	10-AV-00	Van Hool A318	Van Hool	B40D	1995

854-858 — Van Hool A300 — Van Hool — B39D — 1999

854	SX	23-EG-30	856	SX	23-EG-32	857	SX	35-EH-18	858	SX	97-EX-90
855	SX	23-EG-31									

859	SX	78-FL-13	Van Hool A318	Van Hool	B40D	1995

860-868 — Volvo B10M-55 — - — AB77D — 1995

860	MO	00-01-ZE	862	AZ	27-37-ZD	865	MO	95-40-ZG	867	MO	58-96-ZG
861	MO	27-38-ZD	863	AZ	58-95-ZG	866	MO	95-41-ZG	868	MO	02-98-ZI

869	SX	78-FL-12	Van Hool A318	Van Hool	B36D	1996
876	VA	45-49-PP	MAN UEL292	MAN	B49D	1990
878	VA	29-08-PT	MAN SR292	MAN	B53D	1987

881-899 — DAF SB3000 — BC59D 1993-96

No.	Depot	Reg	No.	Depot	Reg	No.	Depot	Reg	No.	Depot	Reg
881	AZ	00-98-EE	887	AZ	00-99-EE	891	AZ	54-26-CQ	895	AZ	74-13-CQ
882	AZ	94-97-CQ	888	AZ	01-01-EE	892	AZ	54-22-CQ	897	AZ	75-99-HH
883	AZ	94-96-CQ	889	AZ	01-02-EE	893	AZ	54-27-CQ	898	AZ	76-01-HH
885	AZ	94-95-CQ	890	AZ	98-88-EF	894	AZ	36-97-CQ	899	AZ	15-89-HS
886	AZ	94-98-CQ									

No.	Depot	Reg	Chassis	Body	Type	Year
900	MO	83-69-SC	Hyundai	Hyundai	M8	2001
901	MO	61-AZ-55	Hyundai	Hyundai	M8	2001

906-913 — Mercedes-Benz O303 — Mercedes-Benz — BC49D* 1980-91 — *seating varies

No.	Depot	Reg	No.	Depot	Reg	No.	Depot	Reg	No.	Depot	Reg
906	VA	77-65-PE	909	VA	09-20-LU	910	SE	09-21-LU	913	VA	09-24-LU
908	VA	33-65-QL									

No.	Depot	Reg	Chassis	Body	Type	Year
921	AL	29-06-GT	Toyota 43P850		C23F	1994
922	AL	77-75-IG	Toyota Coaster HB31R	Caetano Optimo	C21F	1997
923	AL	72-87-JX	Toyota Coaster HB31R	Caetano Optimo	C21F	1997
924	AL	74-25-HH	Toyota 43P850		C23F	1994
931	AL	VX-75-25	Scania K113 CLB	-	C49F	1991
932	AL	71-21-IH	Scania L113 CLB	-	C51F	1997
933	AL	95-13-IO	Scania L113 CLB	-	C51F	1997
934	AL	89-99-IP	Scania K113 CLB	-	C51F	1997
935	AL	90-00-IP	Scania K113 CLB	-	C51F	1997
936	AL	43-01-JL	Scania K113 CLB	-	C51F	1998
937	AL	05-10-JO	Scania K113 CLB	-	C51F	1998
938	AL	05-16-IX	Volvo B10B	-	C51F	1997
939	AL	05-19-IX	Volvo B10B	-	C51F	1997
940	AL	78-13-LM	MAN 18370 A	-	C51F	1998
941	AL	93-26-PA	MAN 18310 A	-	C51F	2000
942	AL	93-31-PA	MAN 18310 A	-	C51F	2000
943	AL	93-28-PA	MAN 18310 A	-	C51F	2000

944-948 — MAN 18-350 — C55F 2001

No.	Depot	Reg	No.	Depot	Reg	No.	Depot	Reg	No.	Depot	Reg
944	AZ	29-48-SE	946	AL	29-52-SE	947	AZ	29-53-SE	948	AZ	29-54-SE
945	AL	29-51-SE									

No.	Depot	Reg	Chassis	Body	Type	Year
950	AL	93-HC-66	Mercedes-Benz 396.493	-	C55F	1998
956	AL	04-DC-40	Mercedes-Benz 396.493	-	C55F	1998
957	AL	63-DF-94	Mercedes-Benz 396.493	-	C55F	1999

960-967 — Mercedes-Benz OH1627L — C51F 1996

No.	Depot	Reg	No.	Depot	Reg	No.	Depot	Reg	No.	Depot	Reg
960	AZ	24-28-HH	962	AZ	24-32-HH	964	AZ	24-34-HH	966	AZ	24-36-HH
961	AL	24-29-HH	963	AL	24-33-HH	965	AZ	24-35-HH	967	AZ	24-37-HH

968-982 — Mercedes-Benz O1829 — C52F 1997

No.	Depot	Reg	No.	Depot	Reg	No.	Depot	Reg	No.	Depot	Reg
968	AZ	19-51-IU	972	AZ	43-67-JA	976	AZ	43-65-JA	980	AZ	43-78-JA
969	AZ	19-83-IU	973	AZ	43-77-JA	977	AZ	43-66-JA	981	AZ	54-17-JA
970	AZ	43-62-JA	974	AZ	43-76-JA	978	AZ	43-72-JA	982	AZ	43-68-JA
971	AZ	43-63-JA	975	AZ	43-75-JA	979	AZ	43-74-JA			

No.	Depot	Reg	Chassis	Body	Type	Year
983	AZ	93-25-PA	MAN 18350A	-	C51F	2000
984	AZ	93-30-PA	MAN 18310A	-	C51F	2000
985	AZ	89-55-RD	MAN 18310	-	C55F	2001

990-994 — Mercedes-Benz O408 — Mercedes-Benz — BC49D 1995

No.	Depot	Reg	No.	Depot	Reg	No.	Depot	Reg	No.	Depot	Reg
990	MO	05-68-XE	992	AV	05-71-XE	993	AV	33-02-XE	994	AL	33-03-XE
991	MO	05-70-XE									

Depots: Almada (AL); Azeitao (AZ); Moita (MO); Sesimbra (SE); Seixal (SX) and Varzinha (VA).

ARRIVA NOROESTE

Arriva (Iasa-Finisterre), Poligono de Sabon, Parcela 31-32, 15142 Arteixo, La Coruña, España

250	LU	C-2011-BB	Mercedes-Benz O303/15	Irizar	C55F	1992
251	SA	C-2012-BB	Mercedes-Benz O303/15	Irizar	C55F	1992
255	FE	C-7264-BB	Pegaso 5226	Castrosua	C55F	1992
256	LU	C-7265-BB	Pegaso 5226	Castrosua	C55F	1992
257	SA	C-7266-BB	Pegaso 5226	Castrosua	C55F	1992
258	CO	C-7267-BB	Pegaso 5226	Castrosua	C55F	1992
264	FE	C-9126-BD	Pegaso 5226	Castrosua	C55F	1993
265	FE	C-9127-BD	Pegaso 5226	Castrosua	C55F	1993
266	FE	C-9128-BD	Pegaso 5226	Castrosua	C55F	1993
267	FE	C-9129-BD	Pegaso 5226	Castrosua	C55F	1993
268	LU	LU-5964-O	Kässbohrer S215HD	Kässbohrer Setra	C55F	1993
269	CO	LU-5965-O	Kässbohrer S215HD	Kässbohrer Setra	C55F	1993
270	LU	C-9130-BD	Volvo B12	Irizar	C55D	1993
271	LU	C-9131-BD	Volvo B12	Irizar	C55D	1993
286	FE	C-1998-BH	Scania K113TLA	Irizar Dragon	C(81)D	1994
299	FE	C-0041-BD	Kässbohrer S215HD	Kässbohrer Setra	C55D	1993
300	CO	C-4724-BJ	Mercedes-Benz O404 RH	Irizar	C55D	1994
301	SA	C-4725-BJ	Mercedes-Benz O404 RH	Irizar	C55D	1994
303	FE	LU-4913-O	Pegaso 5226	Castrosua	C56D	1993
304	CO	C-2809-BK	Pegaso 5226	Hispano Carrocera	C55D	1994
307	LU	C-9810-BK	Pegaso CC95.9.E18	Unvi	C36D	1995
309	CO	C-3742-BL	Mercedes-Benz O1117	Ferqui	C36C	1995
315	FE	C-6101-BN	Mercedes-Benz O1117	Ferqui	C36C	1996
316	FE	C-6424-BN	Mercedes-Benz O1117	Ferqui	C36C	1996
317	FE	C-6425-BN	Mercedes-Benz O1117	Ferqui	C36C	1996
322	LU	C-5538-BT	Setra Seida 412MH	Setra	C55D	1997
323	CO	C-5539-BT	Setra Seida 412MH	Setra	C55D	1997
324	LU	C-5748-BT	Setra Seida 412MH	Setra	C55D	1997
325	LU	C-5749-BT	Setra Seida 412MH	Setra	C55D	1997
326	LU	C-0297-BU	MAN 10.220	Ferqui	C38C	1997
327	FE	C-0358-BV	MAN 10.220	Ferqui	C38C	1997
328	LU	C-0359-BV	MAN 10.220	Ferqui	C38C	1997
329	FE	C-0360-BV	MAN 10.220	Ferqui	C38C	1997
330	CO	C-3683-BX	MAN 13.220	Ugarte	C43D	1998
331	CO	C-3684-BX	MAN 13.220	Ugarte	C43D	1998
332	LU	C-3685-BX	MAN 13.220	Ugarte	C43D	1998
333	LU	C-3686-BX	MAN 13.220	Ugarte	C43D	1998
334	LU	C-7698-BY	MAN 13.220	Ugarte	C43D	1998
336	FE	C-7700-BY	MAN 13.220	Ugarte	C43D	1998
337	CO	C-7701-BY	MAN 13.220	Ugarte	C43D	1998
338	LU	C-0336-CB	Scania K94IB	OVI	C47D	1999
339	FE	C-0337-CB	Scania K94IB	OVI	C47D	1999
341	FE	C-0339-CB	Scania K94IB	OVI	C47D	1999
400	LU	C-8493-BZ	Iveco Mago 59.12	Indcar	C27D	1999
401	SA	C-8494-BZ	Iveco Mago 59.12	Indcar	C27D	1999
402	LU	C-8495-BZ	Iveco Mago 59.12	Indcar	C27D	1999
403	FE	C-8496-BZ	Iveco Mago 59.12	Indcar	C27D	1999
474	FE	C-9544-BF	Pegaso 5226	Castrosua	C56D	1993
479	FE	C-4402-BM	MAN 18.310	Castrosua	C56D	1995
482	FE	C-9561-BP	MAN 18.310	Castrosua	C56D	1996
486	LU	C-5304-BX	MAN 18.350	Irizar	C57D	1999
487	SA	C-5305-BX	MAN 18.350	Irizar	C57D	1999
491	SA	C-5395-CF	Volvo B12	Irizar Century	C50D	1999
492	LU	C-5396-CF	Volvo B12	Irizar Century	C50D	1999
493	FE	C-5397-CF	Volvo B12	Irizar Century	C50D	1999
494	FE	C-5398-CF	Volvo B12	Irizar Century	C50D	1999
495	CO	C-5399-CF	Volvo B12	Irizar Century	C50D	1999
496	CO	C-5400-CF	Volvo B12	Irizar Century	C50D	1999
497	FE	C-5401-CF	Volvo B12	Irizar Century	C50D	1999
498	FE	C-5402-CF	Volvo B12	Irizar Century	C50D	1999
499	LU	C-8930-CF	Volvo B12	Irizar Century	C50D	1999
500	CO	C-8928-CF	Volvo B12	Irizar Century	C50D	1999
501	LU	C-8929-CF	Volvo B12	Irizar Century	C50D	1999
502	CO	C-9814-CF	Volvo B12	Irizar Century	C50D	1999
504	SA	C-9816-CF	Volvo B12	Irizar Century	C50F	1999

Number 76 in the Autocares Mallorca fleet is IB-9451-DD, a MAN 18.310 with Sunsundegui Stylo bodywork. It is seen here in Soller bus station about to depart for Tunel. *Colin Martin*

505	LU	C-9817-CF	Volvo B12	Irizar Century	C50F	1999
507	CO	C-0638-CG	Volvo B12	Irizar Century	C50F	1999
508	FE	C-0639-CG	Volvo B10M	Irizar InterCentury	C54F	1999
510	CO	C-0641-CG	Volvo B10M	Irizar InterCentury	C54F	1999
511	LU	C-0642-CG	Volvo B10M	Irizar InterCentury	C54F	1999
512	CO	C-0643-CG	Volvo B10M	Irizar InterCentury	C54F	1999
513	FE	C-0644-CG	Volvo B10M	Irizar InterCentury	C54F	1999
514	FE	C-0645-CG	Volvo B10M	Irizar InterCentury	C54F	1999
515	FE	C-0646-CG	Volvo B10M	Irizar InterCentury	C54F	1999
517	LU	C-0648-CG	Volvo B12	Irizar Century	C50F	1999
518	LU	C-0649-CG	Volvo B12	Irizar Century	C50F	1999
519	LU	C-0650-CG	Volvo B10M	Irizar InterCentury	C54F	1999
520	FE	C-0651-CG	Volvo B10M	Irizar InterCentury	C54F	1999
521	CO	C-0625-CG	Volvo B10M	Irizar InterCentury	C54F	1999
522	CO	C-0653-CG	Volvo B10M	Irizar InterCentury	C54F	1999
523	CO	C-0654-CG	Volvo B10M	Irizar InterCentury	C54F	1999
524	LU	C-0655-CG	Volvo B12	Irizar Century	C50F	1999
525	FE	C-0656-CG	Volvo B10M	Irizar InterCentury	C54F	1999
526	FE	C-0657-CG	Volvo B10M	Irizar InterCentury	C54F	1999
527	CO	C-0658-CG	Volvo B10M	Irizar InterCentury	C54F	1999
528	CO	C-0659-CG	Volvo B10M	Irizar InterCentury	C54F	1999
529	FE	C-0660-CG	Volvo B10M	Irizar InterCentury	C54F	1999
530	CO	C-0661-CG	Volvo B10M	Irizar InterCentury	C54F	1999
532	LU	4278-BSW	Volvo B12	Irizar Century	C55F	1996
533	CO	4276-BSW	Volvo B12	Sunsundegui	C56F	1996
534	CO	3838-BWJ	Volvo B12	Irizar Century	C55F	1995
535	CO	3839-BWJ	Volvo B12	Irizar Century	C55F	1996
536	CO	4016-BWJ	Volvo B12	Irizar Century	C55F	1997
537	FE	0471-BZN	Scania 420	Irizar Century	C71F	2002
538	FE	0547-BZN	Scania 420	Irizar Century	C71F	2002
539	SA	0343-BZN	Scania K114	Irizar Century	C59F	2002
540	LU	0517-BZN	Scania K114	Irizar Century	C59F	2002
541	FE	7452-BZN	Scania K114	Irizar Century	C59F	2002
542	LU	0324-BZN	Scania K114	Irizar Century	C59F	2002

543	LU	9571-BZN	Scania K114	Irizar Century	C59F	2002
544	CO	0359-BZN	Scania K114	Irizar Century	C59F	2002
545	LU	0402-BZN	Scania K114	Irizar Century	C59F	2002
546	FE	5007-CZN	Volvo B10B	Noge	C57F	2000
547	SA	5051-CZN	Volvo B10B	Noge	C57F	2000
548	SA	5084-CZN	Volvo B10B	Noge	C57F	2000
549	SA	5104-CZN	Volvo B10B	Noge	C57F	2000
550	LU	C-7703-BU	Scania L113 CLA	Irizar Century	C55F	1997
551	CO	C-0806-BT	Scania L113 CLA	Irizar Century	C55F	1997
552	LU	C-7704-BU	Scania L113 CLA	Irizar Century	C55F	1997
553	FE	8173-CZR	Scania L113 CLB	Irizar InterCentury	C55F	1996
554	SA	7192-CZV	Volvo B10B	Noge	C57F	2000
555	FE	7218-CZV	Scania L113 CLB	Irizar InterCentury	C55F	1996
556	FE	9516-CZV	Volvo B10B	Noge	C57F	2000
557	FE	5671-CZY	Volvo B10B	Noge	C57F	2000
558	CO	9882-DPK	Irisbus Eurorider C35	Irizar InterCentury	C59F	2005
559	CO	9891-DPK	Irisbus Eurorider C35	Irizar InterCentury	C59F	2005
560	CO	9881-DPK	Irisbus Eurorider C35	Irizar InterCentury	C59F	2005
561	LU	9885-DPK	Irisbus Eurorider C35	Irizar InterCentury	C59F	2005
562	CO	9895-DPK	Irisbus Eurorider C35	Irizar InterCentury	C59F	2005
563	LU	9921-DPK	Irisbus Eurorider C35	Irizar InterCentury	C59F	2005
564	CO	9913-DPK	Irisbus Eurorider C35	Irizar InterCentury	C59F	2005
565	FE	9916-DPK	Irisbus Eurorider C35	Irizar InterCentury	C59F	2005
566	FE	9899-DPK	Irisbus Eurorider C35	Irizar InterCentury	C59F	2005
567	CO	9902-DPK	Irisbus Eurorider C35	Irizar InterCentury	C59F	2005
569	LU	2314-DWL	MAN 18-350	Noge	C57F	2000
571	LU	1993-FFM	Irisbus Eurorider C35	Irizar InterCentury	C59F	2006
572	FE	1997-FFM	Irisbus Eurorider C35	Irizar InterCentury	C59F	2006
573	CO	5043-FFX	Irisbus Eurorider C35	Irizar InterCentury	C59F	2006
574	FE	7070-FFV	Irisbus Eurorider C35	Irizar InterCentury	C59F	2006
575	FE	7084-FFV	Irisbus Eurorider C35	Irizar InterCentury	C59F	2006
578	FE	6457-FFW	Irisbus Eurorider C35	Irizar InterCentury	C59F	2006
579	FE	M-0287-SY	Volvo B10B	Castrosua	B40D	2000
580	FE	3481-FFP	MAN 18-420	Noge	C55F	2008
581	FE	3457-FFP	MAN 18-420	Noge	C55F	2008
582	SA	1653-FFT	MAN 18-420	Noge	C55F	1997
583	SA	3119-DKY	MAN R07 RH464	Lion's Coach	C55F	2005
584	FE	5395BVT	MAN 18-460	Noge	C55F	2002
585	FE	5681-BKF	MAN 18,460	Irizar InterCentury	C55F	2001
586	SA	7497-BDD	MAN 18.420	Noge	C55F	2000
587	SA	7498-BDD	MAN 18.420	Noge	C55F	2000
588	LU	7666-GPN	Volvo B12B	Irizar InterCentury	C55F	2000
589	FE	3194-DJV	Scania K124 IB	Irizar InterCentury	C55F	1999
590	FE	-	Volvo B10B	Castrosua Magnus	C40D	1998
591	u	-	Volvo B10B	Castrosua Magnus	C40D	1998
592	u	-	Volvo B10B	Castrosua Magnus	C40D	1998

Depots: La Coruña (CO); Ferrol (FE); Lugo (LU) and Santiago de Compostela (SA)

AUTOCARES MALLORCA

Autocares Mallorca, Camino Vell Mal Pas, Alcudia
Bus Nort Balear, Gremi Fusters, Poligono Son Castello, Palma

35	AM	PM-4846-BZ	Iveco 391E	Castrosua CS40	B39D	1995
36	AM	PM-4851-BZ	Iveco 391E	Castrosua CS40	B39D	1995
37	AM	PM-0457-CB	Iveco 391E	Ugarte CX-Elite	C55D	1995
38	AM	PM-1248-CB	Iveco 391E	Ugarte CX-Elite	C55D	1995
39	AM	PM-0304-CH	Iveco 391E	Castrosua CS40	B39D	1996
40	AM	PM-0305-CH	Iveco 391E	Castrosua CS40	B39D	1995
42	AM	IB-1249-CM	Iveco 80E18	Indcar Mago	C30F	1997
43	AM	PM-9734-CM	Iveco 391E	Irizar InterCentury	BC55D	1997
44	AM	PM-9735-CM	Iveco 391E	Irizar InterCentury	BC55D	1997
45	AM	PM-3530-CN	Iveco 391E	Castrosua CS40	B39D	1997
46	AM	IB-3531-CN	Iveco 391E	Castrosua CS40	B39D	1997
47	AM	IB-8194-CV	Iveco 391E	Irizar Century	C55D	1998

48	AM	IB-7901-CW	Iveco 391E	Unvi Cidade II	B26D	1998
51	AM	IB-2184-CZ	Mercedes-Benz O405	Mercedes-Benz	B55D	1998
53	AM	IB-3540-DG	Iveco 391E	Ayats Atlas	C55D	1999
56	AM	IB-5157-DG	Iveco Daily 35-10	Iveco	C13D	1999
57	AM	IB-5158-DG	Iveco Daily 35-10	Iveco	C13D	1999
58	AM	IB-3046-DN	Iveco 391E	Noge Touring	C55D	2000
60	AM	IB-9413-DN	Iveco 391E	Unvi Cidade II	B44D	2000
61	AM	IB-9414-DN	Iveco 391E	Unvi Cidade II	B44D	2000
62	AM	IB-4796-DP	Iveco 391E	Ugarte Nobus	C55D	2000
63	AM	IB-4737-CY	MAN 1190	Arabus	C35D	1988
64	AM	IB-5685-CY	Iveco 391E	Irizar InterCentury	BC53D	1998
65	AM	IB-5686-CY	Iveco 391E	Irizar InterCentury	BC53D	1998

66-70

Iveco EuroRider 397E.12.35 — Irizar InterCentury — BC55D — 2002-03

66	AM	8867BWL	**68**	AM	8784BWL	**69**	AM	7280CHJ	**70**	AM	7321CHJ
67	AM	8678BWL									

71-76

Iveco EuroRider 397E — Unvi Cidade II — B44D — 2003

71	AM	2543CHR	**73**	AM	2671CHR	**75**	AM	6244CJD	**76**	AM	6293CJD
72	AM	2630CHR	**74**	AM	2717CHR						

77	AM	IB-0120-DF	Iveco EuroRider	OVI Radial	BC45D	1999
80	AM	0359-DYW	Irisbus EuroRider	Irizar Century	C55D	2006
81	AM	0388-DYW	Irisbus EuroRider	Irizar Century	C55D	2006
82	AM	3129-CHG	Iveco EuroRider	Irizar InterCentury	BC55D	1996
83	AM	4735-FSL	Irisbus EuroRider	Irizar InterCentury	BC55D	2007
84	AM	IB-4069-BZ	Iveco	UNVI Mago	C25D	1995
85	AM	7430-GFL	Irisbus EuroRider 397E	Andecar Viana	C55D	2008
75	BN	IB-7717-CL	Ford Transit	Ford	M14	1997
76	BN	IB-9451-DD	MAN 18.310	Sunsundegui Stylo	B55D	1999
78	BN	IB-7573-CN	Iveco EuroRider 391E	Ugarte CX-Elite	C55D	1997
81	BN	9830-BWT	Iveco EuroRider 391E.12.35	Irizar InterCentury	C55D	2002
86	BN	3283-CHJ	Iveco EuroRider 397E.12.35	Irizar InterCentury	C55D	1996
88	BN	3061-CHG	Iveco EuroRider 397E.12.35	Irizar InterCentury	C55D	1996
89	BN	3290-CHG	Iveco EuroRider 397E.12.35	Irizar InterCentury	C55D	1996
91	BN	C-2524-BT	Mercedes-Benz O1829	Irizar	C55D	1989
93	BN	8953-FRG	Irisbus EuroRider 397E.12.35	Irizar InterCentury	C55D	2007
94	BN	5666-GDM	Irisbus C65	Indcar	C18F	2008
95	BN	IB-4666-CT	MAN	Ayats	C80D	1997
96	BN	7884-BHR	Iveco Daily 80E18	Indcar Mago	C16F	2001
98	BN	5448-CFR	MAN 18.410	Andecar	C55D	2003
99	BN	5933-CHK	MAN 18.410	Andecar	C55D	2003

ESFERA BUS

Pol Industrial Fin de Semana. Avda, Gumersindo Llorente 54, 28022 Madrid

7	M-8290-NT	Renault FR1	Irizar Century	C55F	1992
10	M-2880-UL	Renault FRH	Irizar Century	C55F	1997
13	M-7603-YZ	Renault FRX	Andecar Viana	C55F	2000
15	96-4-BHC	Mercedes-Benz O404	Ugarte Nobus	C55F	2001
18	8124-CHX	MAN 10.225	Andecar Sensca	C30F	2003
21	M-3721-XH	Iveco EuroRider 35	Noge Touring	C55F	1999
24	3911-CMN	MAN 18.463	Andecar Viana	C55F	2003
25	4389-CNB	MAN 18.463	Noge Touring	C50F	2003
26	2426-BHX	Iveco EuroRider 38	Andecar Viana	C55F	2001
27	9334-DHN	MAN 18.463	Andecar Viana	C55F	2005
28	4716-DJW	MAN 18.463	Noge Touring	C50F	2005
29	2250-CHP	MAN 10.225	Andecar Seneca	C28F	2003
30	4929-DPK	Volkswagen	Andecar 111.1	C18F	2005
31	4966-DPK	Volkswagen	Andecar 111.1	C18F	2005
32	9459-DPR	Volkswagen	Andecar 111.1	C18F	2005
33	8232-CJJ	Mercedes-Benz Sprinter 413	Noge Sprinter	C16F	2003
39	6104-CKW	Volvo B12B	Irizar PB	C53F	2003
40	0650-BHY	Volvo B12B	Irizar PB	C54F	2001

Tib's 73, 2671-CHR is one of six Iveco EuroRiders 3 with Unvi Cidade II bodywork from the 2003 delivery. It is seen at Puerto Alcudia. *Colin Martin*

41	0651-BHY	Volvo B12B	Irizar PB	C54F	2001
42	2139-BTK	MAN 18.463	Noge Touring	C55F	2002
43	1924-GDM	Iveco EuroRider 397E	Noge Titanium	C50F	2008
44	2023-FFM	Iveco EuroRider 397E	Irizar InterCentury	C59F	2006
45	7079-FFV	Iveco EuroRider 397E	Irizar InterCentury	C59F	2006
46	5399-FFW	Iveco EuroRider 397E	Irizar InterCentury	C59F	2006
47	7434-GPN	Iveco EuroRider 35	Andecar	C55F	1998
48	8146-DWX	MAN 18.463	Noge Touring	C55F	2002
49	5769-BGL	MAN 18.463	Noge Touring	C55F	2001
50	6876-BNY	MAN 18.463	Noge Touring	C55F	2001
51	2414-DRW	MAN 18.463	Noge Touring	C55F	2005
61	M-2261-ZC	Volvo B12B	Noge Touring	C55F	2000
72	M-4072-SK	Scania K113 CLB	Irizar Century	C55F	1995
73	8124-CHX	MAN 10.225	Ferqui	C35F	2000
75	8105-BFY	Scania K124 EB	Noge Titanium	C55F	2001
79	4642-CGX	Mercedes-Benz OC500	Irizar Century	C55D	2003
80	8144-CMP	Volvo B7R	Irizar Century	C50D	2003
81	7840-CSK	Mercedes-Benz OC500	Irizar Century	C55D	2004
82	6693-DBS	MAN 10.225	Ferqui Solera	C33F	2004
83	6374-DGP	Mercedes-Benz OC500	Andecar	C55D	2004
84	1939-DLH	Mercedes-Benz 923	Beulas Gianino	C30F	2005
85	1671-DSL	Volvo B7R	Irizar Century	C55F	2005
86	9607-GPS	Iveco Eurobus 38	Noge Touring	C55F	2000
87	9344-BMW	MAN 18.350	Irizar PB	C54F	2001
88	5356-BTK	MAN 18.460	Noge Touring	C55F	2002

Note: Coaches 1-60 operate in Esfera colours while 61-90 carry Fray names and livery.

DeBLAS

Arriva DeBlas - C/Fraguas, 27 Poligon Ind Ust - 28925 Alcorcon, Madrid, Espana

343	M-6172-XG	Volvo B10MA	-	AB67D	1999
344	M-6958-XF	Volvo B10MA	-	AB67D	1999
345	M-6166-XG	Volvo B10MA	-	AB67D	1999
346	M-6169-XG	Volvo B10MA	-	AB67D	1999
347	M-6171-XG	Volvo B10MA	-	AB67D	1999
348	M-6168-XG	Volvo B10BLE	-	B36D	1999
349	M-6167-XG	Volvo B10BLE	-	B36D	1999
350	M-6170-XG	Volvo B10BLE	-	B36D	1999
351	M-6237-YF	Volvo B10MA	-	AB67D	1999
353	M-6245-YF	Volvo B10MA	-	AB67D	1999
355	M-6241-YF	Volvo B10MA	-	AB67D	1999
356	M-6242-YF	Volvo B10MA	-	AB67D	1999
357	M-6239-YF	Volvo B10MA	-	AB67D	1999
358	M-6240-YF	Volvo B10MA	-	AB67D	1999
359	M-6244-YF	Volvo B10MA	-	AB67D	1999
360	M-5681-YG	Volvo B10MA	-	AB67D	1999
361	M-5682-YG	Volvo B10MA	-	AB67D	1999
363	M-5685-YG	Volvo B10MA	-	AB67D	1999
365	M-5679-YG	Volvo B10MA	-	AB67D	1999
367	M-5675-YG	Volvo B10MA	-	AB67D	1999
368	M-5674-YG	Volvo B10MA	-	AB67D	1999
372	M-5676-YG	Volvo B10MA	-	AB67D	1999
373	M-5677-YG	Volvo B10MA	-	AB67D	1999
374	M-5678-YG	Volvo B10MA	-	AB67D	1999
385	636-BBN	Iveco EuroRider		C35F	2000
386	6884-BDY	Volvo B10BLE	-	N42D	2001
387	4411-BFK	Volvo B7L	-	N40D	2001
388	0359-BPV	Iveco EuroRider 38		S63D	2001
389	3564-BXB	Iveco EuroRider 29A	Noge Catalan Star	C51D	2002
390	3571-BXB	Iveco EuroRider 29A	Noge Catalan Star	C51D	2002
391	2348-BXC	Iveco EuroRider 29A	Noge Catalan Star	C51D	2002
392	2366-BXC	Iveco EuroRider 29A	Noge Catalan Star	C51D	2002
393	9355-BXG	Volvo B10BLE	-	N42D	2002
394	4680-BXH	Volvo B10BLE	-	N42D	2002
395	4698-BXH	Volvo B10BLE	-	N42D	2002
396	4689-BXH	Volvo B10BLE	-	N42D	2002
397	9664-BXG	Volvo B10BLE	-	N42D	2002
398	9716-BXZ	Volvo B12BLE	-	N58D	2002
399	7809-CCC	Volvo B12BLE	-	N58D	2002
400	7868-CCC	Volvo B12BLE	-	N58D	2002
401	7736-CCC	Volvo B12BLE	-	N58D	2002
402	7729-CCC	Volvo B12BLE	-	N58D	2002
403	7628-CCC	Volvo B12BLE	-	N58D	2002
404	9385-CCC	Volvo B12BLE	-	N58D	2002
405	9382-CCC	Volvo B12BLE	-	N58D	2002
406	7839-CCC	Volvo B12BLE	-	N58D	2002
407	7861-CCC	Volvo B12BLE	-	N58D	2002
408	9069-CFZ	Iveco EuroRider 38		S63D	2003
409	0408-CHB	Iveco EuroRider Cityclass		N35D	2003
410	0876-CGZ	Iveco EuroRider Cityclass		N35D	2003
411	8724-CGX	Iveco EuroRider Cityclass		N35D	2003
412	4323-CGY	Iveco EuroRider Cityclass		N35D	2003
413	8186-CHY	Iveco EuroRider Cityclass		N35D	2003
414	9007-CGN	Volvo B12BLE	-	N58D	2003
415	3977-CHP	Volvo B12BLE	-	N58D	2003
416	7750-CHG	Volvo B12BLE	-	N58D	2003
418	4009-CHP	Volvo B12BLE	-	N58D	2003
419	0375-CHR	Volvo B12BLE	-	N58D	2003
420	7743-CHG	Volvo B12BLE	-	N58D	2003
421	7755-CHG	Volvo B12BLE	-	N58D	2003
422	7763-CHG	Volvo B12BLE	-	N58D	2003
423	3978-CHP	Volvo B12BLE	-	N58D	2003
424	7744-CHG	Volvo B12BLE	-	N58D	2003
425	3284-CNM	Volvo B12BLE	-	N58D	2003
426	1565-CNM	Volvo B12BLE	-	N58D	2003

427	1555-CNM	Volvo B12BLE	-	N58D	2003
428	1523-CNM	Volvo B12BLE	-	N58D	2003
429	1541-CNM	Volvo B12BLE	-	N58D	2003
430	3288-CNM	Volvo B12BLE	-	N58D	2003
431	1503-CNM	Volvo B12BLE	-	N58D	2003
432	1493-CNM	Volvo B12BLE	-	N58D	2003
433	6350-CSW	Volvo B12BLE	-	N58D	2004
434	1706-CSX	Volvo B12BLE	-	N58D	2004
435	6386-CSW	Volvo B12BLE	-	N58D	2004
436	6375-CSW	Volvo B12BLE	-	N58D	2004
437	6363-CSW	Volvo B12BLE	-	N58D	2004
438	6448-CSW	Volvo B12BLE	-	N58D	2004
439	6356-CSW	Volvo B12BLE	-	N58D	2004
440	6434-CSW	Volvo B12BLE	-	N58D	2004
441	6454-CSW	Volvo B12BLE	-	N58D	2004
442	6461-CSW	Volvo B12BLE	-	N58D	2004
443	6495-CSW	Volvo B12BLE	-	N58D	2004
444	0712-CTJ	Volvo B12BLE	-	N58D	2004
445	8214-CSW	Iveco EuroRider Cityclass		N35D	2004
446	6659-CSW	Iveco EuroRider Cityclass		N35D	2004
447	6575-CSW	Iveco EuroRider Cityclass		N35D	2004
448	6587-CSW	Iveco EuroRider Cityclass		N35D	2004
449	6610-CSW	Iveco EuroRider Cityclass		N35D	2004
450	6638-CSW	Iveco EuroRider Cityclass		N35D	2004
451	6623-CSW	Iveco EuroRider Cityclass		N35D	2004
452	6650-CSW	Iveco EuroRider Cityclass		N35D	2004
453	1963-CXX	Volvo B12BLE	-	N58D	2004
454	3003-CXW	Volvo B12BLE	-	N58D	2004
455	2986-CXW	Volvo B12BLE	-	N58D	2004
456	3063-CXW	Volvo B12BLE	-	N58D	2004
457	1959-CXX	Volvo B12BLE	-	N58D	2004
458	3089-CXW	Volvo B12BLE	-	N58D	2004
459	4727-DDK	Volvo B12BLE	-	N58D	2004
460	4755-DDK	Volvo B12BLE	-	N58D	2004
461	4735-DDK	Volvo B12BLE	-	N58D	2004
462	4738-DDK	Volvo B12BLE	-	N58D	2004
463	4744-DDK	Volvo B12BLE	-	N58D	2004
464	4740-DDK	Volvo B12BLE	-	N58D	2004
465	0132-DHZ	Volvo B12BLE	-	N58D	2005
466	2316-DJF	Volvo B12BLE	-	N58D	2005
467	1246-DJB	Volvo B12BLE	-	N58D	2005
468	0092-DHZ	Volvo B12BLE	-	N58D	2005
469	2311-DJF	Volvo B12BLE	-	N58D	2005
470	6221-DMS	Volvo B12BLE	-	N58D	2005
471	6194-DMS	Volvo B12BLE	-	N58D	2005
472	6190-DMS	Volvo B12BLE	-	N58D	2005
473	6201-DMS	Volvo B12BLE	-	N58D	2005
474	6210-DMS	Volvo B12BLE	-	N58D	2005
475	6206-DMS	Volvo B12BLE	-	N58D	2005
476	6173-DMS	Volvo B12BLE	-	N58D	2005
477	6215-DMS	Volvo B12BLE	-	N58D	2005
478	6181-DMS	Volvo B12BLE	-	N58D	2005
479	6231-DMS	Volvo B12BLE	-	N58D	2005
480	6239-DMS	Volvo B12BLE	-	N58D	2005
481	6227-DMS	Volvo B12BLE	-	N58D	2005
482	6186-DMS	Volvo B12BLE	-	N58D	2005
483	7070-FBL	Volvo B12BLE	-	N58D	2006
484	7055-FBL	Volvo B12BLE	-	N58D	2006
485	7085-FBL	Volvo B12BLE	-	N58D	2006
486	7180-FBL	Volvo B12BLE	-	N58D	2006
487	7130-FBL	Volvo B12BLE	-	N58D	2006
488	7167-FBL	Volvo B12BLE	-	N58D	2006
489	7152-FBL	Volvo B12BLE	-	N58D	2006
490	7191-FBL	Volvo B12BLE	-	N58D	2006
491	4411-FBP	Volvo B12BLE	-	N58D	2006
492	5198-FBR	Volvo B12BLE	-	N58D	2006
493	4302-FBP	Volvo B12BLE	-	N58D	2006
494	4428-FBP	Volvo B12BLE	-	N58D	2006
495	4118-FJM	Volvo B12BLE	-	AN65D	2006
496	9653-FTL	Volvo B12BLE	-	AN65D	2007
497	3167-FST	Volvo B12BLE	-	N45D	2007
498	0694-FSZ	Volvo B7RLE	-	N45D	2007
499	0640-FSZ	Volvo B7RLE	-	N45D	2007

Can Picafort is the location for this view of 39 in the Mallorca fleet. IB0304CH, is an Iveco 391 with Castrosua CS40 with standard dual-door bodywork. *Colin Martin*

500	0660-FSZ	Volvo B7RLE	-	N45D	2007
501	0671-FSZ	Volvo B7RLE	-	N45D	2007
502	9639-FTL	Volvo B12BLE	-	AN65D	2007
503	9571-FTL	Volvo B12BLE	-	AN65D	2007
504	9554-FTL	Volvo B12BLE	-	AN65D	2007
505	0686-FSZ	Volvo B12BLE	-	N45D	2007
506	0678-FSZ	Volvo B12BLE	-	N45D	2007
507	4785-FTF	Volvo B12BLE	-	N45D	2007
508	3059-FYH	Volvo B7RLE	-	N45D	2007
509	3016-FYH	Volvo B7RLE	-	N45D	2007
510	3056-FYH	Volvo B12BLE	-	AN65D	2007
511	1235-FYJ	Volvo B12BLE	-	AN65D	2007
512	3041-FYH	Volvo B12BLE	-	AN65D	2007
513	1241-FYJ	Volvo B12BLE	-	N45D	2007
514	3065-FYH	Volvo B12BLE	-	N45D	2007
515	5167-GBS	Volvo B12BLE	-	N45D	2007
516	5724-GDD	Volvo B7RLE	-	N45D	2008
517	1540-GDD	Volvo B7RLE	-	N45D	2008
518	1571-GDD	Volvo B7RLE	-	N45D	2008
519	1588-GDD	Volvo B7RLE	-	N45D	2008
520	1617-GDD	Volvo B7RLE	-	N45D	2008
521	2142-GDK	Volvo B7RLE	-	N45D	2008
522	2138-GDK	Volvo B7RLE	-	N45D	2008
523	5734-GDD	Volvo B7RLE	-	N45D	2008
524	5664-GDM	Volvo B7RLE	-	N45D	2008
525	4782-GDJ	Volvo B7RLE	-	N45D	2008
526	2126-GDK	Volvo B7RLE	-	N45D	2008
527	2133-GDK	Volvo B7RLE	-	N45D	2008
528	2135-GDK	Volvo B7RLE	-	N45D	2008
529	4750-GDJ	Volvo B7RLE	-	N45D	2008
530	2123-GDK	Volvo B7RLE	-	N45D	2008
531	5667-GDM	Volvo B7RLE	-	N45D	2008
532	4763-GDJ	Volvo B7RLE	-	N45D	2008
533	4775-GDJ	Volvo B7RLE	-	N45D	2008
534	0666-GFP	Volvo B7RLE	-	N45D	2008
535	7083-GFN	Volvo B7RLE	-	N45D	2008
536	4297-GFV	Volvo B7RLE	-	N45D	2008
537	7140-GFN	Volvo B7RLE	-	N45D	2008
538	6800-GFN	Volvo B7RLE	-	N45D	2008
539	7015-GFN	Volvo B7RLE	-	N45D	2008
540	0734-GFP	Volvo B7RLE	-	N45D	2008

541	6901-GFN	Volvo B7RLE	-		N45D	2008
542	6914-GFN	Volvo B7RLE	-		N45D	2008
543	7182-GFN	Volvo B7RLE	-		N45D	2008
544	7026-GFN	Volvo B7RLE	-		N45D	2008
545	0653-GFP	Volvo B7RLE	-		N45D	2008
546	6979-GFN	Volvo B7RLE	-		N45D	2008
547	0621-GFP	Volvo B7RLE	-		N45D	2008
548	6883-GFN	Volvo B7RLE	-		N45D	2008
549	0636-GFP	Volvo B7RLE	-		N45D	2008
550	7065-GFN	Volvo B7RLE	-		N45D	2008
551	0683-GFP	Volvo B7RLE	-		N45D	2008
552	7336-GMC	Iveco Daily A65C18	Irisbus		N18D	2009
553	7345-GMC	Iveco Daily A65C18	Irisbus		N18D	2009
554	7341-GMC	Iveco Daily A65C18	Irisbus		N18D	2009
555	1476-GPS	Scania K360	-		N57D	2009
556	1454-GPS	Scania K360	-		N57D	2009
557	1466-GPS	Scania K360	-		N57D	2009
558	1451-GPS	Scania K360	-		N57D	2009
559	1504-GPS	Scania K360	-		N57D	2009
560	1486-GPS	Scania K360	-		N57D	2009
561	1495-GPS	Scania K360	-		N57D	2009
562	1653-GPS	Scania K360	-		N57D	2009
563	1445-GPS	Scania K360	-		N57D	2009
564	1590-GPS	Scania K360	-		N57D	2009
565	1586-GPS	Scania K360	-		N57D	2009
566	4170-GPS	Scania K360	-		N57D	2009
567	1314-GPS	Scania K360	-		N57D	2009
568	1606-GPS	Scania K360	-		N57D	2009
569	3972-GSJ	Volvo B7R	-		N46D	2009
570	6466-GSJ	Volvo B7R	-		N46D	2009
571	6472-GSJ	Volvo B7R	-		N46D	2009
572	6456-GSJ	Volvo B7R	-		N46D	2009
573	6489-GSJ	Volvo B7R	-		N46D	2009
574	6517-GSJ	Volvo B7R	-		N46D	2009
575	6501-GSJ	Volvo B7R	-		N46D	2009
576	6483-GSJ	Volvo B7R	-		N46D	2009
577	6478-GSJ	Volvo B7R	-		N46D	2009

Digital pictures of all the Arriva continental fleets are most welcome and, when used in the Handbooks, a royalty fee is payable. Another view of the Mallorca fleet shows MAN 11.90 number 63, IB-4737-CY, with Arabus coach work. *Colin Martin*

ARRIVA ITALY - SAB

SAB Autoservizi srl, Piazza Marconi 4, 24122 Bergamo

39	BGA52588	Iveco 370.97.S24	Portesi			B22D	1991	
40	BGA50162	Iveco 370.97.S24	Portesi			B22D	1991	
42	BGA50161	Iveco 370.97.S24	Portesi			B22D	1991	
76	AW749PY	Mercedes-Benz O303/9R	Mercedes			C38D	1990	
80	BGD12750	Mercedes-Benz O303/10R	Mercedes			C40D	1994	
84	BGA40904	Mercedes-Benz O303/10R	Bianchi			C58D	1990	
86	AH911KM	Iveco 380.10.29 EuroClass	Orlandi			B25D	1996	
87	AH915KM	Iveco 380.10.29 EuroClass	Orlandi			B25D	1996	
114	AD666TP	Iveco 370.10S.24	Desimon			C58D	1990	
115	AH401KF	Iveco 380.10.29 EuroClass	Orlandi			B25D	1995	
116	AH878KF	Iveco 380.10.29 EuroClass	Orlandi			B25D	1995	
120	AH875KF	Iveco 380.10.29 EuroClass	Orlandi			B25D	1995	
138	BGA65439	Kässbohrer SG221 UL	Kässbohrer Setra			AB58D	1991	
139	BGA74947	Kässbohrer SG221 UL	Kässbohrer Setra			AB58D	1991	
140	BGB18812	Kässbohrer SG221 UL	Kässbohrer Setra			AB58D	1992	

142-145

		Setra S 215 UL	Kässbohrer			B27D	1991-92	
142	BGB51904	143	BGB51903	144	BGB01838	145	BGB01837	

159	BS458WY	Cacciamali TCI 970 Sigma 2	Cacciamali		B22D	2001	
160	BS460WY	Cacciamali TCI 970 Sigma 2	Cacciamali		B22D	2001	
164	AN015PP	Iveco 315.8.18	Orlandi		BC31D	1996	
165	AN014PP	Iveco 315.8.18	Orlandi		BC31D	1996	
166	AN013PP	Iveco 315.8.18	Orlandi		BC31D	1996	

168-186

		Cacciamali TCI 970 Sigma 2	Cacciamali			B22D	2001-03	
168	BS456WY	172	BS790WZ	176	BS777WT	181	BV382VR	
169	BS459WY	173	BS791WZ	177	BV355VS	185	BX177BE	
170	BS457WY	174	BS895WZ	179	BV335VS	186	CE896TB	
171	BS560WT	175	BS896WZ					

187	CW712PC	Irisbus EuroRider 397.10.31	10.8m		B16D	2004

261-264

		Iveco 370.12.S30	Bianchi		B22D	1991
261	BGA48629	262	BGA52589	263	BGA48630	264	BGA52590

308	BGA55605	Mercedes-Benz O303/15R	Bianchi		C55D	1991
309	BGA55606	Mercedes-Benz O303/15R	Bianchi		C55D	1991
310	BGB54150	Kässbohrer S215 HRI	Kässbohrer Setra		BC77D	1992

321-329

		Iveco 380.12.35 EuroClass	Orlandi		Regional bus	1995-96
321	AH880KF	324	AH882KF	326	AH912KM	328	AH914KM
322	AH403KF	325	AH400KF	327	AH910KM	329	AH909KM
323	AH881KF						

332-346

		Iveco 393.12.35 My Way	Irisbus-Orlandi		Regional bus	2000
332	BG305PC	336	BG301PC	340	BG297PC	344	BG293PC
333	BG304PC	337	BG300PC	341	BG296PC	345	BG292PC
334	BG303PC	338	BG299PC	342	BG295PC	346	BG291PC
335	BG302PC	339	BG298PC	343	BG294PC		

347	CP755CX	Mercedes-Benz 0405 NU	Mercedes	Regional bus	1992
348	AW278TP	Mercedes-Benz O404	Mercedes	Regional bus	1998
349	AW279TP	Mercedes-Benz O404	Mercedes	Regional bus	1998

350-364

		Mercedes-Benz O408	Mercedes		Regional bus	1997
350	AT083SN	353	AT084SN	356	AT080SN	358	AT088SN
351	AT086SN	354	AT087SN	357	AT079SN	364	AT085SN
352	AT081SN	355	AT082SN				

Three articulated Kässbohrer Setra SG221 ULs form part of the rural fleet that serve the area around Bergamo. Most vehicles call into the depot during the day for fuel and 140, BGB18812, is seen about to enter the washing bay. *Bill Potter*

365-387

			Mercedes-Benz O405 NU		Mercedes-Benz		Regional bus		1998
365	AW205TM	371	AW386TM	377	AW383TM	383	AW396TM		
366	AW220TM	372	AW387TM	378	AW395TM	384	AW392TM		
367	AW203TM	373	AW388TM	379	AW384TM	385	AW394TM		
368	AW206TM	374	AW382TM	380	AW391TM	386	BE193NY		
369	AW204TM	375	AW389TM	381	AW393TM	387	BE194NY		
370	AW219TM	376	AW390TM	382	AW397TM				

388-398

			Mercedes-Benz Citaro O530 NU		Mercedes-Benz		Regional bus		2001
388	BN683RW	391	BN689RW	394	BN681RW	397	BN690RW		
389	BN688RW	392	BP287ZA	395	BN687RW	398	BP288ZA		
390	BN677RW	393	BN693RW	396	BN694RW				

403	AT989SM	Kässbohrer S300 NC	Kässbohrer Setra	City bus	1991
404	AN974PP	BredaMenarini M 221.1	Menarini	City bus	1997

405-418

			Mercedes-Benz Citaro O530 NU		Mercedes-Benz		Regional bus		2000-01
405	BN678RW	411	BN692RW	414	BN682RW	417	BM871EW		
406	BP289ZA	412	BN691RW	415	BN679RW	418	BN680RW		
407	BN684RW	413	BP292ZA	416	BN686RW				

419-422

			Mercedes-Benz O407		Mercedes		Regional bus		1992
419	BZ825WZ	420	BZ826WZ	421	BZ827WZ	422	BZ828WZ		

423-429

			Mercedes-Benz O407		Mercedes		Regional bus		1992
423	CP756CZ	425	CP757CZ	427	CP754CZ	429	CP496CZ		
424	CP752DA	426	CP495CZ	428	CP753CZ				

430-447

			Iveco 393.12.35 My Way		Iveco		Regional bus		2000
430	BM961EV	435	BM262EW	440	BM259EW	444	BM874EW		
431	BM962EV	436	BM263EW	441	BM257EW	445	BM875EW		
432	BM963EV	437	BM260EW	442	BM872EW	446	BM876EW		
433	BM964EV	438	BM264EW	443	BM873EW	447	BM877EW		
434	BM261EW	439	BM258EW						

Arriva's SAB operation is based in the Italian town of Bergamo. In addition to the local bus network some coaching activity is provided. Pictured returning to the depot is 456, CR045AH, which is used as the local football team coach during the winter season. Note the application of the Arriva logo. *Bill Potter*

448-451

						Iveco 393.12.35 My Way	Iveco-Orlandi	Regional bus	2000
448	BM569EY	449	BM571EY	450	BM570EY	451	BM568EY

452	CE897TB	Irisbus 393.12.35 My Way	Irisbus-Orlandi	Regional bus	2003
453	CH278PD	Kässbohrer S300 NC	Kässbohrer Setra	City bus	1993
454	CH633NZ	Kässbohrer S300 NC	Kässbohrer Setra	City bus	1992
455	CR046AH	Irisbus Domino 2001 HD	Irisbus Orlandi	Coach	2004
456	CR045AH	Irisbus Domino 2001 HD	Irisbus Orlandi	Coach	2004
457	CT986EC	Mercedes-Benz Citaro O530 NU	Mercedes-Benz	Regional bus	2005
458	CT987EC	Mercedes-Benz Citaro O530 NU	Mercedes-Benz	Regional bus	2005
459	CT988EC	Mercedes-Benz Integro O550 UL	Mercedes-Benz	Regional bus	2005
488	BG907343	Mercedes-Benz O303/15R	Bianchi	Coach	1988
493	CB768MJ	Iveco 370.12.S30	Orlandi	Regional bus	1992
494	BGB29553	Iveco 370.12.S30	Orlandi	Coach	1992
495	BGB29554	Iveco 370.12.S30	Orlandi	Coach	1992
496	BGB31233	Iveco 370.12.S30	Orlandi	Coach	1992
498	AT356TE	Mercedes-Benz O350 Tourismo	Mercedes	Coach	1997
499	AT537TE	Mercedes-Benz O350 Tourismo	Mercedes	Coach	1997

501-511

						Mercedes-Benz O404	Mercedes	Coach	1992-93
501	AW352RV	505	AW145PZ	507	AW888PZ	510	BE213NY
503	AW144PZ	506	AW146PZ	508	AW488RA	511	BF264NR

512	CD086FF	Mercedes-Benz O350 Tourismo	Mercedes	Coach	2002
513	CD743FE	Mercedes-Benz O350 Tourismo	Mercedes	Coach	2002

514-517

						Irisbus Domino 2001 HD	Irisbus Orlandi	Regional bus	2004
514	CR045AH	515	CR046AH	516	CR991AH	517	CR992AH

550-555

						Mercedes-Benz O407	Mercedes	Regional bus	1994-95 Arriva Danmark, 2005
550	CW217AL	552	CW219AL	554	CW221AL	555	CW222AL
551	CW218AL	553	CW220AL

In 2007 a batch of the shorter Irisbus Crossway was delivered to SAB. Comprising sixteen vehicles they are generally found on the rural routes of Lombardy away from Bergamo. Seen in Albino as it heads out of the centre is 648, **DH424GP.** *Bill Potter*

556	CT698ZF	Mercedes-Benz Integro 0550 UL	Mercedes-Benz			Interurban	2001		
557	CW898AM	Mercedes-Benz Citaro 0530 LU	Mercedes-Benz			Regional bus	2003		
558	DD561RG	MAN NL263 11.95m	MAN			Regional bus	2002		
559	DE933XJ	Mercedes-Benz 0405 NU	Mercedes-Benz			Regional bus	1996		

560-564
Mercedes-Benz Integro 0550 UL — Mercedes-Benz — Interurban — 2008

560	DK366WP	562	DP678KW	563	DR090CR	564	DR220CR
561	DN633DG						

600-603
Mercedes-Benz Citaro 0530NU — Mercedes-Benz — Regional bus — 2001

600	CT412ZF	601	BP695ZY	602	BP541ZY	603	CT104ZF

613-617
Irisbus Turbocity CityClass U491 — Irisbus — Regional bus — 2006-07

613	DC797TX	615	DE473TG	616	DE607TG	617	DE673TG
614	DE513TG						

618-623
BredaMenarini M 240 10.5m — Bredabus — Urban — 2008

618	DL054SN	620	DL655SN	622	DK779WP	623	DK895WP
619	DK777WP	621	DK778WP				

624	DN234DG	Irisbus CityClass 491	Irisbus		Urban	2008
625	DN235DG	Irisbus CityClass 491	Irisbus		Urban	2008
626	DN236DG	Irisbus CityClass 491	Irisbus		Urban	2008

631-642
Irisbus Ares N 10.6m — Irisbus — Regional bus — 2005

631	CW708AL	634	CW710AL	637	CW829AL	640	CW078AM
632	CW707AL	635	CW709AL	638	CW830AL	641	CW353AM
633	CW706AL	636	CW758AL	639	CW957AL	642	CW354AM

643-658
Irisbus Crossway 10.5m — Irisbus — Regional bus — 2007

643	DH076GP	647	DH073GP	651	DH071GP	655	DH070GP
644	DH075GP	648	DH424GP	652	DH662GP	656	DH462GP
645	DH074GP	649	DH663GP	653	DH664GP	657	DH069GP
646	DH423GP	650	DH072GP	654	DH425GP	658	DH068GP

659-674 — Irisbus Crossway 10.5m* — Irisbus — Regional bus — 2008 *668-70 are 12.8m

659	DN425DG	663	DN287DG	667	DP211KW	671	DR783CR
660	DN431DG	664	DN280DG	668	DP212KW	672	DR784CR
661	DN278DG	665	DN288DG	669	DP213KW	673	DT364EE
662	DN279DG	666	DN281DG	670	DP214KW	674	DT365EE

675-686 — Irisbus Crossway 10.5m — Irisbus — Regional bus — 2010

675	EC682ME	678	EC685ME	681	EC756ME	684	EC759ME
676	EC683ME	679	EC686ME	682	EC757ME	685	EC760ME
677	EC684ME	680	EC687ME	683	EC758ME	686	EC761ME

687	EC762ME	risbus Crossway 12m	Irisbus	Regional bus	2010
688	EC763ME	risbus Crossway 12m	Irisbus	Regional bus	2010

701-724 — MAN Lion's City U 12m — MAN — Regional bus — 2007

701	DE474TG	707	DE515TG	713	DE665TG	719	DE518TG
702	DE475TG	708	DE519TG	714	DE666TG	720	DE670TG
703	DE476TG	709	DE602TG	715	DE667TG	721	DE606TG
704	DE477TG	710	DE603TG	716	DE668TG	722	DE671TG
705	DE478TG	711	DE604TG	717	DE669TG	723	DE880TG
706	DE514TG	712	DE605TG	718	DE517TG	724	DE672TG

725-734 — MAN Lion's City U 12m — MAN — Regional bus — 2008

725	DN246DG	728	DN249DG	731	DN252DG	733	DN254DG
726	DN247DG	729	DN250DG	732	DN253DG	734	DN255DG
727	DN248DG	730	DN251DG				

955	EC689ME	Toyota Coaster BB50R	Caetano Optimo V	C18F	2010
956	EC688ME	Toyota Coaster BB50R	Caetano Optimo V	C18F	2010
963	DT392VE	Menarini M231	Irisbus	Suburban	1999
964	DR063CR	Probus 215 SCB	Probus	Regional	2009

965-968 — Cacciamali TCI 840 — Cacciamali — Interurban 2008

965	DR525CR	966	DR447CR	967	DR448CR	968	DR449CR

969-977 — Mercedes-Benz Sprinter 515 — Sprinter 65 — Minibus — 2008

969	DE709TG	972	DG873MV	974	DG875MV	976	DG877MV
970	DE710TG	973	DG874MV	975	DG876MV	977	DG878MV
971	DG872MV						

978	BX755BF	Iveco Daily F45.12	Iveco	Regional bus	2001
979	BS105XA	Iveco EuroPolis 9.15	Iveco	City bus	2001
980	BS224XA	Iveco EuroPolis 9.15	Iveco	City bus	2001
981	AW170TP	Mercedes-Benz Vario O814	Beluga	Coach	1987
984	CE543TA	Fiat Ducato L2.8JTD	Fiat	Coach	2003
985	BX274BG	Iveco 65.C15 THESI	Cacciamali	Regional bus	2001
986	BY309EF	Iveco 65.C15 THESI	Cacciamali	Regional bus	2002
987	BX275BG	Iveco 65.C15 THESI	Cacciamali	Regional bus	2001
988	BY308EF	Iveco 65.C15 THESI	Cacciamali	Regional bus	2002
991	AT949TT	Iveco Daily F45.12	Iveco	Regional bus	1997
992	AT948TT	Iveco Daily F45.12	Iveco	Regional bus	1997
993	AT947TT	Iveco Daily F45.12	Iveco	Regional bus	1997
994	AT950TT	Iveco Daily F45.12	Iveco	Regional bus	1997
995	BE248NZ	Iveco Daily F45.12	Iveco	Regional bus	1999
996	BE249NZ	Iveco Daily F45.12	Iveco	Regional bus	1999
999	AW385TM	Fiat Ducato	Fiat	Regional bus	1996
1011	BGB28561	Iveco 370.12.S30	Orlandi	Regional bus	1992
1013	BGB28562	Iveco 370.12.S30	Orlandi	Regional bus	1992
1067	BGA57919	Iveco 370.10S.24	Iveco	Regional bus	1991
1069	BGB11432	Kässbohrer SG 221 UL	Kässbohrer Setra	Regional bus	1992

1081-1086 — Mercedes-Benz O530GNU — Mercedes-Benz Citaro — Regional bus — 2001

1081	BS585XB	1083	BS844XB	1085	BS988WY	1086	BS101WY
1082	BS455WY	1084	BS578WY				

1087	BB553TB	BredaMenarini M 321	BredaMenarini	City bus	1999
1113	BGA68889	Volvo B10M	Portesi	Regional bus	1991
1114	BGA68890	Volvo B10M	Portesi	Regional bus	1991

An interesting vehicle in the SAB fleet is 1087, BB553TB, a BredaMenarini City bus from 1999 and the only example of the type in the fleet. It is seen in the orange livery carried by buses on city services. *Bill Potter*

1201-1210

Volvo B7LA — City/Regional bus 2000-01

1201	CH280PD	1204	CH483PD	1207	CH096NZ	1209	CH635NZ
1202	CH281PD	1205	CH563PD	1208	CH140NZ	1210	CH636NZ
1203	CH484PD	1206	CH139NZ				

1211-1216

Mercedes-Benz O405GN Mercedes-Benz AN57D 1994 Arriva Denmark, 2005-07

1211	CW968VS	1213	CW969VS	1215	u/r	1216	u/r
1212	CW969VS	1214	CW969VS				

1217	DK894WP	BredaMenarini M 321 18m	BredaMenarini	City bus	1999
1219	DR668ZB	BredaMenarini M 321 18m	BredaMenarini	City bus	1999

SIA

Società Italiana Autoservizi SpA, Via Cassala 3/a, 25126 Brescia

34	BSE72407	Iveco 315.8.18	Orlandi	BC32D	1993
35	BSF08559	Iveco 370.12.S30	Dallavia	C46D	1994
38	AZ 085MC	Iveco 380.12.38 EuroClass HD	Orlandi	C51D	1998
39	AZ 423MC	Mercedes-Benz O404/15R HD	Mercedes-Benz	C56D	1998
40	AZ 431MC	Mercedes-Benz O404/15R HD	Mercedes-Benz	C56D	1998
41	BE 792ZJ	Iveco 380.12.38 EuroClass HD	Orlandi	C51D	1999
42	BT062GC	Iveco 391.12.35 EuroRider	Orlandi	C51D	2001
45	CD209BW	Mercedes-Benz O350	Mercedes-Benz Tourismo	C51D	2002
46	CD124BW	Mercedes-Benz O350	Mercedes-Benz Tourismo	C51D	2002
47	CD125BW	Mercedes-Benz O350	Mercedes-Benz Tourismo	C51D	2002
48	DK751HY	Irisbus Domino HD	Irisbus	C55D	2007
86	AZ783MD	Iveco 370.12.SE35 12m	Orlandi	BC55D	1998
87	AZ784MD	Iveco 370.12.SE35 12m	Orlandi	BC55D	1998
96	CY322CX	BredaMenarini 220-LU	Bredabus	N21D	1996

No.	Reg	Model	Body	Type	Year	Notes
97	CY323CX	BredaMenarini 220-LU	Bredabus	N21D	1996	
98	DK670HY	BredaMenarini M240 NU	Bredabus	N18D	2001	
99	DK653HY	BredaMenarini M240 NU	Bredabus	N18D	2001	

122-126 — Mercedes-Benz Citaro O530 GNU 18m — AN48D — 2001

122	BV 951 DY	124	BV 579 DW	125	BV 580 DW	126 BV 585 DW
123	BV 581 DW					

No.	Reg	Model	Body	Type	Year	Notes
127	CP730TT	Mercedes-Benz Citaro O530 GNU	Mercedes-Benz	AN48D	1998	
128	CN584HF	Mercedes-Benz Citaro O530 GNU	Mercedes-Benz	AN50D	1998	
129	CN334HF	Mercedes-Benz Citaro O530 GNU	Mercedes-Benz	AN50D	1998	
131	DB388GE	Mercedes-Benz O405 G	Mercedes-Benz	AN61D	1995	
132	DK654HY	BredaMenarini M321 U	Bredabus	AN30D	1995	

133-143 — Mercedes-Benz Citaro O530 GNU — AN57D — 2008-09

133	DN323MS	136	DN380MS	139	DN379MS	142 DN318MS
134	DN325MS	137	DN322MS	140	DN319MS	143 DV449RG
135	DN324MS	138	DN321MS	141	DN320MS	

No.	Reg	Model	Body	Type	Year	Notes
144	CZ104GY	Mercedes-Benz Citaro O530 GNU		AN56D	2004	Arriva Netherlands, 2010

145-147 — Mercedes-Benz Citaro O530 GNU — AN57D — 2010

145	CZ131GY	146	CZ120GY	147	CZ121GY

No.	Reg	Model	Body	Type	Year
163	BSE62369	Iveco 315.8.18 7.6m	Orlandi	B30D	1993

168-172 — Iveco 315.8.S18 7.6m — Orlandi — B30D — 1996-98

168	AF870XR	170	AF869XR	171	AZ350NF	172 AZ351NF
169	AF868XR					

173-183 — Cacciamali TCI 840 — Cacciamali — BC35D — 2008

173	DN862MS	176	DP018HG	179	DP125HG	182 DP128HG
174	DP020HG	177	DP019HG	180	DP126HG	183 DP129HG
175	DP017HG	178	DP021HG	181	DP127HG	

185-188 — Toyota Coaster BB50R — Caetano Optimo V — C26F — 2010

185	CZ122GY	186	CZ123GY	187	CZ128GY	188 CZ129GY

No.	Reg	Model	Body	Type	Year
200	DL831NA	Mercedes-Benz O550 Integro L	Mercedes-Benz	B69D	2008
201	CZ105GY	Mercedes-Benz O550 Integro L	Mercedes-Benz	B49D	2004
202	CZ103GY	Mercedes-Benz O550 Integro L	Mercedes-Benz	B49D	2004

250-290 — Mercedes-Benz O408 — Mercedes-Benz — B53D — 1996-97

250	AF436XX	261	AF440XX	272	AP634NW	282	AP636NW
251	AF701XX	262	AF441XX	273	AP481NW	283	AP632NW
252	AF437XX	263	AF787XX	274	AP490NW	284	AP635NW
253	AF710XX	265	AF705XX	275	AP683NW	285	AP489NW
254	AF708XX	266	AF709XX	276	AP491NW	286	AP488NW
256	AF707XX	267	AP487NW	277	AP492NW	287	AP486NW
257	AF702XX	268	AP482NW	278	AP493NW	288	AP631NW
258	AF703XX	269	AP495NW	279	AP494NW	289	AP633NW
259	AF704XX	270	AP485NW	280	AP483NW	290	AP682NW
260	AF439XX	271	AP496NW	281	AP484NW		

291-295 — Mercedes-Benz O405 NU — Mercedes-Benz — N46D — 1998

291	BH071WK	293	BH073WK	294	BH074WK	295 BH075WK
292	BH072WK					

296-322 — Mercedes-Benz O530 NU — Mercedes-Benz Citaro — N46D — 2001

296	BT242GD	303	BT108GD	310	BT763GD	317	BV403DV
297	BT100GD	304	BT109GD	311	BT107GD	318	BV582DW
298	BT101GD	305	BT110GD	312	BT244GD	319	BV402DV
299	BT102GD	306	BT112GD	313	BT764GD	320	BV583DW
300	BT103GD	307	BT111GD	314	BT761GD	321	BV401DV
301	BT104GD	308	BT106GD	315	BT243GD	322	BV584DW
302	BT105GD	309	BV404DV	316	BT762GD		

No.	Reg	Model	Body	Type	Year
323	CG989SP	Mercedes-Benz O530 NU	Mercedes-Benz Citaro	N46D	2003
324	CV103XV	Mercedes-Benz O530 NU	Mercedes-Benz Citaro	N46D	2005

One of five Mercedes-Benz Citaro O530 GNU buses added to the Brescia fleet in 2001, 124, BV579DW, carried your editor through to Lake Garda where this picture was taken. This link is one of the principal routes operated by SIA. *Bill Potter*

350-362

Mercedes-Benz O345   Mercedes-Benz Conecto   NC44D   2001

350	CL043AY	354	CL982AY	357	CL190AY	360	CL979AY
351	CL042AY	355	CL983AY	358	CL191AY	361	CL985AY
352	CL980AY	356	CL981AY	359	CL984AY	362	CL099AY
353	CL189AY						

438	AD 459WC	Iveco 370.97.S24	Portesi	B43D	1995

440-450

Irisbus Ares 10.6m   Irisbus   B41D   2006

440	CY857CZ	443	CY860CZ	446	CY863CZ	449	CY866CZ
441	CY858CZ	444	CY861CZ	447	CY864CZ	450	CY867CZ
442	CY859CZ	445	CY862CZ	448	CY865CZ		

451-470

Irisbus Crossway 10.66m   Irisbus   B41D   2007-08

451	DE784SB	456	DE785SB	461	DN005MS	466	DN012MS
452	DE951SB	457	DE948SB	462	DN006MS	467	DN641MS
453	DE950SB	458	DN002MS	463	DN007MS	468	DN642MS
454	DH572CS	459	DN003MS	464	DN008MS	469	DN639MS
455	DE949SB	460	DN004MS	465	DN889MS	470	DN640MS

509	AP382NT	Mercedes-Benz O408	Mercedes-Benz	B53D	1997
510	AZ605ND	Mercedes-Benz O408	Mercedes-Benz	B53D	1998
511	AZ736NF	Mercedes-Benz O405 N2	Mercedes-Benz	N38D	1998
512	BE684ZJ	Iveco EuroRider 391.12.29	Orlandi	B53D	1999
513	BR642FF	Iveco EuroRider 391.12.29	Orlandi	B53D	2000
514	BR112FG	Iveco EuroRider 391.12.29	Orlandi	B53D	2000

647-658

Iveco 370.12.SE35   Iveco   B55D   1995-96

647	AF 404XJ	650	AF 405XJ	653	AF 395XJ	656	AF 392XJ
648	AF 417XL	651	AF 396XJ	654	AF 393XJ	657	AF 401XJ
649	AF 394XJ	652	AF 406XJ	655	AF 403XJ	658	AF 391XJ

The latest intake of buses for SIA is a batch of MAN Lion's City buses. Illustrating the type is 720, DV718RG, seen here setting out from the depot on its next duty. Many workings commence from the depot, with their first pick-up point at the nearby bus station. *Bill Potter*

659-690

			Iveco MyWay 393.12.35		Iveco		B48D		2000
659	BM 314 FV	676	BM 417 FV	681	BM 689 FV	686	BM 692 FV
666	BM 685 FV	677	BM 418 FV	682	BM 690 FV	687	BM 555 FF
667	BM 321 FV	678	BM 687 FV	683	BM 420 FV	688	BM 554 FF
668	BM 686 FV	679	BM 419 FV	684	BM 691 FV	689	BM 553 FF
674	BM 416 FV	680	BM 688 FV	685	BM 326 FV	690	BM 552 FF
675	BM 325 FV						

691-698

Iveco ArWay 393.12.35 — Irisbus — B49D — 2007

691	DE787SB	693	DE786SB	695	DE720SB	697	DE721SB
692	DE947SB	694	DE719SB	696	DE788SB	698	DE789SB

699-712

Iveco Crossway 12m — Irisbus — B49D — 2008

699	DN056MS	703	DN339MS	707	DN697MS	710	DN696MS
700	DN013MS	704	DN057MS	708	DN801MS	711	DN863MS
701	DN011MS	705	DN010MS	709	DN865MS	712	DN695MS
702	DN014MS	706	DN800MS				

713-726

MAN Lion's City U 12m — MAN — N44D — 2009-10

713	DV714RG	717	DV767RG	721	DV719RG	724	CZ129GY
714	DV715RG	718	DV766RG	722	CZ127GY	725	CZ130GY
715	DV716RG	719	DV765RG	723	CZ128GY	726	CZ131GY
716	DV717RG	720	DV718RG				

803-810

Kässbohrer S300 NC — Kässbohrer Setra — N30D — 1993-94

803	AP 003NZ	805	AP 005NZ	807	AP 007NZ	809	AP 009NZ
804	AP 004NZ	806	AP 006NZ	808	AP 008NZ	810	AP 010NZ

811-831

Mercedes-Benz O405N — Mercedes-Benz — N38D — 1998-99

811	AZ 933NE	817	AZ 112NF	822	AZ 935NE	827	AZ 119NF
812	AZ 932NE	818	AZ 114NF	823	AZ 934NE	828	AZ 937NE
813	AZ 108NF	819	AZ 115NF	824	AZ 938NE	829	AZ 107NF
814	AZ 110NF	820	AZ 936NE	825	AZ 117NF	830	BE 794ZJ
815	AZ 109NF	821	AZ 116NF	826	AZ 118NF	831	BE 793ZJ
816	AZ 113NF						

832	CN335HF	Mercedes-Benz O530 NU 12m	Mercedes-Benz Citaro	N35D	1997

833-836

BredaMenarini Avancity — Breda — N22D — 2009

833	DY072NZ	834	DY069NZ	835	DY068NZ	836	DY071NZ

ASF

ASF Autolinee SRL, Via Asiago 16/18, 22100 Como, Italy

1003	AX556YS	Iveco 315.8.18 Poker	Iveco	ALI	19	
1004	BB758KB	Iveco 315.8.18 Orlandi	Iveco	ALI	19	
1005	BE009MY	Cacciamali A59	Cacciamali	ALI	19	
1006	AX556YS	Iveco 315.8.18 Orlandi	Iveco	ALI	19	

1007-1012

		Iveco Daily 65C		Cacciamali		ALI	19	
1007	BV211SX	**1009**	BZ619TB	**1011**	CJ091XJ		**1012**	CJ336XJ
1008	BV382SX	**1010**	CJ754XH					

1013	DC049JP	Toyota Optimo BB50L	Caetano Optimo	ALI	19	
1014	DC048JP	Toyota Optimo BB50L	Caetano Optimo	ALI	19	
1015	DF658ZA	Iveco Daily 65C	Cacciamali	ALI	19	
1016	DM119KV	Iveco A50	Tourys	ALI	19	
1017	DR546KK	Volkswagen Crafter	Volkswagen	ALI	19	
1105	DK018JP	Iveco 370.10.24	Portesi	ALI	20	
1106	DK019JP	Iveco 370.10.24	Portesi	ALI	20	
1130	AG409TE	Iveco 370E.9.27	Dalla Via	ALI	19	

1131-1135

		MAN 11.220		De Simon		ALI	19	
1131	AN759EX	**1133**	AX548YS	**1134**	AX549YS		**1135**	AX550YS
1132	AN758EX							

1136	BE011MY	Iveco 370.10.24	Portesi	ALI	20	
1137	BE650MY	Mercedes-Benz O303	Mercedes-Benz	ALI	19	
1138	BE154MY	Mercedes-Benz O303	Mercedes-Benz	ALI	19	
1140	BJ809NR	Cacciamali TCI970	Cacciamali	ALI	19	
1141	BJ708NR	Cacciamali TCI970	Cacciamali	ALI	19	
1142	BJ593NR	Cacciamali TCI970	Cacciamali	ALI	19	

1143-1145

		MAN 11.220		De Simon		ALI	19	
1143	BP587PP	**1144**	BP588PP	**1145**	BP841PP		**1145**	BP840PP

1147	BP737PR	Mauri SAS	?	ALI	19	
1148	CF472HJ	Cacciamali Engin TCI 800	Cacciamali	ALI	19	
1149	CL515JL	Cacciamali Engin TCI 800	Cacciamali	ALI	19	

1150-1157

		Cacciamali Engin TCI 800		Cacciamali		ALI	19	
1150	CZ353MH	**1152**	DE764YY	**1154**	DF092YZ		**1156**	DF075YZ
1151	CZ363MH	**1153**	DF073YZ	**1155**	DF091YZ		**1157**	DF076YZ

1158	DF129YZ	Cacciamali TCI 972	Cacciamali	ALI	19	
1159	DM142KV	Cacciamali Engin TCI 800	Cacciamali	ALI	19	
1160	DM204KV	Cacciamali Engin TCI 800	Cacciamali	ALI	19	

1161-1166

		Cacciamali TCI 972		Cacciamali		ALI	20	
1161	DM348KV	**1163**	DM153KV	**1165**	DK989JP		**1166**	DM079KV
1162	DK988JP	**1164**	DM103KV					

1263	CO947141	Iveco 370.10.24 10.6M	Iveco	Regional	19	
1266	CO896829	Sitcar 161.24	Sitcar	Regional	19	
1267	CO896828	Iveco 370.10.24 10.6m	Iveco	Regional	19	
1268	CO050966	Iveco 370.10.24 10.6m	Iveco	Regional	19	
1270	AG319TM	BredaMenariniBus M120/1E	Breda	Regional	19	
1272	BP079ZY	Mauri SAS	?	ALI	19	
1273	CF221HH	Volvo B12B	Volvo 8700	Coach	19	
1274	CR764PP	Irisbus EuroRider 397.10.31	Crossway	Coach	20	
1275	CX613DW	De Simon Starbus LN2801	?	Coach	20	
1276	CX243ZG	Scania IN3	de Simon	Coach	20	
1277	CX242ZG	Scania IN3	de Simon	Coach	20	
1278	CZ078MH	Scania IN3	de Simon	Coach	20	
1279	CZ079MH	Scania IN3	de Simon	Coach	20	
1280	DT814FX	Iveco Crossway 12m	Irisbus	Regional	2009	
1324	COA04084	Iveco 370.12.25	Iveco	Regional	19	
1325	COA45564	Siccar 166.30	?	Regional	19	
1331	COA92635	Iveco 370.12.25	Iveco	Regional	19	

Lake Como is situated some 100 metres behind 1280, DT814FX, as it collects a passenger on a journey to Colico. The town is a central point in the area with many routes converging on the town. *Bill Potter*

1332	COB18826	Iveco 370.12.25	Iveco	Regional	19	
1333	COB18823	Iveco 370.12.25	Iveco	Regional	19	
1337	COD46831	Iveco 370.12.30	Iveco	Regional	19	
1338	COD44785	Iveco 370.12.30	Iveco	Regional	19	
1340	AE301HL	Iveco 370.12.30	Iveco	Regional	19	
1341	AG738TG	BredaMenariniBus M120/1E	Breda	Regional	19	
1343	AP467VW	Iveco 391E.12.29	Iveco	Regional	19	
1344	AP909VY	Iveco 391E.12.29	Iveco	Regional	19	
1346	BX353BR	Irisbus 391E.12.29	Irisbus	Regional	20	
1347	BZ748TD	Mercedes-Benz O550 Integro	Mercedes-Benz	Regional	20	
1348	DP481CA	Ayats Bravo 1 391E	Ayats	Coach	20	

1349-1354
Irisbus 399 EL75 — Irisbus — Regional — 20

1349	CL436JJ	**1351**	CL765JJ	**1353**	CL894JJ	**1354** CL435JJ
1350	CL457JJ	**1352**	CL895JJ			

1355-1359
de Simon IL3 — de Simon — Regional

1355	CL476JK	**1357**	CX240ZG	**1358**	CX239ZG	**1359** CX238ZG
1356	CX241ZG					

1360-1364
Irisbus Karosa C956 — Irisbus — Regional

1360	DC275JP	**1362**	CZ620MH	**1363**	CZ621MH	**1364** CZ622MH
1361	CZ619MH					

1365	DE444YY	Scania OmniLink	Scania	Regional		
1366	DE787YY	Scania OmniLink	Scania	Regional		
1367	DE765YY	Scania OmniLink	Scania	Regional		
1504	CL640JL	Irisbus 380.12.35	-	Regional		
1601	BZ596SZ	Irisbus 380.10.35	-	Regional		
2001	DT627FX	Irisbus Europolis TCC760	Cacciamali	ALS	2009	
2002	DS960PK	Irisbus Europolis TCC760	Cacciamali	ALS	2009	
2127	CO949209	Inbus U150	Sicca 181 CU			

2132-2136 — Irisbus 200E 9.23m — Irisbus — ALS

2132 BK746MB	**2134** BK983MB	**2135** BK686MB	**2136** BK984MB
2133 BK867MB			

2201 DK306JP	Irisbus Cityclass 491E 10.8m	Irisbus	ALS
2202 DK307JP	Irisbus Cityclass 491E 10.8m	Irisbus	ALS
2203 DK308JP	Irisbus Cityclass 491E 10.8m	Irisbus	ALS

2257-2262 — Iveco 571.10.20 — Iveco — ALS

2257 CO949206	**2259** CO949207	**2261** CO961281	**2262** CO974967
2258 CO949208	**2260** CO949205		

2265 COA04085	BredaMenariniBus M201/NS	Breda	Regional

2266-2275 — BredaMenariniBus M220/NS — Breda — Regional

2266 COB29650	**2269** COD46236	**2272** AA627ZZ	**2274** AE138HH
2267 COB29651	**2270** COD46235	**2273** AA628ZZ	**2275** AE139HH
2268 COB29652	**2271** COD46234		

2277-2292 — Irisbus Cityclass 491E 10.8m — Irisbus — ALS

2277 BJ632NR	**2281** BJ594NR	**2285** BJ123NR	**2289** BJ407NR
2278 BJ034NR	**2282** BJ633NR	**2286** BJ032NR	**2290** BJ595NR
2279 BJ356NR	**2283** BJ357NR	**2287** BJ406NR	**2291** BJ300NR
2280 BJ592NR	**2284** BJ707NR	**2288** BJ301NR	**2292** BJ825NR

2293-2299 — Irisbus Cityclass 491E 10.8m — Irisbus — ALS

2293 DC616JP	**2295** DC618JP	**2297** DK310JP	**2299** DK305JP
2294 DC617JP	**2296** DK311JP	**2298** DK309JP	

2301-2304 — Irisbus Cityclass 491E 10.8m — Irisbus — ALS

2301 AP587WA	**2302** AP594WA	**2303** AP589WA	**2304** AP588WA

2305 AX007XR	Mercedes-Benz O405 N	Mercedes-Benz	B--D	19
2306 AP310WA	BredaMenariniBus M221	Menarini	B--D	
2307 BE589MZ	Irisbus Cityclass 491E 12m	Irisbus	B--D	
2308 BE007MY	Mercedes-Benz O405 N	Mercedes-Benz	B--D	19

Scania OmniCity 2340, CC697FB, sits at the bus station is Como having arrived from Lecco. *Bill Potter*

Pictured crossing the rail line that links Como with Milan is BredaMenariniBus 2403, COB53310. *Bill Potter*

2309-2313

2309-2313		Setra S300 NC		Setra		N D		
2309	BE004MY	**2311**	BE015MY	**2312**	BE018MY		**2313**	BE017MY
2310	BE014MY							

2314	BJ124MP	BredaMenariniBus M240	Menarini	B--D	

2315-2337

2315-2337		Mercedes-Benz Citaro O530		Mercedes-Benz		N--D		
2315	BJ631NR	**2321**	BJ469NR	**2327**	BJ527NR		**2333**	BJ401NR
2316	BJ840NP	**2322**	BJ528NR	**2328**	BJ467NR		**2334**	BJ673NR
2317	BJ247NR	**2323**	BJ248NR	**2329**	BJ465NR		**2335**	BJ400NR
2318	BJ529NR	**2324**	BJ630NR	**2330**	BJ705NR		**2336**	BJ675NR
2319	BJ808NR	**2325**	BJ399NR	**2331**	BJ674NR		**2337**	BJ466NR
2320	BJ468NR	**2326**	BJ122NR	**2332**	BJ402NR			

2338	BP450PP	Irisbus Cityclass 491E 12m	Irisbus	N--D	
2339	CR869PN	Irisbus Cityclass 491E 12m	Irisbus	N--D	
2340	CC697FB	Scania OmniCity CN94 UB	Scania	N--D	
2341	CL979JK	Solaris Urbino 12m	Solaris	N--D	
2342	CX551DW	MAN NL202	MAN	N--D	
2346	DC408JP	Solaris Urbino 12m	Solaris	N--D	

2343-2351

2343-2351		BredaMenariniBus M240 11.9m		Breda		Regional		
2343	CX336ZG	**2345**	CX338ZG	**2348**	DF174YZ		**2350**	DF173YZ
2344	CX337ZG	**2347**	DE445YY	**2349**	DF191YZ		**2351**	DF190YZ

2371	COB18825	BredaMenariniBus 12m	Siccar 286	Regional	
2372	COB18824	BredaMenariniBus 12m	Siccar 286	Regional	

2373-2379

2373-2379		Irisbus 590E 12m		Irisbus		ALS		
2373	AG312TM	**2375**	AG314TM	**2377**	AG316TM		**2379**	AG318TM
2374	AG313TM	**2376**	AG315TM	**2378**	BC671FV			

2380-2386

2380-2386		Setra S300 NC		Setra		N D		
2380	AN821EW	**2382**	AN466EW	**2384**	AN461EW		**2386**	AN901EW
2381	AN463EW	**2383**	AN464EW	**2385**	AN462EW			

2388-2399

2388-2399		Irisbus 591E 12m		Irisbus		ALS		
2388	AP709VW	**2391**	AP465VW	**2394**	AP590WA		**2397**	AP586WA
2389	AP710VW	**2392**	AP464VW	**2395**	AP593WA		**2398**	AP591WA
2390	AP466VW	**2393**	AX027XR	**2396**	AP592WA		**2399**	AP595WA

2401	COB18827	BredaMenariniBus 17.5m	Siccar 386	AB--D	
2402	COB19901	BredaMenariniBus 17.5m	Siccar 386	AB--D	
2403	COB53310	BredaMenariniBus 17.5m	Siccar 386	AB--D	
2404	AG486TT	Irisbus 590E 17.5m	Irisbus	AB--D	

2405	AG487TT	Irisbus 590E 17.5m	Irisbus	AB--D
2406	BC378FV	MAN NG272 17.9m	MAN	AB--D
2407	DS959PK	BredaMenariniBus M321 18m	Menarini	AB--D
2408	CD964PW	BredaMenariniBus M321 18m	Menarini	AB--D
2409	u	BredaMenariniBus M321 18m	Menarini	AB--D
2501	DH553VP	Scania OmniLink 13.6m	Scania	N--D
3001	CR744PP	Iveco A50 7.8m	Iveco	M
3003	CR506PR	Mercedes-Benz Sprinter 616	Mercedes-Benz	M
3004	CX354ZG	BredaMenariniBus M231/V 7.8m	Menarini	N--D
3005	CX339ZG	BredaMenariniBus M231/V 7.8m	Menarini	N--D
3006	CX340ZG	BredaMenariniBus M231/V 7.8m	Menarini	N--D
3007	DS609PK	Iveco A50 7.8m	Iveco	M
3013	M18S4895	Iveco Dailybus 49	Iveco	M
3101	AX547YS	Cacciamali TCM920	Cacciamali	
3143	COB96830	Inbus U150	Sicca 181 C	B
3144	COB96831	Inbus U150	Sicca 181 C	B
3145	AB648AD	MAN 11.190	-	B
3146	AG586TT	Cacciamali TCM890 9m	Cacciamali	B

3147-3153 Irisbus 200E 9.23m Irisbus N--D

3147	BJ017NP	3149	BJ018NP	3151	BJ020NP	3153	BJ526NR
3148	BJ019NP	3150	BJ016NP	3152	BK745MB		

3154	BP159ZZ	Mercedes-Benz O520 Cito	Mercedes-Benz	N20D	19
3155	BP160ZZ	Mercedes-Benz O520 Cito	Mercedes-Benz	N20D	19
3156	CF220HH	Mercedes-Benz O520 Cito	Mercedes-Benz	N20D	19

3201-3208 BredaMenariniBus M240 Menarini N--D

3201	DE447YY	3203	DF147YZ	3205	DF127YZ	3207	DF077YZ
3202	DE424YY	3204	DF128YZ	3206	DF149YZ	3208	DF074YZ

3210	DM969KV	Cacciamali TCN105 10.5m	Cacciamali	N--D
3211	DP074CA	Cacciamali TCN105 10.5m	Cacciamali	N--D
3212	DP669CA	Cacciamali TCN105 10.5m	Cacciamali	N--D

3276-3290 Fiat 471 Fiat B--D

3276	MI7L6079	3287	MI5F8167	3289	MI5F8166	3290	MI7L6077
3277	MI7L6079	3288	MI5F8165				

3291	AG400TN	Fiat 490	Fiat	B--D
3292	AP596WA	Cacciamali TCN105 10.5m	Cacciamali	N--D

3293-3299 BredaMenariniBus M240 Menarini N--D

3293	CR932PR	3295	CX341ZG	3297	CX353ZG	3299	DE423YY
3294	CT198VY	3296	CX352ZG	3298	DE446YY		

3336	M16T4450	Fiat 480	Fiat	B--D
3337	M16V7772	de Simon UL55 12m	de Simon	

3338-3342 BredaMenariniBus M220 Menarini B--D

3338	AG377TH	3340	AG378TH	3341	AG374TH	3342	AG375TH
3339	AG375TH						

3343	AN465EW	Setra S300 NC	Setra	N D
3344	AP625VZ	Setra S300 NC	Setra	N D

3345-3349 Iveco 491E 12m Iveco N--D

3345	AP584WA	3347	AP583WA	3348	BE613MY	3349	BE612MY
3346	AP585WA						

3350	BJ035NR	Irisbus 491E 11.9m	Irisbus	N--D
3351	BJ706NR	Irisbus 491E 11.9m	Irisbus	N--D
3352	BJ033NR	Irisbus 491E 11.9m	Irisbus	N--D
3403	M13G0815	Inbus 17.5m	Sicca 383 C	B
3404	M13G0814	Inbus 17.5m	Sicca 383 C	B
3405	M11L7207	Inbus 17.5m	Sicca 383 C	B
3407	M11L7209	Inbus 17.5m	Sicca 383 C	B
3408	AP009VV	Mercedes-Benz O405 GN	Mercedes-Benz	AB--D
3409	AP010VV	Mercedes-Benz O405 GN	Mercedes-Benz	AB--D
3410	AN645EY	Mercedes-Benz O405 GN	Mercedes-Benz	AB--D
3411	DT527FX	BredaMenariniBus M321 18m	Menarini	AB--D

SAIA

SAIA Trasporti, Via Foro Boario 4/b, 25124 Brescia.

Additional depots are located at Palazzolo sull'Oglio, Orzinuovi, Fiesse, Pralboino and Desenzano del Garda.

1	BSB72612	Menarini M101/1 12m	Menarini	C54D	1990
17	AN 528 JX	Iveco 380.12.38.	Irisbus-Orlandi	C55D	1997
19	AP 139 NW	Renault Iliade GTX	Renault	C55D	1997
21	AP 209 NZ	Renault Iliade GTX	Renault	C55D	1998
25	BR 459 ZT	Renault Iliade GTX	Renault	C57D	2001
29	BS D23781	Iveco 70	Cacciamali	C41D	1990
31	BS B97340	Irisbus 389E.12.43	Iveco	C57D	2003
33	CY103CX	Iveco Daily	Iveco	C34D	1996
35	DB054GE	Mercedes-Benz Tourismo 0350	Mercedes-Benz	C55D	2006
37	DE537SB	Iveco Daily	Iveco	C20D	2003
39	DE722SB	Iveco Domino	Iveco	C55D	2007
41	EB505VB	Iveco Daily A50	Iveco	BC18F	2010
150	AP 425NW	MAN NG272	MAN	AN48D	1993
156	AF 284XK	Volvo B10B	Barbi	B53D	1995

158-178		Mercedes-Benz 0408	Mercedes-Benz	B53D	1996-97

158	AF 957XX	164	AF 706XX	170	AP 033NX	176	AP 036NX
160	AF 958XX	166	AF 438XX	172	AP 034NX	178	AP 037NX
162	AF 959XX	168	AP 032NX	174	AP 035NX		

180	AZ 944NF	Mercedes-Benz 0405 NU	Mercedes-Benz	N38D	1998
182	AZ 710NF	Mercedes-Benz 0405 NU	Mercedes-Benz	N46D	1998
184	AZ 927NF	Mercedes-Benz 0405 NU	Mercedes-Benz	N46D	1998
190	AY 420CV	De Simon UL Scania	Desimon	B45D	1998
192	BA 087SM	Iveco 391E.12.35/M	Padane	B55D	1999
194	BE 218DN	Mauri 18EP30-1	Mauri	N64D	1999
196	BN 300SX	Mercedes-Benz Integro 0550	Mercedes-Benz	BC51D	2000
198	BN 518SX	Mercedes-Benz Integro 0550	Mercedes-Benz	BC53D	2000
200	BN 695SX	Mercedes-Benz Integro 0550	Mercedes-Benz	BC53D	2000
204	BR 094FE	Ayats Bravo I	Ayats	C76D	2000
206	BR 096FE	Mercedes-Benz Integro 0550	Mercedes-Benz	BC53D	2000
208	BR 095FE	Mercedes-Benz Integro 0550	Mercedes-Benz	BC53D	2000

SIA and SAIA now share the same depot in Brescia with many of the office functions being combined. Parked in the depot is SIA's 86, AZ783MD an Iveco 370.12.SE35 with an Orlandi Domino dual-purpose body.
Bill Potter

210-236

			Irisbus 393.12.35 My Way	Irisbus-Orlandi		B47D	2000

No.	Reg	No.	Reg	No.	Reg	No.	Reg
210	BR 928FE	218	BM 324FV	226	BM 320FV	232	BM 315FV
212	BR 964FE	220	BM 316FV	228	BM 323FV	234	BM 415FV
214	BR 772FE	222	BM 317FV	230	BM 313FV	236	BM 318FV
216	BM 322FV	224	BM 319FV				

No.	Reg	Type	Body	Seating	Year
238	BP 180BG	MAN NL263 F	Autodromo	N48D	2000
240	BP 177BG	MAN NL263 F	Autodromo	N48D	2000

242-254

			Mercedes-Benz Citaro O530 NU	Mercedes-Benz		N46D	2001

No.	Reg	No.	Reg	No.	Reg	No.	Reg
242	BT 351GC	246	BT 348GC	250	BT 537GC	254	BT 204GD
244	BT 350GC	248	BT 349GC	252	BT 538GC		

No.	Reg	Type	Body	Seating	Year
256	BT203GD	Ayats Bravo I	Ayats	C75D	2000
258	BT941GD	Mercedes-Benz Citaro O530 NU	Mercedes-Benz	N46D	2001
260	BT940GD	Mercedes-Benz Citaro O530 NU	Mercedes-Benz	N46D	2001
262	BV410DV	Mercedes-Benz Citaro O530 NU	Mercedes-Benz	N46D	2001
266	BV873DZ	Renault Agora Moovy	Renault	BC48D	2001
268	BV874DZ	Renault Agora Moovy	Renault	BC48D	2001
272	BZ169XN	MAN SU 313	MAN	BC52D	2002
274	BZ170XN	MAN SU 313	MAN	BC52D	2002
276	CF122JN	Irisbus 399E My Way	Irisbus Orlandi	B48D	2003
278	CJ391BX	Iveco 380.12.35.	Orlandi	B55D	1995
280	CJ309BY	MAN SG292 18m	MAN	AB63D	1993

282-300

			Mercedes-Benz Conecto O345	Mercedes-Benz		BC44D	2001

No.	Reg	No.	Reg	No.	Reg	No.	Reg
282	CL542AX	288	CL544AX	294	CL052AY	298	CM023EW
284	CL543AX	290	CL220AX	296	CL5624Y	300	CL561AY
286	CL541AX	292	CL560AY				

No.	Reg	Type	Body	Seating	Year
304	CP892TT	MAN NU313	MAN	B48D	1996
306	CP893TT	MAN NU313	MAN	B48D	1996
308	CP894TT	MAN NU313	MAN	B48D	1996
310	CP895TT	MAN NU313	MAN	B48D	1996
312	CP891TT	MAN NU313	MAN	B48D	1996
322	CR330HK	Mercedes-Benz Integro O550 UL	Mercedes-Benz	BC69D	2004
324	CT379CZ	Setra S324 UL	Setra	AC79D	1997
326	CT896XV	Mercedes-Benz O407	Mercedes-Benz	BC49D	1994
328	CT896XV	Mercedes-Benz O407	Mercedes-Benz	BC49D	1994

330-342

			Irisbus MyWay 399E.12.35	Irisbus		B48D	2005

No.	Reg	No.	Reg	No.	Reg	No.	Reg
330	CV667XV	334	CV671XV	338	CV669XV	342	CV673XV
332	CV672XV	336	CV668XV	340	CV670XV		

No.	Reg	Type	Body	Seating	Year
344	CY157CZ	Mercedes-Benz Integro O550 UL	Mercedes-Benz	BC69D	2006
346	BR335FF	Mercedes-Benz Integro O550 UL	Mercedes-Benz	BC53D	2003
348	CJ565BY	Mercedes-Benz Integro O550 UL	Mercedes-Benz	BC53D	2003
350	DB510GE	Setra S319 NF	Setra	BC57D	1998
354	DB865WS	Mercedes-Benz Citaro O530 NU	Mercedes-Benz	N42D	2006
356	DE260SB	Iveco 680.12.30	Iveco	AB73D	1989
358	DE361SB	MAN Lion's City U (A20)	MAN	N44D	2007
360	DE362SB	MAN Lion's City U (A20)	MAN	N44D	2007

362-392

			Irisbus Arway	Irisbus		B49D	2007

No.	Reg	No.	Reg	No.	Reg	No.	Reg
362	DE360SB	370	DE724SB	378	DH331CS	386	DH335CS
364	DE792SB	372	DE791SB	380	DH332CS	388	DH244CS
366	DH851CS	374	DE725SB	382	DH333CS	390	DH245CS
368	DE723SB	376	DH330CS	384	DH334CS	392	DF336CS

No.	Reg	Type	Body	Seating	Year
394	LD687NA	MAN Lion's City U	MAN	N44D	2008

396-406

			Irisbus Crossway	Irisbus		N49D	2008

No.	Reg	No.	Reg	No.	Reg	No.	Reg
396	DN058MS	400	DN067MS	404	DN062MS	406	DN059MS
398	DN060MS	402	DN061MS				

No.	Reg	Type	Body	Seating	Year
408	DN364MS	Mercedes-Benz Citaro O530 GNU	Mercedes-Benz	AN57D	2008
410	DN363MS	Mercedes-Benz Citaro O530 GNU	Mercedes-Benz	AN57D	2008
412	DN864MS	Cacciamali 840 TCI 8.48m	Cacciamali	N35D	2009

Carrying the SAIA fleet name is 404, DN062MS, one of six Irisbus Crossway buses added to the operation in 2008. Most of these rural buses are fitted with curtains used to keep out the sun. *Bill Potter*

414-442

				Irisbus Crossway		Irisbus		N49D	2009	
414	DN373MS	422	DN366MS	430	DN377MS			438	DN375MS	
416	DN367MS	424	DN365MS	432	DN370MS			440	DN378MS	
418	DN441MS	426	DN374MS	434	DN372MS			442	DN371MS	
420	DN440MS	428	DN376MS	436	DN369MS					

444	DV444RG	Mercedes-Benz Citaro O530 GNU	Mercedes-Benz	AN57D	2009	
446	DV487RG	Mercedes-Benz Citaro O530 GNU	Mercedes-Benz	AN57D	2009	

448-454

				MAN Lion's City A20		MAN	N44D	2009	
448	DV713RG	450	DV712RG	452	DV651RG			454	DV711RG

456	CZ100GY	Mercedes-Benz Citaro O530 GNU	Mercedes-Benz	AN56D	2004	Arriva Netherlands, 2010
458	CZ102GY	Mercedes-Benz Integro O550	Mercedes-Benz	BC49F	2004	Arriva Netherlands, 2010
460	CZ101GY	Mercedes-Benz Integro O550	Mercedes-Benz	BC53F	2004	Arriva Netherlands, 2010
462	CZ111GY	MAN Lion's City U	MAN	N44D	2010	
464	CZ112GY	MAN Lion's City U	MAN	N44D	2010	
466	CZ113GY	Irisbus Crossway 12m	Irisbus	BC49D	2010	
468	CZ114GY	Irisbus Crossway 12m	Irisbus	BC49D	2010	
470	CZ115GY	Irisbus Crossway 12m	Irisbus	BC49D	2010	
472	CZ116GY	Irisbus Crossway 12m	Irisbus	BC49D	2010	
474	CZ118GY	Mercedes-Benz Citaro O530 GNU	Mercedes-Benz	AN57D	2010	
476	CZ118GY	Mercedes-Benz Citaro O530 GNU	Mercedes-Benz	AN57D	2010	
478	CZ119GY	Toyota Coaster BB50L	Caetano Optimo V	C29D	2010	

SAL

SAL srl, Via della Pergola 2, 23900 Lecco, Italy

3002	AN848EV	MAN 11.190	Macchi	B31D	1996
3005	AN942EW	MAN 11.190	Macchi	B31D	1997
3013	COD59447	MAN 11.190	Macchi	B31D	1994
3015	AN438EW	Kässbohrer S300 NC	Kässbohrer Setra	N35D	1992
3016	AN439EW	Setra S 300 NC	Setra	N35D	1997
3017	AN440EW	Kässbohrer S300 NC	Kässbohrer Setra	N35D	1993
3026	AG533TR	BredaMenarini M 3001.12L	BredaMenarinbus	B43D	1996
3027	AG534TR	BredaMenarini M 3001.12L	BredaMenarinbus	B43D	1996
3029	AN731EW	BredaMenarini M 221	BredaMenarinbus	N37D	1997
3034	AN988EW	Kässbohrer S300 NC	Kässbohrer Setra	N35D	1991
3035	COB83012	BredaMenarini M120/1	BredaMenarinbus	B48D	1992
3057	COD59602	Setra S212 H	Setra	B48D	1994
3063	AN080EZ	Mercedes-Benz O303/15R	Bianchi	C54D	1987
3064	AP574VZ	Mercedes-Benz O303/15R	Bianchi	C54D	1986
3065	AN939EY	Mercedes-Benz O303/15R	Bianchi	C54D	1986
3106	BB199KC	Mercedes-Benz O303/14R	Mercedes	BC50D	1999
3109	BE328MY	Iveco Daily F45.12	Iveco	B20D	1999
3114	BF634TD	Mercedes-Benz O408	Mercedes	N54D	1997
3115	BF635TD	Mercedes-Benz O408	Mercedes	N54D	1997
3116	BF636TD	Mercedes-Benz O408	Mercedes	N54D	1997
3117	BF637TD	Mercedes-Benz O408	Mercedes	N54D	1997
3118	BF638TD	Mercedes-Benz O408	Mercedes	N54D	1997
3119	BF830TD	Iveco Daily F45.12	Iveco	B27D	1998
3120	BF829TD	Iveco Daily F45.12	Iveco	B29D	2000
3121	BF828TD	Iveco Daily F45.12	Iveco	B29D	2000
3122	BY901MN	Iveco 393.12.35 My Way	Iveco	B49D	2000
3123	BK965MA	Mercedes-Benz O404	Mercedes	BC51D	1993
3124	BJ017NR	Iveco 393.12.35 My Way	Iveco	B49D	2000
3125	BJ015NR	Iveco 393.12.35 My Way	Iveco	BC49D	2000
3126	BJ018NR	Iveco 393.12.35 My Way	Iveco	B49D	2000
3127	BJ016NR	Iveco 393.12.35 My Way	Iveco	B49D	2000
3128	BJ014NR	Iveco 393.12.35 My Way	Iveco	B49D	2000
3129	BJ012NR	Iveco 393.12.35 My Way	Iveco	B49D	2000
3130	BJ013NR	Iveco 393.12.35 My Way	Iveco	B49D	2000
3131	BP600PP	MAN 11.220	DeSimon Starline 55.12	B30D	2001
3132	BP722PP	MAN 11.220	DeSimon Starline 55.12	B30D	2001

Pictured arriving in Lecco is SAL 3130, BJ013NR, an Iveco My Way bus. All SAL vehicles are numbered in the 3xxx series but the initial digit is omitted from the vehicles.
Bill Potter

Urban colours are carried on SAL's 3134, BP261PR, an Iveco EuroPolis model. The Setra S300 seen behind was withdrawn shortly after the picture was taken. *Bill Potter*

3133	BP262PR	Iveco EuroPolis 9.15	Iveco	N27D	2001
3134	BP261PR	Iveco EuroPolis 9.15	Iveco	N27D	2001
3135	BP260PR	Iveco EuroPolis 9.15	Iveco	N27D	2001
3136	BP259PR	Iveco EuroPolis 9.15	Iveco	N27D	2001
3137	CX401YW	Iveco EuroPolis 10.50	Iveco	N30D	2001
3138	BP539ZY	Iveco EuroPolis 10.50	Iveco	N30D	2001
3143	BP538ZY	Mercedes-Benz Citaro O530 NU	Mercedes	N44D	2001
3146	BV937SX	Iveco Daily F45.12	Iveco	B30D	2001
3147	BZ 262 SZ	Mercedes-Benz O350 TURISMO	Mercedes	B55D	2002
3148	CD147SA	MAN 11.220	DeSimon Starline 55.12	B35D	2002
3149	BZ646TB	Cacciamali TCI 970 Sigma 2	Cacciamali	BC42D	2002
3150	CL586JJ	Mercedes-Benz Tourismo O340	Mercedes	C45D	2001
3151	CL587JJ	Mercedes-Benz Tourismo O340	Mercedes	C45D	2001
3152	CL478JL	MAN 272 UL 12m	MAN	B54D	1993
3153	CL479JL	MAN 272 UL 12m	MAN	B54D	1993
3154	CL501JL	MAN 272 UL 12m	MAN	B54D	1993
3155	CL502JL	MAN 272 UL 12m	MAN	B54D	1995
3156	CL477JL	MAN 313 UL 12m	MAN	B54D	1997
3157	CL503JL	MAN 313 UL 10.4m	MAN	B42D	1997
3158	CR428PP	Mercedes-Benz O404	Noleggio	C51D	1992
3159	CR005PR	MAN 313 UL 10.4m	MAN	BC47D	1999
3160	CR670PR	MAN 272 UL 12m	MAN	B54D	1994
3161	CR669PR	MAN 272 UL 12m	MAN	B54D	1994
3162	CR668PR	MAN 292 UL 12m	MAN	B54D	1993
3163	CT017VY	Mercedes-Benz Citaro O530	Mercedes	N44D	2001
3164	CR189PR	Mercedes-Benz Citaro O530	Mercedes	N44D	2001
3165	CR190PR	Mercedes-Benz Citaro O530	Mercedes	N44D	2001
3166	CR191PR	Mercedes-Benz Citaro O530	Mercedes	N44D	2001
3167	CR804PN	Irisbus MyWay 393.12.35	Irisbus	B49D	2005
3168	CR803PN	Irisbus MyWay 393.12.35	Irisbus	B49D	2005
3169	CR856PN	Irisbus MyWay 393.12.35	Irisbus	B49D	2005
3170	CR855PN	Irisbus MyWay 393.12.35	Irisbus	B49D	2005
3171	CX050YW	Toyota Coaster BB50L	Caetano Optimo V	C29D	2005
3172	CX294YW	Iveco TurboDaily 59	Cacciamali	B23D	1999

An interesting purchase by Arriva in 2009 is the Cacciamali TCI 840. These are to be found in several fleets with three allocated to SAL. Awaiting departure from Lecco rail station is 3206, DN859NX. *Bill Potter*

3173	CX884ZG	Mercedes-Benz Integro O550 UL	Mercedes-Benz	BC67D	2006
3174	DC413JP	Mercedes-Benz O405G	Mercedes-Benz	AB61D	1995
3175	DE651YY	Irisbus TurboDaily 59	Irisbus	B20D	2006
3176	DE954YY	Iveco Ducato	Iveco	M14	2007
3177	DF616YZ	Iveco TurboDaily 59	Iveco	B20D	1999
3179	DF317ZA	Irisbus Crossway 491.12.29	Irisbus	B43D	2007
3180	DF315ZA	Irisbus Crossway 491.12.29	Irisbus	N22D	2007
3181	DF014YZ	MAN Lion's City U (A20)	MAN	N48D	2007
3182	DF353YZ	MAN Lion's City U (A20)	MAN	N48D	2007
3183	DF011YZ	MAN Lion's City U (A20)	MAN	N48D	2007
3184	DF013YZ	MAN Lion's City U (A20)	MAN	N48D	2007
3185	DF012YZ	MAN Lion's City U (A20)	MAN	N48D	2007
3186	DF157YZ	MAN Lion's City U (A20)	MAN	N48D	2007
3187	DF158YZ	MAN Lion's City U (A20)	MAN	N48D	2007
3188	AH841CY	Cacciamali Tema 207	Cacciamali	B43D	1996
3189	BZ283SY	BredaMenarini M321	BredaMenarinI	AB40D	1999
3190	DM091JM	Irisbus Crossway 491.10.29	Irisbus	B43D	2008
3191	DM092JM	Irisbus Crossway 491.10.29	Irisbus	B43D	2008
3192	DM093JM	Irisbus Crossway 491.10.29	Irisbus	B43D	2008
3193	DM094JM	Irisbus Crossway 491.10.29	Irisbus	B43D	2008
3194	DM306JM	Iveco TurboDaily 59	Iveco	B29D	2008
3203	DM305JM	MAN Lion's City U (A20)	MAN	N53D	2008
3204	DR843GP	Irisbus Crossway 491.12.29	Irisbus	B53D	2009
3205	DR844GP	Irisbus Crossway 491.10.29	Irisbus	B45D	2009
3206	DN859NX	Cacciamali TCI 840	Cacciamali	B36D	2009
3207	DN861NX	Cacciamali TCI 840	Cacciamali	B36D	2009
3208	DN860NX	Cacciamali TCI 840	Cacciamali	B36D	2009
3209	DR930GP	Iveco A45.10	Iveco	B41D	1997
3210	DV581HE	Irisbus Crossway SRF162	Irisbus	N47D	2009
3212	ED013BL	Irisbus Crossway 491.10.29	Irisbus	N41D	2010
3213	ED014BL	Irisbus Crossway 491.10.29	Irisbus	N41D	2010
3214	ED012BL	Irisbus Crossway 491.10.29	Irisbus	N41D	2010
3215	ED166BL	Mercedes-Benz O405G	Mercedes-Benz	AB61D	1999
3216	ED151BL	Ikarus 41704A	Ikarus	AB53D	1996

KM

KM SpA, Via Postumia 102, 26100 Cremona

1003	CR389359	Iveco 280 RA7	Cacciamali	B22F	1988	
1004	BG451PH	Iveco 45.10	Iveco	B39F	1995	
1005	BH060WY	Iveco CC80E18M/86	Cacciamali	B46F	2000	
1006	BV937GP	Iveco Scuolabus Turbo Daily	Cacciamali	B33F	1989	
1007	DD102YG	Iveco Tema 207	Cacciamali	B41F	1996	
1008	BV088ZB	Iveco 100E	Cacciamali	B41F	1999	
1009	BV073ZB	Iveco 100E	Cacciamali	B49D	2000	

1030-1036 — Irisbus Cityclass 491.12.29 — Irisbus — N20D* — 2007-08 — *1035/6 are N16D

1030	DD354YG	**1032**	DD355YG	**1034**	DF237PJ	**1036**	DM301JY
1031	DD352YG	**1033**	DD353YG	**1035**	DM300JY		

1037-1040 — Irisbus 200E 10.48m — Irisbus — NC18D — 2009

1037	DN634JT	**1038**	DN716JT	**1039**	DN316JT
1040	DS028EJ				

1041	DX384ZJ	Irisbus 65C17	Cacciamali Urby	C41F	2009	
1074	AL597GD	CAM Bussotto NL202 FU	Autiromo	N25D	1996	
1075	AP257XK	BredaMenarini M 230/1E2	Bredamenarinbus	N13D	1998	
1076	AP258XK	BredaMenarini M 230/1E2	Bredamenarinbus	N12D	1998	

1078-1082 — Kronos 10KV23-U — Mauri — N20D — 2001

1078	BV620GK	**1080**	BV621GK	**1081**	BV826GK
1079	BV680GK			**1082**	BV827GK

1083-1086 — Mercedes-Benz Cito O520 — Mercedes-Benz — N9D — 2002

1083	BV916GS	**1084**	BV014GT	**1085**	BV917GS
				1086	BV936GP

1087	CL922MC	Irisbus Cityclass 491.12.29	Irisbus	N22D	2004	
1088	CR503TW	Irisbus Cityclass 491.12.29	Irisbus	N22D	2005	
1091	CV595BG	Iveco TurboCity 491.10.24	Irisbus	B18D	1992	
1093	DC575NY	Mercedes-Benz Sprinter 416	Mercedes-Benz	N9D	2006	
1094	DF336PJ	BredaMenarini M 230/1E2	Bredamenarinbus	N12D	1998	
1095	DF335PJ	BredaMenarini M 230/1E2	Bredamenarinbus	N12D	1998	

The KM operation is centred on the Italian town on Cremona. Illustrating the fleet is 1160, BS693LE, an Iveco Cityclass bus dating from 2001. As with the SAL fleet the initial number is not displayed on the vehicles.
Bill Potter

Cremona boasts two bus stations and awaiting its departure from the rural one is 1131, BH342WC, an Iveco EuroRider. *Ken McKenzie*

1096-1099

		Irisbus 200E 10.48m	Irisbus	N16D	2008

1096	DM445JY	**1097**	DM212JY	**1098**	DM223JY	**1099**	DM315JY

1103	BSD05103	Iveco 370.12.25L	Iveco	B55D	1990
1105	AF778XJ	Cam Busotto 2LS-SR	Autiromo	B39D	1995
1109	BE301DN	Mercedes-Benz O405NU	Mercedes-Benz	N46D	1999
1110	AZ465NF	Mercedes-Benz O405NU	Mercedes-Benz	N46D	1998
1111	BM984FW	Mercedes-Benz O405NU	Mercedes-Benz	N46D	2000
1113	AF164XD	Iveco 370.12.35	Dalla Via	B55D	1995
1114	AZ469NF	Mercedes-Benz O405NU	Mercedes-Benz	N46D	1998
1128	BSB69662	Iveco 370.12.25L	Iveco	B55D	1990
1129	BSD05102	Iveco 370.12.25L	Iveco	B55D	1990
1130	BH343WC	Iveco EuroRider 391E.12.29	Iveco	B55D	1998
1131	BH342WC	Iveco EuroRider 391E.12.29	Iveco	B55D	1998
1132	AZ468NF	Mercedes-Benz O405 NU	Iveco	N46D	1998

1137-1142

		Ayats 2 Piani	Ayats	NC75D	2001

1137	BM281DX	**1139**	BM283DX	**1141**	BR776FE	**1142**	BR905FE
1138	BM282DX	**1140**	BR775FE				

1143	AF163 XD	Iveco 370.12.35	Dalla Via	B55D	1995
1144	BM 280DX	Iveco 393E.12.35 My Way	Iveco	B51D	2001
1145	BM 285DX	Iveco 393E.12.35 My Way	Iveco	B51D	2001
1146	BM 290DX	Iveco 393E.12.35 My Way	Iveco	B51D	2001
1147	AF747XF	Iveco 370.12.35	Dalla Via	B55D	1995

1148-1155

		Iveco 393E.12.35 My Way	Iveco	B51D	2001

1148	BM291DX	**1150**	BM284DX	**1152**	BM288DX	**1154**	BM292DX
1149	BM286DX	**1151**	BM287DX	**1153**	BM289DX	**1155**	CD523YR

1156	AD940JF	Cacciamali Tema 100	Cacciamali	BC24F	1995
1157	AZ470NF	Mercedes-Benz O405NU	Mercedes-Benz	N46D	1998
1158	DF183PJ	Irisbus Crossway	Irisbus	B41D	2007
1159	AZ467NF	Mercedes-Benz O405NU	Mercedes-Benz	N46D	1998
1160	BS693LE	Iveco 491.12.27 - Cityclass	Iveco	N37D	2001

1161	BS694LE	Iveco 491.12.27 - Cityclass	Iveco		N37D	2001	
1162	BS695LE	Iveco 491.12.27 - Cityclass	Iveco		N37D	2001	

1163-1166		Irisbus MyWay 399E	Irisbus		BC48D	2004	
1163	CR563TW	**1164**	CL684ME	**1165**	CL 685ME	**1166**	CR 504TW

1167	DA573RA	Mercedes-Benz Integro 0550	Mercedes-Benz	C65F	2006	
1168	DA574RA	Mercedes-Benz Integro 0550	Mercedes-Benz	C65F	2006	
1169	DC004WA	Irisbus Daily A50	Irisbus	B14F	2006	
1170	DC005WA	Irisbus Daily A50	Irisbus	B14F	2006	

1171-1184		Irisbus Arway	Irisbus		B49D	2007	
1171	DF025PJ	**1175**	DD456YG	**1178**	DF028PJ	**1182**	DF030PJ
1172	DD458YG	**1176**	DF032PJ	**1179**	DF029PJ	**1183**	DF027PJ
1173	DD459YG	**1177**	DF026PJ	**1180**	DF024PJ	**1184**	DF031PJ
1174	DD457YG						

1185	DM344JY	Irisbus Crossway	Irisbus	BC55F	2008	
1186	DM343JY	Irisbus Crossway	Irisbus	BC55F	2008	
1189	BSD09800	Iveco 370.12.30S	Portesi	B55D	1990	
1190	DH499TY	Toyota Coaster BB50R	Caetano Optimo IV	C27F	2008	
1191	DM302JY	Toyota Coaster BB50R	Caetano Optimo IV	C27F	2008	
1195	AZ466NF	Mercedes-Benz 0405NU	Mercedes-Benz	N46D	1998	
2405	AP785XF	Iveco 370E.12.35 - Domino	Iveco-Orlandi	C55D	1998	
2407	BG322PH	Mercedes-Benz 0404	Dalla Via Palladio	C47D	2000	
2408	BG323PH	Mercedes-Benz 0404	Dalla Via Palladio	C51D	2000	
2410	DF130PJ	Mercedes-Benz Tourismo	Mercedes-Benz	C53D	2003	

SAF

Società Autoservizi FVG SpA, Via Baldasseria Bassa 75, 33100 Udine, Italy

3	AH449YP	Kässbohrer S140 ES	Kässbohrer Setra	C52D		
52	UD662611	Iveco 370.12.25 12m	Iveco	B55D	1991	
53	UD684276	Iveco 370.12.25 12m	Iveco	B55D	1991	
54	UD684277	Iveco 370.12.25 12m	Iveco	B55D	1991	
55	UD684278	Iveco 370.12.25 12m	Iveco	B55D	1991	
56	UD744862	Iveco 370.12.30 12m	Iveco	B55D	1993	
68	AG170CR	Iveco 380.12.35 12m	Iveco	B55D	1996	

80-84		Scania OmniCity K230 UB	Scania		N23F	2009	
80	DW042HN	**82**	DW083HN	**83**	DW044HN	**84**	DW045HN
81	DW043HN						

101	AM920SR	Scania L94IB	Irizar InterCentury 12m	N55D	1997	
104	BD181LG	Scania L94IB	Irizar InterCentury 12m	N55D	1999	
109	BD439LG	Scania L94IB	Irizar InterCentury 12m	N55D	1999	
110	BV193MF	Mercedes-Benz 0350 12m	Mercedes-Benz	C51F	2001	
112	BV651MF	Mercedes-Benz 0350 12m	Mercedes-Benz	C51F	2001	
118	BV238MF	Mercedes-Benz 0350 12m	Mercedes-Benz	C51F	2001	
119	BV194MF	Mercedes-Benz Travego 0580 12m		C51F	2001	
120	BV195MF	Mercedes-Benz Travego 0580 12m		C51F	2001	
123	BV196MF	Mercedes-Benz Travego 0580 12m		BC51D	2001	
129	BW000WE	Neoplan N4426/3	Piani 12m	B86D	2001	
134	AM880SS	De Simon IL3 260 Scania	12m	N53D	1997	
135	AM870SS	De Simon IL3 260 Scania	12m	N53D	1997	
136	AM879SS	De Simon IL3 260 Scania	12m	N53D	1997	
137	BV289MG	Neoplan N4426/3	Piani 12m	B86D	2001	
139	BV423MG	Neoplan N4426/3	Piani 12m	B86D	2001	
144	BV497MG	Neoplan N4426/3	Piani 12m	B86D	2001	
145	BV740MG	Neoplan N4426/3	Piani 12m	B86D	2001	
146	GO232620	Volvo B10B	12m	N55D	1994	
174	AG150CR	Iveco 380.12.35	Iveco	N55D	1996	
175	AG160CR	Iveco 380.12.35	Iveco	N55D	1996	
176	AG180CR	Iveco 380.12.35	Iveco	N55D	1996	
177	AG510CS	Iveco 370E.12.35	Iveco	N55D	1996	
178	AG520CS	Iveco 370E.12.35	Iveco	N55D	1996	

193	DD878HP	Setra S431 DT	Setra	C80D	2007	
194	UD684510	Iveco Orlandi Poker 315.8.17	Iveco	NC28F	1991	
214	UD729328	Padane Z1		C37F	1987	
215	UD567020	Mercedes-Benz O303/15R		C71D	1988	
220	UD574050	Mercedes-Benz O303/15R		C71D	1988	
221	UD590656	Mercedes-Benz O303/15R		C71D	1988	

230-255

		Mercedes-Benz O303/15R	12m	BC53D*	1989	some now BC71D for schools

230	UD620350	242	UD607008	246	UD639700	252 UD641030
235	UD620370	243	UD607005	247	UD639734	253 UD641740
237	UD616564	244	UD607004	248	UD640292	254 UD641040
240	UD607006	245	UD655850	250	UD656413	255 UD642450
241	UD607007					

258	UD682829	Mercedes-Benz O303/10R	9.23m	BC39D	1991
259	UD683358	Mercedes-Benz O303/13R	10.55m	BC47D	1991
262	UD709540	Mercedes-Benz O303/15R	12m	BC55D	1992
263	UD711714	Mercedes-Benz O408	12m	BC53D	1992
265	UD732805	Mercedes-Benz O408	12m	BC53	1993
267	AA307WH	Mercedes-Benz O340	12m	C53D	1994
275	AE458RW	Mercedes-Benz O408	12m	BC53D	1994
276	AE459RW	Mercedes-Benz O408	12m	B53D	1994

281-290

		Mercedes-Benz Tourismo O350	12m	C53F	1995-96

281	AG351CC	286	AK847RC	287	AG240CM	290	CF317HL

291-305

		Mercedes-Benz O408	12m	B53D	1996

291	AG347CC	295	AG355CC	299	AG359CC	303	AG363CC
292	AG348CC	296	AG356CC	300	AG360CC	304	AG364CC
293	AG349CC	297	AG357CC	301	AG361CC	305	AG365CC
294	AG350CC	298	AG358CC	302	AG362CC		

306	BB861RY	Mercedes-Benz Sprinter 412	Soro	B18F	1999
307	BB953RY	Mercedes-Benz Sprinter 412	Soro	B18F	1999
308	BV362MF	Mercedes-Benz Sprinter 416	Mercedes-Benz	B18F	2001
309	BE837FE	Mercedes-Benz Sprinter 412	Soro	B18F	1999
310	BE838FE	Mercedes-Benz Sprinter 412	Soro	B18F	1999
311	BF907DX	Mercedes-Benz Sprinter 412	Soro	B18F	1999
312	AG190CY	Iveco Orlandi 380.12.35		B55D	1996
313	AG910CZ	Iveco 370E.12.35		B55D	1996
314	AG900CZ	Iveco 370E.12.35		B55D	1996
316	AT960HF	Iveco Daily 6.86m		B19F	1997
319	AZ300WB	Neoplan N 4026/3 12m		B88F	1998
320	AZ488VF	Iveco 315.8.18 7.58m		B30F	1998
321	AZ489VF	Iveco EuroRider 391E.12.29		B53D	1998
322	AZ490VF	Iveco EuroRider 391E.12.29		B53D	1998
324	AZ088WB	Iveco EuroRider 391E.12.29		B53D	1998
325	AZ089WB	Iveco EuroRider 391E.12.29		B53D	1998
326	AZ099WB	Iveco EuroRider 391E.12.29		B53D	1998
327	AZ100WB	Iveco Orlandi Euroclass 380.12.35		B55D	1998
328	BD310FZ	Iveco Orlandi Euroclass 380.12.35 12m		B55D	1999
329	BF242DX	Neoplan Centroliner N4026/3	12m	C88F	1999
330	BH578XR	Neoplan Centroliner N4026/3	12m	C88F	2000

331-342

		Volvo B10B 12m	Volvo	N53D	2000

331	BH855XR	334	BH114XS	337	BH117XS	340	BH120XS
332	BV048MG	335	BH115XS	338	BH118XS	341	BH121XS
333	BH857XR	336	BH116XS	339	BH119XS	342	BH122XS

349	DW091HN	Cacciamali TCI 840	Cacciamali	N33F	2009
350	DW092HN	Cacciamali TCI 840	Cacciamali	N33F	2009
359	AG490CL	Neoplan Centroliner N4026/3	12m	C88F	1996
360	AG500CL	Neoplan Centroliner N4026/3	12m	C88F	1996

361-365

		Neoplan Transliner N316 SHD	12m	C53F	1998

361	AT191JA	363	BE331FE	364	AT390JA	365	AT590JA
362	AT192JA						

369-373

		Neoplan Centroliner N4026/3	12m	C88F	1998

369	AZ389VF	371	AZ840VF	372	AZ047VG	373	AZ411VG
370	AZ046VG						

374	AZ899VF	Neoplan N122/3	12m			C75F	1998
375	BH568XR	Neoplan N4026/3	12m			C88F	2000
376	BH569XR	Neoplan N4026/3	12m			C88F	2000
377	BH674XT	Volvo B10B 10.8m	Volvo			B45D	2000
378	BH673XT	Volvo B10B 10.8m	Volvo			B45D	2000

379-400   Volvo B10B 12m   Volvo   N53D   2000

379	BH229XV	385	BH235XV	391	BJ051RB	396	BJ056RB
380	BH230XV	386	BH236XV	392	BJ052RB	397	BJ057RB
381	BH231XV	387	BH237XV	393	BJ053RB	398	BJ058RB
382	BH232XV	388	BH238XV	394	BJ054RB	399	BJ059RB
383	BH233XV	389	BJ049RB	395	BJ055RB	400	BJ060RB
384	BH234XV	390	BJ050RB				

446-449   De Simon Intercity IL3   12m   N53D   2001

446	BS311RN	447	BS312RN	448	BS318RN	449	BS319RN

450	CF318HL	Mercedes-Benz Tourismo O350		C51D	2003
461	AZ090WB	Irizar Century 12.37A		C38D	1998

462-476   De Simon Intercity IL3 12m   N53D   1999

462	AZ807WB	466	AZ046WC	470	AZ812WB	474	AZ816WB
463	AZ808WB	467	AZ047WC	471	AZ813WB	475	AZ858WB
464	AZ809WB	468	AZ048WC	472	AZ814WB	476	AZ859WB
465	AZ810WB	469	AZ811WB	473	AZ815WB		

477	BJ031RB	MAN 11.22 8.82m	De Simon Starline	B34D	2000
478	BJ028RB	Iveco Daily A45E12 6.86m		B19F	2000
479	BJ029RB	Iveco Daily A45E12 6.86m		B19F	2000
480	BJ030RB	Iveco Daily A45E12 6.86m		B19F	2000
481	BJ677RB	Volvo B10B 12m		N53F	2000

482-486   Volvo B10B 10.8m   N45D   2000

482	BJ493RB	484	BJ674RB	485	BJ675RB	486	BJ676RB
483	BJ673RB						

488-493   Neoplan Euroliner N316 SHD   Neoplan   C51F   2000

488	BJ450RC	490	BH780XY	492	BH782XY	493	BH783XY
489	BJ369RC	491	BH781XY				

494	BJ244RC	Iveco Daily A45E12 6.86m		C19F	2000
495	BJ889RC	Mercedes-Benz Sprinter 416		N18D	2000
497	BJ473RD	De Simon Intercity IN3	10.67m	N47D	2000
498	BJ474RD	De Simon Intercity IN3	10.67m	N47D	2000
499	BS884RN	MAN 11.220	Beulas Ministar	C35D	2001
505	BE330FE	Volvo B12B	Barbi Echo	C51D	1999
506	BM877SA	Iveco EuroRider 391E.12.35	Orlandi Domino	C48D	2001
507	BM837SA	Iveco EuroRider 391E.12.35	Orlandi Domino	C48D	2001
508	CN237SF	Iveco EuroRider 391E.12.35	Orlandi Domino	C48D	2001
509	BM809SA	Iveco EuroRider 391E.12.35	Orlandi Domino	C48D	2001
510	BM810SA	Iveco EuroRider 391E.12.35	Orlandi Eurorider	BC53D	2001
511	BM832SA	Iveco EuroRider 391E.12.35	Orlandi Eurorider	BC53D	2001
512	BM831SA	Iveco EuroRider 391E.12.35	Orlandi Eurorider	BC53D	2001
513	BS487RN	Iveco EuroRider 391E.12.35	Orlandi Eurorider	BC53D	2001
514	BM972SA	Iveco EuroRider 391E.12.35	Orlandi Eurorider	BC53D	2001
515	BW410WE	Iveco EuroRider 391.10.35	Orlandi Eurorider	BC45D	2002
516	BZ715EZ	Mercedes-Benz Tourismo O350		C46F	1997
517	BW854WF	Mercedes-Benz Tourismo O350		C46F	1997
518	CN236SF	Mercedes-Benz Tourismo O350		C46F	1997
519	BZ548EZ	Mercedes-Benz Tourismo O350		C46F	1997
520	CB526YE	Mercedes-Benz Tourismo O350		C53F	2003
521	CY519VV	Mercedes-Benz Integro O550	Mercedes-Benz	BC40F	2006
522	CY520VV	Mercedes-Benz Integro O550	Mercedes-Benz	BC40F	2006
523	BZ046FA	Iveco 370E.12.35	Dalla Via DV39D Top Line	C50F	2002
524	BZ047FA	Iveco 370E.12.35	Dalla Via DV39D Top Line	C50F	2002
525	BZ048FA	Iveco 370E.12.35	Dalla Via DV39D Top Line	C50F	2002
526	CF530HL	Neoplan Centroliner N4426/3		B86D	2003
527	CF531HL	Neoplan Centroliner N4426/3		B86D	2003
528	CF532HL	Neoplan Centroliner N4426/3		B86D	2003
529	CF533HL	Neoplan Centroliner N4426/3		B86D	2003
530	CF569HL	Mercedes-Benz Tourismo O350		C51F	2003
531	DC970GD	Caccimali Tema 206 9.3m		N16F	2006

532	DW252HN	Caccimali Tema 206 9.3m			N16F	1999	
534	CW419WG	Mercedes-Benz 412	Sora		B25F	1994	
535	CW420WG	Mercedes-Benz Sprinter 412	Sora		N25F	2000	
536	CW421WG	Mercedes-Benz Sprinter 412	Sora		N25F	2005	
537	CY521VV	Mercedes-Benz Integro O550	Mercedes-Benz		C40D	2006	
538	CY522VV	Mercedes-Benz Integro O550	Mercedes-Benz		C40D	2006	
539	CY523VV	Mercedes-Benz Integro O550	Mercedes-Benz		C40D	2006	
541	CY524VV	Mercedes-Benz Integro O550	Mercedes-Benz		C40D	2006	
542	CY525VV	Mercedes-Benz Integro O550	Mercedes-Benz		C40D	2006	
543	CY526VV	Mercedes-Benz Integro O550	Mercedes-Benz		C40D	2006	
544	CY527VV	Mercedes-Benz Integro O550	Mercedes-Benz		C40D	2006	
545	CY528VV	Mercedes-Benz Integro O550	Mercedes-Benz		C40D	2006	
546	CY529VV	Mercedes-Benz Integro O550	Mercedes-Benz		C40D	2006	
547	CY530VV	Mercedes-Benz Integro O550	Mercedes-Benz		C40D	2006	
548	DB816WD	Scania L124UB6 13.7m	Beulas Aura N		C42D	2006	
549	DA386XH	MAN - 9.9m	Beulas Cygnus		C39D	2006	
550	CW300WG	Scania L124UB6 13.7m	Beulas Aura N		C40D	2006	
557	CR405TD	Scania L124UB6 13.7m	Beulas Aura N		C63F	2005	
558	CR406TD	Scania L124UB6 13.7m	Beulas Aura N		C63F	2005	

568-573

Iveco 391E.12.29 — Orlandi EuroRider — NC53D — 2001

568	BM937SA	570	BM939SA	572	BM878SA	573	BM879SA
569	BM938SA	571	BS486RN				

574-600

Scania — De Simon Intercity IL3. — BC53D — 2001

574	BS017RN	581	BS098RN	588	BS062RN	595	BS291RN
575	BS003RN	582	BS001RN	589	BS061RN	596	BS290RN
576	BS018RN	583	BS126RN	590	BS139RN	597	BS176RN
577	BS019RN	584	BS138RN	591	BS161RN	598	BS288RN
578	BS063RN	585	BS002RN	592	BS162RN	599	BS310RN
579	BS099RN	586	BS137RN	593	BS163RN	600	BS265RN
580	BS097RN	587	BS125RN	594	BS175RN		

601	DW065HN	Irisbus Arway 12.8m	Irisbus	N53D	2009
602	BV841MF	De Simon Intercity IL3.	12m	BC53D	2001
603	DW066HN	Irisbus Arway 12.8m	Irisbus	N53D	2009
604	DW067HN	Irisbus Arway 12.8m	Irisbus	N53D	2009
605	BV842MF	De Simon Intercity IL3.	12m	BC53D	2001
606	DW068HN	Irisbus Arway 12.8m	Irisbus	N53D	2009
607	BV871MF	De Simon Intercity IL3.	12m	BC53D	2001
608	BW007WE	De Simon Intercity IL3.	12m	BC53D	2001
609	DW069HN	Irisbus Arway 12.8m	Irisbus	N53D	2009
610	DW070HN	Irisbus Arway 12.8m	Irisbus	N53D	2009
611	DW071HN	Irisbus Arway 12.8m	Irisbus	N53D	2009
612	DW072HN	Irisbus Arway 12.8m	Irisbus	N53D	2009
613	DW073HN	Irisbus Arway 12.8m	Irisbus	N53D	2009
614	CR404TD	Beulas Ministar N MAN	9.8m	C39F	2005
616	DW074HN	Irisbus Arway 12.8m	Irisbus	N53D	2009
620	CR407TD	Beulas Ministar N MAN	13.7m	C63F	2005

622-642

Mercedes-Benz Integro O550 U — Mercedes-Benz — BC53D — 2003

622	CD882SA	628	CD888SA	633	CD893SA	638	CJ747PJ
623	CH505AJ	629	CD889SA	634	CD894SA	639	CJ748PJ
624	CD884SA	630	CD890SA	635	CD895SA	640	CN331SF
625	CD885SA	631	CD891SA	636	CD896SA	641	CN332SF
626	CD886SA	632	CD892SA	637	CD897SA	642	CN333SF
627	CD887SA						

643	CJ495PJ	De Simon Intercity IN3.	10.67m	BC47D	2004
644	CJ496PJ	De Simon Intercity IN3.	10.67m	BC47D	2004

645-649

Mercedes-Benz Integro O550 U — Mercedes-Benz — BC53D — 2005

645	CR895TB	647	CR896TB	648	CR899TB	649	CR898TB
646	CR897TB						

650	CY531VV	De Simon Intercity IN3.	10.67m	BC67D	2005

655-658

MAN 11.220 8.88m — Beulas Midistar 1 — C35D — 2005

655	CR901TB	656	CR900TB	657	CR903TB	658	CR902TB

In addition to the buses in Italy, Arriva operates the cable car that links Albino at the lower end with Selvino up in the Lombardy hills. Seen at the upper station which connects with some bus services, is one of the two cars used. *Bill Potter*

668	CR906TB	MAN 11.220 7m	Noge	C22F	2005		
669	CR905TB	MAN 11.220 7m	Noge	C22F	2005		
673	CR904TB	MAN 11.220 10mm	Dalla Itziano	C47D	2005		
680-688		Neoplan Centroliner N4426/3	Neoplan	C86D	2006		
680	CY532VV	**682** CY533VV	**683** CY534VV			**688**	CY535VV
692	DK726LP	TVM Marbus B4	Marbus Viveo	C30D	2008		
693	DK728LP	TVM Marbus B4	Marbus Viveo	C30D	2008		
694-698		De Simon Millle Miglia	de Simon	BC47D	2008		
694	DK203GD	**696** DK205GD	**697** DK206GD			**698**	DK207GD
695	DK204GD						
699	DF612TL	MAN 11.220	Beaulas Midistar N	C39D	2008		
701	DD719HP	Mercedes-Benz Travego O580	Mercedes-Benz	C53D	2007		
702	DS614LV	Mercedes-Benz Travego O580	Mercedes-Benz	C53D	2009		
703	DS615LV	Mercedes-Benz Travego O580	Mercedes-Benz	C53D	2009		
704	DS616LV	Mercedes-Benz Travego O580	Mercedes-Benz	C53D	2009		
707	DD720HP	Mercedes-Benz Travego O580	Mercedes-Benz	C53D	2007		
711-718		MAN 11.22 8.82m	De Simon	N34D	1998		
711	AT195HT	**713** AT243JA	**715** AT245JA			**717**	AT247JA
712	AT196HT	**714** AT244JA	**716** AT246JA			**718**	AT248JA
719-726		Mercedes-Benz O404 10RH	Tiziano 9.22m	BC39D	2001-02		
719	BS354RP	**721** BS632RP	**723** BS634RP			**725**	BZ915FA
720	BS631RP	**722** BS633RP	**724** BS635RP			**726**	BZ916FA
727-730		De Simon Intercity IN3.	10.67m	B47D	2003		
727	CD795SA	**728** CD796SA	**729** CD797SA			**730**	CD798SA
734	DW093HN	Scania OmniExpress	Scania	NC47F	2009		
735	DW094HN	Scania OmniExpress	Scania	NC47F	2009		

Arriva's cable carseen almost mid way down from Selvino which is in the background. Both Arriva and the local SAB names are carried and Arriva tickets issued. *Bill Potter*

738-750

Irisbus Arway SFR160 — Irisbus — NC57D* — 2007

738	DF455TL	742	DF459TL	745	DF461TL	748	DF458TL
739	DF466TL	743	DF463TL	746	DF462TL	749	DF457TL
740	DF465TL	744	DF460TL	747	DD093HP	750	DF456TL
741	DF464TL						

751	DK450GD	Mercedes-Benz Travego O580	Mercedes-Benz	C53D	2008
752	DK451GD	Mercedes-Benz Travego O580	Mercedes-Benz	C53D	2008
753	DP021AY	Mercedes-Benz Sprinter 515	Mercedes-Benz	N16D	2008
754	DP557AY	Iveco Dailybus	Iveco	N19F	2008
755	DP344AY	Neoplan Skyliner N1122/3	Neoplan	C73D	2008

756-760

Scania OmniExpress — Scania — NC47D — 2008

756	DP540AY	758	DP542AY	759	DP543AY	760	DP544AY
757	DP541AY						

761	DP555AY	TVM Marbus B4	Marbus Viveo	C30D	2008

762-770

Irisbus Arway SFR160 — Irisbus — NC55D — 2008

762	DP492AY	764	DP494AY	766	DP496AY	769	DP498AY
763	DP493AY	765	DP495AY	768	DP497AY	770	DP499AY

767	BF288DX	Volvo B10B	12m	N53D	1999

771-775

MAN Lion's City A21 — MAN — N27D — 2008

771	DP545AY	773	DP547AY	774	DP548AY	775	DP549AY
772	DP546AY						

776-781

Bredamenarinibus Avancity L CNG 12m — N20 — 2005

776	CR907TB	778	CR909TB	780	CR910TB	781	CR912TB
777	CR908TB	779	CR911TB				

782	DP600AY	Irisbus Europolis 200E. 7.96m	Cacciamali	M9	2008
783	DP601AY	Irisbus Europolis 200E. 7.96m	Cacciamali	M9	2008
784	DF454TL	Irisbus Cityclass 491E.12.87	Irisbus	N22D	2007

785-799 Bredamenarinibus M240 LU3 11.96m   N22D* 2003-04 *seating varies

785	CN334SF	789	CF108HM	793	CH061AH		797	CH250AH
786	CN335SF	790	CF109HM	794	CH062AH		798	CH251AH
787	CN336SF	791	CF110HM	795	CH063AH		799	CH252AH
788	CF107HM	792	CH060AH	796	CH064AH			

No.	Reg	Type	Variant/Length	Seating	Year
800	CD435SA	De Simon 15 MT	14.80m	N65D	2002
801	DP602AY	Scania OmniCity CN94UB	Scania	N23D	2008
802	DP631AY	Scania OmniCity CN94UB	Scania	N23D	2008
803	DP603AY	Scania OmniCity CN94UB	Scania	N23D	2008
822	BH018XV	Irisbus CityClass 491E.12.22 CNG		N28D	2000
825	AT029HT	Autodromo MAN 232 CNG	Bassotto Metano	N25D	1997
833	BH019XV	Irisbus CityClass 491E.12.22 CNG		N28D	2000
835	AT718HV	Autodromo MAN 232 CNG	Bassotto Metano	N25D	1997
838	AT031HT	Autodromo MAN 232 CNG	Bassotto Metano	N25D	1997
839	AT719HV	Autodromo MAN 232 CNG	Bassotto Metano	N25D	1997
840	BH020XV	Irisbus CityClass 491E.12.22 CNG		N28D	2000
850	BV903MF	Irisbus CityClass 491E.12.22 CNG		N28D	2000
851	AT720HV	Autodromo MAN 232 CNG	Bassotto Metano	N25D	1997
854	BH022XV	Irisbus CityClass 491E.12.22 CNG		N28D	2000
855	BH023XV	Irisbus CityClass 491E.12.22 CNG		N28D	2000
856	BH024XV	Irisbus CityClass 491E.12.22 CNG		N28D	2000
857	AT721HV	Autodromo MAN 232 CNG	Bassotto Metano	N25D	1997
858	BH025XV	Irisbus CityClass 491E.12.22 CNG		N28D	2000
859	BH026XV	Irisbus CityClass 491E.12.22 CNG		N28D	2000
860	BH027XV	Irisbus CityClass 491E.12.22 CNG		N28D	2000
861	BH028XV	Irisbus CityClass 491E.12.22 CNG		N28D	2000
862	BH029XV	Irisbus CityClass 491E.12.22 CNG		N28D	2000
863	BH030XV	Irisbus CityClass 491E.12.22 CNG		N28D	2000
864	BH031XV	Irisbus CityClass 491E.12.22 CNG		N28D	2000
874	AT030HT	Autodromo MAN 232 CNG	Bassotto Metano	N25D	1997
875	AT032HT	Autodromo MAN 232 CNG	Bassotto Metano	N25D	1997
876	AT033HT	Autodromo MAN 232 CNG	Bassotto Metano	N25D	1997
877	AT034HT	Autodromo MAN 232 CNG	Bassotto Metano	N25D	1997
878	BM940SA	Irisbus CityClass 491E.12.22 Methanol		N28D	2001
879	BM941SA	Irisbus CityClass 491E.12.22 Methanol		N28D	2001
880	BM847SA	Irisbus CityClass 491E.12.22 Methanol		N28D	2001
881	BM848SA	Irisbus CityClass 491E.12.22 Methanol		N28D	2001
882	BM849SA	Irisbus CityClass 491E.12.22 Methanol		N28D	2001
883	BM880SA	Irisbus CityClass 491E.12.22 Methanol		N28D	2001
884	CD013SA	Mercedes-Benz Cito O520	9.59m	N17D	2002
885	CD014SA	Mercedes-Benz Cito O520	9.59m	N17D	2002
886	CD015SA	Mercedes-Benz Cito O520	9.59m	N17D	2002
887	BZ627FA	Mercedes-Benz Cito O520	8.09m	N11D	2002
888	BZ628FA	Mercedes-Benz Cito O520	8.09m	N11D	2002
889	CD799SA	Bredamenarinibus M240GNC Exobus	10.79m	N18D	2003
890	CD800SA	Bredamenarinibus M240GNC Exobus	10.79m	N18D	2003
891	CD801SA	Bredamenarinibus M240GNC Exobus	10.79m	N18D	2003
892	CD802SA	Bredamenarinibus M240GNC Exobus	10.79m	N18D	2003
893	CD803SA	Bredamenarinibus M240GNC Exobus	10.79m	N18D	2003
894	CH253AH	Bredamenarinibus M240GNC Exobus	10.79m	N18D	2003
895	CH254AH	Bredamenarinibus M240GNC Exobus	10.79m	N18D	2003
896	CH255AH	Bredamenarinibus M240GNC Exobus	10.79m	N18D	2003
897	CH256AH	Bredamenarinibus M240GNC Exobus	10.79m	N18D	2003
898	DF467TL	Mercedes-Benz Sprinter		N11D	2007
900	CF714HL	Iveco Daily 49.10.1/N-3,6 POLL		N9F	1992

TRIESTE TRASPORTI

Trieste Trasporti SpA, Via dei Lavoratori, 2 - 34144 Trieste

565	CP877FT	Irisbus Europolis TCC685	Cacciamali	City bus	2004
566	CP870FT	Irisbus Europolis TCC685	Cacciamali	City bus	2004
591	CB258YE	Irisbus Europolis 924	Cacciamali	City bus	2002
592	CB350YE	Irisbus Europolis 924	Cacciamali	City bus	2002
593	CB351YE	Irisbus Europolis 924	Cacciamali	City bus	2002

594-598   Irisbus Urbano 203E.9.26   Irisbus   City bus   2007

594	DF677SY	596	DF679SY	597	DF676SY	598	DF678SY
595	DF698SY						

601	BM667RA	Setra S315 HD	Setra	C--F	-
603	BM762RA	Mercedes-Benz O404	Mercedes-Benz	C--F	-
604	BM761RA	Irisbus Dalla via 370E	Paliadio	C--F	-
605	BV038ZE	Neoplan Staliner N516	Neoplan	C--F	-
606	BV678ZC	Irisbus Domino 2001 HDH	Irisbus	C--F	-
607	CB743YE	Irisbus Orlandi	Irisbus	C--F	-
615	BM666RA	Iveco 380.12.38	Iveco	C--F	-
616	BM668RA	Iveco 380.12.38	Iveco	C--F	-
641	BM868RA	Iveco CC80E18M/86	Cacciamali	School bus	2000
642	BV039ZB	Iveco CC80E18M/86	Cacciamali	School bus	2000
643	BV074ZB	Iveco CC80E18M/86	Cacciamali	School bus	2000
646	BV072ZB	Iveco CC80E18M/86	Cacciamali	School bus	2000
647	BM605RA	Iveco 100	Cacciamali	School bus	2000
648	CB849YE	Iveco 100	Cacciamali	School bus	2000

791-795   BredaMenarini M340   BredaMenarinbus   City bus   2004

791	CP804BT	793	CP803BT	794	CP802BT	795	CP801BT
792	CP794BT						

801-832   Irisbus CityClass 491.12.29   Irisbus   City bus   2001

801	BM827RA	809	BM594RA	817	BM522RA	825	BM598RA
802	BM399RA	810	BM595RA	818	BM681RA	826	BM599RA
803	BM398RA	811	BM518RA	819	BM597RA	827	BM601RA
804	BM397RA	812	BM455RA	820	BM519RA	828	BM520RA
805	BM396RA	813	BM596RA	821	BM453RA	829	BM678RA
806	BM521RA	814	BM454RA	822	BM456RA	830	BM602RA
807	BM680RA	815	BM395RA	823	BM517RA	831	BM603RA
808	BM457RA	816	BM452RA	824	BM677RA	832	BM604RA

901-914   Mercedes-Benz Citaro O530GN   Mercedes-Benz   AN50D   2008

901	DJ143MF	905	DJ099MF	909	DP813GW	912	DP815GW
902	DJ101MF	906	DJ145MF	910	DP814GW	913	DP824GW
903	DJ146MF	907	DJ148MF	911	DP841GW	914	DP825GW
904	DJ100MF	908	DJ144MF				

1001-1005   Autodrome ALE Zerai 7,7/3P E3   Autiromo   City bus   2001-03

1001	BV785ZB	1003	BV787ZB	1004	BV786ZB	1005	CB450YE
1002	BV788ZB						

1006-1009   Rampini ALE Zerai 7,7/3P E3   Rampini   City bus   2008

1006	DP842GW	1007	DP843GW	1008	DP844GW	1009	DP845GW

1011-1020   Breda Menarini M231/E3   BredaMenarinbus   City bus   2001

1011	BV501ZB	1014	BV562ZB	1017	BV561ZB	1019	BV656ZB
1012	BV502ZB	1015	BV503ZB	1018	BV637ZB	1020	BV655ZB
1013	BV635ZB	1016	BV636ZB				

1021	CP854BT	Breda Menarini M231/E3	BredaMenarinbus	City bus	2005

1031-1049
Breda Menarini M240/E3 NU — BredaMenarinbus — City bus — 2001

1031	BV504ZB	1036	BV507ZB	1041	BV567ZB	1046	BV559ZB
1032	BV505ZB	1037	BV508ZB	1042	BV512ZB	1047	BV560ZB
1033	BV506ZB	1038	BV509ZB	1043	BV513ZB	1048	BV570ZB
1034	BV565ZB	1039	BV510ZB	1044	BV568ZB	1049	BV571ZB
1035	BV566ZB	1040	BV511ZB	1045	BV569ZB		

1050-1080
Breda Menarini M240/E3 NU — Bredamenarinbus — City bus — 2002-03

1050	CB352YE	1058	CB410YE	1066	CB413YE	1074	CB127YE
1051	CB180YE	1059	CB411YE	1067	CB414YE	1075	CB152YE
1052	CB181YE	1060	CB259YE	1068	CB415YE	1076	CB128YE
1053	CB409YE	1061	CB260YE	1069	CB416YE	1077	CB129YE
1054	CB182YE	1062	CB261YE	1070	CB417YE	1078	CB151YE
1055	CB183YE	1063	CB262YE	1071	CB418YE	1079	CB150YE
1056	CB195YE	1064	CB263YE	1072	CB125YE	1080	CB149YE
1057	CB196YE	1065	CB412YE	1073	CB126YE		

1101-1110
Breda Menarini M240/E3 LU 3P — Bredamenarinbus — City bus — 2002

1101	CB264YE	1104	CB238YE	1107	DA977MK	1109	CB241YE
1102	CB197YE	1105	CB239YE	1108	CB198YE	1110	CB266YE
1103	CB237YE	1106	CB265YE				

1151-1170
Breda Menarini M240/E3 LU 18m — Bredamenarinbus — City bus — 2002-03

1151	CB419YE	1156	CB355YE	1161	CB358YE	1166	CB425YE
1152	CB420YE	1157	CB430YE	1162	CB422YE	1167	CB426YE
1153	CB267YE	1158	CB421YE	1163	CB423YE	1168	CB427YE
1154	CB353YE	1159	CB356YE	1164	CB424YE	1169	CB359YE
1155	CB354YE	1160	CB357YE	1165	CB429YE	1170	CB428YE

1201	CB835YE	Scania OmniCity CN94UB	Scania	City bus	2003
1202	DJ024MF	Irisbus Citelis C12B	Irisbus	City bus	2007
1203	DB870YH	Mercedes-Benz Cito O520	Mercedes-Benz	Citybus	2006
1204	DB998YH	Mercedes-Benz Cito O520	Mercedes-Benz	Citybus	2006
1205	DS995CZ	Irisbus Cityclass 491E.10.29	Irisbus	Citybus	2009

1211-1261
Irisbus Cityclass 491E.10.29 — Irisbus — Citybus — 2004-05

1211	CP716FT	1224	CP864FT	1237	CT628SW	1250	CT973SW
1212	CP713FT	1225	CP865FT	1238	CT625SW	1251	CT977SW
1213	CP708FT	1226	CP866FT	1239	CT626SW	1252	CT971SW
1214	CP705FT	1227	CP867FT	1240	CT630SW	1253	CT981SW
1215	CP715FT	1228	CP868FT	1241	CT624SW	1254	CT969SW
1216	CP714FT	1229	CP869FT	1242	CT623SW	1255	CT980SW
1217	CP712FT	1230	CP871FT	1243	CT972SW	1256	CT979SW
1218	CP706FT	1231	CP872FT	1244	CT622SW	1257	CT975SW
1219	CP717FT	1232	CP873FT	1245	CT620SW	1258	CT976SW
1220	CP707FT	1233	CP874FT	1246	CT621SW	1259	CT982SW
1221	CP710FT	1234	CP875FT	1247	CT983SW	1260	CT970SW
1222	CP711FT	1235	CP876FT	1248	CT974SW	1261	CT978SW
1223	CP709FT	1236	CT627SW	1249	CT629SW		

1262-1278
Irisbus Cityclass 491E.10.29 — Irisbus — Citybus — 2007

1262	DF695SY	1267	DF714SY	1271	DF718SY	1275	DF759SY
1263	DF697SY	1268	DF736SY	1272	DF748SY	1276	DF773SY
1264	DF717SY	1269	DF775SY	1273	DF738SY	1277	DF774SY
1265	DF715SY	1270	DF737SY	1274	DF751SY	1278	DF750SY
1266	DF716SY						

1301-1306
Mercedes-Benz Citaro O530 — Mercedes-Benz — Citybus — 2006-07

1301	DF640SY	1303	DF623SY	1305	DF610SY	1306	DF611SY
1302	DF608SY	1304	DF609SY				

1401-1425
Irisbus Cityclass 491E.10.29 — Irisbus — Citybus — 2007

1401	DF979SY	1408	DJ015MF	1414	DJ058MF	1420	DJ062MF
1402	DF981SY	1409	DJ018MF	1415	DJ021MF	1421	DJ064MF
1403	DF984SY	1410	DJ017MF	1416	DJ016MF	1422	DJ061MF
1404	DF983SY	1411	DJ069MF	1417	DJ065MF	1423	DJ054MF
1405	DF982SY	1412	DJ063MF	1418	DJ057MF	1424	DJ055MF
1406	DJ019MF	1413	DJ056MF	1419	DJ066MF	1425	DJ060MF
1407	DJ020MF						

Trieste lies to the east of the Gulf of Venice many kilometres from the other Italian operations, and adjacent to Slovenia. A major fleet renewal programme took place from 2004 with the introduction of the Irisbus CityClass. Illustrating the type is 1273, DF738SY, from the 2007 delivery. *Mark Lyons*

1426-1441

		Irisbus Citalis 12m		Irisbus		Citybus		2008-09
1426	DP921GW	1430	DP918GW	1434	DP890GW	1438	DP887GW	
1427	DP919GW	1431	DP920GW	1435	DP884GW	1439	DA487MJ	
1428	DP922GW	1432	DP886GW	1436	DA468MJ	1440	DP888GW	
1429	DP883GW	1433	DP889GW	1437	DA486MJ	1441	DP885GW	

1601-1607

		Breda Menarini 231/5		Breda Menarini		Citybus		2008
1601	DP896GW	1603	DP893GW	1605	DP891GW	1607	DP892GW	
1602	DP894GW	1604	DP897GW	1606	DP895GW			

SADEM - SADAV

SADEM SpA, Via della Repubblica 14, 10095 Grugliasco, Italy

SAPAV SpA, Corso Torino 396, 10064 Pinerolo, Italy

2005-2009

Iveco Cityclass 370E.12.35 — N37D 1999

2005	BA840NC	2007	BB831NA	2008	BB832NA	2009 BB833NA
2006	BA841NC					

2010	DS569SL	Irisbus Europolis 200E.8.13	Cacciamali	N16D	1999
2011	DS729SL	Irisbus Europolis 200E.8.13	Cacciamali	N16D	1999
2012	DY534DK	Iveco Europolis 200E.10.20	Cacciamali	N16D	1999
2013	DS556SL	Irisbus Europolis 200E.8.13	Cacciamali	N16D	1999
2014	DY533DK	Iveco Europolis 200E.10.20	Cacciamali	N16D	1999
2015	DY535DK	Iveco Europolis 200E.10.20	Cacciamali	N16D	1999
2016	BS281BZ	Breda Menarini M240LS		N35D	2001
2017	BS475BZ	Breda Menarini M240LS		N35D	2001
2018	BX855GH	Irisbus Europolis 200E.8.13		N17D	2001
2019	BY642KX	Iveco 65C15/70	Orlandi Happy	B24F	2002
2020	CK216HV	Breda Menarini M240LS		N37D	2003
2021	CK217HV	Breda Menarini M240LS		N37D	2003
2022	CK218HV	Breda Menarini M240LS		N37D	2003
2023	DY723DJ	Irisbus Crossway SFR161		N22F	2009

2901	CW113HA	Iveco Daily 50C15PRB		B22F	2005

3006-3023

Iveco Euroclass 380.12.35 — B51D 1995-96

3006	AH209VN	3012	AH484VN	3016	AK560DN	3021	AK021DP
3007	AH208VN	3013	AH885VZ	3017	AK017DP	3022	CM568JF
3009	AZ210NK	3014	AH884VZ	3019	AK019DP	3023	AK078DP
3010	AH485VN	3015	AK559DN	3020	AK020DP		

3024-3027

Iveco Orlandi Sicca 391E.12.29 — B53D 1998

3024	AT109DG	3025	AT110DG	3026	AT296DG	3027	AT585DG

3028	BS894BZ	Iveco Daily A45E.12 6.86m		B16F	1998

3029-3033

Iveco Domino 370E.12.35 — B53D 1998

3029	AW895LA	3031	AW894LA	3032	AW893LA	3033	AW897LA
3030	AW896LA						

3034	AW599LD	Iveco 370E.12.27	Orlandi Poker	B43D	1998

3037-3041

Iveco Eurorider 391E.12.29 — Orlandi Sicca B53F 1999

3037	BB375NB	3039	BB347MY	3040	BB348MY	3041	BB349MY
3038	BB376NB						

3042	BE206GS	Iveco 370E.12.27	Orlandi Poker	B43D	1999
3043	BE209GS	Iveco 370E.12.27	Orlandi Poker	B43D	1999
3044	BE207GS	Iveco 370E.12.27	Orlandi Poker	B43D	1999

3045-3053

Iveco Euroclass 380.12.35 — B55D 1999

3045	BE210GS	3048	BE821GS	3050	BE524GT	3052	BE521GT
3046	BE820GS	3049	BE522GT	3051	BE523GT	3053	BE520GT

3054-3058

Iveco 370E.9.27 — Orlandi Poker B43D 1999

3054	BG356KB	3056	BG358KB	3057	BG359KB	3058	BG361KB
3055	BG357KB						

3059	BG727KB	Iveco Daily A45E.12		B19F	1999

3060-3064

Iveco 370E.9.27 — Orlandi Poker B43D 1999

3060	BG478KC	3062	BG480KC	3063	BG481KC	3064	BG482KC
3061	BG479KC						

3065-3070 — Irisbus Myway 393E.12.35 — BC51D — 2001

3065	BS075BJ	3067	BS077BJ	3069	BS079BJ	3070	BS080BJ
3066	BS076BJ	3068	BS078BJ				

3071	BS979BW	Iveco Daily 65.15	Orlandi Happy	B20F	2001

3072-3080 — Irisbus Myway 393E.12.35 — B51D — 2001-02

3072	BV767HW	3075	BX110GH	3077	BY056KY	3079	BY390KY
3073	BV768HW	3076	BX756GH	3078	BY057KY	3080	BY392KY
3074	BV769HW						

3081	CD357AA	Mercedes-Benz Vario 0815	Sitcar Beluga	C24D	2002

3082-3088 — Irisbus Myway 399.12.35 — N51D — 2003

3082	CF155EN	3084	CF157EN	3086	CF159EN	3088	CF161EN
3083	CF156EN	3085	CF158EN	3087	CF160EN		

3089	CF517EP	Mercedes-Benz Vario 0815	Sitcar Beluga	C24D	2003
3090	CG735EF	Irisbus Myway 399.12.35		N51D	2003
3091	CJ175DG	Mercedes-Benz Vario 0815	Sitcar Beluga	C28D	2003

3093-3098 — Irisbus Eurorider 397E.12.35 — Orlando Domino — C49D — 2003

3093	CK625HV	3095	CK951HV	3097	CK355HW	3098	CK354HW
3094	CK818HV	3096	CK083HW				

3099-3108 — Irisbus Euroclass 389.12.35 — Orlandi — B50D — 2003-04

3099	CK478HX	3102	CK832HX	3105	CM704JD	3107	CM051JE
3100	CK479HX	3103	CK833HX	3106	CM705JD	3108	CM052JE
3101	CK587HX	3104	CK834HX				

3109	CN181JE	Irisbus Euroclass 389.10.35	Orlandi	B42D	2004
3110	CN182JE	Irisbus Euroclass 389.10.35	Orlandi	B42D	2004

3111-3116 — Irisbus Myway 399.12.35 — N51D — 2004

3111	CN755CA	3113	CN438CB	3115	CN529CB	3116	CR205NB
3112	CN437CB	3114	CN528CB				

3117	CR634NB	Mercedes-Benz Vario 0815	Sitcar Beluga	C28D	2005

3118-3125 — Irisbus Euroclass 389.12.35 — Orlandi — B50D — 2005

3118	CV568KL	3120	CV570KL	3122	CV751KL	3124	CV753KL
3119	CV569KL	3121	CV750KL	3123	CV752KL	3125	CV754KL

3126-3130 — Irisbus Eurorider 397E.12.35 — Orlandi Domino — C49D — 2005-06

3126	CW652HB	3128	CW654HB	3129	CW107HC	3130	CZ265AL
3127	CW653HB						

3131-3136 — Irisbus Euroclass 389.12.35 — Orlandi — N50D — 2006

3131	CZ515AL	3133	CZ517AL	3135	CZ519AL	3136	CZ520AL
3132	CZ516AL	3134	CZ518AL				

3137	CZ702AL	Cacciamali Grifone TCI 8.40		NC33D	2006
3138	CZ703AL	Cacciamali Grifone TCI 8.40		NC33D	2006
3139	CZ836AL	Irisbus Myway 399 EL75		N47D	2006
3140	DD632GY	Irisbus Eurorider 397E.12.35	Orlando Domino HD	C49D	2006
3141	DD819GY	Irisbus Eurorider 397E.12.35	Orlando Domino HD	C49D	2006
3142	DD938GY	Irisbus Eurorider 397E.12.35	Orlando Domino HD	C49D	2006
3143	DM566PF	Iveco 370E.9.27	Orlando Sicca-Poker	B43D	1999
3144	DM565PF	Iveco 370E.9.27	Orlando Sicca-Poker	B43D	1999
3145	DM061PG	Iveco 370E.9.27	Orlando Sicca-Poker	B43D	1999

3146-3152 — Irisbus Crossway GX127 — Irisbus — N49F — 2009

3146	P	DY724DJ	3148	P	DY557DJ	3150	P	DY583DJ	3152 D DY763DJ
3147	P	DY556DJ	3149	P	DY582DJ	3151	D	DY762DJ	

3153	D	u/r	Mercedes-Benz Integro O550	Mercedes-Benz	C53F	2004

4000-4003	Irisbus Euroclass 380.12.35				BC55D	2001	
4000	BS459PM	**4001**	BS460PM	**4002**	BS461PM	**4003**	BS462PM
4004-4012	Irisbus Euroclass 380.10.35				BC47D	2001	
4004	BS580PM	**4007**	BS670PM	**4009**	BS671PM	**4011**	BS673PM
4005	BS581PM	**4008**	BS582PM	**4010**	BS672PM	**4012**	BS674PM
4006	BS669PM						
4013-4019	Irisbus Euroclass 389E.12.35				BC55D	2003-05	
4013	CK537ST	**4015**	CK962SV	**4017**	CS262PP	**4019**	CS264PP
4014	CK594ST	**4016**	CK963SV	**4018**	CS263PP		
4020	DB849BL	Irisbus Arway SFR160	Irisbus	N55D	2007		
4021	DB850BL	Irisbus Arway SFR160	Irisbus	N53D	2007		
4022	DB851BL	Irisbus Arway SFR160	Irisbus	N50D	2007		
4023	DT654CP	Irisbus Crossway SFR160	Irisbus	N49D	2008		
4024	DT653CP	Irisbus Crossway SFR160	Irisbus	N49D	2008		
5001-5008	Irisbus Euroclass 380E.12.38HD	Irisbus		C50D	1996-2001		
5001	BC813JF	**5003**	BS629BT	**5005**	BS999BX	**5007**	CR221NA
5002	BK426DA	**5004**	BS998BX	**5006**	CG736EF	**5008**	CR222NA
5009	DM063PG	Irisbus Eurorider 397E.12.35	Orlandi Domino	C55D	2008		
5501-5510	Irisbus Euroclass 380E.12.43HD	Irisbus		C53D*	1996-2000 *seating varies		
5501	AK890DV	**5504**	AW307NS	**5507**	BL886WF	**5509**	BL758WH
5502	AK889DV	**5505**	BA558CM	**5508**	BL117WH	**5510**	BL757WH
5503	AW574NR	**5506**	BF947MA				
5511	BN898EA	Iveco Eurorider 315E.8.18	Orlandi Sicca-Poker	C20D	2000		
5512	BN895EA	Iveco Eurorider 370E.9.27	Orlandi Sicca-Poker	C41D	2000		
5513	BS050BL	Irisbus Euroclass HD 380.12.38		C55D	2001		
5514	DF307CW	Irisbus Euroclass HD 380.12.38		C55D	2001		
5515	BS442BV	Irisbus Euroclass HD 380.12.38		C55D	2001		
5516	BS441BV	Irisbus Euroclass HD 380.12.38		C55D	2001		
5517	BS895BZ	Mercedes-Benz Vario 0815	Sitcar Beluga	C21F	2001		
5518	CG737EF	Irisbus Euroclass 389E.12.43HD		C53D	2003		
5519	CH347KN	Irisbus Euroclass 389E.12.43HD		C53D	2003		
5520	CV424KR	Irisbus Eurorider 397E.12.43	Orlandi Domino	C55D	2005		
5521	CV425KR	Irisbus Eurorider 397E.12.43	Orlandi Domino	C55D	2005		
5522	DM062PG	Irisbus Eurorider 397E.12.40	Orlandi Domino	C55D	2008		
5523	DW415HM	Iveco Eurorider 315E.12.38		C49D	2002		
5524	DW498HM	Iveco Daily 65.15	Orlandi Happy	C20D	2003		

Note: SADEM was established in 1941, as Società Autotrasporti della Dalmazia e Montenegro.

TRANSCENTRUM BUS

Transcentrum Bus sro, Kancelár, Mladáá Boleslav, Boleslavská 98, Czech Republic

MBA1841	Karosa C734.20	B45D	1986
MBA1842	Karosa C734.20	B45D	1986
MBO9488	Karosa C734.20	B45D	1987
MBA4784	Karosa C734.20	B45D	1988
3S89750	Karosa LC735.40	B45D	1989
3S93729	Karosa C734.1340	B45D	1990
MBA0263	Karosa LC735.1011	B45D	1990
MBA0283	Karosa LC735.1011	B45D	1990
MB8814	Karosa C 734.40	B45D	1990
MB8943	Karosa LC 735.1011	B45D	1990
MB9176	Karosa C 734.1340	B45D	1990
MB9424	Karosa LC736.1014	B46D	1991
MB9478	Karosa C734.1340	B45D	1991
MB9578	Karosa C734.1340	B45D	1991
MB9579	Karosa C734.1340	B45D	1991

MB9870	Karosa C734.1340		B45D	1992
MBA0241	Karosa C734.1340		B45D	1993
MBA0243	Karosa C734.1340		B45D	1993
MBA0847	Karosa C734.1340		B45D	1993
MBA0849	Karosa C734.1340		B45D	1993
MBA0851	Karosa C734.1340		B46D	1994
MBA1045	Karosa LC735.1011		B45D	1994
MBA2308	Karosa C734.1345		B46D	1994
MBA3329	SOR Libchavy	SOR C 7.5	BC26F	1997
MBM9496	Bova Futura FHD 12-340		C50F	1997
MBA3412	Karosa C934.1351		B46D	1997
MBA3413	Karosa C934.1351		B46D	1997
MBM8601	Karosa C934.1351		B46D	1998
MBM8726	Karosa C934.1351		B46D	1999
MBM8727	Karosa C934.1351		B46D	1999
MBM8937	Karosa C934.1351		B46D	1999
7S15851	Karosa C934.1351		B46D	1999
MBM8674	Renault Master L3H2		M16	1999
MBO0442	Bova Futura FHD 12-370		C49F	1999
MBM9119	Bova Futura FHD 12-370		C51F	1999
MBN2772	Bova Magiq HD 120.340		C51F	2000
MBM8985	Mercedes-Benz Vario O814		C24F	2000
MBM9384	Karosa C934.1351		B46D	2000
MBM9385	Karosa C934.1351		B46D	2000
MBN2791	Karosa C934.1351		B46D	2000
MBN2825	Karosa C934.1351		B46D	2000
MBN2963	Karosa C934.1351		B46D	2001
MBN2964	Karosa C934.1351		B46D	2001
MBN3012	Karosa C934.1351		B46D	2001
MBN3029	Karosa C934.1351		B46D	2001
MBO0418	Karosa C955		B52D	2001
7S82318	Dennis Dart SLF	Alexander ALX200	N38D	2001
8S49491	Dennis Dart SLF	Alexander ALX200	N38D	2001
8S49496	Dennis Dart SLF	Alexander ALX200	N38D	2001
8S70547	Dennis Dart SLF	Alexander ALX200	N38D	2001
8S70548	Dennis Dart SLF	Alexander ALX200	N38D	2001
8S70549	Dennis Dart SLF	Alexander ALX200	N38D	2001
8S70551	Dennis Dart SLF	Alexander ALX200	N38D	2001
MBO9460	Karosa C954.1360		B50D	2002
MBO9498	Karosa C954.1360		B50D	2002
1S55743	Karosa C954.1360		B50D	2002
1S56089	Karosa C954.1360		B50D	2002
3S89745	Karosa C954.1360		B50D	2002
3S89748	Karosa C954.1360		B50D	2002
3S89749	Karosa C955.1073		B52D	2002
3S89671	Karosa C954.1360		B54D	2002
3S88827	Karosa C954.1360		B51D	2003
3S89104	SOR Libchavy C10.5		BC47F	2003
3S89105	SOR Libchavy C10.5		BC47F	2003
3S89107	Karosa C954.1360		BD50D	2003
3S89742	SOR Libchavy C10.5		BC45D	2003
3S89743	SOR Libchavy C10.5		BC47D	2003
3S89746	SOR Libchavy C10.5		BC47D	2003
5S36488	SOR Libchavy C10.5		BC47D	2003
5S83464	SOR Libchavy C10.5		BC47D	2003
3S32024	Karosa C956.1074		BC51D	2003
3S21769	Karosa C956.1074		BC51D	2004
3S21779	Karosa C956.1074		BC51D	2004
3S22156	Karosa C954.1360		BC51D	2004
3S22157	Karosa C954.1360		BC51D	2004
3S44223	Karosa C956.1074		BC51D	2004
3S45386	CitroÁn Jumper 2.2		M8	2004
4S90029	CitroÁn Jumper 2.2		M8	2005
4S53670	Irisbus Daily S2000		C20F	2004
4S54621	Karosa C954.1360		BC50D	2005
4S90174	Karosa C954.1360		BC50D	2005
4S90175	Karosa C954.1360		BC50D	2005
5S04694	Karosa C954.1360		BC50D	2005
5S04695	Karosa C954.1360		BC50D	2005
4S54717	VDL Bova Futura FHD 12-380	VDL Bova	C51F	2005
5S19553	Bova Magiq XHD 120.D380		C51F	2006
5S36244	Karosa C954.1360		BC50D	2006
5S36245	Karosa C954.1360		BC50D	2006

5S83083	Karosa C954.1360		BC50D	2006
7S15899	Bova Magiq XHD 139.D430		C59F	2007
7S51162	Renault Master NDD		M16	2007
7S51163	Renault Master NDD		M16	2007
7S52301	Irisbus Crossway 491.12.29	Irisbus	N50D	2007
9S90920	Irisbus Crossway 491.12.29	Irisbus	N50D	2007
7S52303	Irisbus Crossway 491.12.29	Irisbus	N50D	2007
7S52917	Irisbus Crossway 491.12.29	Irisbus	N50D	2007
7S52918	Irisbus Crossway 491.12.29	Irisbus	N50D	2007
8S71071	Irisbus Crossway 491.12.29	Irisbus	N50D	2008
8S71072	Irisbus Crossway 491.12.29	Irisbus	N50D	2008
8S71073	Irisbus Crossway 491.12.29	Irisbus	N50D	2008
8S71949	Irisbus Crossway 491.12.29	Irisbus	N50D	2008
8S71950	Irisbus Crossway 491.12.29	Irisbus	N50D	2008
8S49608	Irisbus Evadys	Irisbus	C50D	2008
8S71403	Irisbus Evadys	Irisbus	C50D	2008
9S57825	Irisbus Crossway 10.5m	Irisbus	N43D	2009
9S57826	Irisbus Crossway 10.5m	Irisbus	N43D	2009
9S57827	Irisbus Crossway 10.5m	Irisbus	N43D	2009
9S91884	Irisbus Crossway 10.5m	Irisbus	N43D	2009

Depots: Boleslavská 98/6, 293 06 Kosmonosy

BOSÁK BUS

Bosák BUS spol sro, Pøíbramská 964, 263 01 Dobøíš, Èeská republika (Czech Republic)

2S70457	Karosa C734.20		B45D	1986
2S70470	Karosa C734.20		B45D	1986
3S08689	Karosa C734.20		B45D	1986
PBA5255	Karosa C734.20		B45D	1986
PB9119	Karosa C734.20		B45D	1986
7S06519	Karosa C734.20		B45D	1987
PB9694	Karosa C734.20		B45D	1987
PB9699	Karosa C734.20		B45D	1987
PBA5257	Karosa C734.20		B45D	1987
PBA5778	Karosa C734.20		B45D	1988
2S70463	Karosa C734.20		B45D	1988
2S70464	Karosa C734.20		B45D	1988
3S08719	Karosa C734.20		B45D	1989
3S08691	Karosa C734.20		B45D	1989
3S08692	Karosa C734.20		B45D	1989
2S70477	Karosa C734.40		B45D	1989
3S08649	Karosa C734.40		B45D	1990
PBA0669	Karosa C734.40		B45D	1990
PBA2209	Karosa C734.40		B45D	1993
3S08700	Karosa B732.1652		B31D	1994
3S08701	Karosa B732.1652		B31D	1994
9S22219	Mercedes-Benz O408	Mercedes-Benz	BC50D	1995
PBA7072	Volvo B10-400		BC56D	1998
PBL4282	Bova Futura FHD 12		C51FT	1999
PBL4283	Bova Futura FHD 12		C51FT	1999
3S08309	Karosa C936.1038		BC46F	2000
PBL4385	Karosa C934.1351		BC49D	2000
PBA6769	Karosa C934.1351		BC45D	2000
PBL1938	Bova Futura FHD 12		C51FT	2000
PBL1939	Bova Futura FHD 12		C51FT	2001
PBA7125	Karosa C935.1039		BC46F	2001
PBA7141	Karosa C935.1039		BC46F	2001
PBA7156	Karosa C935.1039		BC46F	2001
PBK3857	Karosa C955.1073		BC51F	2001
PBL1816	Karosa C955.1073		BC50F	2001
3S08279	Karosa C955.1073		BC49F	2004
3S80139	Karosa C955.1073		BC49F	2005
4S04299	Karosa C955.1073		BC49F	2005

4S04749	Karosa C954.1360		BC49D	2005
4S04759	Karosa C954.1360		BC49D	2005
5S00429	Karosa C954.1360		BC49D	2006
5S00829	Karosa C954.1360		BC50D	2006
5S30469	Karosa C954.1360		BC49D	2006
6S22019	Irisbus Arway SFR160	Irsibus	N49D	2007
8S07039	Irisbus Arway SFR160	Irisbus	N49D	2008
8S07049	Irisbus Arway SFR160	Irisbus	N49D	2008
8S07099	Irisbus Arway SFR160	Irisbus	N49D	2008
8S62129	Irisbus Arway SFR160	Irisbus	N49D	2008
9S22179	Irisbus Arway SFR160	Irisbus	N49D	2009
9S77499	Irisbus Arway SFR160	Irisbus	N49D	2009
9S77509	Irisbus Arway SFR160	Irisbus	N49D	2009

OSNADA

Osnado spol sro, Nádražní 501, 542 24 Svoboda nad Úpou, Czech Republic

TUA2189	Karosa C934.1351		BC49D	1998
3H08907	Karosa B732.20		B31D	1988
TU9865	Karosa LC734.40		B45D	1988
TU8290	Karosa LC734.40		B45D	1988
TU8645	Karosa LC734.40		B45D	1989
TU8646	Karosa LC734.40		B45D	1989
TU8714	Karosa LC735.40		BC49D	1989
TU8689	Karosa LC735.40		BC49D	1989
TU9046	Karosa LC734.40		B45D	1990
TU9060	Karosa LC734.40		B45D	1990
TU9064	Karosa LC734.40		B45D	1990
TU9097	Karosa LC734.40		B45D	1990
1H42071	Karosa LC734.40		B45D	1990
1H42073	Karosa LC734.40		B45D	1990
1H42074	Karosa LC734.40		B45D	1990
2H40464	Karosa LC734.40		B45D	1990
4H46072	Karosa C734.1340		B45D	1990
4H46074	Karosa C734.1340		B45D	1990
4H35045	Karosa LC734.1340		B45D	1990
4H35943	Karosa LC734.1341		B45D	1990
TU9813	Karosa LC735.1011		BC49D	1991
TU9676	Karosa LC735.1011		B45D	1991
4H46073	Karosa LC734.1340		B45D	1992
4H46253	Karosa LC734.1340		B45D	1992
4H46254	Karosa LC734.1340		B45D	1992
TUA2010	Karosa C734.1340		B45D	1992
1H33213	Karosa C734.1340		B45D	1994
TUA1292	Karosa C734.1340		B45D	1995
TUA1411	Karosa C734.1340		B45D	1996
JC8572	Karosa C934.1351		BC49D	1997
TUA2188	Karosa C934.1351		BC49D	1998
TUA2190	Karosa C934.1351		BC49D	1998
TUA2186	SOR C 9.5		NC35D	1998
TUA2187	SOR C 9.5		NC35D	1998
JCH5655	Reanult SFR112	Reanult Iliade RTX	C53F	1999
JCH5637	Karosa LC936.1038		BC49D	1999
JCH5639	Karosa C934.1351		BC49D	1999
JCH5640	Karosa C934.1351		BC49D	1999
JCH5680	Karosa C934.1351		BC49D	1999
JCH5720	Karosa C934.1351		BC49D	1999
JCH5991	Karosa C934.1351		BC49D	2000
JCH5992	Karosa C934.1351		BC49D	2000
JCH5993	Karosa C934.1351		BC49D	2000
3H16290	Karosa C935.1039		BC49D	2000
JCH5971	Karosa B932.1694		B31D	2000
JCH5972	Karosa B941.1964		AB41D	2000
JCI0654	Karosa C935.1039		BC49D	2001
JCI7615	Karosa C955.1073		BC49D	2001
JCH5679	Karosa C934.1351		BC49D	2001

JCI7544	Karosa C954.1360		BC49D	2001
1H49158	Karosa C954.1360		BC49D	2002
1H49159	Karosa C954.1360		BC49D	2002
1H56055	Karosa C955.1073		BC49D	2002
JCI9250	Karosa LC956.1072		BC49D	2002
JCI1265	Karosa B952.1712		B31D	2002
1H65791	SOR Libchavy C10.5		BC47D	2003
1H65793	SOR Libchavy C10.5		BC47D	2003
1H65792	SOR C 10.5		BC35D	2003
2H25015	Karosa B941.1964		AB41D	2003
1H62800	Karosa C956.1072		BC49D	2003
1H63039	Karosa C956.1074		BC49D	2003
1H65170	Karosa C956.1074		BC49D	2003
2H25133	Karosa C956.1074		BC49D	2003
1H65150	Karosa C954.1360		B45D	2003
1H69442	Karosa C954.1360		B45D	2004
1H69443	Karosa C954.1360		B45D	2004
2H16705	Karosa C954.1360		B45D	2004
2H16706	Karosa C954.1360		B45D	2004
1H69440	Karosa C954.1360		BC49D	2004
1H69441	Karosa C954.1360		BC49D	2004
1H96005	Karosa C956.1074		BC49D	2004
2H16708	Karosa C956.1074		BC49D	2004
2H16977	Karosa C956.1074		BC49D	2004
3H16439	Karosa C956.1074		BC49D	2004
3H71440	Karosa C956.1074		BC49D	2004
2H16979	Karosa B952.1716		B31D	2004
1H96008	Mercedes-Benz Sprinter		M9	2004
2H97010	SOR CNG 12		NC41D	2005
2H97020	SOR CNG 12		NC41D	2005
2H78280	Karosa B941.1964		AB41D	2005
2H78323	Karosa C954.1360		BC49D	2005
2H97065	Karosa C954.1360		B45D	2006
2H97066	Karosa C954.1360		B45D	2006
2H97067	Karosa C954.1360		B45D	2006
3H21310	Karosa C954.1360		BC49D	2006
3H21590	Irisbus PU09D2	Irisbus	N34D	2006
3H21570	SOR CNG 12		NC41D	2006
3H21580	SOR CNG 12		NC41D	2006
3H46390	SOR CNG 12		NC41D	2007
3H45580	SOR CNG 12		NC41D	2007
3H46380	SOR CNG 12		NC41D	2007
3H46099	Irisbus Citelis C12B	Irisbus	N34D	2007
3H45890	Irisbus Crossway 10.6m	Irisbus	N43D	2007
4H18157	Irisbus Crossway 10.6m	Irisbus	N43D	2008
3H71480	Irisbus Evadys	Irisbus	C50D	2008
3H71980	Irisbus Evadys	Irisbus	C50D	2008
4H35452	Tedom C12 G	Tedom	N27D	2008
4H18159	SOR CN 10.5		NC35D	2008
4H18158	SOR CN 10.5		NC35D	2008

SAD MICHALOVCE

Slovenská autobusová doprava Michalovce as, Lastomírska, 07180 Michalovce, Slovakia

60018	MI864BG	Karosa C734		B45D	1986
60031	MI756AU	Karosa C734		B45D	1987
60032	MI725AU	Karosa C734		B45D	1987
60040	MI644AS	Karosa B732		B45D	1987
60044	TV143AO	Karosa C734		B45D	1988
60052	MI762CA	Irisbus Crossway GX127	Irisbus	N50D	2008
60053	MI753AR	Karosa LC735		B45D	1988
60057	MI755AU	Karosa C734		B45D	1988
60059	MI623AS	Karosa C734		B45D	1988
60061	MI739AR	Karosa B732		B31D	1988
60073	TV598AH	Karosa C734		B45D	1989
60074	MI622AS	Karosa C734		B45D	1989
60076	MI052AY	Karosa C734		B45D	1989
60081	TV106AO	Karosa B732		B31D	1989
60082	MI739AU	Karosa LC736		B45D	1989
60086	MI736AE	Karosa B732		B31D	1989
60089	MI768AR	Karosa C734		B45D	1989
60091	TV842AC	Karosa C734		B45D	1989
60096	TV105AO	Karosa B731		B31D	1989
60099	MI769AR	Karosa C734		B45D	1989
60103	TV051AO	Karosa C734		B45D	1989
60106	TV101AO	Karosa C734		B45D	1990
60108	MI740AU	Karosa C734		B45D	1990
60109	MI737BG	Karosa C734		B45D	1990
60117	MI748AR	Karosa C734		B45D	1990
60118	MI753AU	Karosa LC735		B45D	1990
60120	MI741AU	Karosa B732		B31D	1990
60126	TV115AO	Karosa C734		B45D	1990
60129	MI750AR	Karosa C734		B45D	1990
60132	MI742AU	Karosa C734		B45D	1990
60134	MI628AS	Karosa C734		B45D	1990
60139	TV076AO	Karosa C734		B45D	1990
60141	TV062AO	Karosa C734		B45D	1990
60144	TV058AO	Karosa C734		B45D	1991
60146	MI811BG	Karosa C734		B45D	1991
60149	TV149AO	Karosa LC736		B45D	1991
60151	TV150AO	Karosa LC736		B45D	1991
60152	MI721AU	Karosa LC736		B46D	1991
60156	MI748AU	Karosa C734		B45D	1991
60159	TV055AO	Karosa B732		B31D	1991
60160	TV053AO	Karosa C734		B45D	1992
60162	MI645AS	Karosa C734		B45D	1992
60163	MI721AR	Karosa C734		B45D	1992
60165	MI632AS	Karosa C734		B45D	1993
60167	TV173BP	Karosa LC736		B45D	1990
60170	MI633AS	Karosa C734		B45D	1992
60171	MI021AY	Karosa C734		B45D	1992
60176	TV081AO	Karosa B731		B31D	1988
60179	MI830BZ	Karosa LC736		B46D	1995
60183	TV145AO	Karosa LC736		B45D	1995
60189	MI729AR	Karosa LC736		B46D	1995
60198	MI747BG	Karosa HD957		B46D	1997
60199	TV667AD	Karosa C734		B45D	1987
60200	MI264AF	Karosa LC936		B49D	1998
60206	TV868AC	Karosa LC936		B45D	1990
60215	MI469AP	Karosa C734		B46D	2000
60221	MI651AS	SOR C 7.5		BC27D	2001
60222	MI234AT	SOR C 7.5		BC27D	2001
60223	MI441AT	Karosa C934		B46D	2001
60224	MI442AT	Karosa C934		B46D	2001
60226	MI821AT	Karosa C954		B50D	2001
60227	MI019AU	Karosa LC956		B51D	2001
60228	TV654AP	SOR C 9.5		BC35D	2001
60231	MI286AU	SOR C 9.5		BC35D	2001

60232	TV820AP	SOR C 9.5		BC35D	2001
60234	MI564AU	SOR C 9.5		BC35D	2001
60237	MI463AX	SlovBus	SlovBus	B46D	2002
60240	TV148AT	SOR C 9.5		BC35D	2002
60241	TV149AT	SOR C 9.5		BC35D	2002
60242	MI591BS	Karosa C954		B50D	2002
60243	TV008AU	SOR C 9.5		BC35D	2003
60244	MI852BG	SOR C 9.5		BC35D	2003
60245	TV391AU	SOR C 9.5		BC35D	2003
60246	MI724BK	SOR C 9.5		BC35D	2003
60247	MI598BB	SOR C 10.5		B47D	2003
60248	MI935BB	SOR C 10.5		B47D	2004
60249	MI936BB	SOR C 10.5		B47D	2004
60250	TV817AV	SOR C 10.5		B47D	2004
60251	TV924AV	SOR C 10.5		B47D	2004
60252	TV925AV	SOR C 10.5		B47D	2004
60253	TV816AV	SOR C 10.5		B47D	2004
60254	MI043BC	SOR C 10.5		B47D	2004
60255	MI044BC	SOR C 10.5		B47D	2004
60256	MI085AY	Karosa B732		B31D	1984
60257	MI537BG	SOR C 10.5		BC47D	2004
60259	MI929BC	Karosa C954		B50D	2004
60260	MI149CD	Irisbus Crossway GX127	Irisbus	N50D	2004
60261	MI924BC	Karosa C954		B50D	2004
60262	MI925BC	Karosa C954		B50D	2004
60263	MI926BC	Karosa C954		B50D	2004
60264	MI927BC	Karosa C954		B50D	2004
60265	MI928BC	Karosa LC956		B49D	2004
60266	MI106BD	SOR C 10.5		B47D	2004
60267	MI647AS	Karosa B734		BC45D	1992
60268	MI408BV	SOR C 10.5		B47D	2004
60269	MI228BG	SOR C 10.5		B47D	2004
60270	MI826BH	SOR C 10.5		B47D	2004
60271	MI789BI	Scania K114IB4	Irizar Century 12.35	C45D	2004
60272	TV110AO	Karosa C734		B45D	1988
60274	MI737AE	Karosa C734		B45D	1992
60275	TV072AO	Karosa C734		B45D	1990
60276	TV138AO	Karosa C734		B45D	1991
60277	TV594AH	Karosa B731		B31D	1986
60278	MI640AS	Karosa C734		B45D	1991
60279	MI033BG	Karosa C734		B45D	1990
60280	MI726AU	Karosa B732		B31D	1987
60281	TV343AA	Karosa LC735		B45D	1988
60283	TV071AO	Karosa C734		B45D	1989
60284	MI724AU	Karosa C734		B45D	1987
60285	MI754AR	Karosa C734		B45D	1996
60286	MI761AU	Karosa LC735		B45D	1990
60287	MI042AY	Karosa C734		B45D	1989
60288	MI438BM	Scania K114IB4	Irizar Century 12.35	C50D	2004
60289	MI439BM	Scania K114IB4	Irizar Century 12.35	C50D	2004
60290	MI722AU	Karosa B732		B31D	1984
60291	MI559CJ	Karosa HD957		B46D	1999
60292	TV086AO	Karosa C734		B45D	1989
60293	TV070AO	Karosa C734		B45D	1989
60294	MI760AR	Karosa C734		B45D	1987
60295	TV136AO	Karosa B732		B31D	1989
60296	MI629AS	Karosa C734		B45D	1990
60298	MI625AS	Karosa C734		B45D	1988
60299	TV142AO	Karosa C734		B45D	1988
60300	MI778BG	Karosa C734		B45D	1996
60301	MI779BG	Karosa C734		B45D	1999
60302	MI776BG	Karosa C734		B45D	1990
60303	MI775BG	Karosa C734		B45D	1990
60304	MI777BG	Karosa C734		B45D	1987
60305	TV057AO	Karosa C734		B45D	1987
60306	TV128AO	Karosa B732		B31D	1988
60307	MI786BG	Karosa C734		B45D	1993
60308	MI787BG	Karosa C734		B45D	1990
60309	MI785BG	Karosa C734		B45D	1993
60310	MI766AR	Karosa C734		B45D	1986
60311	MI735AE	Karosa B732		B31D	1990
60312	TV077AO	Karosa C734		B45D	1987
60313	TV593AH	Karosa C734		B45D	1988

60314	MI626AS	Karosa C734		B45D	1988
60315	MI733AR	Karosa C734		B45D	1989
60315*	TV092AO	Karosa C734		B45D	1984
60316	TV096AO	Karosa C734		B45D	1989
60317	MI624AS	Karosa C734		B45D	1988
60318	MI751AU	Karosa C734		B45D	1992
60319	MI055AY	Karosa B732		B31D	1990
60320	TV085AO	Karosa C734		B45D	1990
60321	MI722AR	Karosa C734		B46D	1996
60322	MI834BG	Karosa LC736		B46D	1990
60323	MI835BG	Karosa LC736		B46D	1996
60324	MI843BG	Karosa C734		B45D	1995
60325	TV314BD	Karosa LC736		B45D	1991
60326	TV796BA	Karosa LC735		B45D	1991
60327	TV317BD	Karosa LC736		B45D	1996
60332	MI857BG	Karosa C734		B45D	1995
60333	TV142BM	Karosa C734		B45D	1995
60334	TV631BM	Karosa C734		B45D	1995
60335	MI922BG	Karosa C734		B45D	1992
60336	MI412BX	SOR C 9.5		BC35D	2002
60337	MI411BX	SOR C 9.5		BC35D	1998
60338	MI410BX	SOR C 9.5		BC35D	2001
60339	MI409BX	SOR C 9.5		BC35D	2001
60340	MI408BX	SOR LC 10.5		BC47D	2001
60341	MI433CC	Karosa C934		B46D	2000
60342	MI365BX	Irisbus Crossway GX	Irisbus	N50D	2007
60343	MI366BX	Irisbus Crossway GX	Irisbus	N50D	2007
60344	MI367BX	Irisbus Crossway GX	Irisbus	N50D	2007
60345	MI368BX	Irisbus Crossway GX	Irisbus	N50D	2007
60346	MI732BX	HungariaBus Starter		B45D	2008
60347	MI796BX	HungariaBus Starter		B45D	2008
60348	TV846BO	Karosa C934		B46D	1998
60349	TV847BO	Karosa C934		B46D	1996
60350	TV848BO	Karosa C934		B46D	1988

60351	MI155CA	Karosa LC736		B46D	1996
60354	TV665BP	Hungarocont Enterprise		N21F	2008
60356	MI763CA	Irisbus Crossway GX	Irisbus	N50D	2008
60357	MI764CA	Irisbus Crossway GX	Irisbus	N50D	2008
60358	MI765CA	Irisbus Crossway GX	Irisbus	N50D	2008
60359	MI766CA	Irisbus Crossway GX	Irisbus	N50D	2008
60360	MI768CA	Irisbus Crossway GX	Irisbus	N50D	2008
60361	MI769CA	Irisbus Crossway GX	Irisbus	N50D	2008
60362	MI773CA	Irisbus Crossway GX	Irisbus	N50D	2008
60363	MI774CA	Irisbus Crossway GX	Irisbus	N50D	2008
60364	MI775CA	Irisbus Crossway GX	Irisbus	N50D	2008
60365	MI776CA	Irisbus Crossway GX	Irisbus	N50D	2008
60366	MI779CA	Irisbus Crossway GX	Irisbus	N50D	2008
60367	MI780CA	Irisbus Crossway GX	Irisbus	N50D	2008
60368	MI781CA	Irisbus Crossway GX	Irisbus	N50D	2008
60369	MI783CJ	Irisbus Crossway GX	Irisbus	N50D	2008
60370	MI783CA	Irisbus Crossway GX	Irisbus	N50D	2008
60371	MI784CA	Irisbus Crossway GX	Irisbus	N50D	2008
60372	MI785CA	Irisbus Crossway GX	Irisbus	N50D	2008
60373	MI786CA	Irisbus Crossway GX	Irisbus	N50D	2008
60374	MI761CA	Irisbus Crossway GX	Irisbus	N50D	2008
60375	TV665BR	Karosa LC736		B45D	1996
60376	MI301CC	Irisbus Crossway GX	Irisbus	N50D	2008
60377	MI302CC	Irisbus Crossway GX	Irisbus	N50D	2008
60378	MI303CC	Irisbus Crossway GX	Irisbus	N50D	2008
60379	MI304CC	Irisbus Crossway GX	Irisbus	N50D	2008
60380	MI305CC	Irisbus Crossway GX	Irisbus	N50D	2008
60381	MI306CC	Irisbus Crossway GX	Irisbus	N50D	2008
60382	MI307CC	Irisbus Crossway GX	Irisbus	N50D	2008
60383	MI308CC	Irisbus Crossway GX	Irisbus	N50D	2008
60384	MI309CC	Irisbus Crossway GX	Irisbus	N50D	2008
60385	MI310CC	Irisbus Crossway GX	Irisbus	N50D	2008
60386	MI311CC	Irisbus Crossway GX	Irisbus	N50D	2008
60387	MI312CC	Irisbus Crossway GX	Irisbus	N50D	2008
60388	MI313CC	Irisbus Crossway GX	Irisbus	N50D	2008
60389	MI314CC	Irisbus Crossway GX	Irisbus	N50D	2008
60390	MI315CC	Irisbus Crossway GX	Irisbus	N50D	2008
60391	MI316CC	Irisbus Crossway GX	Irisbus	N50D	2008
60392	MI317CC	Irisbus Crossway GX	Irisbus	N50D	2008
60393	MI318CC	Irisbus Crossway GX	Irisbus	N50D	2008
60394	MI319CC	Irisbus Crossway GX	Irisbus	N50D	2008
60395	MI320CC	Irisbus Crossway GX	Irisbus	N50D	2008
60396	MI701CC	Irisbus Crossway GX	Irisbus	N50D	2008
60397	MI702CC	Irisbus Crossway GX	Irisbus	N50D	2008
60398	MI703CC	Irisbus Crossway GX	Irisbus	N50D	2008
60399	MI704CC	Irisbus Crossway GX	Irisbus	N50D	2008
60400	MI705CC	Irisbus Crossway GX	Irisbus	N50D	2008
60401	MI706CC	Irisbus Crossway GX	Irisbus	N50D	2008
60402	MI708CC	Irisbus Crossway GX	Irisbus	N50D	2008
60403	MI709CC	Liaz Granus		BC43D	1998
60405	MI013CI	Iveco Daily	Rošero	N27D	2009
60406	MI014CI	Iveco Daily	Rošero	N27D	2009
60407	MI016CI	Iveco Daily	Rošero	N27D	2009
60408	MI017CI	Iveco Daily	Rošero	N27D	2009
60409	MI018CI	Iveco Daily	Rošero	N27D	2009
60410	MI019CI	Iveco Daily	Rošero	N27D	2009
60411	MI147CL	Irisbus Crossway GX	Irisbus	N50D	2009
60412	MI148CL	Irisbus Crossway GX	Irisbus	N50D	2009
60413	MI149CL	Irisbus Crossway GX	Irisbus	N50D	2009
60414	MI150CL	Irisbus Crossway GX	Irisbus	N50D	2009
60415	MI151CL	Irisbus Crossway GX	Irisbus	N50D	2009
60416	MI152CL	Irisbus Crossway GX	Irisbus	N50D	2009
60417	MI153CL	Irisbus Crossway GX	Irisbus	N50D	2009
60418	MI154CL	Irisbus Crossway GX	Irisbus	N50D	2009
60419	MI155CL	Irisbus Crossway GX	Irisbus	N50D	2009
60420	MI156CL	Irisbus Crossway GX	Irisbus	N50D	2009
60421	MI157CL	Irisbus Crossway GX	Irisbus	N50D	2009
60422	MI158CL	Irisbus Crossway GX	Irisbus	N50D	2009
60423	MI159CL	Irisbus Crossway GX	Irisbus	N50D	2009
60424	MI160CL	Irisbus Crossway GX	Irisbus	N50D	2009
60425	MI819CJ	Irisbus Arway SFR160	Irisbus	NC50D	2010
60426	MI820CJ	Irisbus Arway SFR160	Irisbus	NC50D	2010

60427	MI821CJ	Irisbus Arway SFR160	Irisbus	NC50D	2010
60428	MI822CJ	Irisbus Arway SFR160	Irisbus	NC50D	2010
60429	MI823CJ	Irisbus Arway SFR160	Irisbus	NC50D	2010
60430	MI824CJ	Irisbus Arway SFR160	Irisbus	NC50D	2010
60431	MI825CJ	Irisbus Arway SFR160	Irisbus	NC50D	2010
60432	MI826CJ	Irisbus Arway SFR160	Irisbus	NC50D	2010
60433	MI625CK	Dennis Dart SLF	Alexander ALX200	N40D	2001
60434	MI627CK	Dennis Dart SLF	Alexander ALX200	N40D	2001
63331	TV142BM	Karosa C734		B45D	1995

SAD NOVé ZáMKY

Slovenská autobusová doprava Nové Zámky, akciová spolocnost, Považská 2,
940 14 Nové Zámky, Slovakia

117	NZ045BR	Karosa C734	B45D	1985
132	NZ188BR	Karosa C734	B45D	1986
144	NZ208CA	Karosa C734	B45D	1987
149	NZ705BM	Karosa C734	B45D	1987
152	NZ458BU	Karosa C734	B45D	1987
153	NZ755BM	Karosa C734	B45D	1987
157	NZ183BR	Karosa B732	B31D	1987
160	NZ197BR	Karosa C734	B45D	1988
170	NZ194BR	Karosa B732	B31D	1988
173	NZ018BR	Karosa B732	B31D	1988
174	NZ147BR	Karosa B732	B31D	1988
176	NZ026BR	Karosa C734	B45D	1989
180	NZ088AH	Karosa LC735	B45D	1989
181	NZ024BR	Karosa B732	B31D	1989
182	NZ025BR	Karosa B732	B31D	1989
183	NZ186BU	Karosa B732	B31D	1989
184	NZ023BR	Karosa B732	B31D	1989
190	NZ702BM	Karosa C744	AB60D	1989
194	NZ074BU	Karosa C734	B45D	1990
196	NZ775AY	Karosa B732	B31D	1990
197	NZ041BR	Karosa B732	B31D	1990
198	NZ746BM	Karosa B732	B31D	1990
201	NZ754BM	Karosa C734	B45D	1990
204	NZ198BR	Karosa C744	AB60D	1990
206	NZ094AH	Karosa LC736	B46D	1991
265	NZ013BR	Karosa C734	B45D	1994
271	NZ753BM	Karosa C734	B45D	1995
316	NZ744BM	Karosa C734	B45D	1996
516	NZ086BR	Karosa B732	B31D	1993
517	NZ089BR	Karosa B732	B31D	1993
527	NZ325AG	Karosa C934	B46D	1998
544	NZ409AK	Karosa LC936	B47D	1999
588	NZ317AO	Karosa C734	B45D	1989
591	NZ316AO	Karosa C734	B45D	1988
605	NZ315AO	Karosa C734	B45D	1988
608	NZ337AO	Karosa C734	B45D	1987
615	NZ319AO	Karosa C734	B45D	1993
616	NZ340AO	Karosa C734	B45D	1994
618	NZ746AS	Karosa C734	B45D	1996
619	NZ744AS	Slovbus SB134	B44D	1998
722	NZ433AZ	Karosa C734	B46D	2000
723	NZ638AS	Karosa C734	B46D	2000
724	NZ639AS	Karosa C934	B46D	2000
725	NZ354AT	MercedesBenz Vario O815	M19D	2000
726	NZ355AT	MercedesBenz Vario O815	M19D	2000
734	NZ341AU	MercedesBenz Vario O815	M19D	2000
735	NZ337AU	Karosa C934	B46D	2000
753	NZ344BA	Karosa C954	B54D	2001
754	NZ360BA	Karosa C954	B54D	2001

755	NZ709BA	Karosa C954		B50D	2001
756	NZ710BA	Karosa C954		B54D	2001
940	NZ119CO	Karosa C734		B45D	1986
945	NZ349BU	Karosa C734		B45D	1987
946	NZ366BU	Karosa C734		B45D	1987
947	NZ382BU	Karosa C734		B45D	1987
954	NZ360BU	Karosa C734		B45D	1986
964	NZ283BU	Karosa C734		B45D	1988
965	NZ365BU	Karosa LC735		B45D	1988
970	NZ347BU	Karosa C734		B45D	1988
973	NZ368BU	Karosa LC735		B45D	1989
974	NZ392BU	Karosa LC736		B45D	1989
978	NZ363BU	Karosa B732		B31D	1989
980	NZ359BU	Karosa C734		B45D	1989
981	NZ358BU	Karosa C734		B45D	1989
983	NZ355BU	Karosa C734		B45D	1989
985	NZ395BU	Karosa C744		AB60D	1989
986	NZ339BU	Karosa C744		AB60D	1989
990	NZ799BV	Karosa C734		B45D	1990
993	NZ397BU	Karosa B731		B31D	1990
996	NZ364BU	Karosa C734		B45D	1992
999	NZ356BU	Karosa C734		B46D	1993
1003	NZ341BU	Karosa B732		B33D	1994
1007	NZ369BU	Karosa LC736		B46D	1995
1010	NZ433BU	Karosa LC936		B49D	1998
1011	NZ337BU	Karosa C934		B46D	1998
1014	NZ956CP	Karosa C935		B47D	1999
1015	NZ895CP	Karosa C934		B46D	2000
1016	NZ957CP	Karosa C934		B46D	2000
1030	NZ892CP	MercedesBenz Vario O815		M19D	2000
1031	NZ894CP	Karosa C934		B46D	2000
1032	NZ953CP	Karosa C954		B50D	2001
1033	NZ954CP	Karosa C954		B50D	2001
1034	NZ958CP	Karosa C954		B50D	2001
1035	NZ264BU	Karosa C954		B54D	2001
1258	NZ436BU	Karosa LC735		B45D	1987
1259	NZ428BU	Karosa C734		B45D	1987
1260	NZ451BU	Karosa C734		B45D	1987
1261	NZ254BU	Karosa C734		B45D	1987
1262	NZ426BU	Karosa C734		B45D	1987
1265	NZ449BU	Karosa C734		B45D	1987
1266	NZ416BU	Karosa C734		B45D	1987
1268	NZ448BU	Karosa C734		B45D	1988
1271	NZ429BU	Karosa C734		B45D	1988
1272	NZ446BU	Karosa C734		B45D	1988
1274	NZ439BU	Karosa LC735		B45D	1988
1276	NZ414BU	Karosa B732		B31D	1988
1277	NZ400BU	Karosa B732		B31D	1988
1278	NZ413BU	Karosa B732		B31D	1988
1281	NZ455BU	Karosa B732		B31D	1989
1282	NZ248BU	Karosa B732		B31D	1989
1284	NZ445BU	Karosa C734		B45D	1989
1289	NZ415BU	Karosa C734		B45D	1989
1293	NZ435BU	Karosa C734		B45D	1990
1294	NZ442BU	Karosa C734		B45D	1990
1295	NZ384BU	Karosa C734		B45D	1990
1296	NZ443BU	Karosa C734		B45D	1990
1297	NZ422BU	Karosa C734		B45D	1992
1300	NZ252BU	Karosa C734		B45D	1994
1381	NZ255BU	Karosa C734		B45D	1993
1382	NZ408BU	Karosa B732		B31D	1993
1436	NZ423BU	Karosa C734		B45D	1992
1452	NZ269BU	Karosa LC735		B45D	1990
1454	NZ272BU	Karosa LC736		B45D	1991
1457	NZ207CA	Karosa C734		B46D	1995
1484	NZ596CS	SOR V 7.5		B26D	1997
1509	NZ852CN	Karosa C934		B46D	1998
1524	NZ825CS	Slovbus SB134		B44D	1999
1526	NZ850CN	Karosa C734		B45D	1995
1605	NZ427BU	Karosa C734		B45D	1987
1607	NZ425BU	Karosa C734		B46D	1990
1611	NZ856CN	Karosa C734		B45D	1995
1612	NZ399BU	Karosa C734		B45D	1988

1613	NZ434BU	Karosa LC736	B45D	1988
1614	NZ851CN	Karosa LC735	B46D	1990
1615	NZ456BU	Karosa LC736	B46D	1996
1622	NZ404BU	Karosa LC735	B45D	1987
1661	NZ823CS	MercedesBenz Vario O815	M19D	2000
1662	NZ438BU	MercedesBenz Vario O815	M19D	2000
1664	NZ417BU	Karosa C934	B46D	2000
1674	NZ598CS	Karosa C954	B50D	2001
1678	NZ402BU	Karosa C954	B54D	2001
1682	NZ594BG	Karosa C954	B50D	2003
1683	NZ578BG	Karosa C954	B50D	2003
1684	NZ593BG	Karosa C954	B54D	2003
1688	NZ937BI	Karosa LC956	B53D	2003
1689	NZ935BI	Karosa LC956	B53D	2003
1690	NZ934BI	Karosa LC956	B51D	2003
1691	NZ938BI	Karosa LC956	B53D	2003
1700	NZ258NK	SOR LC 10.5	B45D	2003
1701	NZ774CU	SOR LC 10.5	B45D	2003
1702	NZ260BK	SOR LC 10.5	B45D	2003
1703	NZ428BK	Ikarus E98	B48D	2000
1704	NZ429BK	Ikarus E595.55	B51D	1999
1711	NZ134BD	Karosa C734	B45D	1986
1712	NZ130BD	Karosa LC735	B45D	1986
1713	NZ136BD	Karosa C734	B45D	1987
1714	NZ158BD	Karosa LC735	B45D	1987
1715	NZ159BD	Karosa C734	B45D	1987
1716	NZ647BL	MAN HJS432	B47D	2001
1717	NZ663CN	MAN SL232	B45D	2001
1718	NZ883CJ	MAN SL232	B45D	2001
1719	NZ657BL	MAN HJS432	B45D	2001
1720	NZ172BD	MAN HJS432	B47D	2001
1721	NZ182BD	Karosa C735	B45D	1988
1722	NZ183BD	Karosa C735	B45D	1988
1723	NZ085BN	Karosa C734	B45D	1988
1724	NZ260DH	Karosa C734	B45D	1989
1725	NZ679BN	Karosa C734	B45D	1987
1726	NZ680BN	Karosa C734	B45D	1989
1730	NZ684BO	Karosa C734	B45D	1986
1731	NZ701BO	Karosa C734	B45D	1986
1732	NZ099CN	Karosa C934	B54D	2004
1733	NZ703BO	Karosa C934	B54D	2004
1734	NZ704BO	Karosa C934	B54D	2004
1735	NZ705BO	Karosa C934	B54D	2004
1736	NZ706BO	Karosa C934	B54D	2004
1737	NZ708BO	Karosa C934	B54D	2004
1738	NZ709BO	Karosa C934	B54D	2004
1739	NZ710BO	Karosa C954	B54D	2004
1740	NZ711BO	Karosa C954	B50D	2004
1741	NZ712BO	Karosa C954	B54D	2004
1910	NZ715BM	Karosa B952	B32D	2004
1911	NZ716BM	Karosa B952	B32D	2004
1914	NZ748BM	Karosa B732	B31D	1987
1915	NZ749BM	Karosa B732	B31D	1988
1920	NZ836BS	Karosa C734	B45D	1989
1921	NZ078BT	Karosa B731	B31D	1990
1927	NZ513BV	Karosa LC735	B45D	1987
1928	NZ812BV	Karosa C734	B45D	1988
1929	NZ921BM	Karosa LC735	B45D	1988
1930	NZ922BM	Karosa LC735	B45D	1989
1931	NZ830DK	Karosa LC735	B45D	1988
1933	NZ048BU	Karosa C734	B45D	1989
1934	NZ050BU	Karosa C734	B45D	1989
1935	NZ428BY	Karosa C734	B45D	1988
1936	NZ429BY	Karosa LC735	B45D	1989
1937	NZ829BY	Karosa LC736	B46D	1990
1938	NZ062BU	Karosa LC735	B45D	1988
1939	NZ063BU	Karosa C734	B45D	1988
1940	NZ064BU	Karosa C734	B45D	1990
1941	NZ065BU	Karosa C734	B45D	1989
1942	NZ066BU	Karosa LC736	B46D	1988
1943	NZ067BU	Karosa C734	B45D	1989
1945	NZ070BU	Karosa C734	B45D	1990
1946	NZ071BU	Karosa LC735	B45D	1989

1948	NZ085BU	Karosa C734		B45D	1988
1949	NZ086BU	Karosa C734		B45D	1989
1950	NZ091BU	Karosa C734		B45D	1990
1951	NZ092BU	Karosa C734		B45D	1989
1952	NZ106BU	Karosa C734		B45D	1989
1953	NZ109BU	Karosa LC735		B45D	1989
1954	NZ113BU	Karosa C734		B45D	1991
1955	NZ122BU	Karosa LC735		B45D	1989
1956	NZ126BU	Karosa C734		B45D	1990
1963	NZ072CB	Karosa C734		B45D	1993
1964	NZ073CB	Karosa C734		B45D	1990
1965	NZ259CB	Karosa LC736		B46D	1995
1966	NZ261CB	Karosa C734		B45D	1990
1967	NZ124BU	Karosa C734		B46D	1993
1968	NZ725CB	Karosa C734		B45D	1990
1969	NZ728CB	Karosa C734		B46D	1994
1970	NZ729CB	Karosa C734		B45D	1993
1971	NZ749CB	Karosa LC735		B46D	1990
1972	NZ163CC	Karosa C734		B45D	1990
1973	NZ162CC	Karosa C734		B45D	1990
1974	NZ118BU	Karosa C734		B45D	1990
1975	NZ151BU	Karosa C734		B46D	1995
1976	NZ153BU	Karosa C734		B46D	1994
1996	NZ217BU	Karosa C734		B46D	1995
1997	NZ218BU	Karosa C734		B46D	1995
2001	NZ226BU	Karosa C734		B46D	1994
2002	NZ228BU	Karosa C734		B46D	1994
2003	NZ245BU	Karosa C734		B46D	1994
2004	NZ632BU	Karosa C734		B46D	1995
2007	NZ261BU	Karosa C734		B46D	1995
2008	NZ263BU	Karosa C734		B46D	1994
2013	NZ273BU	Karosa C734		B46D	1995
2016	NZ274BU	Karosa C734		B45D	1993
2017	NZ275BU	Karosa C734		B46D	1995
2018	NZ754CL	Karosa C734		B46D	1994
2019	NZ187CM	Karosa C734		B46D	1993
2020	NZ189CM	Karosa C734		B46D	1995
2021	NZ192CM	Karosa C734		B46D	1995
2022	NZ193CM	Karosa C734		B46D	1994
2026	NZ335BU	Karosa C734		B46D	1995
2027	NZ334BU	Karosa B732		B31D	1993
2028	NZ652CR	Autosan Granus H10		B43D	1998
2029	NZ387BU	Karosa B732		B31D	1993
2030	NZ388BU	Karosa C734		B43D	1996
2031	NZ457BU	Karosa B732		B31D	1993
2032	NZ894BU	Autosan Granus H10		B43D	1998
2033	NZ087CT	Autosan Granus H10		B43D	1998
2034	NZ089CT	Autosan Granus H10		B43D	1998
2035	NZ091CT	Autosan Granus H10		B43D	1998
2036	NZ463BU	Karosa C734		B45D	1993
2037	NZ464BU	Karosa C734		B46D	1995
2038	NZ387CA	Karosa C734		B45D	1994
2039	NZ930CU	Irisbus Crossway GX	Irisbus	N54D	2007
2040	NZ931CU	Irisbus Crossway GX	Irisbus	N54D	2007
2041	NZ932CU	Irisbus Crossway GX	Irisbus	N48D	2007
2042	NZ933CU	Irisbus Crossway GX	Irisbus	N54D	2007
2043	NZ934CU	Irisbus Crossway GX	Irisbus	N54D	2007
2044	NZ020CV	HungariaBus Starter		B45D	2007
2045	NZ147CV	HungariaBus Starter		B45D	2007
2046	NZ479CV	Irisbus Crossway GX	Irisbus	N48D	2007
2048	NZ152CA	Karosa C734		B46D	1995
2049	NZ875CV	Karosa C734		B46D	1998
2050	NZ153CA	Karosa C734		B46D	1995
2051	NZ154CA	Karosa C734		B46D	1995
2052	NZ156CA	Karosa C734		B46D	1995
2053	NZ155CA	Karosa C734		B46D	1996
2075	NZ688CY	HungariaBus Starter		B45D	2008
2083	NZ549DB	Irisbus Crossway	Irisbus	N50D	2008
2084	NZ554DB	Irisbus Crossway	Irisbus	N50D	2008
2085	NZ556DB	Irisbus Crossway	Irisbus	N50D	2008
2086	NZ557DB	Irisbus Crossway	Irisbus	N50D	2008
2087	NZ558DB	Irisbus Crossway	Irisbus	N50D	2008
2088	NZ559DB	Irisbus Crossway	Irisbus	N50D	2008

2089	NZ560DB	Irisbus Crossway	Irisbus	N50D	2008
2090	NZ561DB	Irisbus Crossway	Irisbus	N50D	2008
2091	NZ564DB	Irisbus Crossway	Irisbus	N50D	2008
2092	NZ567DB	Irisbus Crossway	Irisbus	N50D	2008
2093	NZ568DB	Irisbus Crossway	Irisbus	N50D	2008
2094	NZ570DB	Irisbus Crossway	Irisbus	N50D	2008
2095	NZ571DB	Irisbus Crossway	Irisbus	N50D	2008
2096	NZ572DB	Irisbus Crossway	Irisbus	N50D	2008
2097	NZ573DB	Irisbus Crossway	Irisbus	N50D	2008
2098	NZ067DF	Irisbus Crossway	Irisbus	N50D	2008
2099	NZ621DB	Irisbus Crossway	Irisbus	N50D	2008
2000	NZ624DB	Irisbus Crossway	Irisbus	N50D	2008
2101	NZ625DB	Irisbus Crossway	Irisbus	N50D	2008
2102	NZ627DB	Irisbus Crossway	Irisbus	N50D	2008
2102	NZ628DB	Irisbus Crossway	Irisbus	N50D	2008
2104	NZ629DB	Irisbus Crossway	Irisbus	N50D	2008
2105	NZ630DB	Irisbus Crossway	Irisbus	N50D	2008
2106	NZ631DB	Irisbus Crossway	Irisbus	N50D	2008
2107	NZ632DB	Irisbus Crossway	Irisbus	N50D	2008
2108	NZ633DB	Irisbus Crossway	Irisbus	N50D	2008
2109	NZ634DB	Irisbus Crossway	Irisbus	N50D	2008
2110	NZ635DB	Irisbus Crossway	Irisbus	N50D	2008
2111	NZ636DB	Irisbus Crossway	Irisbus	N50D	2008
2112	NZ637DB	Irisbus Crossway	Irisbus	N50D	2008
2445	NZ733DF	Irisbus Crossway	Irisbus	N50D	2008
2446	NZ734DF	Irisbus Crossway	Irisbus	N50D	2008
2447	NZ738DF	Irisbus Crossway	Irisbus	N50D	2008
2448	NZ735DF	Irisbus Crossway	Irisbus	N50D	2008
2449	NZ736DF	Irisbus Crossway	Irisbus	N50D	2008
2450	NZ882DF	Irisbus Crossway	Irisbus	N50D	2008
2451	NZ889DF	Irisbus Crossway	Irisbus	N50D	2008
2452	NZ886DF	Irisbus Crossway	Irisbus	N50D	2008
2453	NZ884DF	Irisbus Crossway	Irisbus	N50D	2008
2454	NZ885DF	Irisbus Crossway	Irisbus	N50D	2008
2455	NZ071DG	Irisbus Crossway	Irisbus	N50D	2008
2456	NZ064DG	Irisbus Crossway	Irisbus	N50D	2008
2457	NZ076DG	Irisbus Crossway	Irisbus	N50D	2008
2458	NZ077DG	Irisbus Crossway	Irisbus	N50D	2008
2459	NZ066DG	Irisbus Crossway	Irisbus	N50D	2008
2460	NZ075DG	Irisbus Crossway	Irisbus	N50D	2008
2461	NZ073DG	Irisbus Crossway	Irisbus	N50D	2008
2462	NZ072DG	Irisbus Crossway	Irisbus	N50D	2008
2463	NZ063DG	Irisbus Crossway	Irisbus	N50D	2008
2464	NZ065DG	Irisbus Crossway	Irisbus	N50D	2008
2465	NZ068DG	Irisbus Crossway	Irisbus	N50D	2008
2466	NZ074DG	Irisbus Crossway	Irisbus	N50D	2008
2467	NZ067DG	Irisbus Crossway	Irisbus	N50D	2008
2479	NZ011DN	MAN ÜL 353		BC50D	1999
2480	NZ012DN	MAN ÜL 353		BC50D	1999
2481	NZ013DN	MAN ÜL 353		BC50D	1999
2482	NZ014DN	MAN ÜL 353		BC50D	1999
2483	NZ992DM	MAN ÜL 353		BC50D	1999
2484	NZ016DN	MAN ÜL 353		BC50D	1999
2485	NZ017DN	MAN ÜL 353		BC50D	1999
2486	NZ018DN	MAN ÜL 353		BC50D	1999
2487	NZ019DN	MAN ÜL 353		BC50D	1999
2488	NZ033DN	MAN ÜL 353		BC50D	1999
2489	NZ035DN	MAN ÜL 353		BC50D	1999
2490	NZ138DN	MAN ÜL 353		BC50D	1999
2491	NZ280DN	MAN ÜL 353		BC50D	1999
2492	NZ139DN	MAN ÜL 353		BC50D	1999
2493	NZ140DN	MAN ÜL 353		BC50D	1999
2494	NZ150DN	MAN ÜL 353		BC50D	1999
2495	NZ682DN	MAN ÜL 353		BC50D	1999
2496	NZ148DN	MAN ÜL 353		BC50D	1999
2497	NZ852DO	Irisbus Citelis LE	Irisbus	N35D	2009
2498	NZ853DO	Irisbus Citelis LE	Irisbus	N35D	2009

VT-TRANSMAN

VT Transman kft., 8000 Székesfehérvár, Videoton Ipari Park, Berényi út 72-100, Hungary

CCP-958	Ikarus 256.50	Ikarus	B45D	1981
BHC-492	Ikarus 256.50	Ikarus	BC45D	1985
BPV-127	Ikarus 280.47	Ikarus	AB35D	1985
EZZ-075	Ikarus 280.03	Ikarus	AB56D	1986
AVC-494	Ikarus 256.50E	Ikarus	BC45D	1986
CJY-365	Ikarus 256	Ikarus	B47D	1986
GNX-378	Ikarus 256	Ikarus	B43D	1987
GNX-379	Ikarus 256.54	Ikarus	B86D	1987
GNX-380	Ikarus 256.54	Ikarus	B86D	1987
GNX-381	Ikarus 256.54	Ikarus	B86D	1987
GNX-382	Ikarus 256.54	Ikarus	B44D	1987
GNX-395	Ikarus 280	Ikarus	AB47D	1987
JOY-216	Ikarus 280	Ikarus	AB47D	1987
JOY-217	Ikarus 280	Ikarus	AB47D	1987
JOY-220	Ikarus 280	Ikarus	AB47D	1987
JOY-221	Ikarus 280	Ikarus	AB47D	1987
JOY-223	Ikarus 280	Ikarus	AB47D	1987
DUL-094	Ikarus 256.50	Ikarus	B46D	1987
BPB-322	Ikarus 256.50E	Ikarus	BC45D	1987
GTY-302	Rakos 350 Union	Rakos	BC52D	1988
GTY-303	Rakos 350 Union	Rakos	BC52D	1988
GVL-649	Ikarus 435.23	Ikarus	BC65D	1988
FLF-254	Ikarus 250.59	Ikarus	B40D	1988
AGT-518	Ikarus 250.59	Ikarus	BC44D	1988
AGX-552	Ikarus 250	Ikarus	BC49D	1988
BSM-648	Ikarus 256.50	Ikarus	B47D	1988
CCP-831	Ikarus 256.50	Ikarus	B45D	1988

CJD-475	Ikarus 256.50E	Ikarus	B45D	1988
AAK-608	Ikarus 256.50E	Ikarus	BC45D	1989
BHK-756	Ikarus 250.59	Ikarus	BC49D	1989
BPP-581	Ikarus 256.50	Ikarus	BC46D	1989
BPU-105	Ikarus 256.50	Ikarus	BC44D	1990
BRA-619	Ikarus 256.50	Ikarus	B47D	1990
BRA-655	Ikarus 256.50	Ikarus	B45D	1990
BRC-285	Ikarus 260.32	Ikarus	B40D	1990
AAI-515	Ikarus 256.50V	Ikarus	BC47D	1990
AEU-221	Ikarus 250.59	Ikarus	BC40D	1990
ANZ-478	Ikarus 250.72	Ikarus	BC47D	1990
DOG-798	Mercedes-Benz 208	Mercedes-Benz	M13	1990
BOS-058	Ikarus 256.50E	Ikarus	BC40D	1991
BOS-262	Ikarus 260.32	Ikarus	BC40D	1992
FJZ-283	Ikarus 435.06	Ikarus	AB58D	1994
EYB-348	Ikarus 415.27	Ikarus	B42D	1994
DUD-687	Ikarus 256.50E	Ikarus	B44D	1996
FKC-725	Ikarus 256.50E	Ikarus	B45D	1996
FKC-730	Ikarus 256	Ikarus	B43D	1996
FKC-857	Ikarus 250	Ikarus	B44D	1996
FKC-862	Ikarus 256.50	Ikarus	B40D	1996
GTU-487	Ikarus 543.24	Ikarus	B29F	1998
FLM-022	Hungaria Bus 122L	HB	BC41D	1998
CKC-433	Rakos 350 Union	Rakos	BC44D	1999
CKC-434	Rakos 350 Union	Rakos	BC52D	1999
CKC-437	Rakos 350 Union	Rakos	BC51D	1999
FIZ-259	Rakos 350 Union	Rakos	BC52D	1999
VID-301	Ikarus 256	Ikarus	B44D	1999
VID-302	Ikarus 256	Ikarus	B44D	1999
VID-303	Ikarus 256	Ikarus	B44D	1999
VID-304	Ikarus 256	Ikarus	B44D	1999
VID-305	Ikarus 256	Ikarus	B44D	1999
VID-306	Ikarus 256	Ikarus	B44D	1999
VID-307	Ikarus 256	Ikarus	B44D	1999
VID-309	Ikarus 256	Ikarus	B44D	1999
VID-310	Ikarus 256	Ikarus	B44D	1999
VID-311	Ikarus 256	Ikarus	B44D	1999
VID-312	Ikarus 256	Ikarus	B44D	1999
VID-313	Ikarus 256	Ikarus	B44D	1999

One of the latest acquisitions by Arriva is the Hungarian fleet of VT-Transman. Seen here is GVL649, an Ikarus 435 of 1988 vintage. *Arriva*

VID-314	Ikarus 256	Ikarus	B44D	1999
VID-315	Ikarus 256	Ikarus	B44D	1999
VID-316	Ikarus 256	Ikarus	B44D	1999
VID-317	Ikarus 256	Ikarus	B44D	1999
VID-318	Ikarus 256	Ikarus	B44D	1999
VID-321	Ikarus 256	Ikarus	B44D	1999
VID-322	Ikarus 256	Ikarus	B44D	1999
VID-323	Ikarus 256	Ikarus	B44D	1999
VID-324	Ikarus 256	Ikarus	B44D	1999
VID-325	Ikarus 256	Ikarus	B44D	1999
VID-326	Volkswagen LT46	Volkswagen	M19	1999
VID-327	Volkswagen LT46	Volkswagen	M19	1999
VID-328	Volkswagen LT46	Volkswagen	M19	1999
JOY-538	Ikarus 263.01	Ikarus	B25D	1999
JOY-539	Ikarus 263.01	Ikarus	B25D	1999
JOY-540	Ikarus 263.01	Ikarus	B25D	1999
JOY-541	Ikarus 263.01	Ikarus	B25D	1999
KAZ-049	Ikarus 263.10	Ikarus	B25D	1999
KAZ-050	Ikarus 263.10	Ikarus	B25D	1999
KAZ-051	Ikarus 263.10	Ikarus	B25D	1999
KAZ-052	Ikarus 263.10	Ikarus	B25D	1999
KAZ-053	Ikarus 263.10	Ikarus	B25D	1999
KAZ-054	Ikarus 263.10	Ikarus	B25D	1999
KAZ-055	Ikarus 263.10	Ikarus	B25D	1999
KAZ-056	Ikarus 263.10	Ikarus	B25D	1999
KAZ-057	Ikarus 263.10	Ikarus	B25D	1999
KAZ-058	Ikarus 263.10	Ikarus	B25D	1999
KTX-217	Ikarus 263.10	Ikarus	B25D	1999
KTX-218	Ikarus 263.10	Ikarus	B25D	1999
KTX-245	Ikarus 263.10	Ikarus	B25D	1999
KOC-345	MAN ÜL353	MAN	BC54D	1999
KOC-355	MAN ÜL353	MAN	BC54D	1999
FLM-025	MAN ÜL353	MAN	BC53D	2000
FLX-854	MAN ÜL353	MAN	BC54D	2000

FLX-856	MAN ÜL353	MAN	BC54D	2000
FLX-857	MAN ÜL353	MAN	BC54D	2000
FLX-858	MAN ÜL353	MAN	BC54D	2000
FLX-859	MAN ÜL353	MAN	BC54D	2000
FLX-861	MAN ÜL353	MAN	BC54D	2000
FLX-862	MAN ÜL353	MAN	BC54D	2000
FLX-863	MAN ÜL353	MAN	BC54D	2000
FLX-864	MAN ÜL353	MAN	BC54D	2000
FJV-160	MAN SL233	MAN	B45D	2000
FJZ-261	MAN SL233	MAN	B45D	2000
FJZ-278	MAN SL233	MAN	B45D	2000
FJU-311	MAN SL233	MAN	B45D	2000
FJU-312	MAN SL233	MAN	B45D	2000
HDY-685	Volkswagen LT35	Volkswagen	M16	2000
IEZ-464	Volkswagen LT46	Volkswagen	M19	2000
LSM-498	Mercedes-Benz Cito O520	Mercedes-Benz	N-F	2001
LSY-889	Mercedes-Benz Cito O520	Mercedes-Benz	N-F	2001
LSZ-994	Mercedes-Benz Cito O520	Mercedes-Benz	N-F	2001
LSZ-995	Mercedes-Benz Cito O520	Mercedes-Benz	N-F	2001
LSZ-996	Mercedes-Benz Cito O520	Mercedes-Benz	N-F	2001
LLT-062	MAN Lion's City A23	MAN	AN51D	2001
LLT-063	MAN Lion's City A23	MAN	AN51D	2000
LLT-064	MAN Lion's City A23	MAN	AN51D	2001
LLT-065	MAN Lion's City A23	MAN	AN51D	2001
LLT-066	MAN Lion's City A23	MAN	AN51D	2001
FJV-144	MAN SL233	MAN	B45D	2001
FJV-154	MAN SL233	MAN	B45D	2001
FJV-155	MAN SL233	MAN	B45D	2001
FJX-658	MAN SL233	MAN	B45D	2001
FJX-684	MAN SL233	MAN	B45D	2001
HSJ-445	MAN SL233	MAN	B32D	2001
HSJ-446	MAN SL233	MAN	B32D	2001
HSJ-447	MAN SL233	MAN	B32D	2001
HSJ-448	MAN SL233	MAN	B32D	2001
HSJ-449	MAN SL233	MAN	B32D	2001
HSJ-450	MAN SL233	MAN	B32D	2001
HSJ-451	MAN SL233	MAN	B32D	2001
HSJ-452	MAN SL233	MAN	B32D	2001
HSJ-453	MAN SL233	MAN	B32D	2001
HSJ-454	MAN SL233	MAN	B32D	2001
HSJ-455	MAN SL233	MAN	B32D	2001
HSJ-456	MAN SL233	MAN	B32D	2001
HSJ-457	MAN SL233	MAN	B32D	2001
HSJ-458	MAN SL233	MAN	B32D	2001
HSJ-459	MAN SL233	MAN	B32D	2001
HSJ-460	MAN SL233	MAN	B32D	2001
HSJ-461	MAN SL233	MAN	B32D	2001
HSJ-462	MAN SL233	MAN	B32D	2001
HSJ-463	MAN SL233	MAN	B32D	2001
HSJ-464	MAN SL233	MAN	B32D	2001
HSJ-465	MAN SL233	MAN	B32D	2001
HSJ-466	MAN SL233	MAN	B32D	2001
HSJ-467	MAN SL233	MAN	B32D	2001
HSJ-468	MAN SL233	MAN	B32D	2001
HSJ-469	MAN SL233	MAN	B32D	2001
HSJ-470	MAN SL233	MAN	B32D	2001
HSJ-471	MAN SL233	MAN	B32D	2001
HSJ-472	MAN SL233	MAN	B32D	2001
HSJ-473	MAN SL233	MAN	B32D	2001
HSJ-474	MAN SL233	MAN	B32D	2001
HSJ-475	MAN SL233	MAN	B32D	2001
HSJ-476	MAN SL233	MAN	B32D	2001
HSJ-477	MAN SL233	MAN	B32D	2001
HSJ-478	MAN SL233	MAN	B32D	2001
HSJ-479	MAN SL233	MAN	B32D	2001
KLN-090	Volvo B7RLE	Alfa	N27D	2006
KLN-091	Volvo B7RLE	Alfa	N27D	2006
KLN-092	Volvo B7RLE	Alfa	N27D	2006
KLN-093	Volvo B7RLE	Alfa	N27D	2006
KLN-094	Volvo B7RLE	Alfa	N27D	2006
KLN-095	Volvo B7RLE	Alfa	N27D	2006
KLN-096	Volvo B7RLE	Alfa	N27D	2006
KLN-097	Volvo B7RLE	Alfa	N27D	2006

KLN-098	Volvo B7RLE	Alfa	N27D	2006
KOE-130	Volvo B7RLE	Alfa	N27D	2006
KOE-148	Volvo B7RLE	Alfa	N27D	2006
KOE-415	Volvo B7RLE	Alfa	N27D	2006
KPN-499	Volvo B7RLE	Alfa	N27D	2007
KPN-954	Volvo B7RLE	Alfa	N27D	2007
KPN-955	Volvo B7RLE	Alfa	N27D	2007
KPN-963	Volvo B7RLE	Alfa	N27D	2007
KPN-964	Volvo B7RLE	Alfa	N27D	2007
KXM-004	Volvo B7RLE	Alfa	N27D	2007
KXM-005	Volvo B7RLE	Alfa	N27D	2007
KXM-006	Volvo B7RLE	Alfa	N27D	2007
KXM-007	Volvo B7RLE	Alfa	N27D	2007
KXM-008	Volvo B7RLE	Alfa	N27D	2007
KXM-009	Volvo B7RLE	Alfa	N27D	2007
KXM-017	Volvo B7RLE	Alfa	N27D	2007
KXM-018	Volvo B7RLE	Alfa	N27D	2007
KXM-019	Volvo B7RLE	Alfa	N27D	2007
KXM-020	Volvo B7RLE	Alfa	N27D	2007
KXM-021	Volvo B7RLE	Alfa	N27D	2007
KXM-022	Volvo B7RLE	Alfa	N27D	2007
KXM-023	Volvo B7RLE	Alfa	N27D	2007
KXM-024	Volvo B7RLE	Alfa	N27D	2007
KXM-025	Volvo B7RLE	Alfa	N27D	2007
KXM-026	Volvo B7RLE	Alfa	N27D	2007
KXM-027	Volvo B7RLE	Alfa	N27D	2007
KXM-028	Volvo B7RLE	Alfa	N27D	2007
KXM-029	Volvo B7RLE	Alfa	N27D	2007
KXM-030	Volvo B7RLE	Alfa	N27D	2007
KXM-031	Volvo B7RLE	Alfa	N27D	2007
KXM-032	Volvo B7RLE	Alfa	N27D	2007
KXM-033	Volvo B7RLE	Alfa	N27D	2007
KXM-034	Volvo B7RLE	Alfa	N27D	2007
KXM-035	Volvo B7RLE	Alfa	N27D	2007
KXM-036	Volvo B7RLE	Alfa	N27D	2007
KXM-037	Volvo B7RLE	Alfa	N27D	2007
KXM-038	Volvo B7RLE	Alfa	N27D	2007
KXM-039	Volvo B7RLE	Alfa	N27D	2007
KXM-040	Volvo B7RLE	Alfa	N27D	2007
KXM-041	Volvo B7RLE	Alfa	N27D	2007
KXM-042	Volvo B7RLE	Alfa	N27D	2007
KXM-043	Volvo B7RLE	Alfa	N27D	2007
KXM-044	Volvo B7RLE	Alfa	N27D	2007
KXM-045	Volvo B7RLE	Alfa	N27D	2007
FLX-851	Iveco Daily 50C	Iveco	B20F	2007
FLX-852	Iveco Daily 50C	Iveco	B20F	2007
FLX-853	Iveco Daily 50C	Iveco	B20F	2007
FSJ-662	Iveco Daily 50C	Iveco	B20F	2007
FSJ-663	Iveco Daily 50C	Iveco	B20F	2007
FSJ-664	Iveco Daily 50C	Iveco	B20F	2007

A unusual supplier of buses for the fleet is Rakos. Seen in VT Transman colours is 350 Union model with index mark CKC437.
Arriva

Index to UK vehicles

Reg	Region	Reg	Region	Reg	Region	Reg	Region
BX05UWY	London	BX55FXJ	London	CX06BHV	NW & Wales	CX07CSZ	NW & Wales
BX05UWZ	London	BX55FXK	London	CX06BHW	NW & Wales	CX07CTE	NW & Wales
BX05UXC	London	BX55FXL	London	CX06BHY	NW & Wales	CX07CTF	NW & Wales
BX05UXD	London	BX55FXM	London	CX06BHZ	NW & Wales	CX07CTK	NW & Wales
BX07MXT	London	BX55FXO	London	CX06BJE	NW & Wales	CX07CTO	NW & Wales
BX54EBU	Tellings GM	BX55FXP	London	CX06BJF	NW & Wales	CX07CTU	NW & Wales
BX54EBV	Tellings GM	BX55FXR	London	CX06BJJ	NW & Wales	CX07CTV	NW & Wales
BX55FUH	London	BX55FXS	London	CX06BJK	NW & Wales	CX07CTY	NW & Wales
BX55FUJ	London	BX55FXT	London	CX06BJO	NW & Wales	CX07CTZ	NW & Wales
BX55FUO	London	BX55FXU	London	CX06BJU	NW & Wales	CX07CUA	NW & Wales
BX55FUP	London	BX55FXV	London	CX06BJV	NW & Wales	CX07CUC	NW & Wales
BX55FUT	London	BX55FXW	London	CX06BJY	NW & Wales	CX07CUG	NW & Wales
BX55FUU	London	BX55FXY	London	CX06BJZ	NW & Wales	CX07CUH	NW & Wales
BX55FUW	London	BX56VTU	Southern Cs	CX06BKA	NW & Wales	CX07CUJ	NW & Wales
BX55FUY	London	BX56VTV	Southern Cs	CX06BKD	NW & Wales	CX07CUK	NW & Wales
BX55FVA	London	BX56VTW	Southern Cs	CX06BKE	NW & Wales	CX07CUU	NW & Wales
BX55FVB	London	C212GTU	NW & Wales	CX06BKF	NW & Wales	CX07CUV	NW & Wales
BX55FVC	London	CC04MAL	Tellings GM	CX06BKG	NW & Wales	CX07CUW	NW & Wales
BX55FVD	London	CE52UWW	The Shires	CX06BKJ	NW & Wales	CX07CUY	NW & Wales
BX55FVF	London	CJZ9115	Midlands	CX06BKK	NW & Wales	CX07CVA	NW & Wales
BX55FVG	London	CUV122C	London	CX06BKL	NW & Wales	CX07CVB	NW & Wales
BX55FVH	London	CUV217C	London	CX06BKN	NW & Wales	CX08DJJ	NW & Wales
BX55FVJ	London	CUV335C	London	CX06BKO	NW & Wales	CX08DJK	NW & Wales
BX55FVK	London	CX04AXW	NW & Wales	CX06EAK	NW & Wales	CX08DJO	NW & Wales
BX55FVL	London	CX04AXY	NW & Wales	CX06EAM	NW & Wales	CX08DJU	NW & Wales
BX55FVM	London	CX04AXZ	NW & Wales	CX06EAO	NW & Wales	CX09BFM	NW & Wales
BX55FVN	London	CX04AYA	NW & Wales	CX06EAP	NW & Wales	CX09BFN	NW & Wales
BX55FVP	London	CX04AYB	NW & Wales	CX06EAW	NW & Wales	CX09BFO	NW & Wales
BX55FVQ	London	CX04AYC	NW & Wales	CX06EAY	NW & Wales	CX09BFP	NW & Wales
BX55FVR	London	CX04EHV	Midlands	CX06EBA	NW & Wales	CX09BFU	NW & Wales
BX55FVS	London	CX04EHW	Midlands	CX06EBC	NW & Wales	CX09BFV	NW & Wales
BX55FVT	London	CX04EHY	Midlands	CX06EBD	NW & Wales	CX09BFY	NW & Wales
BX55FVU	London	CX04EHZ	Midlands	CX06EBF	NW & Wales	CX09BFZ	NW & Wales
BX55FVW	London	CX04HRN	NW & Wales	CX06EBG	NW & Wales	CX09BGE	NW & Wales
BX55FVY	London	CX04HRP	NW & Wales	CX06EBJ	NW & Wales	CX09BGF	NW & Wales
BX55FVZ	London	CX04HRR	NW & Wales	CX06EBK	NW & Wales	CX09BGK	NW & Wales
BX55FWA	London	CX05AAE	NW & Wales	CX06EBL	NW & Wales	CX09BGO	NW & Wales
BX55FWB	London	CX05AAF	NW & Wales	CX06EBM	NW & Wales	CX09BGU	NW & Wales
BX55FWG	London	CX05AAJ	NW & Wales	CX07COJ	NW & Wales	CX09BGV	NW & Wales
BX55FWH	London	CX05AAK	NW & Wales	CX07COU	NW & Wales	CX09BGW	NW & Wales
BX55FWJ	London	CX05AAN	NW & Wales	CX07CPE	NW & Wales	CX09BGZ	NW & Wales
BX55FWK	London	CX05EOV	NW & Wales	CX07CPF	NW & Wales	CX09BHA	NW & Wales
BX55FWL	London	CX05EOW	NW & Wales	CX07CPK	NW & Wales	CX54DKD	NW & Wales
BX55FWM	London	CX05EOY	NW & Wales	CX07CPN	NW & Wales	CX54DKE	NW & Wales
BX55FWN	London	CX05JVD	NW & Wales	CX07CPO	NW & Wales	CX54DKF	NW & Wales
BX55FWP	London	CX06BGU	NW & Wales	CX07CPU	NW & Wales	CX54DKJ	NW & Wales
BX55FWR	London	CX06BGV	NW & Wales	CX07CPV	NW & Wales	CX54DKK	NW & Wales
BX55FWS	London	CX06BGY	NW & Wales	CX07CPY	NW & Wales	CX54DKL	NW & Wales
BX55FWT	London	CX06BGZ	NW & Wales	CX07CPZ	NW & Wales	CX54DKN	NW & Wales
BX55FWU	London	CX06BHA	NW & Wales	CX07CRF	NW & Wales	CX54DKO	NW & Wales
BX55FWV	London	CX06BHD	NW & Wales	CX07CRJ	NW & Wales	CX54DKU	NW & Wales
BX55FWW	London	CX06BHE	NW & Wales	CX07CRK	NW & Wales	CX54DKV	NW & Wales
BX55FWY	London	CX06BHF	NW & Wales	CX07CRU	NW & Wales	CX54DKY	NW & Wales
BX55FWZ	London	CX06BHJ	NW & Wales	CX07CRV	NW & Wales	CX54DLD	NW & Wales
BX55FXB	London	CX06BHK	NW & Wales	CX07CRZ	NW & Wales	CX54DLF	NW & Wales
BX55FXC	London	CX06BHL	NW & Wales	CX07CSF	NW & Wales	CX54DLJ	NW & Wales
BX55FXE	London	CX06BHN	NW & Wales	CX07CSO	NW & Wales	CX54DLK	NW & Wales
BX55FXF	London	CX06BHO	NW & Wales	CX07CSU	NW & Wales	CX54EPJ	NW & Wales
BX55FXG	London	CX06BHP	NW & Wales	CX07CSV	NW & Wales	CX54EPK	NW & Wales
BX55FXH	London	CX06BHU	NW & Wales	CX07CSY	NW & Wales	CX54EPL	NW & Wales

Reg	Region	Reg	Region	Reg	Region	Reg	Region
CX54EPN	NW & Wales	CX58EUO	NW & Wales	CX58EZA	NW & Wales	DK55FXG	NW & Wales
CX54EPO	NW & Wales	CX58EUP	NW & Wales	CX58EZB	NW & Wales	DK55FXH	NW & Wales
CX55EAA	Scotland West	CX58EUR	NW & Wales	CX58EZC	NW & Wales	DK55FXJ	NW & Wales
CX55EAC	Scotland West	CX58EUT	NW & Wales	CX58EZE	NW & Wales	DK55FXL	NW & Wales
CX55EAE	Scotland West	CX58EUU	NW & Wales	CX58EZF	NW & Wales	DK55FXM	NW & Wales
CX55EAF	NW & Wales	CX58EUV	NW & Wales	CX58EZG	NW & Wales	DK55FXO	NW & Wales
CX55EAG	NW & Wales	CX58EUW	NW & Wales	CX58EZH	NW & Wales	DK55FXR	NW & Wales
CX55EAJ	NW & Wales	CX58EUY	NW & Wales	CX58EZJ	NW & Wales	DK55FXS	NW & Wales
CX55EAK	NW & Wales	CX58EUZ	NW & Wales	CX58EZK	NW & Wales	DK55FXT	NW & Wales
CX55EAM	NW & Wales	CX58EVB	NW & Wales	CX58EZL	NW & Wales	DK55FXU	NW & Wales
CX55EAO	NW & Wales	CX58EVC	NW & Wales	CX58FYU	NW & Wales	DK55FXV	NW & Wales
CX55EAP	NW & Wales	CX58EVD	NW & Wales	CX58FYV	NW & Wales	DK55FXW	NW & Wales
CX55EAW	NW & Wales	CX58EVF	NW & Wales	CX58FYW	NW & Wales	DK55FXX	NW & Wales
CX55EAY	NW & Wales	CX58EVG	NW & Wales	CX58FYY	NW & Wales	DK55FXY	NW & Wales
CX55EBA	NW & Wales	CX58EVH	NW & Wales	CX58FYZ	NW & Wales	DK55FXZ	NW & Wales
CX55EBC	NW & Wales	CX58EVJ	NW & Wales	CX58FZM	NW & Wales	DK55FYA	NW & Wales
CX55EBD	NW & Wales	CX58EVK	NW & Wales	CX58FZN	NW & Wales	DK55FYB	NW & Wales
CX55EBF	NW & Wales	CX58EVL	NW & Wales	CX58FZO	NW & Wales	DK55FYC	NW & Wales
CX55EBG	NW & Wales	CX58EVN	NW & Wales	CX58FZP	NW & Wales	DK55FYD	NW & Wales
CX55EBJ	NW & Wales	CX58EVP	NW & Wales	CX58FZR	NW & Wales	DK55FYE	NW & Wales
CX55FAF	NW & Wales	CX58EVR	NW & Wales	CX58FZS	NW & Wales	DK55FYF	NW & Wales
CX55FAJ	NW & Wales	CX58EVT	NW & Wales	CX58FZT	NW & Wales	DK55FYG	NW & Wales
CX56CDY	NW & Wales	CX58EVU	NW & Wales	CX58FZU	NW & Wales	DK55FYH	NW & Wales
CX56CDZ	NW & Wales	CX58EVV	NW & Wales	CX58FZV	NW & Wales	DK55FYJ	NW & Wales
CX56CEA	NW & Wales	CX58EVW	NW & Wales	CX58FZW	NW & Wales	DK55FYL	NW & Wales
CX56CEF	NW & Wales	CX58EVY	NW & Wales	CX58FZY	NW & Wales	DK55FYM	NW & Wales
CX56CEJ	NW & Wales	CX58EWA	NW & Wales	CX58FZZ	NW & Wales	DK55FYN	NW & Wales
CX56CEK	NW & Wales	CX58EWB	NW & Wales	CX58GAA	NW & Wales	DK55FYO	NW & Wales
CX56CEN	NW & Wales	CX58EWC	NW & Wales	CX58GAO	NW & Wales	DK55FYP	NW & Wales
CX56CEO	NW & Wales	CX58EWD	NW & Wales	CX58GAU	NW & Wales	DK55FYR	NW & Wales
CX56CEU	NW & Wales	CX58EWE	NW & Wales	CX58GBE	NW & Wales	DK55FYS	NW & Wales
CX56CEV	NW & Wales	CX58EWF	NW & Wales	CX58GBF	NW & Wales	DK55FYT	NW & Wales
CX56CEY	NW & Wales	CX58EWG	NW & Wales	CX58GBO	NW & Wales	DK55FYV	NW & Wales
CX56CFA	NW & Wales	CX58EWH	NW & Wales	CX58GBU	NW & Wales	DK55FYW	NW & Wales
CX57BZO	NW & Wales	CX58EWJ	NW & Wales	CX58GBV	NW & Wales	E224WBG	NW & Wales
CX57CYO	NW & Wales	CX58EWK	NW & Wales	CX58GBY	NW & Wales	E227WBG	NW & Wales
CX57CYP	NW & Wales	CX58EWL	NW & Wales	CX58GBZ	NW & Wales	E691NOU	Tellings GM
CX57CYS	NW & Wales	CX58EWM	NW & Wales	CX58GCF	NW & Wales	E766JAR	Original Tour
CX57CYT	NW & Wales	CX58EWN	NW & Wales	D78JHY	Tellings GM	E767JAR	Original Tour
CX57CYU	NW & Wales	CX58EWO	NW & Wales	D170FYM	NW & Wales	E768JAR	Original Tour
CX57CYV	NW & Wales	CX58EWP	NW & Wales	D171FYM	NW & Wales	E769JAR	Original Tour
CX57CYW	NW & Wales	CX58EWR	NW & Wales	D242FYM	NW & Wales	E770JAR	Original Tour
CX57CYX	NW & Wales	CX58EWS	NW & Wales	D553YNO	Original Tour	E771JAR	Original Tour
CX57CYY	NW & Wales	CX58EWT	NW & Wales	D675YNO	Original Tour	E772JAR	Original Tour
CX57CZA	NW & Wales	CX58EWU	NW & Wales	DA51XTC	Midlands	E773JAR	Original Tour
CX58ETY	NW & Wales	CX58EWV	NW & Wales	DA51XTD	Midlands	E774JAR	Original Tour
CX58ETZ	NW & Wales	CX58EWW	NW & Wales	DA51XTE	Midlands	E964JAR	Original Tour
CX58EUA	NW & Wales	CX58EWY	NW & Wales	DG52TYP	Midlands	E965JAR	Original Tour
CX58EUA	NW & Wales	CX58EWZ	NW & Wales	DG52TYS	Midlands	EA520JL	Tellings GM
CX58EUB	NW & Wales	CX58EXA	NW & Wales	DG52TYT	Midlands	EJ020VU	Tellings GM
CX58EUD	NW & Wales	CX58EXB	NW & Wales	DG52TYU	Midlands	EJ020VV	Tellings GM
CX58EUE	NW & Wales	CX58EXC	NW & Wales	DK55FWY	NW & Wales	EJ020VW	Tellings GM
CX58EUF	NW & Wales	CX58EXE	NW & Wales	DK55FWZ	NW & Wales	EJ020VX	Tellings GM
CX58EUH	NW & Wales	CX58EXF	NW & Wales	DK55FXA	NW & Wales	EJ020VY	Tellings GM
CX58EUJ	NW & Wales	CX58EXG	NW & Wales	DK55FXB	NW & Wales	EJ020VZ	Tellings GM
CX58EUK	NW & Wales	CX58EXH	NW & Wales	DK55FXC	NW & Wales	EJ020WA	Tellings GM
CX58EUL	NW & Wales	CX58EXJ	NW & Wales	DK55FXD	NW & Wales	ELZ2362	Midlands
CX58EUM	NW & Wales	CX58EXK	NW & Wales	DK55FXE	NW & Wales	E052HZU	Tellings GM
CX58EUN	NW & Wales	CX58EXL	NW & Wales	DK55FXF	NW & Wales	E052HZV	Tellings GM

EO52OZT	Tellings GM	FJ06ZST	Midlands	FJ55BWG	Midlands	FY58HYV	Midlands
EU05DVW	Original Tour	FJ06ZSU	Midlands	FJ56KFA	Midlands	FY58HYW	Midlands
EU05DVX	Original Tour	FJ06ZSV	Midlands	FJ56KFC	Midlands	FY58HYX	Midlands
EU06BCL	Tellings GM	FJ06ZSW	Midlands	FJ56KFD	Midlands	G2PGL	Tellings GM
EU56FTO	Tellings GM	FJ06ZSX	Midlands	FJ56KFE	Midlands	G34HKY	Tellings GM
EU56GVG	Tellings GM	FJ06ZSY	Midlands	FJ56KFF	Midlands	G35HKY	NW & Wales
EU56GVG	Tellings GM	FJ06ZSZ	Midlands	FJ56KFG	Midlands	G37HKY	Tellings GM
F634LMJ	The Shires	FJ06ZTB	Midlands	FJ56KFK	Midlands	G132YWC	The Shires
F636LMJ	The Shires	FJ06ZTC	Midlands	FJ56KFL	Midlands	G231VWL	The Shires
F637LMJ	The Shires	FJ06ZTD	Midlands	FJ56OBC	Midlands	G235VWL	The Shires
F641LMJ	The Shires	FJ06ZTE	Midlands	FJ56OBD	Midlands	G290UMJ	The Shires
F643LMJ	The Shires	FJ06ZTF	Midlands	FJ56OBE	Midlands	G291UMJ	The Shires
F644LMJ	The Shires	FJ06ZTG	Midlands	FJ56OBG	Midlands	G529VBB	North East
FCZ3413	Midlands	FJ06ZTH	Midlands	FJ56OBH	Midlands	G545VBB	North East
FD02UKB	Midlands	FJ06ZTK	Midlands	FJ56OBK	Midlands	G546VBB	North East
FD02UKC	Midlands	FJ06ZTL	Midlands	FJ56OBL	Midlands	G613BPH	Tellings GM
FD02UKE	Midlands	FJ06ZTM	Midlands	FJ56OBM	Midlands	G614BPH	Tellings GM
FD02UKG	Midlands	FJ06ZTN	Midlands	FJ56OBN	Midlands	G615BPH	Tellings GM
FD02UKJ	Midlands	FJ06ZTO	Midlands	FJ56OBP	The Shires	G624BPH	Southern Cs
FD02UKK	Midlands	FJ06ZTP	Midlands	FJ56PCX	The Shires	G629BPH	Southern Cs
FD02UKL	Midlands	FJ07DWF	Tellings GM	FJ56PCY	The Shires	G630BPH	Southern Cs
FD02UKN	Midlands	FJ07DWG	Tellings GM	FJ56PCZ	The Shires	G631BPH	Southern Cs
FD02UKO	Midlands	FJ07TKA	The Shires	FJ56PDK	The Shires	G633BPH	Southern Cs
FD02UKP	Midlands	FJ07TKC	The Shires	FJ56PDO	The Shires	G634BPH	Southern Cs
FD02UKR	Midlands	FJ07TKE	The Shires	FJ57KGK	Tellings GM	G635BPH	Southern Cs
FD02UKS	Midlands	FJ07TKF	The Shires	FJ58KXF	Midlands	G636BPH	Southern Cs
FD02UKT	Midlands	FJ08DXG	The Shires	FJ58KXG	Midlands	G643BPH	Tellings GM
FD02UKU	Midlands	FJ08DXK	The Shires	FJ58KXH	Midlands	G645UPP	The Shires
FD52GGO	Midlands	FJ08DXL	The Shires	FJ58KXK	Midlands	G646UPP	The Shires
FD52GGP	Midlands	FJ08DXM	The Shires	FJ58KXL	Midlands	G647UPP	The Shires
FD52GGU	Midlands	FJ08DXO	The Shires	FJ58KXM	Midlands	G648UPP	The Shires
FD52GGV	Midlands	FJ08DXP	The Shires	FJ58KXN	Midlands	G649UPP	The Shires
FE51WSU	Midlands	FJ08DXR	The Shires	FJ58KXO	Midlands	G650UPP	The Shires
FE51WSV	Midlands	FJ08KMA	Tellings GM	FJ58KXP	Midlands	G651UPP	The Shires
FE51YWH	Midlands	FJ08KME	Tellings GM	FJ58KXR	Midlands	G652UPP	The Shires
FE51YWJ	Midlands	FJ08KMF	Tellings GM	FJ58KXS	Midlands	G653UPP	The Shires
FE51YWK	Midlands	FJ08KMG	Tellings GM	FJ58KXT	Midlands	G654UPP	The Shires
FE51YWL	Midlands	FJ08LVL	Midlands	FJ58KXU	Midlands	G655UPP	The Shires
FE51YWM	Midlands	FJ08LVM	Midlands	FJ58KXV	Midlands	G656UPP	The Shires
FG56OBF	Midlands	FJ08LVN	Midlands	FJ58KXW	Midlands	G657UPP	The Shires
FJ04PFX	Midlands	FJ08LVO	Midlands	FJ58KXX	Midlands	G725RYJ	Tellings GM
FJ05KWV	Tellings GM	FJ08LVP	Midlands	FJ58KXY	Midlands	GB03TGM	Southern Cs
FJ06ZKK	Tellings GM	FJ08LVR	Midlands	FK52MML	Midlands	GB04LLC	Tellings GM
FJ06ZKL	Tellings GM	FJ08LVS	Midlands	FL52MML	Midlands	GB04TGM	Tellings GM
FJ06ZPV	Midlands	FJ08LVT	Midlands	FN04AFJ	Midlands	GB53BCL	Tellings GM
FJ06ZPW	Midlands	FJ54OTN	Midlands	FN04FSE	Tellings GM	GJ02XZK	Tellings GM
FJ06ZPX	Midlands	FJ54OTP	Midlands	FN04FSF	Tellings GM	GK51SYY	Southern Cs
FJ06ZRL	Midlands	FJ54OTR	Midlands	FN52XBG	Midlands	GK51SYZ	Southern Cs
FJ06ZRN	Midlands	FJ54OTT	Midlands	FY03WZV	Midlands	GK51SZC	Southern Cs
FJ06ZRO	Midlands	FJ54OTV	Midlands	FY58HYH	Midlands	GK51SZD	Southern Cs
FJ06ZRP	Midlands	FJ54OTW	Midlands	FY58HYK	Midlands	GK51SZE	Southern Cs
FJ06ZSD	Midlands	FJ54OTX	Midlands	FY58HYL	Midlands	GK51SZF	Southern Cs
FJ06ZSE	Midlands	FJ55BVT	Midlands	FY58HYM	Midlands	GK51SZG	Southern Cs
FJ06ZSF	Midlands	FJ55BVU	Midlands	FY58HYN	Midlands	GK51SZJ	Southern Cs
FJ06ZSG	Midlands	FJ55BWA	Midlands	FY58HYO	Midlands	GK51SZL	Southern Cs
FJ06ZSK	Midlands	FJ55BWB	Midlands	FY58HYP	Midlands	GK51SZN	Southern Cs
FJ06ZSL	Midlands	FJ55BWC	Midlands	FY58HYR	Midlands	GK52YUW	Southern Cs
FJ06ZSN	Midlands	FJ55BWD	Midlands	FY58HYS	Midlands	GK52YUX	Southern Cs
FJ06ZSO	Midlands	FJ55BWE	Midlands	FY58HYT	Midlands	GK52YUY	Southern Cs
FJ06ZSP	Midlands	FJ55BWF	Midlands	FY58HYU	Midlands	GK52YVB	Southern Cs

GK52YVC	Southern Cs	GN04UEL	Southern Cs	GN06EVU	Southern Cs	GN09AXC	Southern Cs
GK52YVD	Southern Cs	GN04UEM	Southern Cs	GN06EWC	Southern Cs	GN09AXD	Southern Cs
GK52YVE	Southern Cs	GN04UEP	Southern Cs	GN06EWD	Southern Cs	GN09AXF	Southern Cs
GK52YVF	Southern Cs	GN04UER	Southern Cs	GN06EWE	Southern Cs	GN09AXG	Southern Cs
GK52YVG	Southern Cs	GN04UES	Southern Cs	GN07AVB	Southern Cs	GN09AXH	Southern Cs
GK52YVJ	Southern Cs	GN04UET	Southern Cs	GN07AVC	Southern Cs	GN09AXJ	Southern Cs
GK52YVL	Southern Cs	GN04UEU	Southern Cs	GN07AVD	Southern Cs	GN09AXK	Southern Cs
GK53AOA	Southern Cs	GN04UEV	Southern Cs	GN07AVE	Southern Cs	GN09AXM	Southern Cs
GK53AOB	Southern Cs	GN04UEW	Southern Cs	GN07AVF	Southern Cs	GN09AXO	Southern Cs
GK53AOC	Southern Cs	GN04UEX	Southern Cs	GN07AVG	Southern Cs	GN10KWE	Southern Cs
GK53AOD	Southern Cs	GN04UEY	Southern Cs	GN07AVJ	Southern Cs	GN10KWF	Southern Cs
GK53AOE	Southern Cs	GN04UEZ	Southern Cs	GN07AVL	Southern Cs	GN10KWG	Southern Cs
GK53AOF	Southern Cs	GN04UFA	Southern Cs	GN07AVM	Southern Cs	GN10KWH	Southern Cs
GK53AOG	Southern Cs	GN04UFB	Southern Cs	GN07AVN	Southern Cs	GN10KWJ	Southern Cs
GK53AOH	Southern Cs	GN04UFC	Southern Cs	GN07AVO	Southern Cs	GN10KWK	Southern Cs
GK53AOJ	Southern Cs	GN04UFD	Southern Cs	GN07AVP	Southern Cs	GN54MYO	Southern Cs
GK53AOL	Southern Cs	GN04UFE	Southern Cs	GN07DLE	Southern Cs	GN54MYP	Southern Cs
GK53AON	Southern Cs	GN04UFG	Southern Cs	GN07DLF	Southern Cs	GN54MYR	Southern Cs
GK53AOO	Southern Cs	GN04UFH	Southern Cs	GN07DLJ	Southern Cs	GN54MYT	Southern Cs
GK53AOP	Southern Cs	GN04UFJ	Southern Cs	GN07DLK	Southern Cs	GN54MYU	Southern Cs
GK53AOR	Southern Cs	GN04UFK	Southern Cs	GN07DLO	Southern Cs	GN57BNX	Southern Cs
GK53AOT	Southern Cs	GN04UFL	Southern Cs	GN07DLU	Southern Cs	GN57BNY	Southern Cs
GK53AOU	Southern Cs	GN04UFM	Southern Cs	GN07DLV	Southern Cs	GN57BNZ	Southern Cs
GK53AOV	Southern Cs	GN04UFP	Southern Cs	GN07DLX	Southern Cs	GN57BOF	Southern Cs
GK53AOW	Southern Cs	GN04UFR	Southern Cs	GN07DLY	Southern Cs	GN57BOH	Southern Cs
GK53AOX	Southern Cs	GN04UFS	Southern Cs	GN07DLZ	Southern Cs	GN57BOJ	Southern Cs
GK53AOY	Southern Cs	GN04UFT	Southern Cs	GN07DME	Southern Cs	GN57BOU	Southern Cs
GK53AOZ	Southern Cs	GN04UFU	Southern Cs	GN07DMF	Southern Cs	GN57BOV	Southern Cs
GKA449L	NW & Wales	GN04UFV	Southern Cs	GN07DMO	Southern Cs	GN57BPE	Southern Cs
GN04UCW	Southern Cs	GN04UFW	Southern Cs	GN07DMU	Southern Cs	GN57BPF	Southern Cs
GN04UCX	Southern Cs	GN04UFX	Southern Cs	GN07DMV	Southern Cs	GN57BPK	Southern Cs
GN04UCY	Southern Cs	GN04UFY	Southern Cs	GN08CGO	Southern Cs	GN57BPO	Southern Cs
GN04UCZ	Southern Cs	GN04UFZ	Southern Cs	GN08CGU	Southern Cs	GN57BPU	Southern Cs
GN04UDB	Southern Cs	GN04UGA	Southern Cs	GN08CGV	Southern Cs	GN57BPV	Southern Cs
GN04UDD	Southern Cs	GN04UGB	Southern Cs	GN08CGX	Southern Cs	GN57BPX	Southern Cs
GN04UDE	Southern Cs	GN04UGC	Southern Cs	GN08CGY	Southern Cs	GN57BPY	Southern Cs
GN04UDG	Southern Cs	GN04UGD	Southern Cs	GN08CGZ	Southern Cs	GN58BSO	Southern Cs
GN04UDH	Southern Cs	GN04UGE	Southern Cs	GN09AVV	Southern Cs	GN58BSU	Southern Cs
GN04UDJ	Southern Cs	GN04UGF	Southern Cs	GN09AVW	Southern Cs	GN58BSV	Southern Cs
GN04UDK	Southern Cs	GN04UGG	Southern Cs	GN09AVX	Southern Cs	GN58BSX	Southern Cs
GN04UDL	Southern Cs	GN05ANU	Southern Cs	GN09AVY	Southern Cs	GN58BSY	Southern Cs
GN04UDM	Southern Cs	GN05ANV	Southern Cs	GN09AVZ	Southern Cs	GN58BSZ	Southern Cs
GN04UDP	Southern Cs	GN05ANX	Southern Cs	GN09AWA	Southern Cs	GN58BTE	Southern Cs
GN04UDS	Southern Cs	GN05AOB	Southern Cs	GN09AWB	Southern Cs	GN58BTF	Southern Cs
GN04UDT	Southern Cs	GN05AOC	Southern Cs	GN09AWC	Southern Cs	GN58BTO	Southern Cs
GN04UDU	Southern Cs	GN06EBB	Southern Cs	GN09AWG	Southern Cs	GN58BTU	Southern Cs
GN04UDV	Southern Cs	GN06EBF	Southern Cs	GN09AWH	Southern Cs	GN58BTV	Southern Cs
GN04UDW	Southern Cs	GN06EBG	Southern Cs	GN09AWJ	Southern Cs	GN58BTX	Southern Cs
GN04UDX	Southern Cs	GN06EBH	Southern Cs	GN09AWM	Southern Cs	GN58BTY	Southern Cs
GN04UDY	Southern Cs	GN06EUU	Southern Cs	GN09AWO	Southern Cs	GN58BTZ	Southern Cs
GN04UDZ	Southern Cs	GN06EVG	Southern Cs	GN09AWP	Southern Cs	GN58BUA	Southern Cs
GN04UEA	Southern Cs	GN06EVH	Southern Cs	GN09AWR	Southern Cs	GN58BUE	Southern Cs
GN04UEB	Southern Cs	GN06EVJ	Southern Cs	GN09AWU	Southern Cs	GN58BUF	Southern Cs
GN04UEC	Southern Cs	GN06EVK	Southern Cs	GN09AWV	Southern Cs	GN58BUH	Southern Cs
GN04UED	Southern Cs	GN06EVL	Southern Cs	GN09AWW	Southern Cs	GN58BUJ	Southern Cs
GN04UEE	Southern Cs	GN06EVM	Southern Cs	GN09AWX	Southern Cs	GN58BUO	Southern Cs
GN04UEG	Southern Cs	GN06EVP	Southern Cs	GN09AWY	Southern Cs	GN58BUP	Southern Cs
GN04UEH	Southern Cs	GN06EVR	Southern Cs	GN09AWZ	Southern Cs	GN58BUU	Southern Cs
GN04UEJ	Southern Cs	GN06EVT	Southern Cs	GN09AXA	Southern Cs	GN58BUV	Southern Cs
GN04UEK	Southern Cs	GN06EVT	Southern Cs	GN09AXB	Southern Cs	GN58LVA	Southern Cs

Reg	Operator	Reg	Operator	Reg	Operator	Reg	Operator
GN58LVB	Southern Cs	J321BSH	Original Tour	K909SKR	Southern Cs	KE53NFC	The Shires
GN59FVB	Southern Cs	J322BSH	Original Tour	K910SKR	Southern Cs	KE53NFD	The Shires
GN59FVC	Southern Cs	J323BSH	Original Tour	KC03PGE	The Shires	KE53NFF	The Shires
GN59FVD	Southern Cs	J324BSH	Original Tour	KC03PGF	The Shires	KE53NFG	The Shires
GN59FVE	Southern Cs	J325BSH	Original Tour	KC06EVN	Tellings GM	KE54HHF	The Shires
GN59FVF	Southern Cs	J326BSH	Original Tour	KC06EVN	Tellings GM	KE54LNR	The Shires
GN59FVG	Southern Cs	J327BSH	Original Tour	KC06EVP	Tellings GM	KE54LPC	The Shires
GN59FVH	Southern Cs	J328BSH	Original Tour	KC06EVP	Tellings GM	KE54LPF	The Shires
GN59FVJ	Southern Cs	J329BSH	Original Tour	KC51NFO	Southern Cs	KE54LPJ	The Shires
GO03CLA	Tellings GM	J330BSH	Original Tour	KC51PUX	Southern Cs	KE55CKO	The Shires
GO58CHC	Southern Cs	J331BSH	Original Tour	KE03OUK	The Shires	KE55CKP	The Shires
GO58CHD	Southern Cs	J332BSH	Original Tour	KE03OUL	The Shires	KE55CKU	The Shires
GO58CHF	Southern Cs	J334BSH	Original Tour	KE03OUM	The Shires	KE55CTF	The Shires
GO58CHG	Southern Cs	J335BSH	Original Tour	KE03OUN	The Shires	KE55CTK	The Shires
GO58CHH	Southern Cs	J336BSH	Original Tour	KE03OUP	The Shires	KE55CTO	The Shires
GS05TGM	Tellings GM	J337BSH	Original Tour	KE03OUS	The Shires	KE55CTU	The Shires
GSU347	Scotland West	J338BSH	Original Tour	KE03OUU	The Shires	KE55CTV	The Shires
GSU348	Tellings GM	J339BSH	Original Tour	KE03UKK	The Shires	KE55CVA	The Shires
H81DVM	Midlands	J340BSH	Original Tour	KE04CZF	The Shires	KE55CVG	The Shires
H197GRO	The Shires	J341BSH	Original Tour	KE04CZG	The Shires	KE55CVH	The Shires
H202GRO	The Shires	J342BSH	Original Tour	KE04CZH	The Shires	KE55CVJ	The Shires
H769EKJ	Southern Cs	J343BSH	Original Tour	KE04OSU	The Shires	KE55CVK	The Shires
H804RWJ	Tellings GM	J344BSH	Original Tour	KE04OSV	The Shires	KE55CVL	The Shires
HDZ2604	The Shires	J345BSH	Original Tour	KE04PZF	The Shires	KE55CVM	The Shires
HDZ2605	The Shires	J346BSH	Original Tour	KE04PZG	The Shires	KE55FBX	The Shires
HDZ2606	The Shires	J347BSH	Original Tour	KE05FMM	The Shires	KE55FBY	The Shires
HDZ2607	The Shires	J348BSH	Original Tour	KE05FMO	The Shires	KE55FDF	The Shires
HDZ2611	The Shires	J349BSH	Original Tour	KE05FMP	The Shires	KE55FDG	The Shires
HIL2148	Scotland West	J350BSH	Original Tour	KE05FMU	The Shires	KE55GVY	The Shires
HKZ9240	Midlands	J351BSH	Original Tour	KE05FMV	The Shires	KE55GVZ	The Shires
HT05YCP	Tellings GM	J352BSH	Original Tour	KE05FMX	The Shires	KE55GWA	The Shires
HT05YCR	Tellings GM	J433BSH	Original Tour	KE05GOH	The Shires	KE55GWC	The Shires
HT05YCV	Tellings GM	J468OKP	North East	KE07EVX	The Shires	KE55GXR	The Shires
HT05YCX	Tellings GM	JJD545D	London	KE07EVY	The Shires	KE55KPG	The Shires
HT05YCZ	Tellings GM	K27EWC	NW & Wales	KE07EWA	The Shires	KE55KPJ	The Shires
HT05YDA	Tellings GM	K101OHF	Midlands	KE07EWB	The Shires	KE55KTC	The Shires
HT05YDA	Tellings GM	K102OHF	Midlands	KE07EWC	The Shires	KE55KTD	The Shires
HT05YDB	Tellings GM	K103OHF	Midlands	KE51PSZ	The Shires	KE55KTJ	The Shires
HT05YDB	Tellings GM	K105OHF	Midlands	KE51PTO	The Shires	KE57EPA	The Shires
HT05YDC	Tellings GM	K107OHF	Midlands	KE51PTU	The Shires	KE57EPC	The Shires
HT05YDC	Tellings GM	K108OHF	Midlands	KE51PTX	The Shires	KJ02JXT	The Shires
HX04HRD	Tellings GM	K140RYS	North East	KE51PTY	Southern Cs	KL52CWJ	The Shires
HX04HUH	Tellings GM	K320CVX	Yorkshire	KE51PTZ	Southern Cs	KL52CWK	The Shires
HX04HUK	Tellings GM	K321CVX	The Shires	KE51PUA	Southern Cs	KL52CWN	The Shires
HX51LRJ	Tellings GM	K322CVX	The Shires	KE51PUF	Southern Cs	KL52CWO	The Shires
HX51LRK	Tellings GM	K345OFM	Midlands	KE51PUH	Southern Cs	KL52CWP	The Shires
HX51LRL	Tellings GM	K346OFM	Midlands	KE51PUJ	Southern Cs	KL52CWR	The Shires
HX51LRN	Tellings GM	K347OFM	Midlands	KE51PUK	Southern Cs	KL52CWT	The Shires
HX51LRO	Tellings GM	K401HWW	Yorkshire	KE51PUO	Southern Cs	KL52CWU	The Shires
HX51LSO	The Shires	K402HWW	Yorkshire	KE51PUU	Southern Cs	KL52CWV	The Shires
HX55EZF	Midlands	K403HWW	Yorkshire	KE51PUV	Southern Cs	KL52CWW	The Shires
IHZ8821	Midlands	K415BHN	North East	KE51PUY	Southern Cs	KL52CWZ	The Shires
IJZ2331	Midlands	K422BHN	North East	KE51PVD	Southern Cs	KL52CXA	The Shires
J220HGY	North East	K507BHN	North East	KE51PVF	The Shires	KL52CXB	The Shires
J315BSH	Original Tour	K582MGT	North East	KE51PVK	The Shires	KL52CXC	The Shires
J316BSH	Original Tour	K709PCN	North East	KE51PVZ	The Shires	KL52CXD	The Shires
J317BSH	Original Tour	K717PCN	North East	KE53KBO	The Shires	KL52CXE	The Shires
J318BSH	Original Tour	K906SKR	Southern Cs	KE53KBP	The Shires	KL52CXF	The Shires
J319BSH	Original Tour	K907SKR	Southern Cs	KE53NEU	The Shires	KL52CXG	The Shires
J320BSH	Original Tour	K908SKR	Southern Cs	KE53NFA	The Shires	KL52CXH	The Shires

Reg	Operator	Reg	Operator	Reg	Operator	Reg	Operator
KL52CXJ	The Shires	KX09KDN	The Shires	L502TKA	NW & Wales	LF02PTU	London
KL52CXK	The Shires	KX09KDO	The Shires	L505TKA	NW & Wales	LF02PTX	London
KL52CXM	The Shires	KX09KDU	The Shires	L506CPJ	Southern Cs	LF02PTY	London
KL52CXN	The Shires	KX09KDV	The Shires	L507CPJ	Southern Cs	LF02PTZ	London
KL52CXO	The Shires	KX54AVD	The Shires	L508TKA	NW & Wales	LF02PVA	The Shires
KL52CXP	The Shires	KX54AVE	The Shires	L509CPJ	Southern Cs	LF02PVE	London
KL52CXR	The Shires	KX56HCP	Tellings GM	L526FHN	North East	LF02PVJ	London
KL52CXS	The Shires	KX56OVL	Tellings GM	L532EHD	North East	LF02PVK	London
KM51BFX	Tellings GM	KX57FML	Tellings GM	L533FHN	North East	LF02PVL	London
KN52NCD	Tellings GM	KX57OWK	Tellings GM	L551GHN	North East	LF02PVN	London
KN52NDF	Tellings GM	KX57OWM	Tellings GM	L602EKM	The Shires	LF02PVO	London
KN52NDK	Tellings GM	KX57OWO	Tellings GM	L605EKM	Southern Cs	LF08DZW	Tellings GM
KN52NDL	Tellings GM	KX57OWP	Tellings GM	L729VNL	North East	LF08DZX	Tellings GM
KN52NDU	Tellings GM	KX59ACJ	The Shires	L735VNL	North East	LF52UNV	London
KN52NDV	Tellings GM	KX59ACO	The Shires	L736VNL	North East	LF52UNW	London
KN52NDX	Tellings GM	KX59AEE	The Shires	L737VNL	North East	LF52UNX	London
KN52NEJ	Tellings GM	KX59AEF	The Shires	L738VNL	North East	LF52UNY	London
KP51UFL	Tellings GM	KX59CYE	Tellings GM	L739VNL	North East	LF52UNZ	London
KP54BYY	Tellings GM	KX59CYF	Tellings GM	L740VNL	North East	LF52UOA	London
KP54BYZ	Tellings GM	KX59CZA	Tellings GM	L741VNL	North East	LF52UOB	London
KU52EYH	Tellings GM	KX59CZB	Tellings GM	L748VNL	North East	LF52UOC	London
KU52EYJ	Tellings GM	KX59CZC	Tellings GM	L759VNL	North East	LF52UOD	London
KU52RXG	Tellings GM	KX59CZD	Tellings GM	LF02PKA	London	LF52UOE	London
KU52RXT	Tellings GM	KX59CZE	Tellings GM	LF02PKC	London	LF52UOG	London
KU52RYO	Tellings GM	KX59CZF	Tellings GM	LF02PKD	London	LF52UOH	London
KX08HLR	Tellings GM	KX59CZG	Tellings GM	LF02PKE	London	LF52UOJ	London
KX08HLU	Tellings GM	KX59CZH	Tellings GM	LF02PKJ	London	LF52UOK	London
KX08ONC	Tellings GM	KX59CZJ	Tellings GM	LF02PKO	London	LF52UOL	London
KX08ONG	Tellings GM	KX59CZK	Tellings GM	LF02PKU	London	LF52UOM	London
KX09GXW	The Shires	KX59CZL	Tellings GM	LF02PKV	London	LF52UON	London
KX09GXY	The Shires	KX59CZM	Tellings GM	LF02PKX	London	LF52UOO	London
KX09GXZ	The Shires	KX59CZN	Tellings GM	LF02PKY	London	LF52UOP	London
KX09GYA	The Shires	KY51SXD	Midlands	LF02PLJ	London	LF52UOR	London
KX09GYB	The Shires	L25LSX	Scotland West	LF02PLN	London	LF52UOS	London
KX09GYC	The Shires	L94HRF	North East	LF02PLO	London	LF52UOT	London
KX09GYD	The Shires	L95HRF	North East	LF02PLU	London	LF52UOU	London
KX09GYE	The Shires	L127YVK	North East	LF02PLV	London	LF52UOV	London
KX09GYF	The Shires	L136YVK	Yorkshire	LF02PLX	London	LF52UOW	London
KX09GYG	The Shires	L137YVK	Yorkshire	LF02PLZ	London	LF52UOX	London
KX09GYH	The Shires	L141YVK	North East	LF02PMO	London	LF52UOY	London
KX09GYJ	The Shires	L157YVK	North East	LF02PMV	London	LF52UPA	London
KX09GYK	The Shires	L161GYL	North East	LF02PMX	London	LF52UPB	London
KX09GYN	The Shires	L201TKA	Scotland West	LF02PMY	London	LF52UPC	London
KX09GYO	The Shires	L207YCU	Southern Cs	LF02PNE	London	LF52UPD	London
KX09GYP	The Shires	L209KEF	North East	LF02PNJ	London	LF52UPG	London
KX09GYR	The Shires	L210KEF	North East	LF02PNK	London	LF52UPH	London
KX09GYS	The Shires	L210TKA	Scotland West	LF02PNL	London	LF52UPK	London
KX09GYT	The Shires	L211KEF	North East	LF02PNN	London	LF52UPM	London
KX09GYU	The Shires	L212KEF	North East	LF02PNO	London	LF52UPN	London
KX09GYV	The Shires	L219TKA	North East	LF02PNU	London	LF52UPO	London
KX09GYW	The Shires	L220TKA	North East	LF02PNV	London	LF52UPP	London
KX09GYY	The Shires	L225TKA	North East	LF02PNX	London	LF52UPR	London
KX09GYZ	The Shires	L232TKA	North East	LF02PNY	London	LF52UPS	London
KX09GZA	The Shires	L235TKA	Scotland West	LF02POA	London	LF52UPT	London
KX09GZB	The Shires	L244TKA	North East	LF02POH	London	LF52UPV	London
KX09GZC	The Shires	L273FVN	Scotland West	LF02PSO	London	LF52UPW	London
KX09GZD	The Shires	L274FVN	Scotland West	LF02PSU	London	LF52UPX	London
KX09GZE	The Shires	L301TEM	NW & Wales	LF02PSY	London	LF52UPZ	London
KX09KDJ	The Shires	L302TEM	NW & Wales	LF02PSZ	London	LF52URA	London
KX09KDK	The Shires	L303TEM	NW & Wales	LF02PTO	London	LF52URB	London

LF52URC	London	LG03MFE	London	LJ03MGU	London	LJ03MVC	London
LF52URD	London	LG03MFF	London	LJ03MGV	London	LJ03MVD	London
LF52URE	London	LG03MFK	London	LJ03MGX	London	LJ03MVE	London
LF52URG	London	LG03MLL	London	LJ03MGY	London	LJ03MVF	London
LF52URH	London	LG03MLN	London	LJ03MGZ	London	LJ03MVG	London
LF52URJ	London	LG03MLV	London	LJ03MHA	London	LJ03MVT	London
LF52URK	London	LG03MMU	London	LJ03MHE	London	LJ03MVV	London
LF52URL	London	LG03MMV	London	LJ03MHF	London	LJ03MVW	London
LF52URM	London	LG03MMX	London	LJ03MHK	London	LJ03MVX	London
LF52URN	London	LG03MOA	London	LJ03MHL	London	LJ03MVY	London
LF52URO	London	LG03MOF	London	LJ03MHM	London	LJ03MVZ	London
LF52URP	London	LG03MOV	London	LJ03MHN	London	LJ03MWA	London
LF52URR	London	LG03MPF	London	LJ03MHU	London	LJ03MWC	London
LF52URS	London	LG03MPU	London	LJ03MHV	London	LJ03MWD	London
LF52URT	London	LG03MPV	London	LJ03MHX	London	LJ03MWE	London
LF52URU	London	LG03MPX	London	LJ03MHY	London	LJ03MWF	London
LF52URV	London	LG03MPY	London	LJ03MHZ	London	LJ03MWG	London
LF52URW	London	LG03MPZ	London	LJ03MJE	London	LJ03MWK	London
LF52URX	London	LG03MRU	London	LJ03MJF	London	LJ03MWL	London
LF52URY	London	LG03MRV	London	LJ03MJK	London	LJ03MWN	London
LF52URZ	London	LG03MRX	London	LJ03MJU	London	LJ03MWP	London
LF52USB	London	LG03MRY	London	LJ03MJV	London	LJ03MWU	London
LF52USC	London	LG03MSU	London	LJ03MJX	London	LJ03MWV	London
LF52USD	London	LG03MSV	London	LJ03MJY	London	LJ03MWX	London
LF52USE	London	LG03MSX	London	LJ03MKA	London	LJ03MXH	London
LF52USG	London	LG52DAA	London	LJ03MKC	London	LJ03MXK	London
LF52USH	London	LG52DAO	London	LJ03MKD	London	LJ03MXL	London
LF52USJ	London	LG52DAU	London	LJ03MKE	London	LJ03MXM	London
LF52USL	London	LG52DBO	London	LJ03MKF	London	LJ03MXN	London
LF52USM	London	LG52DBU	London	LJ03MKG	London	LJ03MXP	London
LF52USN	London	LG52DBV	London	LJ03MKK	London	LJ03MXR	London
LF52USO	London	LG52DBY	London	LJ03MKL	London	LJ03MXS	London
LF52USS	London	LG52DBZ	London	LJ03MKM	London	LJ03MXT	London
LF52UST	London	LG52DCE	London	LJ03MKN	London	LJ03MXU	London
LF52USU	London	LG52DCF	London	LJ03MKU	London	LJ03MXV	London
LF52USV	London	LG52DCO	London	LJ03MKV	London	LJ03MXW	London
LF52USW	London	LG52DCU	London	LJ03MKX	London	LJ03MXX	London
LF52USX	London	LG52DCV	London	LJ03MKZ	London	LJ03MXY	London
LF52USY	London	LG52DCX	London	LJ03MLE	London	LJ03MXZ	London
LF52USZ	London	LG52DCY	London	LJ03MLF	London	LJ03MYA	London
LF52UTA	London	LG52DCZ	London	LJ03MLK	London	LJ03MYB	London
LF52UTB	London	LG52DDA	London	LJ03MLX	London	LJ03MYC	London
LF52UTC	London	LG52DDE	London	LJ03MLY	London	LJ03MYD	London
LF52UTE	London	LG52DDF	London	LJ03MLZ	London	LJ03MYF	London
LF52UTG	London	LG52DDJ	London	LJ03MMA	London	LJ03MYG	London
LF52UTH	London	LG52DDK	London	LJ03MME	London	LJ03MYH	London
LF52UTL	London	LG52DDL	London	LJ03MMF	London	LJ03MYK	London
LF52UTM	London	LJ03MDV	London	LJ03MMK	London	LJ03MYL	London
LG03MBF	London	LJ03MDX	London	LJ03MSY	London	LJ03MYM	London
LG03MBU	London	LJ03MDY	London	LJ03MTE	London	LJ03MYN	London
LG03MBV	London	LJ03MDZ	London	LJ03MTF	London	LJ03MYP	London
LG03MBX	London	LJ03MEU	London	LJ03MTK	London	LJ03MYR	London
LG03MBY	London	LJ03MFN	London	LJ03MTU	London	LJ03MYS	London
LG03MDE	London	LJ03MFP	London	LJ03MTV	London	LJ03MYT	London
LG03MDF	London	LJ03MFU	London	LJ03MTY	London	LJ03MYU	London
LG03MDK	London	LJ03MFV	London	LJ03MTZ	London	LJ03MYV	London
LG03MDN	London	LJ03MFX	London	LJ03MUA	London	LJ03MYX	London
LG03MDU	London	LJ03MFY	London	LJ03MUB	London	LJ03MYY	London
LG03MEV	London	LJ03MFZ	London	LJ03MUW	London	LJ03MYZ	London
LG03MFA	London	LJ03MGE	London	LJ03MUY	London	LJ03MZD	London

LJ03MZE	London	LJ05BHL	London	LJ05GRZ	London	LJ08CVA	London
LJ03MZF	London	LJ05BHN	London	LJ05GSO	London	LJ08CVB	London
LJ03MZG	London	LJ05BHO	London	LJ05GSU	London	LJ08CVC	London
LJ03MZL	London	LJ05BHP	London	LJ07EBO	London	LJ08CVD	London
LJ04LDA	London	LJ05BHU	London	LJ07EBP	London	LJ08CVF	London
LJ04LDC	London	LJ05BHV	London	LJ07EBU	London	LJ08CVG	London
LJ04LDD	London	LJ05BHW	London	LJ07ECF	London	LJ08CVH	London
LJ04LDF	London	LJ05BHX	London	LJ07ECN	London	LJ08CVK	London
LJ04LDK	London	LJ05BHY	London	LJ07ECT	London	LJ08CVL	London
LJ04LDL	London	LJ05BHZ	London	LJ07ECU	London	LJ08CVM	London
LJ04LDN	London	LJ05BJV	London	LJ07ECW	London	LJ08CVO	London
LJ04LDU	London	LJ05BJX	London	LJ07ECX	London	LJ08CVR	London
LJ04LDX	London	LJ05BJY	London	LJ07ECY	London	LJ08CVS	London
LJ04LDY	London	LJ05BJZ	London	LJ07ECZ	London	LJ08CVT	London
LJ04LDZ	London	LJ05BKA	London	LJ07EDC	London	LJ08CVU	London
LJ04LEF	London	LJ05BKD	London	LJ07EDF	London	LJ08CVV	London
LJ04LEU	London	LJ05BKF	London	LJ07EDK	London	LJ08CVX	London
LJ04LFB	London	LJ05BKY	London	LJ07EDL	London	LJ08CVZ	London
LJ04LFD	London	LJ05BKZ	London	LJ07EDO	London	LJ08CWA	London
LJ04LFE	London	LJ05BLF	London	LJ07EDP	London	LJ08CWC	London
LJ04LFF	London	LJ05BLK	London	LJ07EDR	London	LJ08CXR	London
LJ04LFG	London	LJ05BLN	London	LJ07EDU	London	LJ08CXS	London
LJ04LFH	London	LJ05BLV	London	LJ07EDV	London	LJ08CXT	London
LJ04LFK	London	LJ05BLX	London	LJ07EDX	London	LJ08CXU	London
LJ04LFL	London	LJ05BLY	London	LJ07EEA	London	LJ08CXV	London
LJ04LFM	London	LJ05BMO	London	LJ07EEB	London	LJ08CYC	London
LJ04LFN	London	LJ05BMU	London	LJ07UDD	Original Tour	LJ08CYE	London
LJ04LFP	London	LJ05BMV	London	LJ07XEN	Original Tour	LJ08CYF	London
LJ04LFR	London	LJ05BMZ	London	LJ07XEO	Original Tour	LJ08CYG	London
LJ04LFS	London	LJ05BNA	London	LJ07XEP	Original Tour	LJ08CYH	London
LJ04LFT	London	LJ05BNB	London	LJ07XER	Original Tour	LJ08CYK	London
LJ04LFU	London	LJ05BND	London	LJ07XES	Original Tour	LJ08CYL	London
LJ04LFV	London	LJ05BNE	London	LJ07XET	Original Tour	LJ08CYO	London
LJ04LFW	London	LJ05BNF	London	LJ07XEU	Original Tour	LJ08CYP	London
LJ04LFX	London	LJ05BNK	London	LJ07XEV	Original Tour	LJ08CYS	London
LJ04LFZ	London	LJ05BNL	London	LJ07XEW	Original Tour	LJ09KOE	London
LJ04LGA	London	LJ05GKX	London	LJ08CSO	London	LJ09KOH	London
LJ04LGC	London	LJ05GKY	London	LJ08CSU	London	LJ09KOU	London
LJ04LGD	London	LJ05GKZ	London	LJ08CSV	London	LJ09KOV	London
LJ04LGE	London	LJ05GLF	London	LJ08CSX	London	LJ09KOW	London
LJ04LGF	London	LJ05GLK	London	LJ08CSY	London	LJ09KOX	London
LJ04LGG	London	LJ05GLV	London	LJ08CSZ	London	LJ09KPA	London
LJ04LGK	London	LJ05GLY	The Shires	LJ08CTE	London	LJ09KPE	London
LJ04LGL	London	LJ05GLZ	London	LJ08CTF	London	LJ09KPF	London
LJ04LGN	London	LJ05GME	London	LJ08CTK	London	LJ09KPG	London
LJ04LGV	London	LJ05GMF	London	LJ08CTO	London	LJ09KPK	London
LJ04LGW	London	LJ05GOP	London	LJ08CTV	London	LJ09KPL	London
LJ04LGX	London	LJ05GOU	London	LJ08CTX	London	LJ09KPN	London
LJ04LGY	London	LJ05GOX	London	LJ08CTY	London	LJ09KPO	London
LJ04YWE	London	LJ05GPF	London	LJ08CTZ	London	LJ09KPR	London
LJ04YWS	London	LJ05GPE	London	LJ08CUA	London	LJ09KPT	London
LJ04YWT	London	LJ05GPO	London	LJ08CUE	London	LJ09KPU	London
LJ04YWU	London	LJ05GPU	London	LJ08CUG	London	LJ09KPV	London
LJ04YWV	London	LJ05GPX	London	LJ08CUH	London	LJ09KPX	London
LJ04YWW	London	LJ05GPY	London	LJ08CUK	London	LJ09KPY	London
LJ04YWX	London	LJ05GPZ	London	LJ08CUO	London	LJ09KPZ	London
LJ04YWY	London	LJ05GRF	London	LJ08CUU	London	LJ09KRD	London
LJ04YWZ	London	LJ05GRK	London	LJ08CUV	London	LJ09KRE	London
LJ04YXA	London	LJ05GRU	London	LJ08CUW	London	LJ09KRF	London
LJ04YXB	London	LJ05GRX	London	LJ08CUY	London	LJ09KRG	London

LJ09KRK	London	LJ10CVK	London	LJ51DDY	London	LJ51DKY	London
LJ09KRN	London	LJ10CVL	London	LJ51DDZ	London	LJ51DLD	London
LJ09KRO	London	LJ10CVM	London	LJ51DEU	London	LJ51DLF	London
LJ09KRU	London	LJ10CVN	London	LJ51DFA	London	LJ51DLK	London
LJ09SSO	London	LJ10CVO	London	LJ51DFC	London	LJ51DLN	London
LJ09SSU	London	LJ10CVP	London	LJ51DFD	London	LJ51DLU	London
LJ09SSV	London	LJ10HTT	London	LJ51DFE	London	LJ51DLV	London
LJ09SSX	London	LJ10HTU	London	LJ51DFF	London	LJ51DLX	London
LJ09SSZ	London	LJ10HTV	London	LJ51DFG	London	LJ51DLY	London
LJ09STX	London	LJ10HTX	London	LJ51DFK	London	LJ51DLZ	London
LJ09STZ	London	LJ10HTZ	London	LJ51DFL	London	LJ51ORA	London
LJ09SUA	London	LJ10HUA	London	LJ51DFN	London	LJ51ORC	London
LJ09SUF	London	LJ10HUB	London	LJ51DFO	London	LJ51ORF	London
LJ09SUH	London	LJ10HUK	London	LJ51DFP	London	LJ51ORG	London
LJ09SUO	London	LJ10HUO	London	LJ51DFU	London	LJ51ORH	London
LJ09SUU	London	LJ10HUP	London	LJ51DFX	London	LJ51ORK	London
LJ09SUV	London	LJ10HUU	London	LJ51DFY	London	LJ51ORL	London
LJ09SUX	London	LJ10HUV	London	LJ51DFZ	London	LJ51OSK	London
LJ09SUY	London	LJ10HUY	London	LJ51DGE	London	LJ51OSX	London
LJ09SVA	London	LJ10HUZ	London	LJ51DGF	London	LJ51OSY	London
LJ09SVC	London	LJ10HVA	London	LJ51DGO	London	LJ51OSZ	London
LJ09SVD	London	LJ10HVB	London	LJ51DGU	London	LJ53BAA	London
LJ09SVE	London	LJ10HVC	London	LJ51DGV	London	LJ53BAO	London
LJ09SVF	London	LJ10HVD	London	LJ51DGX	London	LJ53BAU	London
LJ10AWW	London	LJ10HVE	London	LJ51DGY	London	LJ53BAV	London
LJ10AWX	London	LJ10HVF	London	LJ51DGZ	London	LJ53BBE	London
LJ10AXX	London	LJ10HVG	London	LJ51DHA	London	LJ53BBF	London
LJ10AXY	London	LJ10HVH	London	LJ51DHC	London	LJ53BBK	London
LJ10AXZ	London	LJ10HVK	London	LJ51DHD	London	LJ53BBN	London
LJ10AYA	London	LJ10HVL	London	LJ51DHF	London	LJ53BBO	London
LJ10AYB	London	LJ10HVO	London	LJ51DHG	London	LJ53BBU	London
LJ10AYC	London	LJ10HVP	London	LJ51DHK	London	LJ53BBV	London
LJ10AYD	London	LJ10HVR	London	LJ51DHL	London	LJ53BBX	London
LJ10AYE	London	LJ51DAA	London	LJ51DHO	London	LJ53BBZ	London
LJ10AYH	London	LJ51DAO	London	LJ51DHP	London	LJ53BCF	London
LJ10AYK	London	LJ51DAU	London	LJ51DHV	London	LJ53BCK	London
LJ10AYM	London	LJ51DBO	London	LJ51DHX	London	LJ53BCO	London
LJ10AYN	London	LJ51DBU	London	LJ51DHY	London	LJ53BCU	London
LJ10AYO	London	LJ51DBV	London	LJ51DHZ	London	LJ53BCV	London
LJ10AYP	London	LJ51DBX	London	LJ51DJD	London	LJ53BCX	London
LJ10AYR	London	LJ51DBY	London	LJ51DJE	London	LJ53BCY	London
LJ10AYS	London	LJ51DBZ	London	LJ51DJF	London	LJ53BCZ	London
LJ10AYT	London	LJ51DCE	London	LJ51DJK	London	LJ53BDE	London
LJ10AYU	London	LJ51DCF	London	LJ51DJO	London	LJ53BDF	London
LJ10CUH	London	LJ51DCO	London	LJ51DJU	London	LJ53BDO	London
LJ10CUK	London	LJ51DCU	London	LJ51DJV	London	LJ53BDU	London
LJ10CUO	London	LJ51DCV	London	LJ51DJX	London	LJ53BDV	London
LJ10CUU	London	LJ51DCX	London	LJ51DJY	London	LJ53BDX	London
LJ10CUV	London	LJ51DCY	London	LJ51DJZ	London	LJ53BDY	London
LJ10CUW	London	LJ51DCZ	London	LJ51DKA	London	LJ53BDZ	London
LJ10CUX	London	LJ51DDA	London	LJ51DKD	London	LJ53BEO	London
LJ10CUY	London	LJ51DDE	London	LJ51DKE	London	LJ53BEU	London
LJ10CVA	London	LJ51DDF	London	LJ51DKF	London	LJ53BEY	London
LJ10CVB	London	LJ51DDK	London	LJ51DKK	London	LJ53BFA	London
LJ10CVC	London	LJ51DDL	London	LJ51DKL	London	LJ53BFE	London
LJ10CVD	London	LJ51DDN	London	LJ51DKN	London	LJ53BFF	London
LJ10CVE	London	LJ51DDO	London	LJ51DKO	London	LJ53BFK	London
LJ10CVF	London	LJ51DDU	London	LJ51DKU	London	LJ53BFL	London
LJ10CVG	London	LJ51DDV	London	LJ51DKV	London	LJ53BFM	London
LJ10CVH	London	LJ51DDX	London	LJ51DKX	London	LJ53BFN	London

LJ53BFO	London	LJ54BBX	London	LJ54LHR	London	LJ57UTA	London
LJ53BFP	London	LJ54BBZ	London	LJ55BPZ	London	LJ57UTB	London
LJ53BFU	London	LJ54BCE	London	LJ55BRV	London	LJ57UTC	London
LJ53BFX	London	LJ54BCF	London	LJ55BRX	London	LJ57UTE	London
LJ53BFY	London	LJ54BCK	London	LJ55BRZ	London	LJ57UTF	London
LJ53BGF	London	LJ54BCO	London	LJ55BSO	London	LJ58AUC	London
LJ53BGK	London	LJ54BCU	London	LJ55BSU	London	LJ58AUE	London
LJ53BGO	London	LJ54BCV	London	LJ55BSV	London	LJ58AUV	London
LJ53BGU	London	LJ54BCX	London	LJ55BSX	London	LJ58AUW	London
LJ53LDE	Tellings GM	LJ54BCY	London	LJ55BSY	London	LJ58AUX	London
LJ53NFE	London	LJ54BCZ	London	LJ55BSZ	London	LJ58AUY	London
LJ53NFF	London	LJ54BDE	London	LJ55BTE	London	LJ58AVB	London
LJ53NFG	London	LJ54BDF	London	LJ55BTF	London	LJ58AVC	London
LJ53NFT	London	LJ54BDO	London	LJ55BTO	London	LJ58AVD	London
LJ53NFU	London	LJ54BDU	London	LJ55BTU	London	LJ58AVE	London
LJ53NFV	London	LJ54BDV	London	LJ55BTV	London	LJ58AVG	Tellings GM
LJ53NFX	London	LJ54BDX	London	LJ55BTX	London	LJ58AVK	London
LJ53NFY	London	LJ54BDY	London	LJ55BTY	London	LJ58AVT	London
LJ53NFZ	London	LJ54BDZ	London	LJ55BTZ	London	LJ58AVU	London
LJ53NGE	London	LJ54BEO	London	LJ55BUA	London	LJ58AVV	London
LJ53NGF	London	LJ54BEU	London	LJ55BUE	London	LJ58AVX	London
LJ53NGG	London	LJ54BFA	London	LJ55BUP	London	LJ58AVY	London
LJ53NGN	London	LJ54BFE	London	LJ55BUR	London	LJ58AVZ	London
LJ53NGU	London	LJ54BFF	London	LJ55BUS	London	LJ58AWA	London
LJ53NGV	London	LJ54BFK	London	LJ55BUT	London	LJ58AWC	London
LJ53NGX	London	LJ54BFL	London	LJ55BUU	London	LJ58AWF	London
LJ53NGY	London	LJ54BFM	London	LJ55BUV	London	LJ58AWG	London
LJ53NGZ	London	LJ54BFN	London	LJ55BUW	London	LJ58GCF	Tellings GM
LJ53NHA	London	LJ54BFO	London	LJ55BUX	London	LJ58GCK	Tellings GM
LJ53NHB	London	LJ54BFP	London	LJ55BUY	London	LJ59AAE	London
LJ53NHC	London	LJ54BFV	London	LJ55BUZ	London	LJ59AAF	London
LJ53NHD	London	LJ54BFY	London	LJ55BVD	London	LJ59AAK	London
LJ53NHE	London	LJ54BFZ	London	LJ55BVE	London	LJ59AAN	London
LJ53NHF	London	LJ54BGE	London	LJ55BVF	London	LJ59AAO	London
LJ53NHG	London	LJ54BGF	London	LJ55BVG	London	LJ59AAO	London
LJ53NHH	London	LJ54BGK	London	LJ55BVH	London	LJ59AAU	London
LJ53NHK	London	LJ54BGO	London	LJ55BVK	London	LJ59AAU	London
LJ53NHL	London	LJ54BJE	London	LJ55BVL	London	LJ59AAV	London
LJ53NHN	London	LJ54BJF	London	LJ55BVM	London	LJ59AAX	London
LJ53NHO	London	LJ54BJK	London	LJ56AOW	London	LJ59AAY	London
LJ53NHP	London	LJ54BJO	London	LJ56AOX	London	LJ59AAZ	London
LJ53NHT	London	LJ54BJU	London	LJ56AOY	London	LJ59ABF	London
LJ53NHV	London	LJ54BKG	London	LJ56APZ	London	LJ59ABK	London
LJ53NHX	London	LJ54BKK	London	LJ56ARF	London	LJ59ABN	London
LJ53NHY	London	LJ54BKL	London	LJ56ARO	London	LJ59ABO	London
LJ53NHZ	London	LJ54BKN	London	LJ56ARU	London	LJ59ABU	London
LJ53NJF	London	LJ54BKO	London	LJ56ARX	London	LJ59ABV	London
LJ53NJK	London	LJ54BKU	London	LJ56ARZ	London	LJ59ABX	London
LJ53NJN	London	LJ54BKV	London	LJ56ASO	London	LJ59ABZ	London
LJ54BAA	London	LJ54BKX	London	LJ56ASU	London	LJ59ACF	London
LJ54BAO	London	LJ54LGV	London	LJ56ASV	London	LJ59ACO	London
LJ54BAU	London	LJ54LHF	London	LJ56ASX	London	LJ59ACU	London
LJ54BAV	London	LJ54LHG	London	LJ57USS	London	LJ59ACV	London
LJ54BBE	London	LJ54LHH	London	LJ57UST	London	LJ59ACX	London
LJ54BBF	London	LJ54LHK	London	LJ57USU	London	LJ59ACY	London
LJ54BBK	London	LJ54LHL	London	LJ57USV	London	LJ59ACZ	London
LJ54BBN	London	LJ54LHM	London	LJ57USW	London	LJ59ADO	London
LJ54BBO	London	LJ54LHN	London	LJ57USX	London	LJ59ADV	London
LJ54BBU	London	LJ54LHO	London	LJ57USY	London	LJ59ADX	London
LJ54BBV	London	LJ54LHP	London	LJ57USZ	London	LJ59ADZ	London

Reg	Area	Reg	Area	Reg	Area	Reg	Area
LJ59AEA	London	LJ59LXW	London	LJ60AWB	London	M176GRY	North East
LJ59AEA	London	LJ59LXX	London	LJ60AWC	London	M177GRY	North East
LJ59AEB	London	LJ59LXY	London	LJ60AWD	London	M186YKA	North East
LJ59AEC	London	LJ59LXZ	London	LJ60AWE	London	M186YKA	North East
LJ59AED	London	LJ59LYA	London	LJ60AWF	London	M200CBB	Southern Cs
LJ59AEE	London	LJ59LYC	London	LJ60AWG	London	M211YKD	North East
LJ59AEF	London	LJ59LYD	London	LJ60AWK	London	M216YKD	NW & Wales
LJ59AEG	London	LJ59LYF	London	LJ60AWL	London	M303SAJ	North East
LJ59AEK	London	LJ59LYG	London	LJ60AWN	London	M304SAJ	North East
LJ59AEL	London	LJ59LYH	London	LJ60AWO	London	M370FTY	North East
LJ59AEM	London	LJ59LYK	London	LJ60AWP	London	M371FTY	North East
LJ59AEN	London	LJ59LYO	London	LK55ACY	Southern Cs	M372FTY	North East
LJ59AET	London	LJ59LYP	London	LN02HJO	Tellings GM	M373FTY	North East
LJ59AEU	London	LJ59LYS	London	LS06YCR	Tellings GM	M374FTY	North East
LJ59AEV	London	LJ59LYT	London	LS06YCT	Tellings GM	M375FTY	North East
LJ59AEW	London	LJ59LYU	London	LT04CTV	Tellings GM	M376FTY	North East
LJ59AEX	London	LJ59LYV	London	LT04CTV	Tellings GM	M377FTY	North East
LJ59AEY	London	LJ59LYW	London	LT04CTV	Tellings GM	M401EFD	Midlands
LJ59AEZ	London	LJ59LYY	London	LT04CWC	Tellings GM	M402EFD	Midlands
LJ59GTF	London	LJ59LYZ	London	LT04CWL	Tellings GM	M403EFD	Midlands
LJ59GTU	London	LJ59LZB	London	LT06XDU	Tellings GM	M404EFD	Midlands
LJ59GUA	London	LJ59LZC	London	LT56JXU	Tellings GM	M421UNW	Midlands
LJ59GVC	London	LJ59LZD	London	LT56JXV	Tellings GM	M422UNW	Midlands
LJ59GVE	London	LJ59LZF	London	LT56JYN	Tellings GM	M429UNW	NW & Wales
LJ59GVF	London	LJ59LZG	London	LT56JZM	Tellings GM	M430UNW	Midlands
LJ59GVG	London	LJ59LZH	London	LX05GDV	Original Tour	M514WHF	NW & Wales
LJ59GVK	London	LJ59LZK	London	LX05GDY	Original Tour	M519WHF	NW & Wales
LJ59LVH	London	LJ59LZL	London	LX05GDZ	Original Tour	M523WHF	NW & Wales
LJ59LVV	London	LJ59LZM	London	LX05GEJ	Original Tour	M525MPM	Southern Cs
LJ59LVW	London	LJ59LZN	London	LX05HRO	Original Tour	M527WHF	NW & Wales
LJ59LVX	London	LJ60ASX	London	LX05HSC	Original Tour	M530WHF	NW & Wales
LJ59LVY	London	LJ60ATZ	London	LX05KNZ	Original Tour	M532WHF	NW & Wales
LJ59LVZ	London	LJ60AUA	London	LX05KOA	Original Tour	M532WHF	NW & Wales
LJ59LWA	London	LJ60AUC	London	M2SLT	NW & Wales	M536WHF	NW & Wales
LJ59LWF	London	LJ60AUE	London	M20MPS	Midlands	M558WTJ	NW & Wales
LJ59LWG	London	LJ60AUF	London	M52AWW	The Shires	M561WTJ	NW & Wales
LJ59LWH	London	LJ60AUO	London	M100PHA	Midlands	M569YEM	NW & Wales
LJ59LWK	London	LJ60AUP	London	M109RMS	Scotland West	M571YEM	NW & Wales
LJ59LWL	London	LJ60AUR	London	M109XKC	NW & Wales	M572YEM	NW & Wales
LJ59LWM	London	LJ60AUT	London	M110XKC	NW & Wales	M573YEM	NW & Wales
LJ59LWO	London	LJ60AUU	London	M112XKC	NW & Wales	M575YEM	NW & Wales
LJ59LWP	London	LJ60AUV	London	M113BMR	Midlands	M619PKP	Southern Cs
LJ59LWR	London	LJ60AUW	London	M113RMS	Scotland West	M685HPF	North East
LJ59LWS	London	LJ60AUX	London	M113XKC	NW & Wales	M688HPF	North East
LJ59LWT	London	LJ60AUY	London	M114RMS	Scotland West	M689HPF	North East
LJ59LWU	London	LJ60AVB	London	M115RMS	Scotland West	M690HPF	North East
LJ59LWV	London	LJ60AVH	London	M117RMS	Scotland West	M722CGO	Tellings GM
LJ59LWW	London	LJ60AVK	London	M119RMS	Scotland West	M770DRG	North East
LJ59LWX	London	LJ60AVL	London	M120RMS	Scotland West	M803MOJ	Midlands
LJ59LWY	London	LJ60AVM	London	M157WKA	NW & Wales	M804MOJ	Midlands
LJ59LWZ	London	LJ60AVR	London	M160GRY	Scotland West	M819RCP	Yorkshire
LJ59LXA	London	LJ60AVT	London	M160SKR	NW & Wales	M831SDA	Scotland West
LJ59LXB	London	LJ60AVU	London	M161GRY	Tellings GM	M832SDA	Scotland West
LJ59LXP	London	LJ60AVV	London	M161SKR	NW & Wales	M833SDA	Scotland West
LJ59LXR	London	LJ60AVW	London	M162GRY	Tellings GM	M834SDA	Tellings GM
LJ59LXS	London	LJ60AVX	London	M165GRY	Scotland West	M911MKM	Southern Cs
LJ59LXT	London	LJ60AVY	London	M169GRY	Scotland West	M913MKM	Southern Cs
LJ59LXU	London	LJ60AVZ	London	M170GRY	North East	M914MKM	Southern Cs
LJ59LXV	London	LJ60AWA	London	M172GRY	North East	M915MKM	Southern Cs
						M916MKM	Southern Cs

M917MKM	Southern Cs	MX09LXU	NW & Wales	MX59AAE	NW & Wales	N45JPP	The Shires
M918MKM	Southern Cs	MX09LXV	NW & Wales	MX59AAF	NW & Wales	N46JPP	The Shires
M919MKM	Southern Cs	MX09LXW	NW & Wales	MX59AAJ	NW & Wales	N51FWU	Yorkshire
M920MKM	Southern Cs	MX09LXY	NW & Wales	MX59AAK	NW & Wales	N52FWU	Yorkshire
M922PKN	Southern Cs	MX09LXZ	NW & Wales	MX59AAN	NW & Wales	N101YVU	NW & Wales
M923PKN	Southern Cs	MX09LYA	NW & Wales	MX59AAO	NW & Wales	N103YVU	NW & Wales
M925PKN	Southern Cs	MX09LYC	NW & Wales	MX59AAU	NW & Wales	N104YVU	NW & Wales
M948LYR	The Shires	MX09LYD	NW & Wales	MX59AAV	NW & Wales	N105YVU	NW & Wales
M949LYR	The Shires	MX09LYF	NW & Wales	MX59AAY	NW & Wales	N106DWM	NW & Wales
MF52LYY	NW & Wales	MX09LYG	NW & Wales	MX59AAZ	NW & Wales	N107DWM	NW & Wales
MF52LYZ	NW & Wales	MX09LYH	NW & Wales	MX59ABF	NW & Wales	N108DWM	NW & Wales
MF52LZA	NW & Wales	MX09LYJ	NW & Wales	MX59ABK	NW & Wales	N109DWM	NW & Wales
MF52LZB	NW & Wales	MX09OOJ	NW & Wales	MX59ABN	NW & Wales	N110DWM	NW & Wales
MK02BUS	The Shires	MX09OOU	NW & Wales	MX59FFR	NW & Wales	N113DWM	NW & Wales
MK52XNN	NW & Wales	MX09OOV	NW & Wales	MX59FFS	NW & Wales	N114DWM	NW & Wales
MK52XNO	NW & Wales	MX09OOW	NW & Wales	MX59FFT	NW & Wales	N115DWM	NW & Wales
MK52XNP	NW & Wales	MX09OOY	NW & Wales	MX59FFU	NW & Wales	N116DWM	NW & Wales
MK52XNR	NW & Wales	MX09OPA	NW & Wales	MX59FFV	NW & Wales	N117DWM	NW & Wales
MK52XNS	Scotland West	MX09OPB	NW & Wales	MX59FFW	NW & Wales	N118DWM	NW & Wales
MM02ZVH	NW & Wales	MX09OPC	NW & Wales	MX59FFX	NW & Wales	N119DWM	NW & Wales
MM02ZVJ	NW & Wales	MX09OPD	NW & Wales	MX59FFZ	NW & Wales	N120DWM	NW & Wales
MNZ1138	Midlands	MX09OPE	NW & Wales	MX59FGA	NW & Wales	N121DWM	NW & Wales
MR07FDS	Tellings GM	MX09OPF	NW & Wales	MX59FGB	NW & Wales	N122DWM	NW & Wales
MV02XYJ	Scotland West	MX09OPG	NW & Wales	MX59FGD	NW & Wales	N123DWM	NW & Wales
MV02XYK	Scotland West	MX09OPH	NW & Wales	MX59FGE	NW & Wales	N124DWM	NW & Wales
MX09EKK	NW & Wales	MX09OPJ	NW & Wales	MX59FGF	NW & Wales	N125DWM	NW & Wales
MX09EKL	NW & Wales	MX09OPK	NW & Wales	MX59FGG	NW & Wales	N126DWM	NW & Wales
MX09EKM	NW & Wales	MX09OPL	NW & Wales	MX59FGJ	NW & Wales	N127DWM	NW & Wales
MX09EKN	NW & Wales	MX09OPM	NW & Wales	MX59FHB	NW & Wales	N128DWM	NW & Wales
MX09EKO	NW & Wales	MX09OPN	NW & Wales	MX59JJE	NW & Wales	N129DWM	NW & Wales
MX09EKP	NW & Wales	MX09OPO	NW & Wales	MX59JJF	NW & Wales	N130DWM	NW & Wales
MX09EKR	NW & Wales	MX10BZS	NW & Wales	MX59JJK	NW & Wales	N131DWM	NW & Wales
MX09EKT	NW & Wales	MX10BZT	NW & Wales	MX59JJL	NW & Wales	N132DWM	NW & Wales
MX09EKU	NW & Wales	MX10BZU	NW & Wales	MX59JJO	NW & Wales	N133DWM	NW & Wales
MX09EKW	NW & Wales	MX10BZV	NW & Wales	MX59JJU	NW & Wales	N134DWM	NW & Wales
MX09EKY	NW & Wales	MX10BZW	NW & Wales	MX59JJV	NW & Wales	N160VVO	North East
MX09JHH	NW & Wales	MX10BZY	NW & Wales	MX59JJY	NW & Wales	N161VVO	Tellings GM
MX09JHK	NW & Wales	MX10CZC	NW & Wales	MX59JJZ	NW & Wales	N162VVO	North East
MX09JHL	NW & Wales	MX10CZD	NW & Wales	MX59JKZ	NW & Wales	N163VVO	North East
MX09JHO	NW & Wales	MX10CZE	NW & Wales	MX59JZA	NW & Wales	N164VVO	North East
MX09JHU	NW & Wales	MX10CZF	NW & Wales	MX59JZC	NW & Wales	N166PUT	North East
MX09JHV	NW & Wales	MX10CZG	NW & Wales	MX59JZC	NW & Wales	N167PUT	Tellings GM
MX09JHY	NW & Wales	MX10CZH	NW & Wales	MX59JZD	NW & Wales	N168PUT	Midlands
MX09JHZ	NW & Wales	MX10CZJ	NW & Wales	MX59JZE	NW & Wales	N169PUT	Tellings GM
MX09JJE	NW & Wales	MX10CZK	NW & Wales	MX59JZF	NW & Wales	N170PUT	North East
MX09JJF	NW & Wales	MX10DAA	NW & Wales	MX59JZH	NW & Wales	N171PUT	North East
MX09JTY	NW & Wales	MX10DAO	NW & Wales	MX59JZJ	NW & Wales	N172PUT	Tellings GM
MX09LLXK	NW & Wales	MX10DAU	NW & Wales	MXT179	Original Tour	N173PUT	Midlands
MX09LLXL	NW & Wales	MX10DBO	NW & Wales	N24FWU	NW & Wales	N174PUT	North East
MX09LLXM	NW & Wales	MX10DBU	NW & Wales	N28KGS	The Shires	N176PUT	Tellings GM
MX09LLXN	NW & Wales	MX10DBV	NW & Wales	N29KGS	The Shires	N178PUT	North East
MX09LLXO	NW & Wales	MX10DBY	NW & Wales	N32KGS	The Shires	N179PUT	North East
MX09LLXR	NW & Wales	MX10DBZ	NW & Wales	N35JPP	The Shires	N182OYH	North East
MX09LLXS	NW & Wales	MX10DCE	NW & Wales	N36JPP	The Shires	N183OYH	North East
MX09LXE	NW & Wales	MX10DCF	NW & Wales	N37JPP	The Shires	N211DWM	NW & Wales
MX09LXF	NW & Wales	MX10DCO	NW & Wales	N38JPP	The Shires	N212TPK	NW & Wales
MX09LXG	NW & Wales	MX10DCU	NW & Wales	N39JPP	The Shires	N213TPK	NW & Wales
MX09LXH	NW & Wales	MX10DCV	NW & Wales	N41JPP	The Shires	N221TPK	Southern Cs
MX09LXJ	NW & Wales	MX10DCY	NW & Wales	N42JPP	The Shires	N224TPK	Southern Cs
MX09LXT	NW & Wales	MX10DCZ	NW & Wales	N43JPP	The Shires	N225TPK	Southern Cs

N226TPK	Southern Cs	N284CKB	NW & Wales	N524MJO	The Shires	N686GUM	Scotland West
N227TPK	Southern Cs	N284NCN	North East	N524XVN	North East	N687GUM	Scotland West
N228TPK	Southern Cs	N285CKB	NW & Wales	N525XVN	North East	N689GUM	Midlands
N229TPK	Southern Cs	N285NCN	North East	N531DWM	NW & Wales	N689GUM	Scotland West
N230TPK	Southern Cs	N286CKB	NW & Wales	N532DWM	NW & Wales	N690GUM	Midlands
N231TPK	Southern Cs	N287CKB	NW & Wales	N539TPF	Southern Cs	N691GUM	Scotland West
N233TPK	Southern Cs	N287NCN	North East	N578CKA	NW & Wales	N693EUR	The Shires
N234TPK	Southern Cs	N288CKB	NW & Wales	N579CKA	NW & Wales	N694EUR	The Shires
N235TPK	Southern Cs	N288NCN	North East	N580CKA	NW & Wales	N696EUR	The Shires
N236TPK	Southern Cs	N289CKB	NW & Wales	N581CKA	NW & Wales	N697EUR	The Shires
N237VPH	Southern Cs	N289NCN	North East	N582CKA	NW & Wales	N697EUR	The Shires
N238VPH	Midlands	N290CKB	NW & Wales	N583CKA	NW & Wales	N698EUR	The Shires
N239VPH	Southern Cs	N290NCN	North East	N584CKA	NW & Wales	N698EUR	The Shires
N240VPH	Midlands	N291CKB	NW & Wales	N585CKA	NW & Wales	N699EUR	The Shires
N241VPH	Midlands	N292CKB	NW & Wales	N587CKA	NW & Wales	N699EUR	The Shires
N242VPH	Midlands	N293CKB	NW & Wales	N589CKA	NW & Wales	N702EUR	The Shires
N243VPH	Midlands	N294CKB	NW & Wales	N591CKA	NW & Wales	N702EUR	The Shires
N244VPH	Midlands	N295CKB	NW & Wales	N592CKA	NW & Wales	N703EUR	The Shires
N245VPH	Southern Cs	N296CKB	NW & Wales	N593CKA	NW & Wales	N703GUM	NW & Wales
N246VPH	Southern Cs	N297CKB	NW & Wales	N595CKA	NW & Wales	N704EUR	The Shires
N247CKA	NW & Wales	N298CKB	NW & Wales	N599CKA	NW & Wales	N704EUR	The Shires
N247VPH	Southern Cs	N299CKB	NW & Wales	N601DWY	NW & Wales	N705EUR	The Shires
N248VPH	Midlands	N301AMC	North East	N602DWY	NW & Wales	N705EUR	The Shires
N249VPH	Midlands	N301CKB	NW & Wales	N603CKA	NW & Wales	N705TPK	NW & Wales
N250BKK	Southern Cs	N301ENX	Midlands	N603DWY	NW & Wales	N706EUR	The Shires
N250CKA	NW & Wales	N302CKB	NW & Wales	N604CKA	NW & Wales	N706EUR	The Shires
N251BKK	Southern Cs	N302ENX	Midlands	N605CKA	NW & Wales	N706GUM	NW & Wales
N252BKK	Southern Cs	N303CLV	NW & Wales	N605DWY	NW & Wales	N706TPK	NW & Wales
N252CKA	NW & Wales	N303ENX	Midlands	N606CKA	NW & Wales	N707EUR	The Shires
N253BKK	Southern Cs	N304CLV	NW & Wales	N607CKA	NW & Wales	N707GUM	NW & Wales
N253CKA	NW & Wales	N304ENX	Midlands	N607DWY	NW & Wales	N707TPK	NW & Wales
N254BKK	Southern Cs	N305AMC	North East	N608CKA	NW & Wales	N708EUR	The Shires
N255BKK	Southern Cs	N305CLV	NW & Wales	N608DWY	NW & Wales	N708GUM	Scotland West
N255CKA	NW & Wales	N305ENX	Midlands	N609CKA	NW & Wales	N708TPK	NW & Wales
N256BKK	Southern Cs	N306CLV	NW & Wales	N610CKA	NW & Wales	N709EUR	The Shires
N256CKA	NW & Wales	N307CLV	NW & Wales	N610DWY	NW & Wales	N709GUM	Scotland West
N257BKK	Southern Cs	N308CLV	NW & Wales	N611CKA	NW & Wales	N709TPK	NW & Wales
N258BKK	Southern Cs	N322TPK	Southern Cs	N611DWY	NW & Wales	N710EUR	The Shires
N259BKK	Southern Cs	N429XRC	Midlands	N612CKA	NW & Wales	N710GUM	Scotland West
N259CKA	NW & Wales	N430XRC	Tellings GM	N612DWY	NW & Wales	N711EUR	The Shires
N260CKA	NW & Wales	N431XRC	Midlands	N613DWY	NW & Wales	N711GUM	Scotland West
N261CKA	NW & Wales	N432XRC	North East	N615CKA	NW & Wales	N712EUR	The Shires
N262CKA	NW & Wales	N433XRC	Tellings GM	N616CKA	NW & Wales	N712EUR	The Shires
N263CKA	NW & Wales	N474MUS	Scotland West	N619CKA	NW & Wales	N712GUM	Scotland West
N264CKA	NW & Wales	N511XVN	North East	N621CKA	NW & Wales	N713EUR	The Shires
N271CKB	NW & Wales	N512XVN	North East	N621KUA	Yorkshire	N713EUR	The Shires
N272CKB	NW & Wales	N513XVN	North East	N622CKA	NW & Wales	N713TPK	Southern Cs
N273CKB	NW & Wales	N514XVN	North East	N622FJO	The Shires	N714EUR	The Shires
N274CKB	NW & Wales	N515XVN	North East	N622KUA	Yorkshire	N714TPK	Southern Cs
N275CKB	NW & Wales	N516XVN	North East	N623CKA	NW & Wales	N715EUR	The Shires
N276CKB	NW & Wales	N517XVN	North East	N623FJO	The Shires	N715TPK	Southern Cs
N277CKB	NW & Wales	N518XVN	North East	N623KUA	Yorkshire	N716EUR	The Shires
N278CKB	NW & Wales	N519XVN	North East	N624FJO	The Shires	N716TPK	NW & Wales
N279CKB	NW & Wales	N520XVN	North East	N672GUM	Scotland West	N806EHA	Midlands
N281CKB	NW & Wales	N521MJO	The Shires	N674GUM	Midlands	N806XHN	North East
N281NCN	North East	N522MJO	The Shires	N675GUM	Scotland West	N807EHA	Midlands
N282CKB	NW & Wales	N522XVN	North East	N677GUM	Scotland West	N807XHN	North East
N282NCN	North East	N523MJO	Southern Cs	N681GUM	Scotland West	N808XHN	North East
N283CKB	NW & Wales	N523MJO	The Shires	N683GUM	Scotland West	N809XHN	North East
N283NCN	North East	N523XVn	North East	N685GUM	Scotland West	N810XHN	North East

Reg	Region	Reg	Region	Reg	Region	Reg	Region
N908ETM	The Shires	NK09DFMZ	North East	NK57DXX	North East	P81MOR	Midlands
N912ETM	The Shires	NK09DFNZ	North East	NK57DXY	North East	P82MOR	Midlands
N913ETM	The Shires	NK09EJD	North East	NK57DXZ	North East	P130RWR	North East
N950TVK	North East	NK09EJE	North East	NK57DYA	North East	P135GND	NW & Wales
NDZ4521	The Shires	NK09EJF	North East	NK57GWX	North East	P136GND	NW & Wales
NDZ7918	Southern Cs	NK09EJG	North East	NK57GWY	North East	P137GND	NW & Wales
NDZ7919	The Shires	NK09EJJ	North East	NK57GWZ	North East	P138GND	NW & Wales
NDZ7926	Southern Cs	NK09EJL	North East	NK57GXA	North East	P139GND	NW & Wales
NDZ7933	The Shires	NK09EJV	North East	NK57GXB	North East	P140GND	NW & Wales
NDZ7935	The Shires	NK09EJX	North East	NK57GXC	North East	P170VUA	Yorkshire
NEZ9506	Midlands	NK09EJY	North East	NK57GXD	North East	P171VUA	Yorkshire
NK04VMD	Tellings GM	NK09EJZ	North East	NK57GXE	North East	P172VUA	Yorkshire
NK05GVG	North East	NK09EKA	North East	NK57GXF	North East	P173VUA	Yorkshire
NK05GVX	North East	NK09EKB	North East	NK59DLO	North East	P174VUA	Midlands
NK05GVY	North East	NK09EKC	North East	NK59DLU	North East	P175SRO	The Shires
NK05GWA	North East	NK09EKD	North East	NK59DLV	North East	P175UAD	Midlands
NK05GWC	North East	NK09FNC	North East	NK59DLX	North East	P175VUA	Yorkshire
NK05GWD	North East	NK09FND	North East	NK59DLY	North East	P176LKL	Southern Cs
NK05GWE	North East	NK09FNE	North East	NK59DLZ	North East	P176SRO	The Shires
NK05GWF	North East	NK09FNF	North East	NK59DME	North East	P176VUA	Yorkshire
NK05GWG	North East	NK09FNG	North East	NK59DMF	North East	P177LKL	Southern Cs
NK05GWJ	North East	NK09FVR	North East	NK59DMO	North East	P177SRO	The Shires
NK05GWM	North East	NK10CEJ	North East	NK59DMU	North East	P177VUA	Yorkshire
NK05GWN	North East	NK10CEN	North East	NK59DMV	North East	P178LKL	Southern Cs
NK05GWO	North East	NK10CEO	North East	NK59DMX	North East	P178SRO	The Shires
NK05GWU	North East	NK10CEU	North East	NK59DMY	North East	P179SRO	The Shires
NK05GWV	North East	NK10CEV	North East	NK59DMZ	North East	P179VUA	Yorkshire
NK05GWW	North East	NK10CEX	North East	NK59DND	North East	P180LKL	NW & Wales
NK05GWX	North East	NK10CEY	North East	NK59DNE	North East	P180SRO	The Shires
NK05GWY	North East	NK10CFA	North East	NK59DNF	North East	P180VUA	Yorkshire
NK05GXA	North East	NK10CFD	North East	NK59DNJ	North East	P181LKL	Southern Cs
NK05GXB	North East	NK10CFE	North East	NK59DNN	North East	P181SRO	The Shires
NK05GXC	North East	NK10CFF	North East	NKJ785	Original Tour	P181VUA	Yorkshire
NK05GXD	North East	NK10CFG	North East	NL04PKZ	Tellings GM	P182LKL	NW & Wales
NK05GXE	North East	NK10CFJ	North East	NL04RBF	Tellings GM	P182SRO	The Shires
NK05GXF	North East	NK10CFL	North East	NM02DYA	Southern Cs	P182VUA	Yorkshire
NK05GXG	North East	NK10CFM	North East	NVS485	London	P183LKL	NW & Wales
NK05GXH	North East	NK10CFN	North East	OEZ2159	Midlands	P183SRO	The Shires
NK05GXJ	North East	NK10CFO	North East	OKZ9847	Midlands	P183VUA	Yorkshire
NK05GXL	North East	NK10CFP	North East	OSU895	Tellings GM	P184LKL	Southern Cs
NK05GXM	North East	NK10CFU	North East	OUI3925	Midlands	P184SRO	The Shires
NK05GXN	North East	NK10CFV	North East	OV59WJX	Tellings GM	P184VUA	Yorkshire
NK05GXO	North East	NK10CFX	North East	OV59WJY	Tellings GM	P185LKL	Southern Cs
NK05GXW	North East	NK10CFY	North East	OV59WJZ	Tellings GM	P185SRO	The Shires
NK07FZC	North East	NK10CFZ	North East	OV59WKA	Tellings GM	P185VUA	Yorkshire
NK07FZD	North East	NK10CGE	North East	OV59WKB	Tellings GM	P186LKJ	The Shires
NK07FZE	North East	NK10CGF	North East	OV59WKC	Tellings GM	P186SRO	The Shires
NK07FZF	North East	NK10CGG	North East	P3SLT	NW & Wales	P186VUA	Yorkshire
NK07FZG	North East	NK10CGO	North East	P10LPG	Yorkshire	P187LKJ	Southern Cs
NK09BPF	North East	NK10CGU	North East	P41MVU	NW & Wales	P187SRO	The Shires
NK09BPO	North East	NK53HHX	North East	P42MVU	NW & Wales	P187VUA	Yorkshire
NK09BPU	North East	NK53HHY	North East	P43MVU	NW & Wales	P188LKJ	Southern Cs
NK09BPV	North East	NK53HHZ	North East	P45MVU	NW & Wales	P188SRO	The Shires
NK09BPX	North East	NK53HJA	North East	P46MVU	NW & Wales	P188VUA	Yorkshire
NK09BPY	North East	NK53VKA	North East	P49MVU	NW & Wales	P189LKJ	Southern Cs
NK09BPZ	North East	NK55MYR	North East	P52MVU	NW & Wales	P189SRO	The Shires
NK09BRF	North East	NK55MYS	North East	P53MVU	NW & Wales	P189VUA	Yorkshire
NK09BRV	North East	NK55MYT	North East	P56MVU	NW & Wales	P190LKJ	Southern Cs
NK09BRX	North East	NK56HKV	North East	P58MVU	NW & Wales	P190SRO	The Shires
NK09BRZ	North East	NK56HKW	North East	P61MVU	NW & Wales	P190VUA	Yorkshire

Reg	Region	Reg	Region	Reg	Region	Reg	Region
P191LKJ	Southern Cs	P237MKN	Southern Cs	P303HEM	NW & Wales	P420HVX	NW & Wales
P191VUA	Yorkshire	P238MKN	Southern Cs	P305HEM	NW & Wales	P421HVX	Southern Cs
P192LKJ	Southern Cs	P239MKN	Southern Cs	P306FEA	Midlands	P422HVX	NW & Wales
P192VUA	Yorkshire	P240MKN	Southern Cs	P306HEM	NW & Wales	P423HVX	Southern Cs
P193LKJ	Southern Cs	P241MKN	Southern Cs	P307FEA	Midlands	P425HVX	Southern Cs
P193VUA	Yorkshire	P242MKN	Southern Cs	P307HEM	NW & Wales	P426HVX	Southern Cs
P194LKJ	Southern Cs	P243MKN	Southern Cs	P308FEA	Midlands	P427HVX	Southern Cs
P194VUA	Yorkshire	P244MKN	Southern Cs	P308HEM	NW & Wales	P428HVX	Southern Cs
P195LKJ	Southern Cs	P244NBA	NW & Wales	P309FEA	Midlands	P429HVX	Southern Cs
P195VUA	Yorkshire	P245MKN	Southern Cs	P309HEM	NW & Wales	P430HVX	NW & Wales
P196LKJ	Southern Cs	P246MKN	Southern Cs	P310FEA	Midlands	P431HVX	Southern Cs
P196VUA	Yorkshire	P247MKN	Southern Cs	P310HEM	NW & Wales	P456EEF	North East
P197LKJ	Southern Cs	P250APM	Southern Cs	P311FEA	Midlands	P458EEF	North East
P197VUA	Yorkshire	P250NBA	NW & Wales	P311HEM	NW & Wales	P459EEF	North East
P198LKJ	Southern Cs	P251APM	Southern Cs	P312FEA	Midlands	P460EEF	North East
P198VUA	Yorkshire	P253APM	Southern Cs	P312HEM	NW & Wales	P461EEF	North East
P199LKJ	Southern Cs	P254APM	Southern Cs	P313FEA	Midlands	P481DPE	Southern Cs
P199VUA	Yorkshire	P255APM	Southern Cs	P313HEM	NW & Wales	P514CVO	Midlands
P201HRY	Midlands	P256FPK	The Shires	P314FEA	Midlands	P525YJO	The Shires
P201LKJ	Southern Cs	P257FPK	Southern Cs	P314HEM	NW & Wales	P526YJO	The Shires
P201RWR	The Shires	P258FPK	Southern Cs	P315HEM	NW & Wales	P527YJO	The Shires
P202HRY	Midlands	P259FPK	Southern Cs	P316FEA	Midlands	P533MBU	NW & Wales
P202LKJ	Southern Cs	P259FPK	Southern Cs	P316HEM	NW & Wales	P534MBU	NW & Wales
P202RUM	Yorkshire	P260NBA	NW & Wales	P317FEA	Midlands	P535MBU	NW & Wales
P203HRY	Midlands	P261FPK	Southern Cs	P317HEM	NW & Wales	P536MBU	NW & Wales
P203LKJ	Southern Cs	P262FPK	Southern Cs	P318FEA	Midlands	P537MBU	NW & Wales
P204HRY	Midlands	P263FPK	Southern Cs	P318HEM	NW & Wales	P538MBU	NW & Wales
P204LKJ	The Shires	P264FPK	Southern Cs	P319HEM	NW & Wales	P539MBU	NW & Wales
P205HRY	Midlands	P265FPK	Southern Cs	P319HOJ	Midlands	P540MBU	NW & Wales
P205LKJ	Southern Cs	P266FPK	Southern Cs	P320HEM	NW & Wales	P541MBU	NW & Wales
P206HRY	Midlands	P267FPK	Southern Cs	P320HOJ	Midlands	P542MBU	NW & Wales
P206LKJ	Southern Cs	P270FPK	Southern Cs	P321HOJ	Midlands	P543MBU	NW & Wales
P207LKJ	Southern Cs	P271FPK	Southern Cs	P322HOJ	Midlands	P544MBU	NW & Wales
P208LKJ	Southern Cs	P271VRG	North East	P323HOJ	Midlands	P545MBU	NW & Wales
P209LKJ	Southern Cs	P272FPK	Southern Cs	P324HOJ	Midlands	P601RGS	The Shires
P210LKJ	Scotland West	P272VRG	North East	P324HVX	Southern Cs	P607CAY	Midlands
P211LKJ	Scotland West	P273FPK	Southern Cs	P324HVX	The Shires	P609CAY	Southern Cs
P212LKJ	Scotland West	P274VRG	North East	P325HOJ	Midlands	P610CAY	Southern Cs
P213LKJ	Southern Cs	P275FPK	Southern Cs	P326HOJ	Midlands	P613CAY	Southern Cs
P214LKJ	NW & Wales	P275VRG	North East	P326HVX	Yorkshire	P615PGP	North East
P215LKJ	Southern Cs	P276FPK	Southern Cs	P327HOJ	Midlands	P616PGP	North East
P216LKJ	Southern Cs	P276VRG	North East	P328HVX	Southern Cs	P617PGP	North East
P218MKL	Southern Cs	P277FPK	Southern Cs	P329HVX	Southern Cs	P618FHN	North East
P219MKL	Southern Cs	P277VRG	North East	P330HVX	The Shires	P621FHN	North East
P220MKL	Southern Cs	P278VRG	North East	P331HVX	Southern Cs	P627FHN	North East
P221MKL	Southern Cs	P279FPK	Southern Cs	P332HVX	Southern Cs	P631FHN	North East
P223MKL	Southern Cs	P279VRG	North East	P334HVX	The Shires	P633FHN	North East
P224MKL	Southern Cs	P284FPK	Southern Cs	P410CCU	North East	P634PGP	North East
P225MKL	Southern Cs	P286FPK	Southern Cs	P411CCU	North East	P637PGP	North East
P226MKL	Southern Cs	P288FPK	Southern Cs	P412CCU	North East	P638PGP	North East
P227MKL	Southern Cs	P289FPK	Southern Cs	P413CCU	North East	P639LMJ	Tellings GM
P228MKL	Southern Cs	P290FPK	Southern Cs	P414CCU	North East	P640LMJ	Tellings GM
P229MKL	Southern Cs	P291FPK	Southern Cs	P415CCU	North East	P671OPP	The Shires
P230MKL	Southern Cs	P292FPK	Southern Cs	P416CCU	North East	P672OPP	The Shires
P231MKL	Southern Cs	P293FPK	Southern Cs	P417CCU	North East	P673OPP	The Shires
P232MKL	Southern Cs	P294FPK	Southern Cs	P417HVX	Tellings GM	P674OPP	The Shires
P233MKN	Southern Cs	P295FPK	Southern Cs	P418CCU	North East	P801RWU	Scotland West
P234MKN	Southern Cs	P296FPK	Southern Cs	P419CCU	North East	P802RWU	Scotland West
P235MKN	Southern Cs	P301HEM	NW & Wales	P419HVX	NW & Wales	P803RWU	Scotland West
P236MKN	Southern Cs	P302HEM	NW & Wales	P420CCU	North East	P804RWU	Scotland West

P805RWU	Scotland West	P913PWW	Scotland West	PN52XRW	Midlands	R208CKO	North East
P806DBS	Scotland West	P914PWW	Scotland West	PSU969	Midlands	R208GMJ	The Shires
P807DBS	Scotland West	P915PWW	Scotland West	PSU988	Midlands	R208VPU	The Shires
P808DBS	Scotland West	P926MKL	Southern Cs	PSU989	Midlands	R209CKO	North East
P809DBS	Scotland West	P927MKL	Southern Cs	R10WAL	Yorkshire	R209GMJ	The Shires
P810DBS	Scotland West	P928MKL	Southern Cs	R28GNW	Yorkshire	R209VPU	The Shires
P811DBS	Scotland West	P929MKL	Southern Cs	R29GNW	Yorkshire	R210CKO	Southern Cs
P813DBS	Scotland West	P930MKL	Southern Cs	R44BLU	NW & Wales	R210GMJ	The Shires
P814DBS	Scotland West	P931MKL	Southern Cs	R45VJF	Midlands	R211CKO	Southern Cs
P814VTY	North East	P932MKL	Southern Cs	R46VJF	Midlands	R211GMJ	Southern Cs
P815DBS	Scotland West	P933MKL	Southern Cs	R47XVM	NW & Wales	R212CKO	Southern Cs
P816GMS	Scotland West	P934MKL	Southern Cs	R48XVM	NW & Wales	R212GMJ	The Shires
P817GMS	Scotland West	P935MKL	Southern Cs	R51XVM	NW & Wales	R213CKO	NW & Wales
P818GMS	Scotland West	P936MKL	Southern Cs	R54XVM	NW & Wales	R213GMJ	The Shires
P819GMS	Scotland West	P937MKL	Southern Cs	R57XVM	NW & Wales	R214GMJ	The Shires
P820GMS	Scotland West	P938MKL	NW & Wales	R59XVM	NW & Wales	R215GMJ	The Shires
P821GMS	Scotland West	P939MKL	NW & Wales	R103GNW	Yorkshire	R233AEY	NW & Wales
P822GMS	Scotland West	P940MKL	NW & Wales	R118TKO	Southern Cs	R234AEY	NW & Wales
P822RWU	Scotland West	P941MKL	NW & Wales	R119TKO	Southern Cs	R235AEY	NW & Wales
P823GMS	Scotland West	P942MKL	NW & Wales	R120TKO	Southern Cs	R236AEY	NW & Wales
P824GMS	Scotland West	P943MKL	NW & Wales	R121TKO	Southern Cs	R237AEY	NW & Wales
P824RWU	Midlands	P952RUL	Midlands	R122TKO	Southern Cs	R238AEY	NW & Wales
P825KES	Scotland West	P953RUL	NW & Wales	R151GNW	NW & Wales	R239AEY	NW & Wales
P827KES	Scotland West	P954RUL	Midlands	R152GNW	NW & Wales	R255WRJ	NW & Wales
P828KES	Scotland West	P955RUL	Midlands	R153GNW	NW & Wales	R261EKO	Southern Cs
P829KES	Scotland West	P956RUL	Midlands	R165GNW	The Shires	R262EKO	Southern Cs
P830KES	Scotland West	P957RUL	Midlands	R169GNW	Tellings GM	R263EKO	Southern Cs
P831KES	Scotland West	P958RUL	Midlands	R169GNW	The Shires	R264EKO	Southern Cs
P832KES	Scotland West	P959RUL	NW & Wales	R170GNW	Tellings GM	R265EKO	Southern Cs
P833HVX	Southern Cs	P960RUL	NW & Wales	R170GNW	The Shires	R266EKO	Southern Cs
P833HVX	The Shires	P961RUL	NW & Wales	R180VBM	The Shires	R267EKO	Southern Cs
P833KES	Scotland West	P962RUL	Scotland West	R186DNM	Southern Cs	R268EKO	Southern Cs
P833RWU	NW & Wales	P963RUL	Scotland West	R191RBM	The Shires	R269EKO	Southern Cs
P834KES	Scotland West	P964RUL	Scotland West	R192RBM	The Shires	R270EKO	Southern Cs
P835KES	Scotland West	P965RUL	Scotland West	R193RBM	The Shires	R271EKO	Southern Cs
P835RWU	Midlands	P966RUL	Scotland West	R194RBM	The Shires	R272EKO	Southern Cs
P836KES	Scotland West	P967RUL	Scotland West	R195RBM	The Shires	R291KRG	North East
P836RWU	Midlands	P968RUL	Scotland West	R196RBM	The Shires	R292KRG	North East
P837KES	Scotland West	PCZ6034	Midlands	R197RBM	The Shires	R293KRG	North East
P837RWU	Midlands	PIL2160	Tellings GM	R198RBM	The Shires	R294KRG	North East
P838KES	Scotland West	PIL2170	Tellings GM	R199RBM	The Shires	R295KRG	North East
P839KES	Scotland West	PN02HVL	The Shires	R201CKO	NW & Wales	R296CMV	Southern Cs
P839RWU	Midlands	PN02HVM	The Shires	R201RBM	The Shires	R297CMV	Southern Cs
P840KES	Scotland West	PN02HVO	The Shires	R201VPU	The Shires	R298CMV	Southern Cs
P840PWW	Midlands	PN02HVP	The Shires	R202CKO	NW & Wales	R299CMV	Southern Cs
P841PWW	Midlands	PN02HVR	The Shires	R202RBM	The Shires	R301CMV	Southern Cs
P842PWW	Midlands	PN02HVS	The Shires	R203CKO	NW & Wales	R301PCW	NW & Wales
P843PWW	Midlands	PN52XBF	Midlands	R203RBM	The Shires	R302CMV	Southern Cs
P845PWW	Midlands	PN52XBH	Midlands	R204CKO	North East	R302CVU	NW & Wales
P846PWW	Midlands	PN52XRJ	Midlands	R204RBM	The Shires	R303CVU	NW & Wales
P847PWW	Midlands	PN52XRK	Midlands	R204VPU	The Shires	R304CMV	Southern Cs
P848PWW	Midlands	PN52XRL	Midlands	R205CKO	North East	R304CVU	NW & Wales
P849PWW	Midlands	PN52XRM	Midlands	R205RBM	The Shires	R305CMV	Southern Cs
P850PWW	Midlands	PN52XRO	Midlands	R205VPU	The Shires	R305CVU	NW & Wales
P851PWW	Midlands	PN52XRP	Midlands	R206CKO	North East	R307CMV	Southern Cs
P852PWW	Midlands	PN52XRR	Midlands	R206GMJ	Southern Cs	R308CMV	Southern Cs
P853PWW	Midlands	PN52XRS	Midlands	R206VPU	The Shires	R308CVU	NW & Wales
P854PWW	Midlands	PN52XRT	Midlands	R207CKO	North East	R309CVU	NW & Wales
P855PWW	Midlands	PN52XRU	Midlands	R207GMJ	The Shires	R309WVR	NW & Wales
P902DRG	North East	PN52XRV	Midlands	R207VPU	The Shires	R310CMV	Southern Cs

Reg	Region	Reg	Region	Reg	Region	Reg	Region
R310CVU	NW & Wales	R418COO	NW & Wales	R452SKX	The Shires	R615MNU	Midlands
R310NGM	Southern Cs	R418HVX	The Shires	R453KWT	Yorkshire	R616MNU	Midlands
R310WVR	NW & Wales	R418TJW	Midlands	R453SKX	The Shires	R616MNU	North East
R311CVU	NW & Wales	R419COO	NW & Wales	R454KWT	Yorkshire	R617MNU	Midlands
R311NGM	Southern Cs	R419TJW	Midlands	R455KWT	Yorkshire	R618MNU	Midlands
R311WVR	NW & Wales	R420COO	NW & Wales	R455SKX	The Shires	R619MNU	North East
R312CVU	NW & Wales	R420TJW	Midlands	R456KWT	Yorkshire	R620MNU	Midlands
R312NGM	Southern Cs	R421COO	North East	R456SKX	Southern Cs	R621MNU	Midlands
R312WVR	NW & Wales	R421TJW	Midlands	R457KWT	Yorkshire	R622MNU	Midlands
R313CVU	NW & Wales	R422COO	North East	R458KWT	Yorkshire	R624MNU	Midlands
R313NGM	Southern Cs	R422TJW	Midlands	R459KWT	Yorkshire	R625MNU	North East
R313WVR	NW & Wales	R423COO	North East	R460KWT	Yorkshire	R636MNU	North East
R314WVR	NW & Wales	R423RPY	North East	R461KWT	Yorkshire	R637MNU	Southern Cs
R315WVR	NW & Wales	R423TJW	Midlands	R503MOT	Midlands	R638MNU	Midlands
R317WVR	NW & Wales	R424COO	North East	R504MOT	Midlands	R639MNU	North East
R319WVR	NW & Wales	R424RPY	North East	R505MOT	Midlands	R639MNU	Southern Cs
R321WVR	NW & Wales	R424TJW	Midlands	R521UCC	NW & Wales	R640MNU	North East
R322WVR	NW & Wales	R425COO	North East	R522UCC	NW & Wales	R641MNU	North East
R324WVR	NW & Wales	R425RPY	North East	R524TWR	The Shires	R685MHN	NW & Wales
R326WVR	NW & Wales	R425TJW	Midlands	R546ABA	NW & Wales	R69GNW	Yorkshire
R327WVR	NW & Wales	R426COO	North East	R547ABA	NW & Wales	R701KCU	North East
R329TJW	Midlands	R426RPY	North East	R548ABA	NW & Wales	R704MEW	Midlands
R329WVR	NW & Wales	R426TJW	Midlands	R549ABA	NW & Wales	R705MHN	North East
R330TJW	Midlands	R427COO	North East	R550ABA	NW & Wales	R710MHN	North East
R330WVR	NW & Wales	R427RPY	North East	R551ABA	NW & Wales	R711MHN	North East
R331TJW	Midlands	R427TJW	Midlands	R552ABA	NW & Wales	R716MHN	North East
R331WVR	NW & Wales	R428COO	North East	R553ABA	NW & Wales	R759DUB	The Shires
R332TJW	Midlands	R428TJW	Midlands	R554ABA	NW & Wales	R798DUB	Southern Cs
R332WVR	NW & Wales	R429COO	North East	R556ABA	NW & Wales	R809WJA	The Shires
R334TJW	Midlands	R429TJW	Midlands	R557ABA	NW & Wales	R903BKO	Southern Cs
R334WVR	NW & Wales	R430COO	North East	R558ABA	NW & Wales	R904BKO	Southern Cs
R335TJW	Midlands	R430RPY	North East	R559ABA	NW & Wales	R905BKO	Southern Cs
R335WVR	NW & Wales	R431COO	North East	R560ABA	NW & Wales	R906BKO	Southern Cs
R336TJW	Midlands	R431RPY	North East	R561ABA	NW & Wales	R907BKO	Southern Cs
R336WVR	NW & Wales	R432RPY	North East	R561UOT	Midlands	R908BKO	Southern Cs
R337TJW	Midlands	R433RPY	North East	R562ABA	NW & Wales	R909BKO	The Shires
R337WVR	NW & Wales	R434RPY	North East	R563ABA	NW & Wales	R915JNL	North East
R338TJW	Midlands	R435RPY	North East	R564ABA	NW & Wales	R917JNL	North East
R339TJW	Midlands	R436RPY	North East	R565ABA	NW & Wales	R918JNL	North East
R340TJW	Midlands	R437RPY	North East	R567ABA	NW & Wales	R919JNL	North East
R341TJW	Midlands	R438RPY	North East	R568ABA	NW & Wales	R91GNW	NW & Wales
R342TJW	Midlands	R439RPY	North East	R569ABA	NW & Wales	R920RAU	Midlands
R343TJW	Midlands	R440GWY	Yorkshire	R570ABA	NW & Wales	R923JNL	North East
R344TJW	Midlands	R440RPY	North East	R571ABA	NW & Wales	R929RAU	Midlands
R369TWR	The Shires	R441KWT	Yorkshire	R601MHN	NW & Wales	R942VPU	Southern Cs
R370TWR	The Shires	R442KWT	Yorkshire	R602MHN	NW & Wales	R958RCH	Tellings GM
R371TWR	The Shires	R443KWT	Yorkshire	R602WMJ	The Shires	R985FNW	Yorkshire
R372TWR	The Shires	R445KWT	Yorkshire	R603MHN	NW & Wales	R989FNW	Yorkshire
R381JYS	Scotland West	R446KWT	Yorkshire	R603WMJ	The Shires	RA05XEB	Tellings GM
R382JYS	Scotland West	R447KWT	Yorkshire	R604MHN	NW & Wales	RA05XEC	Tellings GM
R383JYS	Scotland West	R447SKX	The Shires	R604WMJ	The Shires	RA53BLJ	Tellings GM
R384JYS	Scotland West	R448KWT	Yorkshire	R605WMJ	The Shires	RA53BLK	Tellings GM
R385JYS	Scotland West	R448SKX	The Shires	R606FBU	NW & Wales	REZ8516	Midlands
R415TJW	Midlands	R449KWT	Yorkshire	R606MHN	NW & Wales	RF57KTT	Tellings GM
R416COO	NW & Wales	R449SKX	The Shires	R607MHN	NW & Wales	RL04EXL	Tellings GM
R416HVX	The Shires	R450KWT	Yorkshire	R607WMJ	The Shires	RL51ZKR	Tellings GM
R416TJW	Midlands	R450SKX	The Shires	R608MHN	NW & Wales	RL51ZKS	Tellings GM
R417COO	NW & Wales	R451KWT	Yorkshire	R608WMJ	The Shires	RN03EOA	Tellings GM
R417HVX	The Shires	R451SKX	The Shires	R609MHN	NW & Wales	RO57PJU	Tellings GM
R417TJW	Midlands	R452KWT	Yorkshire	R614MNU	Midlands	RO57WJM	Tellings GM

Reg	Area	Reg	Area	Reg	Area	Reg	Area
RUI2486	Midlands	S217XPP	The Shires	S273JUA	London	S356KHN	North East
RV57DXO	Tellings GM	S218JUA	London	S274JUA	London	S357KHN	North East
RV57DXY	Tellings GM	S219JUA	London	S275JUA	London	S358KHN	North East
RX07KPG	Tellings GM	S220JUA	London	S276JUA	London	S401ERP	The Shires
RX07KPJ	Tellings GM	S221JUA	London	S277JUA	London	S402ERP	The Shires
RX53LBJ	Tellings GM	S223JUA	London	S278JUA	London	S403ERP	The Shires
RY05AEZ	Tellings GM	S224JUA	London	S279JUA	London	S404ERP	The Shires
RY07BJU	Tellings GM	S225JUA	London	S280JUA	London	S426MCC	The Shires
S2WMS	Midlands	S226JUA	London	S281JUA	London	S427MCC	The Shires
S10BCL	Tellings GM	S227JUA	London	S282JUA	London	S428MCC	The Shires
S146KNK	The Shires	S228JUA	London	S283JUA	London	S429MCC	The Shires
S147KNK	The Shires	S229JUA	London	S284JUA	London	S43BLU	NW & Wales
S148KNK	The Shires	S230JUA	London	S285JUA	London	S45BLU	NW & Wales
S149KNK	The Shires	S231JUA	London	S286JUA	London	S462GUB	Yorkshire
S150KNK	The Shires	S232JUA	London	S287JUA	London	S463GUB	Yorkshire
S151KNK	The Shires	S233JUA	London	S288JUA	London	S464GUB	Yorkshire
S152KNK	The Shires	S234JUA	London	S289JUA	London	S465GUB	Yorkshire
S153KNK	The Shires	S235JUA	London	S290JUA	London	S466GUB	Yorkshire
S154KNK	The Shires	S236JUA	The Shires	S291JUA	London	S467GUB	Yorkshire
S156KNK	The Shires	S237JUA	London	S292JUA	London	S468GUB	Yorkshire
S157KNK	The Shires	S238JUA	London	S301JUA	Tellings GM	S469GUB	Yorkshire
S158KNK	The Shires	S239JUA	London	S302JUA	Tellings GM	S470GUB	Yorkshire
S159KNK	The Shires	S240JUA	London	S303JUA	Tellings GM	S471GUB	Yorkshire
S160KNK	The Shires	S241JUA	London	S304JUA	London	S472ANW	Yorkshire
S161KNK	The Shires	S242JUA	London	S305JUA	London	S473ANW	Yorkshire
S169JUA	London	S243JUA	London	S306JUA	London	S474ANW	Yorkshire
S170JUA	London	S244JUA	London	S307JUA	The Shires	S475ANW	Yorkshire
S171JUA	London	S245JUA	London	S308JUA	The Shires	S476ANW	Yorkshire
S172JUA	London	S246JUA	London	S310JUA	Tellings GM	S477ANW	Yorkshire
S173JUA	London	S247JUA	London	S311JUA	Tellings GM	S478ANW	Yorkshire
S174JUA	London	S248JUA	London	S312JUA	Tellings GM	S479ANW	Yorkshire
S175JUA	London	S248UVR	NW & Wales	S313JUA	Tellings GM	S480ANW	Yorkshire
S176JUA	London	S249JUA	London	S314JUA	Tellings GM	S481ANW	Yorkshire
S177JUA	London	S249UVR	NW & Wales	S315JUA	The Shires	S482ANW	Yorkshire
S178JUA	London	S250JUA	London	S316JUA	The Shires	S483ANW	Yorkshire
S179JUA	London	S250UVR	NW & Wales	S317JUA	The Shires	S484ANW	Yorkshire
S180JUA	London	S251JUA	London	S318JUA	The Shires	S485ANW	Yorkshire
S181JUA	London	S251UVR	NW & Wales	S322JUA	London	S486ANW	Yorkshire
S182JUA	London	S252JUA	London	S341KHN	North East	S487ANW	Yorkshire
S183JUA	London	S253JUA	London	S342KHN	North East	S488ANW	Yorkshire
S202JUA	NW & Wales	S254JUA	London	S343KHN	North East	S489ANW	Yorkshire
S203JUA	NW & Wales	S255JUA	London	S344KHN	North East	S490ANW	Yorkshire
S204JUA	NW & Wales	S256JUA	London	S345KHN	North East	S491ANW	Yorkshire
S205JUA	NW & Wales	S257JUA	London	S345YOG	Midlands	S550BNV	Tellings GM
S206JUA	NW & Wales	S258JUA	London	S346KHN	North East	S553BNV	Tellings GM
S207DTO	Midlands	S259JUA	London	S346YOG	Midlands	S558MCC	NW & Wales
S207JUA	NW & Wales	S260JUA	London	S347YOG	Midlands	S559MCC	NW & Wales
S208DTO	Midlands	S261JUA	London	S348KHN	North East	S610KHN	NW & Wales
S208JUA	NW & Wales	S262JUA	London	S348YOG	Midlands	S611KHN	North East
S209JUA	NW & Wales	S263JUA	London	S349KHN	North East	S612KHN	North East
S20BCL	Tellings GM	S264JUA	London	S349YOG	Midlands	S613KHN	North East
S210JUA	NW & Wales	S265JUA	NW & Wales	S350KHN	North East	S614KHN	NW & Wales
S211JUA	London	S266JUA	NW & Wales	S350YOG	Midlands	S616KHN	North East
S212JUA	London	S267JUA	NW & Wales	S351KHN	North East	S617KHN	North East
S213JUA	London	S268JUA	NW & Wales	S351YOG	Midlands	S618KHN	North East
S214JUA	London	S268JUG	Midlands	S352KHN	North East	S619KHN	North East
S215JUA	London	S269JUA	NW & Wales	S352YOG	Midlands	S620KHN	NW & Wales
S216JUA	London	S270JUA	NW & Wales	S353KHN	North East	S621KHN	North East
S216XPP	The Shires	S271JUA	NW & Wales	S353YOG	Midlands	S622KHN	NW & Wales
S217JUA	London	S272JUA	London	S354KHN	North East	S623KHN	NW & Wales

Reg	Location	Reg	Location	Reg	Location	Reg	Location
S624KHN	Scotland West	S869ONL	North East	SN54HWY	Tellings GM	T209XBV	Original Tour
S625KHN	North East	S870ONL	North East	SN54HWZ	Tellings GM	T210XBV	Original Tour
S626KHN	North East	S872SNB	NW & Wales	SN54HXA	Tellings GM	T211XBV	Original Tour
S627KHN	NW & Wales	S873SNB	NW & Wales	SN54HXB	Tellings GM	T212XBV	Original Tour
S628KHN	NW & Wales	S874SNB	NW & Wales	SN54HXC	Tellings GM	T213XBV	Original Tour
S629KHN	NW & Wales	S875SNB	NW & Wales	SN54HXD	Tellings GM	T214XBV	Original Tour
S630KHN	NW & Wales	S876SNB	NW & Wales	SN54HXE	Tellings GM	T215XBV	London
S631KHN	NW & Wales	S877SNB	NW & Wales	SN54HXF	Tellings GM	T216XBV	London
S632KHN	NW & Wales	S878SNB	NW & Wales	SN55HTX	Yorkshire	T217XBV	London
S633KHN	NW & Wales	S879SNB	NW & Wales	SN55HTY	Yorkshire	T218NMJ	Southern Cs
S634KHN	NW & Wales	S890ONL	North East	SN55HTZ	Yorkshire	T218XBV	London
S635KHN	North East	S891ONL	North East	SN56AXG	The Shires	T219NMJ	The Shires
S636KHN	North East	S892ONL	North East	SN56AXH	The Shires	T219XBV	London
S637KHN	North East	S893ONL	North East	SN58ENX	The Shires	T220XBV	London
S638KHN	North East	S903DUB	The Shires	SN58ENY	The Shires	T222MTB	NW & Wales
S639KHN	North East	SA52MYT	North East	SN58EOA	The Shires	T273JKM	Southern Cs
S640KHN	North East	SCZ9651	Southern Cs	SN58EOB	The Shires	T274JKM	Southern Cs
S642KHN	Scotland West	SCZ9652	Southern Cs	SN58EOC	The Shires	T275JKM	Southern Cs
S643KHN	Scotland West	SF04RGY	Midlands	SN58EOD	The Shires	T276JKM	Southern Cs
S644KJU	Midlands	SF04RHA	North East	SN58EOE	The Shires	T277JKM	Southern Cs
S645KJU	Midlands	SF09LOD	Scotland West	SN58EOF	The Shires	T278JKM	Southern Cs
S646KJU	North East	SF57NMM	Scotland West	SN58EOG	The Shires	T279JKM	Southern Cs
S648KJU	North East	SF57NMO	Scotland West	SN58EOH	The Shires	T280JKM	Southern Cs
S649KJU	North East	SF57NPK	Scotland West	SN58EOJ	The Shires	T281JKM	Southern Cs
S649KJU	Tellings GM	SF57NPL	Scotland West	SN58EOK	The Shires	T282JKM	Southern Cs
S650KJU	Midlands	SF59AWR	Tellings GM	SN58EOM	The Shires	T283JKM	Southern Cs
S652KJU	Midlands	SJ57DDN	Scotland West	SN58EOO	The Shires	T284JKM	Southern Cs
S653KJU	Southern Cs	SJ57DDO	Scotland West	T10BLU	NW & Wales	T285JKM	Southern Cs
S701VKM	Southern Cs	SJ57DDU	Scotland West	T11BLU	NW & Wales	T286JKM	Southern Cs
S702KFT	North East	SJ57DDV	Scotland West	T20CCH	Midlands	T287JKM	Southern Cs
S702VKM	Southern Cs	SJ57DDX	Scotland West	T49JJF	Midlands	T288JKM	Southern Cs
S703KFT	North East	SJ57DDY	Scotland West	T51JJF	Midlands	T289JKM	Southern Cs
S703VKM	Southern Cs	SJ57DDZ	Scotland West	T52JJF	Midlands	T293FGN	London
S704KFT	North East	SK52MLE	Midlands	T53JJF	Midlands	T294FGN	London
S704VKM	Southern Cs	SK52MLF	Midlands	T54JJF	Midlands	T295FGN	London
S705KFT	North East	SK52MLJ	Midlands	T61JBA	Midlands	T296FGN	London
S705VKM	Southern Cs	SK52MLL	Midlands	T62JBA	NW & Wales	T296FGN	NW & Wales
S706KFT	North East	SK52MLN	Midlands	T63JBA	NW & Wales	T297FGN	London
S706VKM	Southern Cs	SK52MLO	Midlands	T64JBA	NW & Wales	T297FGN	NW & Wales
S707KFT	North East	SMK752F	London	T65JBA	NW & Wales	T298FGN	London
S708KFT	North East	SN03LDV	Midlands	T74AUA	North East	T298FGN	NW & Wales
S709KFT	North East	SN03LDX	Midlands	T75AUA	North East	T299FGN	London
S710KFT	North East	SN03LGC	Midlands	T76AUA	North East	T299FGN	NW & Wales
S711KFT	North East	SN03LGD	Midlands	T78AUA	North East	T300FGN	NW & Wales
S712KRG	North East	SN03LGE	Midlands	T79AUA	North East	T301FGN	London
S713KRG	North East	SN03LGF	Midlands	T81AUA	North East	T301FGN	NW & Wales
S714KRG	North East	SN06BPE	Southern Cs	T82AUA	North East	T302FGN	London
S715KRG	North East	SN06BPF	Southern Cs	T83AUA	North East	T302FGN	NW & Wales
S848RJC	NW & Wales	SN06BPK	Southern Cs	T109LKK	Southern Cs	T303FGN	London
S860OGB	Scotland West	SN06BPU	Southern Cs	T110GGO	London	T303FGN	NW & Wales
S861OGB	Scotland West	SN06BPV	Southern Cs	T110LKK	Southern Cs	T304FGN	London
S862OGB	Scotland West	SN06BPX	Southern Cs	T131AUA	Tellings GM	T304FGN	NW & Wales
S863OGB	Scotland West	SN06BPY	Southern Cs	T133AUA	Tellings GM	T305FGN	London
S864OGB	Scotland West	SN06BPZ	Southern Cs	T202XBV	Original Tour	T305FGN	NW & Wales
S865OGB	Scotland West	SN06BRF	Southern Cs	T203XBV	Original Tour	T306FGN	London
S866OGB	Scotland West	SN53ESG	Midlands	T204XBV	Original Tour	T307FGN	London
S867OGB	Scotland West	SN53ESO	Midlands	T205XBV	Original Tour	T308FGN	London
S868OGB	Scotland West	SN54GPK	The Shires	T206XBV	Original Tour	T309FGN	London
S868ONL	North East	SN54GPO	The Shires	T207XBV	Original Tour	T310FGN	London
S869OGB	Scotland West	SN54GPU	The Shires	T208XBV	Original Tour	T311FGN	London

Reg	Location	Reg	Location	Reg	Location	Reg	Location
T312FGN	London	T592CGT	Southern Cs	UAR247Y	Original Tour	V223PCX	Yorkshire
T313FGN	London	T612PNC	NW & Wales	UAR250Y	Original Tour	V224KDA	Midlands
T314FGN	London	T613PNC	NW & Wales	UAR776Y	Original Tour	V224PCX	Yorkshire
T314PNB	NW & Wales	T614PNC	NW & Wales	UK04BCL	Tellings GM	V225KDA	Midlands
T315FGN	London	T615PNC	NW & Wales	UK04TGM	Southern Cs	V225PCX	Yorkshire
T315PNB	NW & Wales	T616PNC	NW & Wales	UK04TGM	Tellings GM	V226KDA	Midlands
T316FGN	London	T617PNC	NW & Wales	UKZ5466	Midlands	V226PCX	Yorkshire
T316PNB	NW & Wales	T618PNC	NW & Wales	V1SFC	Tellings GM	V227KDA	Midlands
T317FGN	London	T619PNC	NW & Wales	V22BLU	NW & Wales	V227PCX	Yorkshire
T317PNB	NW & Wales	T620PNC	NW & Wales	V33BLU	NW & Wales	V228KDA	Midlands
T318FGN	London	T621PNC	NW & Wales	V82EVU	The Shires	V228PCX	Yorkshire
T318PNB	NW & Wales	T622PNC	NW & Wales	V201KDA	Midlands	V229KDA	Midlands
T319FGN	London	T623PNC	NW & Wales	V201PCX	Yorkshire	V229XUB	Yorkshire
T319PNB	NW & Wales	T624EUB	Yorkshire	V202KDA	Midlands	V230HBH	The Shires
T320FGN	London	T625EUB	Yorkshire	V203KDA	Midlands	V230KDA	Midlands
T320PNB	NW & Wales	T626EUB	Yorkshire	V203PCX	Yorkshire	V231HBH	The Shires
T322FGN	London	T627EUB	Yorkshire	V204KDA	Midlands	V231KDA	Midlands
T322PNB	NW & Wales	T628EUB	Yorkshire	V204PCX	Yorkshire	V232HBH	The Shires
T323FGN	London	T629EUB	Yorkshire	V205KDA	Midlands	V232KDA	Midlands
T323PNB	NW & Wales	T630EUB	Yorkshire	V205PCX	Yorkshire	V233HBH	The Shires
T324FGN	London	T631EUB	Yorkshire	V206DJR	North East	V233KDA	Midlands
T324PNB	NW & Wales	T632EUB	Yorkshire	V206KDA	Midlands	V234HBH	The Shires
T325FGN	London	T633EUB	Yorkshire	V206PCX	Yorkshire	V234KDA	Midlands
T405ENV	The Shires	T634EUB	Yorkshire	V207DJR	North East	V235HBH	The Shires
T405SMV	Tellings GM	T635EUB	Yorkshire	V207KDA	Midlands	V235KDA	Midlands
T406ENV	The Shires	T636EUB	Yorkshire	V207PCX	Yorkshire	V236HBH	The Shires
T406SMV	Tellings GM	T637EUB	Yorkshire	V208DJR	North East	V236KDA	Midlands
T407ENV	The Shires	T638EUB	Yorkshire	V208KDA	Midlands	V237HBH	The Shires
T408ENV	The Shires	T639EUB	Yorkshire	V208PCX	Yorkshire	V237KDA	Midlands
T408LGP	The Shires	T691KPU	Midlands	V209DJR	North East	V238HBH	The Shires
T409ENV	The Shires	T695KPU	Midlands	V209KDA	Midlands	V238KDA	Midlands
T410ENV	The Shires	T696KPU	Midlands	V209PCX	Yorkshire	V239HBH	The Shires
T421GGO	London	T698KPU	Midlands	V210DJR	North East	V239KDA	Midlands
T424LGP	The Shires	T701RCN	North East	V210KDA	Midlands	V250HBH	The Shires
T425LGP	The Shires	T702RCN	North East	V210PCX	Yorkshire	V250HBU	Tellings GM
T42PVM	NW & Wales	T820NMJ	Southern Cs	V211DJR	North East	V251HBH	The Shires
T45KAW	The Shires	T821NMJ	Southern Cs	V211KDA	Midlands	V251HBU	Tellings GM
T47WUT	Midlands	T821PNB	NW & Wales	V211PCX	Yorkshire	V252HBH	The Shires
T48WUT	Midlands	T822NMJ	Southern Cs	V212DJR	North East	V253HBH	The Shires
T490KGB	The Shires	T823NMJ	Southern Cs	V212KDA	Midlands	V254HBH	The Shires
T491KGB	The Shires	T824NMJ	Southern Cs	V212PCX	Yorkshire	V255HBH	The Shires
T492KGB	The Shires	T825NMJ	Southern Cs	V213DJR	North East	V255HBU	Tellings GM
T494KGB	The Shires	T826NMJ	Southern Cs	V213KDA	Midlands	V256HBH	The Shires
T495KGB	The Shires	T827NMJ	The Shires	V213PCX	Yorkshire	V257HBH	The Shires
T495KGB	The Shires	T828NMJ	The Shires	V214DJR	North East	V258HBH	The Shires
T526AOB	NW & Wales	T829NMJ	The Shires	V214KDA	Midlands	V259HBH	The Shires
T527AOB	NW & Wales	T911KKM	Southern Cs	V215KDA	Midlands	V260HBH	The Shires
T528AOB	NW & Wales	T912KKM	Southern Cs	V215PCX	Yorkshire	V261HBH	The Shires
T529AOB	NW & Wales	T913KKM	Southern Cs	V216KDA	Midlands	V262HBH	The Shires
T560JJC	NW & Wales	T914KKM	Southern Cs	V216PCX	Yorkshire	V263HBH	The Shires
T561JJC	NW & Wales	T915KKM	Southern Cs	V217KDA	Midlands	V264HBH	The Shires
T562JJC	NW & Wales	T916KKM	Southern Cs	V217PCX	Yorkshire	V265HBH	The Shires
T564JJC	NW & Wales	T917KKM	NW & Wales	V218KDA	Midlands	V266HBH	The Shires
T565JJC	NW & Wales	T918KKM	Southern Cs	V218PCX	Yorkshire	V267HBH	The Shires
T566JJC	NW & Wales	T919KKM	Southern Cs	V219KDA	Midlands	V268HBH	The Shires
T567JJC	NW & Wales	T920KKM	NW & Wales	V220KDA	Midlands	V270HBH	The Shires
T568JJC	NW & Wales	T921KKM	Southern Cs	V220PCX	Yorkshire	V271HBH	The Shires
T569JJC	NW & Wales	T922KKM	NW & Wales	V221KDA	Midlands	V272HBH	The Shires
T570JJC	NW & Wales	TJI1683	Tellings GM	V221PCX	Yorkshire	V273HBH	The Shires
T591CGT	Southern Cs	TWY7	Yorkshire	V223KDA	Midlands	V274HBH	The Shires

Reg	Region	Reg	Region	Reg	Region	Reg	Region
V275HBH	The Shires	V393KVY	The Shires	V581DJC	NW & Wales	V641KVH	Yorkshire
V276HBH	The Shires	V404ENC	NW & Wales	V582DJC	NW & Wales	V642DVU	NW & Wales
V280HBH	The Shires	V405ENC	NW & Wales	V583DJC	NW & Wales	V643DVU	NW & Wales
V281HBH	The Shires	V406ENC	NW & Wales	V584DJC	NW & Wales	V644DVU	NW & Wales
V282HBH	The Shires	V407ENC	NW & Wales	V585DJC	NW & Wales	V645DVU	NW & Wales
V283HBH	The Shires	V408ENC	NW & Wales	V586DJC	NW & Wales	V646DVU	NW & Wales
V284HBH	The Shires	V409ENC	NW & Wales	V587DJC	NW & Wales	V647DVU	NW & Wales
V285HBH	The Shires	V410ENC	NW & Wales	V588DJC	NW & Wales	V648DVU	NW & Wales
V286HBH	The Shires	V411ENC	NW & Wales	V590DJC	NW & Wales	V649DVU	NW & Wales
V287HBH	The Shires	V412ENC	NW & Wales	V591DJC	NW & Wales	V650DVU	NW & Wales
V288HBH	The Shires	V412UNH	The Shires	V601DBC	Midlands	V650LGC	London
V289HBH	The Shires	V413ENC	NW & Wales	V602DBC	Midlands	V651DVU	NW & Wales
V290HBH	The Shires	V413UNH	The Shires	V603DBC	Midlands	V652DVU	NW & Wales
V291HBH	The Shires	V414ENC	NW & Wales	V604DBC	Midlands	V653DVU	NW & Wales
V292HBH	The Shires	V415ENC	NW & Wales	V605DBC	Midlands	V653LWT	North East
V293HBH	The Shires	V421DGT	The Shires	V606DBC	Midlands	V654DVU	NW & Wales
V294HBH	The Shires	V422DGT	The Shires	V607DBC	Midlands	V655DVU	NW & Wales
V311NGD	Scotland West	V423DGT	Midlands	V608DBC	Midlands	V656DVU	NW & Wales
V312NGD	Scotland West	V424DGT	Midlands	V609DBC	Midlands	V657DVU	NW & Wales
V313NGD	Scotland West	V425DGT	Midlands	V609LGC	Scotland West	V658DVU	NW & Wales
V326DGT	London	V426DGT	Midlands	V610DBC	Midlands	V659DVU	NW & Wales
V327DGT	London	V427DGT	Midlands	V610LGC	Scotland West	V660DVU	NW & Wales
V329DGT	London	V428DGT	Midlands	V611DBC	Midlands	V660LGC	London
V330DGT	London	V429DGT	Midlands	V611LGC	Scotland West	V661DVU	NW & Wales
V331DGT	London	V430DGT	Midlands	V612DBC	Midlands	V662DVU	NW & Wales
V332DGT	London	V431DGT	Midlands	V612DNL	North East	V663DVU	NW & Wales
V334DGT	London	V432DGT	London	V612LGC	Scotland West	V664DVU	NW & Wales
V335DGT	London	V433DGT	London	V613LGC	Scotland West	V665DVU	NW & Wales
V336DGT	London	V434DGT	London	V614LGC	Scotland West	V667DVU	NW & Wales
V337DGT	London	V435DGT	London	V615LGC	Scotland West	V668DVU	NW & Wales
V337MBV	Midlands	V501DFT	North East	V616LGC	Scotland West	V669DVU	NW & Wales
V338DGT	London	V502DFT	North East	V617LGC	Scotland West	V670DVU	NW & Wales
V338MBV	Midlands	V503DFT	North East	V618LGC	Scotland West	V671DVU	NW & Wales
V339DGT	London	V504DFT	North East	V619LGC	Scotland West	V672DVU	NW & Wales
V341DGT	London	V505DFT	North East	V620LGC	Scotland West	V672LWT	Tellings GM
V342DGT	London	V506DFT	North East	V621LGC	Scotland West	V673DVU	NW & Wales
V343DGT	London	V507DFT	North East	V622LGC	Scotland West	V673LWT	Tellings GM
V344DGT	London	V508DFT	North East	V623LGC	Scotland West	V674DVU	NW & Wales
V345DGT	London	V509DFT	North East	V624DBN	NW & Wales	V675DVU	NW & Wales
V346DGT	London	V510DFT	North East	V625DVU	NW & Wales	V676DVU	NW & Wales
V347DGT	London	V511DFT	North East	V626DVU	NW & Wales	V701LWT	Scotland West
V348DGT	London	V512DFT	North East	V627DVU	NW & Wales	V703DNL	North East
V349DGT	London	V513DFT	North East	V628DVU	NW & Wales	V705DNL	North East
V34ENC	NW & Wales	V514DFT	North East	V628LGC	London	V706DNL	North East
V351DGT	London	V515DFT	North East	V629DVU	NW & Wales	V707DNL	North East
V352DGT	London	V553ECC	NW & Wales	V630DVU	NW & Wales	V708DNL	North East
V353DGT	London	V554ECC	NW & Wales	V631DVU	NW & Wales	V709DNL	North East
V354DGT	London	V556ECC	NW & Wales	V632DVU	NW & Wales	V710DNL	North East
V355DGT	London	V557ECC	NW & Wales	V633DVU	NW & Wales	V711DNL	North East
V356DGT	London	V571DJC	NW & Wales	V633LGC	London	V712DNL	North East
V357DGT	London	V572DJC	NW & Wales	V634DVU	NW & Wales	V713DNL	North East
V358DGT	London	V573DJC	NW & Wales	V635DVU	NW & Wales	V714DNL	North East
V359DGT	London	V574DJC	NW & Wales	V636DVU	NW & Wales	V715DNL	North East
V35ENC	NW & Wales	V575DJC	NW & Wales	V637DVU	NW & Wales	V715LWT	NW & Wales
V361DGT	London	V576DJC	NW & Wales	V638DVU	NW & Wales	V716DNL	North East
V362DGT	London	V577DJC	NW & Wales	V639DVU	NW & Wales	V717DNL	North East
V363DGT	London	V578DJC	NW & Wales	V640DVU	NW & Wales	V718DNL	North East
V364DGT	London	V579DJC	NW & Wales	V640KVH	Yorkshire	V719DNL	North East
V365DGT	London	V580DJC	NW & Wales	V640LGC	London	V720DNL	North East
V392KVY	The Shires	V580ECC	NW & Wales	V641DVU	NW & Wales	V721DNL	North East

Reg	Region	Reg	Region	Reg	Region	Reg	Region
V722DNL	North East	W109EWU	Yorkshire	W313PPT	North East	W414VGJ	London
V723DNL	North East	W128XRO	The Shires	W314PPT	North East	W415KNH	The Shires
V724DNL	North East	W129XRO	The Shires	W315PPT	North East	W416KNH	The Shires
V726DNL	North East	W131XRO	The Shires	W317PPT	North East	W421XKX	The Shires
V727DNL	North East	W132XRO	The Shires	W319PPT	North East	W422XKX	The Shires
V728DNL	North East	W134XRO	The Shires	W359XKX	The Shires	W423XKX	The Shires
V733DNL	North East	W136VGJ	London	W361XKX	The Shires	W424XKX	The Shires
V734DNL	North East	W136XRO	The Shires	W362XKX	The Shires	W425XKX	The Shires
V735DNL	North East	W137VGJ	London	W363XKX	The Shires	W426XKX	The Shires
V735FPT	Tellings GM	W137XRO	The Shires	W364XKX	The Shires	W427CWX	Tellings GM
V736DNL	North East	W138VGJ	London	W365XKX	The Shires	W427XKX	The Shires
V737DNL	North East	W138XRO	The Shires	W366VGJ	London	W428XKX	The Shires
V738DNL	North East	W139XRO	The Shires	W367VGJ	London	W429XKX	The Shires
V739DNL	North East	W165HBT	Yorkshire	W367XKX	The Shires	W431WGJ	London
V740DNL	North East	W166HBT	Yorkshire	W368VGJ	London	W431XKX	The Shires
V741DNL	North East	W166PNT	North East	W368XKX	The Shires	W432WGJ	London
V742DNL	North East	W174CDN	NW & Wales	W369VGJ	London	W432XKX	The Shires
V743ECU	North East	W183CDN	Southern Cs	W369XKX	The Shires	W433WGJ	London
V744ECU	North East	W198CDN	Southern Cs	W371VGJ	London	W433XKX	The Shires
V745ECU	North East	W216JND	Midlands	W372VGJ	London	W434WGJ	London
V746ECU	North East	W226SNR	Midlands	W373VGJ	London	W434XKX	Southern Cs
V747ECU	North East	W227SNR	Midlands	W374VGJ	London	W435WGJ	London
V748ECU	North East	W228SNR	Midlands	W376VGJ	London	W435XKX	Southern Cs
V897DNB	The Shires	W229SNR	Midlands	W377VGJ	London	W436WGJ	London
VEZ9715	Midlands	W231SNR	Midlands	W378VGJ	London	W436XKX	Southern Cs
VLT5	London	W232SNR	Midlands	W379VGJ	London	W437WGJ	London
VLT6	London	W233SNR	Midlands	W381VGJ	London	W437XKX	Southern Cs
VLT12	London	W234SNR	Midlands	W382VGJ	London	W438WGJ	London
VLT27	London	W235SNR	Midlands	W383VGJ	London	W438XKX	Southern Cs
VLT32	London	W236SNR	Midlands	W384VGJ	London	W439XKX	Southern Cs
VLT47	London	W237SNR	Midlands	W385VGJ	London	W441XKX	Southern Cs
VLT173	London	W238SNR	Midlands	W386VGJ	London	W442CWX	Tellings GM
VLT244	London	W239SNR	Midlands	W387VGJ	London	W442XKX	The Shires
VLT295	London	W241SNR	Midlands	W388VGJ	London	W443XKX	The Shires
VLZ9237	Midlands	W242SNR	Midlands	W389VGJ	London	W445XKX	The Shires
VU06KFA	Midlands	W243SNR	Midlands	W391VGJ	London	W446XKX	The Shires
VX04JHY	Tellings GM	W244SNR	Yorkshire	W392VGJ	London	W447XKX	The Shires
VX10EBN	Southern Cs	W246SNR	Midlands	W393VGJ	London	W452XKX	The Shires
VX10EBO	Southern Cs	W247SNR	Midlands	W394OJC	NW & Wales	W453XKX	The Shires
VX10EBP	Southern Cs	W248SNR	Midlands	W394VGJ	London	W454XKX	The Shires
VX10EBU	Southern Cs	W249SNR	Midlands	W395RBB	Tellings GM	W457XKX	The Shires
VX10EBV	Southern Cs	W251SNR	Midlands	W395VGJ	London	W458XKX	The Shires
VX10EBX	Southern Cs	W269NFF	NW & Wales	W396RBB	Tellings GM	W459XKX	The Shires
VYJ806	London	W292PPT	North East	W396VGJ	London	W461XKX	London
W3CTS	The Shires	W293PPT	North East	W397RBB	North East	W462XKX	London
W12LUE	NW & Wales	W294PPT	North East	W397VGJ	London	W463XKX	London
W69PRG	North East	W295PPT	North East	W398RBB	North East	W464XKX	London
W72PRG	North East	W296PPT	North East	W398VGJ	London	W465XKX	London
W76PRG	North East	W297PPT	North East	W399RBB	North East	W466XKX	London
W78PRG	Scotland West	W298PPT	North East	W399VGJ	London	W467XKX	London
W79PRG	Scotland West	W299PPT	North East	W401VGJ	London	W468XKX	London
W81PRG	North East	W301PPT	North East	W402VGJ	London	W469XKX	London
W82PRG	Scotland West	W302PPT	North East	W403VGJ	London	W471XKX	London
W83PRG	North East	W303PPT	North East	W404VGJ	London	W472XKX	London
W102EWU	Yorkshire	W304PPT	North East	W407VGJ	London	W473XKX	London
W103EWU	Yorkshire	W307PPT	North East	W408VGJ	London	W474XKX	London
W104EWU	Yorkshire	W308PPT	North East	W409VGJ	London	W475XKX	London
W106EWU	Yorkshire	W309PPT	North East	W411VGJ	London	W476XKX	London
W107EWU	Yorkshire	W311PPT	North East	W412VGJ	London	W477XKX	London
W108EWU	Yorkshire	W312PPT	North East	W413VGJ	London	W478EUB	Midlands

Reg	Region	Reg	Region	Reg	Region	Reg	Region
W478XKX	London	W756SBR	North East	X215ANC	NW & Wales	X267OBN	NW & Wales
W479XKX	London	W757SBR	North East	X215JOF	NW & Wales	X268OBN	NW & Wales
W481XKX	London	W758SBR	North East	X216ANC	NW & Wales	X269OBN	NW & Wales
W482EUB	Midlands	W759SBR	North East	X216HCD	Tellings GM	X271OBN	NW & Wales
W482YGS	The Shires	W901UJM	Tellings GM	X216JOF	NW & Wales	X271RFF	NW & Wales
W483EUB	Midlands	W902UJM	Tellings GM	X217ANC	NW & Wales	X272OBN	NW & Wales
W483YGS	The Shires	W903UJM	Tellings GM	X217HCD	Tellings GM	X272RFF	NW & Wales
W484YGS	The Shires	W904UJM	Tellings GM	X217JOF	NW & Wales	X273RFF	NW & Wales
W485YGS	The Shires	W905UJM	Tellings GM	X218ANC	NW & Wales	X274RFF	NW & Wales
W486YGS	The Shires	W906UJM	Tellings GM	X218JOF	NW & Wales	X295MBH	The Shires
W487YGS	The Shires	W907UJM	Tellings GM	X219JOF	NW & Wales	X296MBH	The Shires
W488YGS	The Shires	W986WDS	The Shires	X221ANC	NW & Wales	X297MBH	The Shires
W489YGS	The Shires	WBZ8737	Midlands	X221HCD	Tellings GM	X351AUX	The Shires
W491YGS	The Shires	WLT348	London	X223ANC	NW & Wales	X415FGP	London
W492YGS	The Shires	WLT372	London	X224ANC	NW & Wales	X416AJA	NW & Wales
W493YGS	The Shires	WLT385	London	X226ANC	NW & Wales	X416FGP	London
W494YGS	The Shires	WLT554	London	X227ANC	NW & Wales	X417AJA	NW & Wales
W495YGS	The Shires	WLT664	London	X228ANC	NW & Wales	X417BBD	The Shires
W496YGS	The Shires	WLT676	London	X229ANC	NW & Wales	X417FGP	London
W497YGS	The Shires	WLT719	London	X231ANC	NW & Wales	X418AJA	NW & Wales
W498YGS	The Shires	WLT751	London	X232ANC	NW & Wales	X418BBD	The Shires
W501RBB	North East	WLT807	London	X233ANC	NW & Wales	X418FGP	London
W601YKN	Southern Cs	WLT888	London	X234ANC	NW & Wales	X419AJA	NW & Wales
W602VGJ	Scotland West	WLT892	London	X235ANC	NW & Wales	X419BBD	The Shires
W602YKN	Southern Cs	WLT895	London	X236ANC	NW & Wales	X419FGP	London
W603VGJ	Scotland West	WLT897	London	X237ANC	NW & Wales	X421AJA	NW & Wales
W603YKN	Southern Cs	WLT901	London	X238ANC	NW & Wales	X421FGP	London
W604VGJ	Scotland West	WLT970	London	X239ANC	NW & Wales	X422AJA	NW & Wales
W604YKN	Southern Cs	WLT997	London	X239PGT	London	X422FGP	London
W605VGJ	Scotland West	WR520PJ	Tellings GM	X241ANC	NW & Wales	X423AJA	NW & Wales
W605YKN	Southern Cs	WSU476	Scotland West	X241PGT	London	X423FGP	London
W606VGJ	Scotland West	WSV570	Tellings GM	X242ANC	NW & Wales	X424AJA	NW & Wales
W607VGJ	Scotland West	WT08BUS	Midlands	X242PGT	London	X424FGP	London
W608VGJ	Scotland West	WT58BUS	Midlands	X243HJA	NW & Wales	X425FGP	London
W631RNP	North East	WT58SOT	Midlands	X243PGT	London	X426AJA	NW & Wales
W651CWX	Yorkshire	WX07WTX	Tellings GM	X244HJA	NW & Wales	X426FGP	London
W652CWX	Yorkshire	X13LUE	NW & Wales	X244PGT	London	X427AJA	NW & Wales
W653CWX	Yorkshire	X14LUE	NW & Wales	X246HJA	NW & Wales	X427FGP	London
W654CWX	Yorkshire	X23BLU	NW & Wales	X246PGT	London	X428FGP	London
W656CWX	Yorkshire	X32KON	NW & Wales	X247HJA	NW & Wales	X428HJA	NW & Wales
W657CWX	Yorkshire	X129PTW	Tellings GM	X247PGT	London	X429FGP	London
W658CWX	Yorkshire	X153ENJ	Tellings GM	X248HJA	NW & Wales	X429HJA	NW & Wales
W659CWX	Yorkshire	X157ENJ	Tellings GM	X248PGT	London	X431FGP	London
W661CWX	Yorkshire	X158ENJ	Tellings GM	X249HJA	NW & Wales	X431HJA	NW & Wales
W662CWX	Yorkshire	X201ANC	NW & Wales	X249PGT	London	X432FGP	London
W663CWX	Yorkshire	X202ANC	NW & Wales	X251HJA	NW & Wales	X432HJA	NW & Wales
W664CWX	Yorkshire	X203ANC	NW & Wales	X252HBC	Midlands	X433FGP	London
W665CWX	Yorkshire	X204ANC	NW & Wales	X252HJA	NW & Wales	X433HJA	NW & Wales
W667CWX	Yorkshire	X207ANC	NW & Wales	X253HJA	NW & Wales	X434FGP	London
W668CWX	Yorkshire	X208ANC	NW & Wales	X254HJA	NW & Wales	X434HJA	NW & Wales
W669CWX	Yorkshire	X209ANC	NW & Wales	X256HJA	NW & Wales	X435FGP	London
W671CWX	Yorkshire	X209JOF	NW & Wales	X257HJA	NW & Wales	X435HJA	NW & Wales
W672CWX	Yorkshire	X211ANC	NW & Wales	X258HJA	NW & Wales	X436FGP	London
W673CWX	Yorkshire	X211JOF	NW & Wales	X259HJA	NW & Wales	X436HJA	NW & Wales
W674CWX	Yorkshire	X212ANC	NW & Wales	X261OBN	NW & Wales	X437FGP	London
W681DDN	The Shires	X212JOF	Tellings GM	X262OBN	NW & Wales	X437HJA	NW & Wales
W751SBR	North East	X213ANC	NW & Wales	X263OBN	NW & Wales	X438FGP	London
W752SBR	North East	X213JOF	NW & Wales	X264OBN	NW & Wales	X438HJA	NW & Wales
W753SBR	North East	X214ANC	NW & Wales	X265OBN	NW & Wales	X439FGP	London
W754SBR	North East	X214JOF	NW & Wales	X266OBN	NW & Wales	X439HJA	NW & Wales

X441FGP	London	X677YUG	Yorkshire	Y36TDA	NW & Wales	Y348UON	Midlands
X441HJA	NW & Wales	X678YUG	Yorkshire	Y37KNB	NW & Wales	Y349UON	Midlands
X442FGP	London	X679YUG	Yorkshire	Y37TDA	NW & Wales	Y351UON	Midlands
X442HJA	NW & Wales	X681YUG	Yorkshire	Y38KNB	NW & Wales	Y352UON	Midlands
X443FGP	London	X682YUG	Yorkshire	Y38TDA	NW & Wales	Y353UON	Midlands
X443HJA	NW & Wales	X683YUG	Yorkshire	Y39TDA	NW & Wales	Y354UON	Midlands
X445FGP	London	X684YUG	Yorkshire	Y40TGM	Tellings GM	Y356UON	Midlands
X445HJA	NW & Wales	X685YUG	Yorkshire	Y42HBT	The Shires	Y357UON	Midlands
X446FGP	London	X686YUG	Yorkshire	Y42TDA	NW & Wales	Y358UON	Midlands
X446HJA	NW & Wales	X687YUG	Yorkshire	Y46ABA	NW & Wales	Y361UON	Midlands
X447FGP	London	X688YUG	Yorkshire	Y46HBT	The Shires	Y362UON	Midlands
X447HJA	NW & Wales	X689YUG	Yorkshire	Y46TDA	NW & Wales	Y363UON	Midlands
X448FGP	London	X691YUG	Yorkshire	Y47ABA	NW & Wales	Y364UON	Midlands
X448HJA	NW & Wales	X692YUG	Yorkshire	Y47HBT	The Shires	Y365UON	Midlands
X449FGP	London	X693YUG	Yorkshire	Y48ABA	NW & Wales	Y366UON	Midlands
X451FGP	London	X694YUG	Yorkshire	Y50TGM	Tellings GM	Y367UON	Midlands
X452FGP	London	X695YUG	Yorkshire	Y83HHE	Tellings GM	Y451KBU	NW & Wales
X453FGP	London	X696YUG	Yorkshire	Y102TGH	London	Y451UGC	Southern Cs
X454FGP	London	X701DBT	NW & Wales	Y184TUK	Midlands	Y452KBU	NW & Wales
X457FGP	Southern Cs	X702DBT	NW & Wales	Y20BLU	NW & Wales	Y452UGC	London
X458FGP	Southern Cs	X703DBT	NW & Wales	Y215BGB	North East	Y453KBU	NW & Wales
X459FGP	Southern Cs	X704DBT	NW & Wales	Y22CJW	NW & Wales	Y454KBU	NW & Wales
X471GGO	London	X705DBT	NW & Wales	Y241KBU	NW & Wales	Y457KBU	NW & Wales
X475GGO	London	X706DBT	NW & Wales	Y242KBU	NW & Wales	Y457KNF	NW & Wales
X478GGO	London	X707DBT	NW & Wales	Y243KBU	NW & Wales	Y458KBU	NW & Wales
X481GGO	London	X708DBT	NW & Wales	Y253YBC	Midlands	Y458KNF	NW & Wales
X485GGO	London	X709DBT	NW & Wales	Y254YBC	Midlands	Y459KBU	NW & Wales
X501GGO	London	X715HCD	Tellings GM	Y256YBC	Midlands	Y461KNF	NW & Wales
X502GGO	London	X734MFL	Tellings GM	Y257YBC	Midlands	Y461UGC	Southern Cs
X503GGO	London	X781NWX	Midlands	Y258KNB	North East	Y462KNF	NW & Wales
X504GGO	London	X782NWX	NW & Wales	Y258YBC	Midlands	Y462UGC	Southern Cs
X506GGO	London	X783NWX	Midlands	Y259KNB	North East	Y463KNF	NW & Wales
X507GGO	London	X801AJA	NW & Wales	Y259YBC	Midlands	Y463UGC	Southern Cs
X508GGO	London	X802AJA	NW & Wales	Y261YBC	Midlands	Y464KNF	NW & Wales
X519GGO	London	X803AJA	NW & Wales	Y262YBC	Midlands	Y464UGC	Southern Cs
X521GGO	London	X804AJA	NW & Wales	Y263YBC	Midlands	Y465KNF	NW & Wales
X522GGO	London	X805AJA	NW & Wales	Y264YBC	Midlands	Y465UGC	Southern Cs
X523GGO	London	X806AJA	NW & Wales	Y265YBC	Midlands	Y466KNF	NW & Wales
X524GGO	London	X807AJA	NW & Wales	Y266YBC	Midlands	Y466UGC	Southern Cs
X526GGO	London	X808AJA	NW & Wales	Y267YBC	Midlands	Y467KNF	NW & Wales
X527GGO	London	X809AJA	NW & Wales	Y291PDN	Tellings GM	Y467UGC	Southern Cs
X529GGO	London	X811AJA	NW & Wales	Y291TKJ	Southern Cs	Y468KNF	NW & Wales
X531GGO	London	X812AJA	NW & Wales	Y292PDN	Tellings GM	Y468UGC	Southern Cs
X532GGO	London	X813AJA	NW & Wales	Y292TKJ	Southern Cs	Y469KNF	NW & Wales
X533GGO	London	X814AJA	NW & Wales	Y293PDN	Tellings GM	Y469UGC	Southern Cs
X534GGO	London	X815AJA	NW & Wales	Y293TKJ	Southern Cs	Y471KNF	NW & Wales
X536GGO	London	X816AJA	NW & Wales	Y294PDN	North East	Y471UGC	London
X537GGO	London	X817AJA	NW & Wales	Y294TKJ	Southern Cs	Y472KNF	NW & Wales
X538GGO	London	X818AJA	NW & Wales	Y295PDN	North East	Y472UGC	London
X541GGO	London	X819AJA	NW & Wales	Y295PDN	Tellings GM	Y473KNF	NW & Wales
X546GGO	London	X821AJA	NW & Wales	Y295TKJ	Southern Cs	Y473UGC	London
X646WTN	North East	X822AJA	NW & Wales	Y296TKJ	Southern Cs	Y474UGC	London
X648WTN	North East	X956DBT	NW & Wales	Y297TKJ	Southern Cs	Y475KNF	NW & Wales
X651WTN	North East	XIL8793	Midlands	Y298TKJ	Southern Cs	Y475UGC	London
X653WTN	Southern Cs	XL04XEL	Tellings GM	Y299TKJ	Southern Cs	Y476UGC	London
X654WTN	North East	XYJ440	London	Y301TKJ	Southern Cs	Y477UGC	London
X656WTN	North East	Y21BLU	NW & Wales	Y302TKJ	Southern Cs	Y478UGC	London
X657WTN	North East	Y30TGM	Tellings GM	Y303TKJ	Southern Cs	Y479UGC	London
X675YUG	Yorkshire	Y32TDA	NW & Wales	Y346UON	Midlands	Y481UGC	London
X676YUG	Yorkshire	Y36KNB	NW & Wales	Y347UON	Midlands	Y482UGC	London

During 2010 many of the mid-life buses in the Netherlands have started to migrate to other Arriva fleets. Amsterdam is a major centre of operation and Scania OmniCity 7853, BR-NP-75 is seen in the city. *Mark Doggett*

Y483UGC	London	Y516UGC	London	Y548UGC	London	Y716KNF	NW & Wales
Y484UGC	London	Y517UGC	London	Y548UJC	NW & Wales	Y717KNF	NW & Wales
Y485UGC	London	Y518UGC	London	Y549UGC	London	Y718KNF	NW & Wales
Y486UGC	London	Y519UGC	London	Y549UJC	NW & Wales	Y719KNF	NW & Wales
Y487UGC	London	Y521UGC	The Shires	Y551UJC	NW & Wales	Y721KNF	NW & Wales
Y488UGC	London	Y522UGC	London	Y552UJC	NW & Wales	Y722KNF	NW & Wales
Y489UGC	London	Y523UGC	London	Y581UGC	London	Y723KNF	NW & Wales
Y491UGC	London	Y524UGC	London	Y685EBR	North East	Y724KNF	NW & Wales
Y492UGC	London	Y526UGC	London	Y686EBR	North East	Y726KNF	NW & Wales
Y493UGC	London	Y527UGC	London	Y687EBR	North East	Y727KNF	NW & Wales
Y494UGC	London	Y529UGC	London	Y688EBR	North East	Y728KNF	NW & Wales
Y495UGC	London	Y531UGC	The Shires	Y689EBR	North East	Y729KNF	NW & Wales
Y496UGC	London	Y532UGC	London	Y691EBR	North East	Y733KNF	NW & Wales
Y497UGC	London	Y533UGC	London	Y693EBR	North East	Y744KNF	NW & Wales
Y498UGC	London	Y538VFF	NW & Wales	Y694EBR	North East	Y801DGT	London
Y499UGC	London	Y539VFF	NW & Wales	Y701XJF	Midlands	Y802DGT	London
Y501UGC	London	Y541UGC	London	Y702XJF	Midlands	Y803DGT	London
Y502UGC	London	Y541UJC	NW & Wales	Y703XJF	Midlands	Y804DGT	London
Y503UGC	London	Y542UGC	London	Y704XJF	Midlands	Y805DGT	London
Y504UGC	London	Y542UJC	NW & Wales	Y705XJF	Midlands	Y806DGT	London
Y506UGC	London	Y543UGC	London	Y706XJF	Midlands	YD02PXW	Yorkshire
Y507UGC	London	Y543UJC	NW & Wales	Y707XJF	Midlands	YD02PXX	Yorkshire
Y508UGC	London	Y544UGC	London	Y709XJF	Midlands	YD02PXY	Yorkshire
Y509UGC	London	Y544UJC	NW & Wales	Y711KNF	NW & Wales	YD02PXZ	Yorkshire
Y511UGC	London	Y546UGC	London	Y712KNF	NW & Wales	YD02PYU	Yorkshire
Y512UGC	London	Y546UJC	NW & Wales	Y713KNF	NW & Wales	YD02PYV	Yorkshire
Y513UGC	London	Y547UGC	London	Y714KNF	NW & Wales	YD02PYW	Yorkshire
Y514UGC	London	Y547UJC	NW & Wales	Y715KNF	NW & Wales	YD02PYX	Yorkshire

Pictured in Hall Green while heading for Wigan is 3026 from the North West and Wales operation. This is a VDL SB200 with Wrightbus Pulsar 2 bodywork, a model that features in most of the British fleets. *Richard Godfrey*

YD02PYY	Yorkshire	YG52CFA	Yorkshire	YJ06FXS	The Shires	YJ06YRR	The Shires
YD02PYZ	Yorkshire	YG52CFD	Yorkshire	YJ06FXT	The Shires	YJ06YRS	The Shires
YD02RJJ	Yorkshire	YG52CFE	Yorkshire	YJ06FXU	The Shires	YJ06YRT	The Shires
YD02RJO	Yorkshire	YG52CFF	Yorkshire	YJ06FXV	The Shires	YJ06YRU	The Shires
YD04MFJ	Tellings GM	YG52CFJ	Yorkshire	YJ06LDK	The Shires	YJ06YRY	NW & Wales
YD04MFK	Tellings GM	YG52CFK	Yorkshire	YJ06LFE	The Shires	YJ06YRZ	NW & Wales
YD04MFN	Tellings GM	YG52CFL	Yorkshire	YJ06LFF	The Shires	YJ07BCZ	The Shires
YE06HNT	The Shires	YG52CFM	Yorkshire	YJ06LFG	The Shires	YJ07BEO	The Shires
YE06HNU	The Shires	YG52CFN	Yorkshire	YJ06LFH	The Shires	YJ07BEU	The Shires
YE06HPA	The Shires	YG52CFO	Yorkshire	YJ06LFK	The Shires	YJ07JFY	Tellings GM
YE06HPC	The Shires	YG52CFP	Yorkshire	YJ06LFL	The Shires	YJ07JHH	Tellings GM
YE06HPF	The Shires	YG52CFU	Yorkshire	YJ06LFZ	Southern Cs	YJ07JSU	Scotland West
YE06HPJ	The Shires	YG52CFV	Yorkshire	YJ06WLX	Yorkshire	YJ07JSV	Scotland West
YE06HPK	The Shires	YG52CFX	Yorkshire	YJ06WLZ	Yorkshire	YJ07JSX	Scotland West
YE06HPL	The Shires	YG52CMU	The Shires	YJ06WMA	Yorkshire	YJ07JSY	Scotland West
YE06HPN	The Shires	YJ03PFX	The Shires	YJ06WMC	Yorkshire	YJ07JSZ	Scotland West
YE06HPO	The Shires	YJ04BKF	The Shires	YJ06WMD	Yorkshire	YJ07JVF	The Shires
YE06HPP	The Shires	YJ04HJC	Scotland West	YJ06WME	Yorkshire	YJ07JVU	The Shires
YE06HPU	The Shires	YJ04HJD	Scotland West	YJ06WMF	Yorkshire	YJ07JVV	The Shires
YE06HPX	Southern Cs	YJ04HJE	Scotland West	YJ06WMG	Yorkshire	YJ07JVW	The Shires
YE06HPY	Southern Cs	YJ04HJF	Scotland West	YJ06WMK	Yorkshire	YJ07JVX	The Shires
YE06HPZ	Southern Cs	YJ04HJG	Yorkshire	YJ06WML	Yorkshire	YJ07JVY	The Shires
YE06HRA	The Shires	YJ05JXP	Midlands	YJ06WWV	Yorkshire	YJ07JVZ	The Shires
YE06HRC	The Shires	YJ05JXU	The Shires	YJ06WWX	Yorkshire	YJ07VPW	The Shires
YE06HRD	The Shires	YJ05JXV	The Shires	YJ06WWY	Yorkshire	YJ07VPX	The Shires
YE06HRF	The Shires	YJ05PVT	The Shires	YJ06WWZ	Yorkshire	YJ07VPY	The Shires
YE06HRG	The Shires	YJ05PVW	Tellings GM	YJ06YRO	NW & Wales	YJ07VRC	The Shires
YE06HRJ	The Shires	YJ06ATK	NW & Wales	YJ06YRP	The Shires	YJ07VRD	The Shires

YJ07VRE	The Shires	YJ09CVA	Yorkshire	YJ09MMA	Midlands	YJ55YGW	The Shires
YJ07VRF	The Shires	YJ09CVB	Yorkshire	YJ09MME	Midlands	YJ56ATK	NW & Wales
YJ07VRU	Midlands	YJ09CVC	Yorkshire	YJ09MMF	Midlands	YJ56ATY	The Shires
YJ08DKN	Tellings GM	YJ09CVD	Yorkshire	YJ09MMK	Southern Cs	YJ56ATZ	The Shires
YJ08DLV	Tellings GM	YJ09CVE	Yorkshire	YJ09MMO	Southern Cs	YJ56JYE	Yorkshire
YJ08DVA	Yorkshire	YJ09CVH	Scotland West	YJ09MMU	Southern Cs	YJ56JYF	Yorkshire
YJ08DVB	Yorkshire	YJ09CVK	Scotland West	YJ09OTW	Midlands	YJ56JYG	Yorkshire
YJ08DVC	Yorkshire	YJ09CVL	Scotland West	YJ09OTY	The Shires	YJ56JYH	Yorkshire
YJ08DVF	Yorkshire	YJ09CVM	Scotland West	YJ09OTZ	The Shires	YJ56JYK	Yorkshire
YJ08DVG	Yorkshire	YJ09CVN	Scotland West	YJ09OUA	Midlands	YJ56JYL	Yorkshire
YJ08DVH	Yorkshire	YJ09CVO	Scotland West	YJ09OUB	Midlands	YJ56JYN	Yorkshire
YJ08DVK	Yorkshire	YJ09CVR	Scotland West	YJ10DFP	North East	YJ56JYO	Yorkshire
YJ08DVN	Yorkshire	YJ09CXL	The Shires	YJ10DFU	North East	YJ56JYP	Yorkshire
YJ08DVO	Yorkshire	YJ09ETF	Yorkshire	YJ10DFV	North East	YJ57AZD	Midlands
YJ08DVP	Yorkshire	YJ09EYA	Yorkshire	YJ10DFW	North East	YJ57AZF	Midlands
YJ08DVR	Yorkshire	YJ09EYB	Yorkshire	YJ10DHD	North East	YJ57AZG	Midlands
YJ08DVT	Yorkshire	YJ09EYC	Yorkshire	YJ10DHE	North East	YJ57AZL	Midlands
YJ08DVU	Yorkshire	YJ09EYG	Yorkshire	YJ10DHF	North East	YJ57AZN	Midlands
YJ08DZA	Southern Cs	YJ09EYH	Yorkshire	YJ10DHG	North East	YJ57AZO	Midlands
YJ08DZB	Southern Cs	YJ09EYK	Yorkshire	YJ10DHK	North East	YJ57AZP	Midlands
YJ08DZC	Southern Cs	YJ09EYL	Yorkshire	YJ10DHL	North East	YJ57AZR	Midlands
YJ08DZD	Southern Cs	YJ09EYM	Yorkshire	YJ10DHN	North East	YJ57AZT	Midlands
YJ08DZE	Southern Cs	YJ09EYO	Yorkshire	YJ51JWW	Tellings GM	YJ57AZU	Midlands
YJ08DZF	Southern Cs	YJ09EYP	Yorkshire	YJ53VFY	The Shires	YJ57BEO	Yorkshire
YJ08DZG	Southern Cs	YJ09EYR	Yorkshire	YJ54BSY	Midlands	YJ57BEU	Yorkshire
YJ08DZH	Southern Cs	YJ09EYS	Yorkshire	YJ54BSZ	Midlands	YJ57BKD	Southern Cs
YJ08DZK	Southern Cs	YJ09LBK	Midlands	YJ54CFG	The Shires	YJ57BPZ	Midlands
YJ08DZL	Southern Cs	YJ09LBL	Midlands	YJ54CKE	Midlands	YJ57BRF	Midlands
YJ08DZM	Southern Cs	YJ09LBN	Midlands	YJ54CKF	Midlands	YJ57BRV	Midlands
YJ08DZN	Southern Cs	YJ09MJE	Midlands	YJ54CKG	Scotland West	YJ57BTU	Tellings GM
YJ08ECY	Yorkshire	YJ09MJF	Midlands	YJ54CKK	Scotland West	YJ57BUA	Midlands
YJ08EEB	Yorkshire	YJ09MJK	Midlands	YJ54CPE	The Shires	YJ57BUE	Midlands
YJ08EEF	Yorkshire	YJ09MJV	Midlands	YJ54CPF	The Shires	YJ57BVB	North East
YJ08EEG	Yorkshire	YJ09MJX	Midlands	YJ55BJE	NW & Wales	YJ57BVC	North East
YJ08EEH	Yorkshire	YJ09MJY	Midlands	YJ55BJF	NW & Wales	YJ57BVD	North East
YJ08EEM	Yorkshire	YJ09MKC	Midlands	YJ55BJK	NW & Wales	YJ57BVE	North East
YJ08EEN	Yorkshire	YJ09MKD	Midlands	YJ55BKG	NW & Wales	YJ57BVF	North East
YJ08EEP	Yorkshire	YJ09MKE	Midlands	YJ55BKK	NW & Wales	YJ57BVG	North East
YJ08EER	Yorkshire	YJ09MKF	Midlands	YJ55BKL	NW & Wales	YJ57BVT	Yorkshire
YJ08EES	Yorkshire	YJ09MKG	Midlands	YJ55BKN	NW & Wales	YJ57BVU	Yorkshire
YJ08EET	Yorkshire	YJ09MKK	Midlands	YJ55BKO	NW & Wales	YJ57BVV	Yorkshire
YJ08EEU	Yorkshire	YJ09MKL	Midlands	YJ55BKU	NW & Wales	YJ57BVW	Yorkshire
YJ08EEV	Yorkshire	YJ09MKM	Midlands	YJ55BKV	NW & Wales	YJ57BVX	Yorkshire
YJ08EEW	Yorkshire	YJ09MKN	Midlands	YJ55WOA	The Shires	YJ57BVY	Yorkshire
YJ08XDK	The Shires	YJ09MKO	Midlands	YJ55WOB	The Shires	YJ57BVZ	Yorkshire
YJ09CSU	Yorkshire	YJ09MKP	Midlands	YJ55WOC	The Shires	YJ57BWA	The Shires
YJ09CTV	Yorkshire	YJ09MKU	Midlands	YJ55WOD	The Shires	YJ57BWB	The Shires
YJ09CTX	Yorkshire	YJ09MKV	Midlands	YJ55WOH	The Shires	YJ57BWC	The Shires
YJ09CTY	Yorkshire	YJ09MKX	Midlands	YJ55WOM	The Shires	YJ57BWD	The Shires
YJ09CTZ	Yorkshire	YJ09MKZ	Midlands	YJ55WOR	The Shires	YJ57BWE	The Shires
YJ09CUA	Yorkshire	YJ09MLE	Midlands	YJ55WOU	The Shires	YJ57BWF	The Shires
YJ09CUC	Yorkshire	YJ09MLF	Midlands	YJ55WOV	The Shires	YJ57EJD	The Shires
YJ09CUG	Yorkshire	YJ09MLK	Midlands	YJ55WOX	The Shires	YJ57EJE	The Shires
YJ09CUH	Yorkshire	YJ09MLL	Midlands	YJ55WPO	The Shires	YJ57EJF	The Shires
YJ09CUK	Yorkshire	YJ09MLN	Midlands	YJ55WSV	Southern Cs	YJ57EJG	The Shires
YJ09CUO	Yorkshire	YJ09MLO	Midlands	YJ55WSW	The Shires	YJ57EJK	The Shires
YJ09CUV	Scotland West	YJ09MLV	Midlands	YJ55WSX	The Shires	YJ57EJL	The Shires
YJ09CUW	Scotland West	YJ09MLX	Midlands	YJ55WSY	The Shires	YJ57EJN	Southern Cs
YJ09CUX	Scotland West	YJ09MLY	Midlands	YJ55WSZ	The Shires	YJ57EJN	The Shires
YJ09CUY	Yorkshire	YJ09MLZ	Midlands	YJ55YGV	The Shires	YJ57EKA	Midlands